D0835642

International Rare
Book Prices

MODERN FIRST EDITIONS

1991

International Rare Book Prices

MODERN FIRST EDITIONS

Series Editor: Michael Cole

1991

The Clique

7 Pulleyn Drive, York YO2 2DY, England

International Rare Book Prices – Modern First Editions

ISBN 1 870773 23 3

North America

Spoon River Press, P.O. Box 3676
Peoria, Illinois 61614, U.S.A.

Typesetting by Maxiprint, York, England
Printed and bound by Biddles Ltd., Guildford, England

Contents

General Introduction

Modern First Editions is the third title in the annual series *International Rare Book Prices*. The other titles in the series are *The Arts & Architecture, Early Printed Books, Science & Medicine, Voyages, Travel & Exploration, Literature.*

The series, generally referred to as *IRBP*, provides annual records of the pricing levels of out-of-print, rare or antiquarian books within a number of specialty subject areas and gives likely sources and suppliers for such books in Britain and the United States of America. It is intended to be used by both the experienced bookman and the newcomer to book-collecting.

Sources of information:

The books recorded each year in the various subject volumes of *IRBP* have been selected from catalogues of books for sale issued during the previous year by numerous bookselling firms in Britain and the United States. These firms, listed at the end of this volume, range in nature from the highly specialized, handling books solely with closely defined subject areas, through to large concerns with expertise across a broad spectrum of interests.

Extent of coverage:

IRBP concentrates exclusively on books published in the English language and, throughout the series as a whole, encompasses books published between the 16th century and the 1970s.

The 30,000 or so separate titles recorded in the annual volumes of *IRBP* vary greatly from year to year although naturally there is a degree of overlap, particularly of the more frequently found titles. Consecutive annual volumes do not, therefore, merely update pricings from earlier years; they give substantially different listings of books on each occasion. The value of the *IRBP* volumes lies in providing records of an ever-increasing range of individual titles which have appeared for sale on the antiquarian or rare book market.

Emphasis is placed throughout on books falling within the lower to middle range of the pricing scale (£10 - £250; £$20 - $500) rather than restricting selection to the unusually fine or expensive. In so doing, *IRBP* provides a realistic overview of the norm, rather than the exception, within the booktrade.

Acknowledgements:

We are indebted to those booksellers who have provided their catalogues during 1990 for the purposes of *IRBP*. A list of the contributing booksellers forms an appendix at the rear of this volume.

This appendix forms a handy reference of contacts in Britain and the United States with proven experience of handling books within the individual specialist fields encompassed by the series. The booksellers listed therein are able, between them, to offer advice on any aspect of the rare and antiquarian booktrade.

Many of the listed books will still, at the time of publication, be available for purchase. Readers with a possible interest in acquiring any of the items may well find it worth their while communicating with the booksellers concerned to obtain further and complete details.

Modern First Editions - Notes

A volume devoted solely to modern literary first editions has been included in the *IRBP* series to meet the demands of an international readership for easily accessible and substantial annual records of the ever-changing trends within this specialized field of book collecting.

The 1991 edition of *Modern First Editions* contains in the region of 7,800 entries, including title duplicates, selected from British and U.S. booksellers' catalogues issued during 1990. Approximately 1,200 separate authors are represented.

Unfortunately, the term 'modern first edition', whilst universally accepted as a general concept, has a somewhat imprecise meaning. It is only right, therefore, that its use in this volume is defined.

Period of Coverage:

There is a lack of consensus over a commencement date for 'modern' literature, with claims ranging from the mid-nineteenth century until well into the twentieth. Additionally there are those who would seek to define 'modern' in terms of literary content rather than as a function of comparative age. Our own rule is rigid and simple. The earliest date of publication allowed for entry in *Modern First Editions* is 1900.

Variant first editions:

Having disposed of 'modern', a problem also arises with 'first'. Such word is often qualified by the addition of a further adjective as in 'first English', 'first American', 'first trade' and the like.

As, however, there are collectors for each of these variants of 'first editions', we have not excluded them from selection. All the books cited herein have appeared in specialist modern first edition catalogues, or in first edition sections within general catalogues. In each case, any qualifying adjective mentioned by the bookseller concerned has been recorded.

Authors and order of entry:

Authors are listed alphabetically by surname.

Individual titles are listed alphabetically under each author's name, using the first word of the title ignoring, for alphabetical purposes, the definite and indefinite articles *the, a* and *an.*

Publisher and place of publication:

We have recorded such details of publisher and place of publication as have been supplied by each bookseller or added these details in cases where it has been possible to make such attribution from the other information supplied. On many occasions the bookseller concerned has considered the date of publication alone to be sufficient indication of publishing priority.

Condition:

As the prices of modern first editions are influenced by the minutiae of condition, far more so than in almost any other category of collected book, we have recorded any defect, however minor, mentioned. In like manner, comments on dustwrappers have been noted. Notwithstanding this, it is as well to bear in mind that it is impracticable for booksellers to attempt to describe every nuance of condition that might apply.

Currency conversion:

IRBP lists books offered for sale priced in either pounds sterling (£) or United States dollars ($). For the benefit of readers unaccustomed to one or other of these currencies, an approximate conversion figure in the alternative currency has been provided in parentheses after each entry, as, for example, "**£100 [≃ $191]**", or, "**$60 [≃ £31]**". The conversion is based upon an exchange rate of £1 sterling ≃ US $1.91 (US $1 ≃ £0.525 sterling), the approximate rate applicable at the date of going to press.

It must be stressed that the conversion figures in parentheses are provided merely as an indication of the approximate pricing level in the currency with which the reader may be most familiar and that fluctuations in exchange rates will make these approximations inaccurate to a greater or lesser degree.

Caveat:

Whilst the greatest care has been taken in transcribing entries from catalogues, it should be understood that it is inevitable that an occasional error will have passed unnoticed. Obvious mistakes, usually typographical in nature, observed in catalogues have been corrected. The accuracy in bibliographical matters of the cataloguers concerned has not been questioned.

The Clique

Modern First Editions 1990 Catalogue Prices

Abbey, Edward

- Appalachian Wilderness. New York: Dutton, 1970. Correct 1st edition in large format. Dustwrapper. *(Lopez)* **$150 [≃£78]**
- Confessions of a Barbarian. Santa Barbara: Capra, 1986. Wrappers (lightly dust soiled). *(Lopez)* **$25 [≃£13]**
- The Monkey Wrench Gang. Edinburgh: Canongate, (1978). 1st UK edition. Price-clipped dustwrapper. *(Between the Covers)* **$100 [≃£52]**

Abish, Walter

- Duel Site. New York: Tibor De Nagy Editions, 1970. One of 300. Wrappers. His 1st book. *(Alphabet)* **$65 [≃£33]**
- Duel Site. New York: Tibor de Nagy, 1970. Wrappers. Author's 1st book. *(Any Amount)* **£22.50 [≃$44]**

Ableman, Paul

- I Hear Voices. Paris: Olympia Press, 1958. Inscription. Dustwrapper. *(Glyn's)* **£18 [≃$34]**

Abrahams, Peter

- Return to Goli. London: Faber, 1953. Price-clipped dustwrapper. *(Alphabet)* **$65 [≃£33]**

Abse, Dannie

- Funland. Portland Univ: 1971. One of 100 signed. Wrappers. Author's presentation copy. *(Whiteson)* **£25 [≃$47]**

Achebe, Chinua

- Anthills of the Savanna. London: 1987. Uncorrected proof copy. Publication date in ink on half-title. Printed wrappers. *(Blakeney)* **£12.50 [≃$24]**
- Things Fall Apart. London: 1958. Uncorrected proof copy. Printed wrappers. Dustwrapper. His 1st book. *(Blakeney)* **£75 [≃$143]**

Ackerley, J.R.

- (Contributes to) Cambridge Poets 1914-1920. Cambridge: Heffer, 1920. Slight foxing. Spine very slightly faded. *(Words Etcetera)* **£30 [≃$57]**
- Hindoo Holiday. London: 1932. Dustwrapper (slightly dusty). *(Words Etcetera)* **£45 [≃$86]**
- Micheldever and Other Poems. McKelvie: 1972. One of 350 (this copy unnumbered). Wrappers. *(Moorhouse)* **£12 [≃$23]**
- Poems by Four Authors [Ackerley, Campbell, Davison, Kendon]. Cambridge: Bowes & Bowes, 1923. Boards darkened at edges. *(Woolmer)* **$95 [≃£49]**
- The Prisoners of War. London: Chatto & Windus, 1925. His 1st book. *(Woolmer)* **$125 [≃£65]**
- We Think the World of You. London: Bodley Head, 1960. Slight spotting on top and foredge. Dustwrapper (slightly soiled and faded on spine, back panel slightly creased). *(Virgo)* **£25 [≃$47]**

Ackroyd, Peter

- Chatterton. London: London Limited Editions, 1987. One of 150 [sic], signed. Original glassine dustwrapper. *(Michael Johnson)* **£40 [≃$76]**
- Chatterton. London: London Limited Editions, 1987. One of 100 [sic], signed. Original glassine. *(Blakeney)* **£55 [≃$105]**
- Chatterton. London: Hamilton, 1987. Dustwrapper. Signed by the author. *(Dyke)* **£25 [≃$47]**
- Country Life. Ferry Press: 1978. One of 350. Signed by the author. Wrappers. *(David Rees)* **£55 [≃$105]**
- Country Life. Ferry Press: 1978. One of 350. Wrappers. *(Halsey)* **£15 [≃$28]**
- Dickens. London: London Limited Editions, 1990. One of 150 signed. Cloth backed boards. Cellophane dustwrapper.

(Words Etcetera) **£40 [≃$76]**
- The Diversions of Purley. London: Hamilton, 1987. Dustwrapper. *(Lewton)* **£9.50 [≃$19]**
- Ezra Pound. London: Thames and Hudson, 1980. Dustwrapper. *(Lewton)* **£24 [≃$46]**
- First Light. Hamish Hamilton, 1989. Uncorrected proof copy. Printed wrappers, month of publication (May) written on upper wrapper. *(David Rees)* **£35 [≃$67]**
- First Light. Hamish Hamilton, 1989. Dustwrapper. Signed by the author. *(David Rees)* **£15 [≃$28]**
- First Light. Hamish Hamilton, 1989. Dustwrapper. Signed by the author. *(Michael Johnson)* **£24 [≃$46]**
- Hawksmoor. London: Hamish Hamilton, 1985. Dustwrapper. *(David Rees)* **£30 [≃$57]**
- The Last Testament of Oscar Wilde. London: Hamilton, 1983. Dustwrapper. *(Dyke)* **£25 [≃$47]**
- The Last Testament of Oscar Wilde. Hamish Hamilton, 1983. Dustwrapper. *(David Rees)* **£25 [≃$47]**
- London Lickpenny. Ferry Press: 1973. One of 500. Wrappers. *(First Issues)* **£45 [≃$86]**
- T.S. Eliot. London: 1984. Dustwrapper (entirely unfaded at spine). *(Blakeney)* **£30 [≃$57]**

Acton, Harold
- Memoirs of an Aesthete. London: 1948. Two corners slightly bumped. *(Clearwater)* **£28 [≃$53]**

Adams, Richard
- The Girl in a Swing. New York: Knopf, 1980. 1st (suppressed) issue. Deckle edged paper. Author's presentation inscription. *(Green Meadow)* **£95 [≃$182]**
- The Plague Dogs. London: Allen Lane, 1977. Dustwrapper. *(Marlborough B'shop)* **£8.50 [≃$17]**
- Shardik. London: Allen Lane, 1974. Dustwrapper. *(Green Meadow)* **£25 [≃$47]**
- Watership Down. London: Rex Collings, 1972. Dustwrapper (upper cover very slightly faded). *(Sotheran's)* **£368 [≃$706]**
- Watership Down. New York: Macmillan, [1972]. Dustwrapper. Inscribed by the author. *(Heritage)* **$150 [≃£78]**

Agee, James
- A Death in the Family. New York: 1957. 1st issue. Spine extremities and lower edge front cover minimally sunned. Dustwrapper (spine minimally rubbed). *(Polyanthos)* **$50 [≃£26]**
- A Death in the Family. London: 1958. 1st English edn. Bumped at bottom of spine. Bookseller's sticker. Dustwrapper. *(Blakeney)* **£35 [≃$67]**
- The Morning Watch. Boston: 1951. Touch of fading at edges. Dustwrapper (spine faded, light wear at edges). *(Woolmer)* **$75 [≃£39]**
- The Morning Watch. Boston: 1951. Dustwrapper. *(Houle)* **$125 [≃£65]**
- A Way of Seeing: Photographs by Helen Levitt. New York: Viking, [1965]. Dustwrapper. *(Dermont)* **$200 [≃£104]**

Aiken, Conrad
- The Kid. London: John Lehmann, 1947. 1st English edition. Unopened. Dustwrapper. *(Chapel Hill)* **$50 [≃£26]**
- The Kid. London: John Lehmann, 1947. 1st English edition. Dustwrapper (small chips). Author's inscription (1958). *(Houle)* **$85 [≃£44]**
- The Morning Song of Lord Zero. New York: OUP, 1963. Dustwrapper (very slightly soiled). Inscribed by Aiken. *(Black Sun)* **$90 [≃£46]**
- Prelude. New York: Random House, 1929. One of 475. Wrappers. *(Nouveau)* **$125 [≃£65]**
- Skylight One. London: John Lehmann, [1951]. 1st English edition. Dustwrapper (nicks). Author's inscription (1955). *(Houle)* **$125 [≃£65]**
- Thee. Drawings by Leonard Baskin. New York: (1967). One of 100 signed. Slipcase. *(Black Sun)* **$175 [≃£91]**

Aiken, Joan
- More than You Bargained For. London: Cape, 1955. Dustwrapper. *(Green Meadow)* **£35 [≃$67]**

Albee, Edward
- Counting the Waves and Listening. New York: 1977. Dustwrapper. Signed presentation copy from the author. *(Polyanthos)* **$35 [≃£18]**
- Everything in the Garden. New York: Atheneum, 1968. Dustwrapper. Signed by the author. *(Antic Hay)* **$65 [≃£33]**
- Seascape. New York: Atheneum, 1975. Price-clipped dustwrapper. Inscribed by the author. *(Heritage)* **$100 [≃£52]**
- Tiny Alice. A Play. New York: Atheneum, 1965. Signed by the author on label mounted on endpaper. *(Heritage)* **$150 [≃£78]**

- Tiny Alice. New York: Atheneum, 1965. Dustwrapper (small nick, short tear). Signed by the author. *(Antic Hay)* **$85 [≈£44]**
- Who's Afraid of Virginia Woolf? New York: Atheneum, 1962. Price-clipped dustwrapper. *(Antic Hay)* **$150 [≈£78]**
- Who's Afraid of Virginia Woolf? London: 1964. Dustwrapper (one small chip). *(Buckley)* **£40 [≈$76]**
- The Zoo Story, The Death of Bessie Smith, The Sandbox. New York: 1960. Spine very lightly sunned, extremities minimally rubbed. Dustwrapper (spine and edges slightly sunned). Signed presentation copy from the author. *(Polyanthos)* **$75 [≈£39]**
- The Zoo Story & Other Plays. London: 1962. Dustwrapper (slightly sunned). *(Buckley)* **£60 [≈$115]**

Aldington, Richard

- A.E. Housman and W.B. Yeats. Peacocks Press: 1955. One of 350. Tissue dustwrapper (frayed and chipped). *(Ellis)* **£30 [≈$57]**
- (Translates) Alcestis by Euripides. London: Chatto & Windus, 1930. One of 260 signed. Tissue dustwrapper (worn at edges). *(Woolmer)* **$85 [≈£44]**
- All Men Are Enemies. London: Chatto & Windus, 1933. One of 110 signed by the author. Edges and prelims lightly foxed. Buckram backed boards, t.e.g. *(Sotheran's)* **£148 [≈$284]**
- All Men Are Enemies. London: Chatto & Windus, 1933. One of 110 signed. *(Woolmer)* **$150 [≈£78]**
- Artifex. London: Chatto & Windus, 1935. Dustwrapper (slight browning to spine). *(Houle)* **$50 [≈£26]**
- At All Costs. London: 1930. Very slight spotting. Original glassine envelope. *(Blakeney)* **£12 [≈$23]**
- At All Costs. London: 1930. One of 275 signed. (covers worn, spine stained at ends). Cellophane dustwrapper (very defective). *(King)* **$45 [≈£23]**
- At All Costs. London: Heinemann, 1930. One of 275 signed. Corners rubbed. Glassine dustwrapper. *(Tiger Books)* **£55 [≈$105]**
- The Colonel's Daughter. London: 1931. One of 210 signed. Edges and endpapers foxed, spine faded. *(Ellis)* **£75 [≈$143]**
- The Colonel's Daughter. London: Chatto & Windus, 1931. One of 210 signed. Spine faded. *(Woolmer)* **$85 [≈£44]**
- The Colonel's Daughter. London: Chatto & Windus, 1931. One of 210 signed. *(Fenning)* **£24.50 [≈$47]**
- The Complete Poems. London: 1948. Edges browned. Dustwrapper (nicked, rubbed, lacks piece at head of spine). *(Ellis)* **£25 [≈$47]**
- D.H. Lawrence. London: Chatto & Windus, 1930. Wrappers. *(Woolmer)* **$35 [≈£18]**
- Death of a Hero. London: 1929. Dustwrapper. *(First Issues)* **£100 [≈$191]**
- Death of a Hero. Paris: Babou and Kahane, 1930. 1st unexpurgated edition. One of 300. 2 vols. Wrappers. Tissue dustwrappers (worn). *(Woolmer)* **$175 [≈£91]**
- A Dream in the Luxembourg. London: Chatto & Windus, 1930. Dustwrapper (slightly soiled). *(Tiger Books)* **£30 [≈$57]**
- A Dream in the Luxembourg. London: 1930. One of 308 signed. *(Fenning)* **£24.50 [≈$47]**
- The Eaten Heart. Chapelle-Reanville: Hours Press, 1929. One of 200 signed. Light spotting to endpapers. Corners lightly rubbed. *(Patterson)* **£125 [≈$239]**
- The Eaten Heart. Hours Press: 1929. One of 200 signed. Corners and edges rubbed and slightly bumped, covers very slightly scratched. *(Virgo)* **£100 [≈$191]**
- Jane Austen. Calif: Ampersand Press, 1948. Cellophane dustwrapper (couple of tears). *(Words Etcetera)* **£50 [≈$95]**
- Jane Austen. Pasadena: Ampersand Press, 1948. Spine slightly faded. *(Woolmer)* **$45 [≈£23]**
- Last Straws. Paris: Hours Press, 1930. One of 500 (of 700) unsigned. End pages browning. Marbled boards, bumped at spine. *(Paul Brown)* **£35 [≈$67]**
- Last Straws. Paris: Hours Press, 1930. One of 700. Endpapers and foredge browned and spotted. Cover edges rubbed, spine extremities crushed. *(Virgo)* **£45 [≈$86]**
- Love and the Luxembourg. New York: 1930. One of 475 signed. T.e.g. *(Polyanthos)* **$35 [≈£18]**
- Love and the Luxembourg. New York: Covici, Friede, 1930. One of 474 signed. *(Woolmer)* **$50 [≈£26]**
- The Love of Myrrhine and Konallis. Chicago: Covici, 1926. One of 150 signed. Bookplate removed. Dustwrapper (few nicks, moderate soil, short tears). *(Antic Hay)* **$125 [≈£65]**
- Roads to Glory. London: Chatto & Windus, 1930. One of 360 signed. Tissue dustwrapper (worn). *(Woolmer)* **$125 [≈£65]**
- Roads to Glory. London: Chatto & Windus, 1930. Dustwrapper. *(Virgo)* **£65 [≈$124]**
- Soft Answers. London: Chatto & Windus, 1932. One of 110 signed. Foredge slightly

spotted. Spine slightly faded. *(Virgo)* **£70 [≃$134]**

- Stepping Heavenward. Florence: Orioli, 1931. One of 808 signed. Unopened. Dustwrapper. *(Polyanthos)* **$75 [≃£39]**
- Stepping Heavenward. Florence: Orioli, 1931. One of 808 signed. Dustwrapper. *(Woolmer)* **$75 [≃£39]**
- Stepping Heavenward. Florence: G. Orioli, 1931. One of 808 signed by the author. Unopened. Dustwrapper. *(Sotheran's)* **£68 [≃$130]**
- A Tourist's Rome. Draguignan: The Melissa Press, (1961). Wrappers. *(Woolmer)* **$50 [≃£26]**
- Two Stories. London: 1930. One of 530 signed. Cloth backed boards (corners and edges trifle rubbed). *(Words Etcetera)* **£15 [≃$28]**
- Two Stories. London: 1930. One of 500 signed. *(Lewton)* **£25 [≃$47]**
- Two Stories. [London]: 1930. One of 530 signed by the author. Unopened. Dustwrapper. *(Heritage)* **$100 [≃£52]**
- A Wreath for San Gemignano. London: Heinemann, 1946. Price-clipped dustwrapper. *(Tiger Books)* **£25 [≃$47]**

Aldiss, Brian

- An Age. London: Faber, 1967. Dustwrapper. *(Sklaroff)* **£35 [≃$67]**
- The Brightfount Diaries. London: 1955. Price-clipped dustwrapper (slightly frayed, nicked). His 1st book. *(Ellis)* **£85 [≃$163]**
- The Brightfount Diaries. London: 1955. Review pasted to half-title. Dustwrapper (spine chipped). His 1st book. *(McCann)* **£30 [≃$57]**
- The Brightfount Diaries. London: 1955. Dustwrapper (chipped and rubbed). His 1st book. *(Buckley)* **£30 [≃$57]**
- The Brightfount Diaries. London: Faber, 1955. Dustwrapper. Author's presentation copy. His 1st book. *(Whiteson)* **£90 [≃$172]**
- The Canopy of Time. London: Faber, 1959. Dustwrapper (slightly chipped, two short tears). Signed by the author. *(David Rees)* **£25 [≃$47]**
- Cities and Stones. London: Faber, 1966. Dustwrapper (slightly darkened). *(Marlborough B'shop)* **£8 [≃$15]**
- Earthworks. London: Faber, 1965. Dustwrapper. *(Sklaroff)* **£25 [≃$47]**
- The Eighty-Minute Hour. London: 1974. Dustwrapper. Signed by the author. *(Ellis)* **£30 [≃$57]**
- Farewell to a Child. Priapus Poets: 1982. One of 350. Unopened. Signed by the author. *(First Issues)* **£15 [≃$28]**
- The Hand-Reared Boy. London: Weidenfeld & Nicolson, 1977. Dustwrapper. Signed by the author (1985). *(Marlborough B'shop)* **£15 [≃$28]**
- Helliconia Spring. London: Cape, 1982. Dustwrapper. *(Ash)* **£10 [≃$19]**
- Last Orders and Other Stories. London: 1977. Dustwrapper. *(Words Etcetera)* **£15 [≃$28]**
- The Malacia Tapestry. London: Cape, 1976. Uncorrected proof copy. Wrappers. *(Sklaroff)* **£25 [≃$47]**
- The Moment of Eclipse. London: Faber, 1970. Dustwrapper. *(Lewton)* **£12.50 [≃$24]**
- A Rude Awakening. London: Cape, 1978. Dustwrapper. Signed by the author. *(Lewton)* **£12.50 [≃$24]**
- A Rude Awakening. London: Weidenfeld & Nicolson, 1978. Dustwrapper. Signed by the author. *(Ash)* **£20 [≃$38]**
- A Soldier Erect. Weidenfeld & Nicolson, 1971. Dustwrapper (very slightly torn). *(Sklaroff)* **£8 [≃$15]**
- The World & Nearer Ones. London: 1979. Dustwrapper. Signed by the author. *(Buckley)* **£18 [≃$34]**

Alexander, David

- The Madhouse in Washington Square. Phila: Lippincott, 1958. Dustwrapper (designed by Warhol). *(Janus)* **$35 [≃£18]**

Algren, Nelson

- Chicago: City on the Make. Garden City: Doubleday, 1951. Dustwrapper. Author's inscription. *(Alphabet)* **$65 [≃£33]**
- The Man with the Golden Arm. Garden City: Doubleday, 1949. Dustwrapper (light edgewear). Signed by the author. *(Heritage)* **$250 [≃£130]**
- The Man with the Golden Arm. New York: 1949. Spine little sunned, covers little soiled. Dustwrapper (some closed tears, spine sunned, extremities chipped, few small edge tears, little soiled). Author's signed presentation copy. *(Polyanthos)* **$85 [≃£44]**
- The Man With the Golden Arm. New York: 1949. Dustwrapper (slightly chipped). *(Sclanders)* **£25 [≃$47]**
- The Neon Wilderness. Garden City: Doubleday, 1947. Slight browning of front endpaper from old clippings. Earliest dustwrapper, with adverts for other books on rear panel. *(Antic Hay)* **$125 [≃£65]**

- A Walk on the Wild Side. New York: Farrar, Straus & Cudahy, 1956. A few faint marks. Dustwrapper (slightly rubbed). Signed, inscribed and dated by the author. *(Ash)* **£100 [≃$191]**
- Who Lost an American? New York: Macmillan, [1963]. Dustwrapper. Inscribed by the author. *(Heritage)* **$100 [≃£52]**

Allbeury, Ted

- All Our Tomorrows. London: Granada, 1982. Dustwrapper. *(Mordida)* **$35 [≃£18]**
- The Alpha List. London: Granada, 1979. Dustwrapper. *(Mordida)* **$40 [≃£20]**
- The Girl from Addis. London: Granada, 1984. Dustwrapper. Author's presentation inscription. *(Limestone Hills)* **$65 [≃£33]**
- The Girl from Addis. London: Granada, 1984. Stamp on front endpaper. Dustwrapper. *(Mordida)* **$40 [≃£20]**
- The Judas Factor. London: New English Library, 1984. Uncorrected proof copy. Dustwrapper. *(Limestone Hills)* **$50 [≃£26]**
- The Man with the President's Mind. London: Peter Davies, 1977. Dustwrapper. *(Mordida)* **$50 [≃£26]**
- Mission Berlin. New York: Walker, 1986. 1st American edition (published in England as The Only Good German). Dustwrapper. *(Mordida)* **$20 [≃£10]**
- Palomino Blonde. London: Peter Davies, 1975. Price-clipped dustwrapper. *(Mordida)* **$65 [≃£33]**
- The Seeds of Treason. London: New English Library, 1986. Dustwrapper. *(Mordida)* **$30 [≃£15]**
- Shadow of Shadows. London: Granada, 1982. Dustwrapper. *(Mordida)* **$30 [≃£15]**
- A Wilderness of Mirrors. London: New English Library, 1988. Dustwrapper. Signed by the author. *(Limestone Hills)* **$45 [≃£23]**

Allen, Woody

- The Floating Light Bulb. New York: Random House, (1982). Dustwrapper. *(Lopez)* **$25 [≃£13]**
- Getting Even. New York: 1971. Name and address. Dustwrapper. *(Pettler & Liebermann)* **$35 [≃£18]**

Allingham, Margery

- The Allingham Casebook. London: 1969. Proof copy. *(Buckley)* **£25 [≃$47]**
- Cargo of Eagles. London: Chatto & Windus, 1968. Dustwrapper. *(Mordida)* **$35 [≃£18]**
- The China Governess. Garden City: Doubleday, 1962. 1st edition (precedes the English edition). Dustwrapper. *(Mordida)* **$40 [≃£20]**
- Coroner's Pidgin. London: Heinemann, 1945. Dustwrapper (slightly chipped, small pieces missing from head of spine). *(Limestone Hills)* **$55 [≃£28]**
- The Galantrys. By Margery Allingham Carter. Boston: Little, Brown, 1943. 1st American edition. Edges spotted and stained. Price-clipped dustwrapper (spine faded, several short closed tears, wear at corners). *(Mordida)* **$25 [≃£13]**
- Hide My Eyes. London: Chatto & Windus, 1958. Dustwrapper. *(Mordida)* **$45 [≃£23]**
- The Mind Readers. London: Chatto & Windus, 1965. Price-clipped dustwrapper. *(Mordida)* **$30 [≃£15]**
- The Tiger in the Smoke. London: 1952. Dustwrapper (slightly chipped). *(Buckley)* **£15 [≃$28]**

Alther, Lisa

- Kinflicks. London: Chatto & Windus, 1976. Dustwrapper. *(Sklaroff)* **£20 [≃$38]**

Alvarez, A.

- Lost. London: Turret Books, 1968. One of 250 signed. Spine sunned. *(King)* **$60 [≃£31]**

Amado, Jorge

- The Miracle of the Birds. Targ Editions: 1983. One of 250 signed. Tissue dustwrapper. *(Nouveau)* **$100 [≃£52]**

Ambler, Eric

- Ability to Kill. London: 1962. Uncorrected proof. Text in withdrawn 1st state with the essay on Bodkin Adams. Printed wrappers, slightly rubbed & soiled, date & published price on front wrapper. Author's presentation inscription. *(Blakeney)* **£125 [≃$239]**
- The Care of Time. New York: Farrar Straus Giroux, [1981]. One of 300 signed by the author. Slipcase. *(Heritage)* **$75 [≃£39]**
- A Coffin for Dimitrios. New York: Knopf, 1939. 1st American edition (published in England as The Mask of Dimitrios). Dustwrapper (edge worn at spine). *(Alphabet)* **$200 [≃£104]**
- Epitaph for a Spy. New York: Knopf, 1952. 1st American edition. Dustwrapper (few nicks). *(Houle)* **$150 [≃£78]**
- The Light of Day. 1962. Uncorrected proof copy. Wrappers (soiled and a little torn). *(Words Etcetera)* **£25 [≃$47]**
- State of Siege. New York: Knopf, 1956. 1st

American edition. Dustwrapper. *(Dermont)* **$25 [≃£13]**

- State of Siege. New York: Knopf, 1956. 1st American edition, published in England as The Night-Comers. Minor browning endpapers. Dustwrapper (short tear). *(Antic Hay)* **$40 [≃£20]**

Amis, Kingsley

- Colonel Sun. By Robert Markham. London: Cape, 1968. Price-clipped dust- wrapper. *(Dyke)* **£35 [≃$67]**
- The Darkwater Hall Mystery. Tragara Press: 1978. One of 165. Wrappers. *(First Issues)* **£95 [≃$182]**
- Dear Illusion. Covent Garden Press: 1972. One of 100 signed. Yellow pictorial wrappers (small patch of abrasion to lower panel). *(First Issues)* **£85 [≃$163]**
- Dear Illusion. London: Covent Garden Press, 1972. One of 100 signed. Pictorial wrappers (small patch of abrasion to lower panel). *(First Issues)* **£85 [≃$163]**
- Difficulties With Girls. London: Hutchinson, 1988. One of 500 numbered advance proofs. Pictorial wrappers. *(David Rees)* **£18 [≃$34]**
- Ending Up. London: Cape, 1974. Uncorrected proof copy. A few marks. Wrappers. *(Glyn's)* **£30 [≃$57]**
- The Evans Country. Eynsham: Fantasy Press, 1962. Wrappers slightly dusty & sunned at the spine, staples rusty. *(Blakeney)* **£20 [≃$38]**
- The Folks That Live on the Hill. London: Hutchinson, 1990. Dustwrapper. Signed by the author. *(David Rees)* **£18 [≃$34]**
- I Want It Now. London: Cape, 1968. Uncorrected proof copy. Wrappers. Proof dustwrapper (slightly rubbed). *(David Rees)* **£25 [≃$47]**
- Jake's Thing. London: Hutchinson, 1978. Dustwrapper. *(Marlborough B'shop)* **£10 [≃$19]**
- The James Bond Dossier. London: Cape, 1965. Dustwrapper. *(Lewton)* **£17.50 [≃$34]**
- A Look Round the Estate. Harcourt: 1968. 1st US edition. Dustwrapper. *(Nouveau)* **$40 [≃£20]**
- Lucky Jim. New York: Doubleday, 1954. 1st American edition. Dustwrapper (slightly chipped at spine ends, spine darkened and slightly soiled). *(First Issues)* **£100 [≃$191]**
- Lucky Jim. New York: Doubleday, 1954. Top boards waterstained. Dustwrapper. *(Nouveau)* **$90 [≃£46]**
- My Enemy's Enemy. London: 1962. Dustwrapper (spine slightly browned). *(Words Etcetera)* **£45 [≃$86]**
- (Edits) The New Oxford Book of English Light Verse. New York: OUP, 1978. Dustwrapper (few nicks). *(Houle)* **$45 [≃£23]**
- One Fat Englishman. London: Gollancz, 1963. Dustwrapper. *(David Rees)* **£12 [≃$23]**

Amis, Martin

- Dead Babies. New York: Knopf, 1976. 1st American edition. Boards a bit faded at edge. Dustwrapper (spine slightly faded). *(Alphabet)* **$40 [≃£20]**
- Einstein's Monsters. London: Cape, 1987. Dustwrapper. Signed by the author. *(David Rees)* **£20 [≃$38]**
- Einstein's Monsters. London: Cape, 1987. Dustwrapper, wraparound band. *(Dyke)* **£18 [≃$34]**
- Einstein's Monsters. New York: Harmony, (1987). 1st American edition. Uncorrected proof copy. Wrappers (lightly rubbed). *(Lopez)* **$35 [≃£18]**
- Invasion of the Space Invaders. London: Hutchinson, 1982. Wrappers. Signed by the author. *(David Rees)* **£35 [≃$67]**
- London Fields. London: Cape, 1989. Uncorrected proof copy. Printed wrappers. *(David Rees)* **£85 [≃$163]**
- London Fields. London: London Limited, 1989. One of 150 signed. Marbled paper & cloth over boards. Dustwrapper. *(Nouveau)* **$110 [≃£57]**
- London Fields. London: Cape, 1989. Dustwrapper. Signed by the author. *(Moorhouse)* **£18 [≃$34]**
- London Fields. London: Cape, 1989. Dustwrapper. *(Dyke)* **£10 [≃$19]**
- Money. London: Cape, 1984. Uncorrected proof copy. Printed wrappers. *(David Rees)* **£90 [≃$172]**
- Money. London: Cape, 1984. Price-clipped dustwrapper. Signed by the author. *(David Rees)* **£45 [≃$86]**
- Money. London: Cape, 1984. Dustwrapper (inside rear flap slightly soiled). Signed by the author. *(Michael Johnson)* **£36 [≃$69]**
- Money. London: Cape, 1984. Dustwrapper. *(Dyke)* **£35 [≃$67]**
- The Moronic Inferno. London: Cape, 1986. Dustwrapper. Signed by the author. *(David Rees)* **£20 [≃$38]**
- The Moronic Inferno. London: Cape, 1986. Dustwrapper. Signed by the author. *(Michael Johnson)* **£24 [≃$46]**

- Other People. London: Cape, 1981. Dustwrapper. Signed by the author. *(David Rees)* **£45 [≈$86]**
- Other People. London: Cape, 1981. Dustwrapper. *(Dyke)* **£30 [≈$57]**
- Other People. London: Cape, 1981. Dustwrapper. *(Lewton)* **£40 [≈$76]**
- Other People. London: Cape, 1981. dustwrapper. Signed by the author. *(Lewton)* **£50 [≈$95]**
- The Rachel Papers. London: 1973. Dustwrapper. Signed by the author. *(Egret)* **£225 [≈$431]**
- The Rachel Papers. London: Cape, 1973. Dustwrapper (touch faded at spine, extremities slightly rubbed, two tiny ink spots showing only on the reverse). His 1st book. *(Moorhouse)* **£225 [≈$431]**
- The Rachel Papers. New York: Knopf, 1974. 1st American edition. Dustwrapper (internally repaired). Signed by the author. *(Michael Johnson)* **£28 [≈$53]**
- The Rachel Papers. New York: Knopf, 1974. 1st American edition. Dustwrapper (half inch tear). *(Alphabet)* **$85 [≈£44]**
- The Rachel Papers. New York: Knopf, 1974. 1st American edition. Dustwrapper. His 1st book. *(Dermont)* **$45 [≈£23]**
- Success. London: Cape, 1978. dustwrapper. Signed by the author. *(David Rees)* **£90 [≈$172]**
- Success. London: Cape, 1978. Dustwrapper. *(Dyke)* **£60 [≈$115]**
- Success. New York: Harmony, 1987. 1st American edition. Dustwrapper. Signed by the author. *(Michael Johnson)* **£25 [≈$47]**
- Success. London: Cape, 1978. dustwrapper. Signed by the author. *(Moorhouse)* **£85 [≈$163]**

Ammons, A.R.

- Corsons Inlet. Cornell UP: (1965). Edges very slightly dusty. dustwrapper. *(Woolmer)* **$50 [≈£26]**
- Expressions of Sea Level. Ohio State: UP, (1963). Dustwrapper (spine faded). *(Woolmer)* **$75 [≈£39]**

Anderson, Forrest

- Sea Pieces and Other Poems. New York: Cassowary Press, 1935. One of 155. Dustwrapper (top edge chipped). *(Woolmer)* **$125 [≈£65]**

Anderson, Margaret

- My 30 Years War. New York: 1930. *(Words Etcetera)* **£50 [≈$95]**

Anderson, Poul

- Murder Bound. New York: Macmillan, 1962. Advance review copy. Some browning. Dustwrapper (very slight soiling rear panel). *(Janus)* **$135 [≈£70]**
- Perish by the Sword. New York: Macmillan, 1959. Advance review copy. Some browning. Dustwrapper (very slight wear). *(Janus)* **$135 [≈£70]**

Anderson, Sherwood

- Alice and the Lost Novel. London: Woburn Books, 1929. One of 550 (of 580) signed. Small bump lower edge. Minor browning endpapers. Dustwrapper (spine lightly browned, small stain front panel). *(Antic Hay)* **$175 [≈£91]**
- Beyond Desire. New York: Liveright, [1932]. One of 165 signed. Cloth. *(Antic Hay)* **$275 [≈£143]**
- Kit Brandon. New York: 1936. Dustwrapper (lightly chipped). *(Pettler & Liebermann)* **$50 [≈£26]**
- Many Marriages. New York: B.W. Huebsch, 1923. Dustwrapper (a few slight nicks along edges). *(Black Sun)* **$200 [≈£104]**
- A New Testament. New York: Boni & Liveright, 1927. One of 265 signed. Some offsetting from ribbon marker. Vellum and boards (spine browned). *(Antic Hay)* **$150 [≈£78]**
- Perhaps Women. New York: (1931). Cloth (some cover discolouration). Dustwrapper (chipped and sunned). *(King)* **$75 [≈£39]**
- Perhaps Women. New York: 1931. Rear board slightly bowed. Dustwrapper. *(Pettler & Liebermann)* **$75 [≈£39]**

Andrezel, Pierre

- Pseudonym used by Dinesen, Isak (Karen Blixen), q.v.

Angelou, Maya

- Just Give Me a Cool Drink of Water 'fore I Die. New York: 1971. Price-clipped dustwrapper. Signed by the author. *(Polyanthos)* **$30 [≈£15]**

Anouilh, Jean

- Poor Bitos. London: Methuen, [1964]. 1st English edition. Dustwrapper (some rubbing). *(Antic Hay)* **$25 [≈£13]**
- Restless Heart. Methuen, 1957. Dustwrapper. *(Ash)* **£20 [≈$38]**

Archer, Jeffrey

- Kane and Abel. London: 1979. Dustwrapper.

(Roberts) **£12.50 [≃$24]**

- Not a Penny More, Not a Penny Less. London: Cape, 1976. Dustwrapper (slightly creased). *(Tiger Books)* **£35 [≃$67]**
- The Prodigal Daughter. Hodder & Stoughton, 1982. Dustwrapper. Signed by the author. *(David Rees)* **£12 [≃$23]**

Arensberg, Ann

- Sister Wolf. New York: Knopf, 1980. Cloth and boards. Dustwrapper. Signed by the author. Her 1st book. *(Antic Hay)* **$40 [≃£20]**

Arlen, Michael

- The Green Hat. London: Collins, 1924. Modern morocco gilt in art deco style, original cloth preserved at rear. *(Ash)* **£250 [≃$479]**

Arnow, Harriette

- The Dollmaker. New York: Macmillan, 1954. Advance pre-publication excerpt. Small paper clip mark front cover. Wrappers. *(Lopez)* **$200 [≃£104]**

Ashbery, John

- As We Know. New York: Viking, (1979). Dustwrapper. *(Woolmer)* **$35 [≃£18]**
- The Double Dream of Spring. New York: Dutton, 1970. 1st (cloth) edition, with full endpapers. 1st issue, with rounded spine. Dustwrapper (tiny tear and crease). Signed by the author. *(Antic Hay)* **$85 [≃£44]**
- Fragment. LA: Black Sparrow, 1969. One of 750 in wrappers. Signed by the author. *(Polyanthos)* **$35 [≃£18]**
- Houseboat Days. New York: Viking, (1977). Dustwrapper. *(Woolmer)* **$35 [≃£18]**
- Self-Portrait in a Convex Mirror. New York: 1975. Edges of covers very slightly sunned. Dustwrapper (tiny chip top of spine). Signed by the author. *(Polyanthos)* **$30 [≃£15]**
- Shadow Train. New York: 1981. Dustwrapper. Signed by the author. *(Polyanthos)* **$20 [≃£10]**
- Three Madrigals. New York: Poet's Press, 1968. One of 150 signed. Wrappers. Signed additionally by the author on title. *(Antic Hay)* **$100 [≃£52]**
- A Wave. New York: Viking, (1984). Dustwrapper. Author's presentation inscription. *(Woolmer)* **$85 [≃£44]**

Ashford, Daisy

- The Young Visiters. London: Chatto & Windus, 1919. Slight traces of erasure on title. Modern morocco gilt by Bayntun-Riviere. *(Ash)* **£250 [≃$479]**

Asimov, Isaac

- Foundation and Empire. New York: Gnome Press, [1952]. Dustwrapper (slightly rubbed, small tear and crease). *(Dermont)* **$150 [≃£78]**
- Pebble in the Sky. Garden City: Doubleday, 1950. Dustwrapper (slightly rubbed). Signed by the author. His 1st book. *(Houle)* **$425 [≃£221]**

Aspen

- Aspen. The Magazine in a Box. Editor-in-Chief and Publisher, Phyllis Johnson. New York: Roaring Fork Press, 1965-71. Issues 1-10 in 9 vols, all published. Fine. Some original mailing cartons preserved. *(Blakeney)* **£1,800 [≃$3,455]**

Astaire, Fred

- Dancing Shoes. New York: 1959. Price-clipped dustwrapper (bit chipped at rear). *(Pettler & Liebermann)* **$40 [≃£20]**

Atwood, Margaret

- Bluebeard's Egg. London: 1987. Dustwrapper. Signed by the author. *(Egret)* **£25 [≃$47]**
- Bodily Harm. Toronto: 1981. 1st Canadian edition. Special advance copy. Wrappers. *(Words Etcetera)* **£50 [≃$95]**
- Bodily Harm. New York: 1982. Uncorrected proof copy. Wrappers. Signed by the author. *(Polyanthos)* **$40 [≃£20]**
- Cat's Eye. (Toronto): McClelland & Stewart, (1988). Uncorrected proof copy. Wrappers. *(Lopez)* **$55 [≃£28]**
- Dancing Girls and Other Stories. New York: 1982. Dustwrapper. Signed by the author. *(Polyanthos)* **$35 [≃£18]**
- "The Gentle Science of Art" and "All Fools Day at the Early English Text Society", by Shakesbeat Latweed [pseudonym], [in] Acta Victoriana V. LXXXVI:1. Toronto: Autumn 1961. Pictorial wrappers (slightly sunned along stapled edge). *(Polyanthos)* **$50 [≃£26]**
- The Handmaid's Tale. London: Cape, 1986. Dustwrapper. *(Lewton)* **£12.50 [≃$24]**
- The Handmaid's Tale. London: 1986. Dustwrapper. Signed by the author. *(Egret)* **£30 [≃$57]**
- The Handmaid's Tale. London: 1986. Dustwrapper. *(Egret)* **£20 [≃$38]**
- Interlunar. Toronto: OUP, 1984. Wrappers. Signed by the author. *(Polyanthos)* **$35 [≃£18]**

- The Journals of Susanna Moodie. Toronto: Oxford, 1970. Wrappers (lightly rubbed). *(Lopez)* **$40 [≃£20]**
- The Journals of Susanna Moodie. London: 1970. Pictorial wrappers. *(McCann)* **£18 [≃$34]**
- Life Before Man. Toronto: M & S, 1979. "Special Preview Edition". Advance copy. Printed wrappers. Signed by the author. *(Alphabet)* **$110 [≃£57]**
- Notes Towards a Poem that can never be written. [Toronto]: Salamander Press, [1981]. One of 200 signed. Wrappers. *(Dermont)* **$100 [≃£52]**
- Power Politics. Toronto: Anansi Press, 1971. 1st Canadian edition. Wrappers. Author's signed presentation copy. *(Moorhouse)* **£40 [≃$76]**
- Procedures for Underground. Toronto: 1970. Name. Wrappers (some wear). *(David Rees)* **£20 [≃$38]**
- Second Words. Boston: 1984. Dustwrapper. Signed by the author. *(Polyanthos)* **$40 [≃£20]**
- Selected Poems II. Boston: 1987. Proof copy. Wrappers. Signed by the author. *(Polyanthos)* **$50 [≃£26]**
- Survival: A Thematic Guide to Canadian Literature. Toronto: Anansi, 1972. Dustwrapper. *(Alphabet)* **$50 [≃£26]**
- True Stories. Toronto: OUP, 1981. Printed wrappers. *(Antic Hay)* **$15 [≃£7]**
- True Stories. Cape Poetry Paperbacks, 1982. Wrappers. Signed by the author. *(Polyanthos)* **$30 [≃£15]**
- Two-Headed Poems. New York: 1978. Dustwrapper. Signed by the author. *(Polyanthos)* **$40 [≃£20]**
- You Are Happy. Toronto: 1974. Wrappers. Signed by the author. *(David Rees)* **£25 [≃$47]**
- You Are Happy. Toronto: OUP, 1974. Printed wrappers. *(Antic Hay)* **$25 [≃£13]**

Auchincloss, Louis

- The Dark Lady. Boston: Houghton, Mifflin, 1977. Price-clipped dustwrapper. Signed by the author. *(Antic Hay)* **$45 [≃£23]**
- The Winthrop Covenant. Boston: Houghton, Mifflin, 1976. Dustwrapper. Signed by the author. *(Antic Hay)* **$50 [≃£26]**
- The Winthrop Covenant. Boston: Houghton Mifflin, 1976. 1st trade edition. Price-clipped dustwrapper (small abrasion rear panel). Signed by the author on a tipped-in leaf. *(Chapel Hill)* **$50 [≃£26]**

Auden, W.H.

- Academic Graffiti. London: 1971. Dustwrapper (slightly sunned). *(Buckley)* **£12 [≃$23]**
- A Certain World. London: 1971. Dustwrapper. *(Buckley)* **£25 [≃$47]**
- City Without Walls. London: 1969. Uncorrected proof. Printed wrappers, name & date on front wrapper. *(Blakeney)* **£20 [≃$38]**
- City Without Walls. London: 1969. Uncorrected proof copy. Wrappers. *(First Issues)* **£75 [≃$143]**
- City Without Walls. London: 1969. Dustwrapper. *(First Issues)* **£25 [≃$4,943]**
- Collected Poems. London: 1976. Dustwrapper. *(Words Etcetera)* **£18 [≃$34]**
- The Collected Poetry. New York: 1945. Dustwrapper. *(Polyanthos)* **$75 [≃£39]**
- The Dance of Death. London: 1933. Bottom edges of boards a little rubbed. Dustwrapper (slightly chipped). *(Clearwater)* **£100 [≃$191]**
- Homage to Clio. London: 1960. Slight foxing and browning of front free endpaper. Dustwrapper. *(Roberts)* **£18 [≃$34]**
- Louis Macneice. A Memorial Address. Privately Printed: 1963. One of 250. Wrappers, very slightly marked. *(Edrich)* **£85 [≃$163]**
- Making Knowing and Judging. Oxford: Clarendon Press, 1956. Printed wrappers. *(Limestone Hills)* **$40 [≃£20]**
- Making, Knowing & Judging. OUP: 1956. Wrappers. *(Lewton)* **£17.50 [≃$34]**
- Making, Knowing and Judging: An Inaugural Lecture. Oxford: 1956. Wrappers. *(David Rees)* **£12 [≃$23]**
- Mountains. London: Faber, 1954. Wrappers. *(David Rees)* **£8 [≃$15]**
- Mountains. London: Ariel Poems, 1954. In original mailing envelope. *(Polyanthos)* **$25 [≃£13]**
- Natural Linguistics. Poem of the Month Club. Signed by the author. *(Whiteson)* **£25 [≃$47]**
- Nones. London: Faber, 1952. Name on endpaper. Dustwrapper (very slightly chipped). *(Virgo)* **£35 [≃$67]**
- Nones. London: Faber, 1952. Dustwrapper. *(Nouveau)* **$70 [≃£36]**
- The Old Man's Road. New York: Voyages, 1956. One of 50 (of 750) signed. Wrappers. Dustwrapper. *(Dermont)* **$650 [≃£338]**
- The Old Man's Road. New York: Voyages Press, 1956. One of 750. Wrappers (slightly

darkened at edges). *(Woolmer)* **$75 [≃£39]**

- The Orators An English Study. London: Faber, (1932). Dustwrapper (darkened, lacks a good part of spine). *(Woolmer)* **$85 [≃£44]**
- Paul Bunyan. London: 1976. Wrappers. *(Buckley)* **£10 [≃$19]**
- Poems. New York: Random House, 1934. 1st American edition. Endpapers and edges browned. Gilt on spine dull. Dustwrapper (soiled, browned and worn). *(Virgo)* **£50 [≃$95]**
- Selected Poems. London: 1938. Dustwrapper. *(Clearwater)* **£25 [≃$47]**
- Selected Poems. London: Faber, 1938. 1st state gilt decorated spine. Endpapers slightly spotted. Dustwrapper (damaged). *(Hazeldene)* **£25 [≃$47]**
- Selected Poems. London: 1938. Dustwrapper. *(Words Etcetera)* **£25 [≃$47]**
- (Edits) Selected Songs of Thomas Campion. Boston: Godine, 1973. One of 250. Slipcase. *(Black Sun)* **$75 [≃£39]**
- The Shield of Achilles. London: Faber, 1955. Dustwrapper (chipped, some closed tears). *(Virgo)* **£27.50 [≃$53]**
- The Shield of Achilles. New York: Random House, [1955]. Dustwrapper (soiled). *(Chapel Hill)* **$65 [≃£33]**
- Some Poems. London: 1940. Slight water stain at spine. dustwrapper. *(Buckley)* **£20 [≃$38]**
- Spain. London: 1937. Wrappers somewhat worn at the spine. *(Blakeney)* **£30 [≃$57]**
- Spain. London: Faber, 1937. Wrappers (slightly faded, foot of spine slightly damaged). *(Virgo)* **£85 [≃$163]**
- Spain. London: 1937. Wrappers (slightly rubbed and creased, two stains to back cover). *(Ellis)* **£60 [≃$115]**
- Spain. London: Faber, (1937). Wrappers with slight wear at bottom edge. *(Woolmer)* **$75 [≃£39]**
- Thank You, Fog. London: Faber, 1974. Uncorrected proof copy. Review slip. Printed wrappers. *(David Rees)* **£25 [≃$47]**
- (Edits) Van Gogh, a Self Portrait [in] Letters. London: 1961. Dustwrapper. *(Words Etcetera)* **£35 [≃$67]**

Auden, W.H. & Isherwood, Christopher

- The Ascent of F6. London: 1936. Dustwrapper (chipped, nicked, spine slightly tanned and with a 2-inch closed tear). *(Ellis)* **£75 [≃$143]**

Auden, W.H. & MacNeice, Louis

- Letters from Iceland. London: Faber, 1937. Bookplate. *(Halsey)* **£20 [≃$38]**
- Letters from Iceland. London: Faber, (1937). Covers a little faded. Price-clipped dustwrapper (some edge wear). *(Woolmer)* **$75 [≃£39]**

Auster, Paul

- (Translates) A Little Anthology of Surrealist Poems. New York: Siamese Banana Press, (1972). Mimeographed sheets. Stapled. *(Between the Covers)* **$175 [≃£91]**
- Moon Palace. London: Faber, 1989. Dustwrapper. Signed by the author. *(Moorhouse)* **£25 [≃$47]**
- The New York Trilogy. London: Faber, 1987. Dustwrapper. *(David Rees)* **£30 [≃$57]**
- The New York Trilogy. London: Faber, 1987. Dustwrapper. Signed by the author. *(David Rees)* **£45 [≃$86]**
- The New York Trilogy. London: 1987. Dustwrapper. *(Sclanders)* **£35 [≃$67]**

Ayckbourn, Alan

- Joking Apart. London: 1979. Dustwrapper. Inscribed by the author. *(Words Etcetera)* **£45 [≃$86]**
- Sisterly Feelings. London: 1981. Dustwrapper. Inscribed by the author. *(Words Etcetera)* **£45 [≃$86]**

Bach, Richard

- Stranger to the Ground. New York: Harper & Row, [1963]. 1st edition ('F-N'). Dustwrapper. *(Houle)* **$75 [≃£39]**

Bagnold, Enid

- Poems. The Whittington Press & William Heinemann: (1978). One of 150 signed. *(Woolmer)* **$75 [≃£39]**

Bailey, Paul

- At the Jerusalem. London: Cape, 1967. Dustwrapper. *(Lewton)* **£25 [≃$47]**
- An English Madam. London: Cape, 1982. Dustwrapper. *(Lewton)* **£5 [≃$9]**
- Gabriel's Lament. London: Cape, 1986. Dustwrapper. *(Lewton)* **£7.50 [≃$15]**
- Peter Smart's Confessions. London: Cape, 1977. Dustwrapper. *(Lewton)* **£9.50 [≃$19]**

Bainbridge, Beryl

- Another Part of the Wood. London: 1968. Uncorrected proof copy. Printed wrappers, spine slightly cocked. *(Blakeney)* **£35 [≃$67]**

- Another Part of the Wood. London: Hutchinson, 1968. Dustwrapper. Signed by the author. *(Lewton)* **£55 [≃$105]**
- Another Part of the Wood. London: 1968. Spine very slightly faded. Dustwrapper (little creased). *(Blakeney)* **£35 [≃$67]**
- The Bottle Factory Outing. London: Duckworth, 1974. Dustwrapper. *(Dyke)* **£20 [≃$38]**
- The Dressmaker. London: 1973. Dustwrapper. *(Words Etcetera)* **£30 [≃$57]**
- English Journey. London: 1984. *(Words Etcetera)* **£12 [≃$23]**
- Harriet Said ... London: Duckworth, 1972. Signature. Dustwrapper. *(Lewton)* **£24 [≃$46]**
- Harriet Said. London: 1972. Dustwrapper. *(Words Etcetera)* **£30 [≃$57]**
- Injury Time. London: Duckworth, 1977. Dustwrapper. *(Lewton)* **£12.50 [≃$23]**
- A Quiet Life. New York: Braziller, 1977. 1st US edition. Dustwrapper. *(Marlborough B'shop)* **£9 [≃$17]**
- Sweet William. London: Duckworth, 1975. Dustwrapper. *(Lewton)* **£12.50 [≃$23]**
- Watson's Apology. Duckworth, 1984. Uncorrected proof copy. Plain wrappers. Proof dustwrapper (somewhat rubbed). *(David Rees)* **£12 [≃$23]**
- A Weekend with Claude. London: 1967. Slight abrasion to flyleaf. Dustwrapper. Her 1st book. *(Words Etcetera)* **£125 [≃$239]**
- A Weekend with Claude. London: Hutchinson New Authors, 1967. Dustwrapper (laminate on rear panel chipped). Her 1st book. *(Moorhouse)* **£50 [≃$95]**
- Winter Garden. London: Duckworth, 1980. Dustwrapper. *(Lewton)* **£9.50 [≃$19]**

Baldwin, James

- Blues for Mr. Charlie. New York: Dial, 1964. Dustwrapper (lightly rubbed, one short tear). *(Nouveau)* **$50 [≃£26]**
- The Devil Finds Work. New York: Dial, 1976. Imitation leather. Dustwrapper. Signed by the author. *(Antic Hay)* **$100 [≃£52]**
- The Fire Next Time. New York: Dial, 1963. Price-clipped dustwrapper (minor rubbing at extremities). *(Nouveau)* **$40 [≃£20]**
- Giovanni's Room. New York: Dial Press, 1956. Dustwrapper. *(Houle)* **$225 [≃£117]**
- Giovanni's Room. New York: Dial, 1956. Few spots on top & foredges. Price-clipped dust- wrapper (lightly chipped). *(Nouveau)* **$100 [≃£52]**
- Giovanni's Room. London: Michael Joseph, 1957. 1st UK edition. Dustwrapper. *(Paul Brown)* **£22.50 [≃$44]**
- Giovanni's Room. London: 1957. Dustwrapper (scuffed, closed tear). *(Buckley)* **£30 [≃$57]**
- Go Tell it on the Mountain. New York: 1953. Spine slightly faded. His 1st book. *(Buckley)* **£25 [≃$47]**
- Go Tell It on the Mountain. New York: Knopf, 1953. Dustwrapper (spine slightly faded). His 1st book. *(Lopez)* **$650 [≃£338]**
- Go Tell it on the Mountain. London: Michael Joseph, 1954. Price-clipped dustwrapper. *(Sklaroff)* **£120 [≃$230]**
- If Beale Street Could Talk. New York: 1974. Dustwrapper. *(Polyanthos)* **$20 [≃£10]**
- Just Above My Head. New York: Dial, [1979]. Dustwrapper. Signed by the author. *(Antic Hay)* **$100 [≃£52]**
- Tell Me How Long the Train's Been Gone. New York: 1968. Dustwrapper. *(Polyanthos)* **$40 [≃£20]**
- Tell Me How Long the Train's Been Gone. London: 1968. Lower spine slightly bumped. Dustwrapper. *(Polyanthos)* **$30 [≃£15]**

Ballard, J.G.

- The Atrocity Exhibition. London: Cape, 1970. Price-clipped dustwrapper (spine faded). Signed by the author. *(David Rees)* **£60 [≃$115]**
- The Atrocity Exhibition. London: Cape, 1970. Dustwrapper (1 small tear), red spine lettering much less faded than usual. *(Dyke)* **£40 [≃$76]**
- The Atrocity Exhibition. London: 1970. Dustwrapper. *(Sclanders)* **£60 [≃$115]**
- The Burning World. New York: Berkley, 1964. Wrappers. *(Moorhouse)* **£20 [≃$38]**
- Concrete Island. London: Cape, 1974. Dustwrapper. Signed by the author. *(David Rees)* **£40 [≃$76]**
- Crash. London: Cape, 1973. Dustwrapper. *(Dyke)* **£40 [≃$76]**
- The Crystal World. New York: Farrar Straus Giroux, (1966). 1st American edition. Dustwrapper (very slightly rubbed). *(Lopez)* **$85 [≃£44]**
- The Day of Creation. London: Gollancz, 1987. One of 100 signed. Slipcase. *(David Rees)* **£75 [≃$143]**
- The Day of Creation. London: Gollancz, 1987. Dustwrapper. Signed by the author (1987). *(Marlborough B'shop)* **£20 [≃$38]**
- The Day of Creation. New York: 1988.

Dustwrapper. Signed by the author. *(Polyanthos)* **$35 [≃£18]**

- The Day of Forever. London: Panther Paper Backs, 1967. The true 1st edition. Paper slightly browned. Spine a little creased & rubbed. *(Blakeney)* **£10 [≃$19]**
- The Drought. London: Cape, 1965. Dustwrapper. *(Lewton)* **£100 [≃$191]**
- The Drowned World. New York: Berkley Medallion Books, 1962. True 1st edition. Pages slightly browned. Paperback covers rubbed at edges of spine. *(Virgo)* **£50 [≃$95]**
- The Drowned World & The Wind from Nowhere. New York: Doubleday, 1965. Upper hinge weak. Dustwrapper (slightly rubbed). *(Moorhouse)* **£65 [≃$124]**
- Empire of the Sun. London: Gollancz, 1984. 1st issue dustwrapper, with 2 reviews on rear panel. *(Alphabet)* **$65 [≃£33]**
- Empire of the Sun. London: Gollancz, 1984. 1st issue dustwrapper, with the Graham Greene quotation on rear panel. *(Ash)* **£25 [≃$47]**
- Empire of the Sun. London: Gollancz, 1984. Dustwrapper. *(Limestone Hills)* **$50 [≃£26]**
- Empire of the Sun. London: Gollancz, 1984. Dustwrapper. *(Dyke)* **£20 [≃$38]**
- Empire of the Sun. London: Gollancz, 1984. 2nd issue dustwrapper, with 6 blurbs on rear panel. *(Alphabet)* **$35 [≃£18]**
- Empire of the Sun. London: Gollancz, 1984. 3rd issue dustwrapper. *(Moorhouse)* **£10 [≃$19]**
- Empire of the Sun. London: Gollancz, 1984. Dustwrapper. *(Lewton)* **£11.50 [≃$23]**
- Empire of the Sun. London: Gollancz, 1984. Dustwrapper. Signed by the author. *(Sklaroff)* **£50 [≃$95]**
- Hello America. London: 1981. Dustwrapper. *(McCann)* **£18 [≃$34]**
- High Rise. London: Cape, 1970. Dustwrapper. *(David Rees)* **£30 [≃$57]**
- Love and Napalm: Export U.S.A. New York: Grove Press, 1972. 1st published edition. Dustwrapper. *(Moorhouse)* **£45 [≃$86]**
- Low-Flying Aircraft. London: Cape, 1976. Dustwrapper. Signed by the author. *(Virgo)* **£40 [≃$76]**
- Myths of the Near Future. London: Cape, 1982. Dustwrapper. Signed by the author. *(David Rees)* **£20 [≃$38]**
- Myths of the Near Future. London: Cape, 1982. Dustwrapper. Signed by the author. *(Virgo)* **£35 [≃$67]**
- Myths of the Near Future. London: Cape, 1982. Dustwrapper. *(Dyke)* **£15 [≃$28]**
- Myths of the Near Future. London: Cape, 1982. Dustwrapper. *(David Rees)* **£10 [≃$19]**
- Passport to Eternity. New York: Berkley, 1963. Wrappers (slightly creased). *(Moorhouse)* **£12 [≃$23]**
- Terminal Beach. New York: Berkley, 1963. Wrappers. *(Moorhouse)* **£20 [≃$38]**
- Terminal Beach. New York: Berkley Medallion Books, 1964. True 1st edition. Pages browned at edges. Small hole in corner of front cover. Signed by the author. *(Virgo)* **£50 [≃$95]**
- The Unlimited Dream Company. London: Cape, 1979. Price-clipped dustwrapper. Signed by the author. *(David Rees)* **£25 [≃$47]**
- The Unlimited Dream Company. London: Cape, 1979. Dustwrapper. *(Dyke)* **£15 [≃$28]**
- The Unlimited Dream Company. London: Cape, 1979. Dustwrapper. *(Lewton)* **£20 [≃$38]**
- The Unlimited Dream Company. London: Cape, 1979. Dustwrapper. *(Limestone Hills)* **$60 [≃£31]**
- The Voices of Time and Other Stories. New York: Berkley, 1962. Ownership label inside front cover. Wrappers. *(Moorhouse)* **£15 [≃$28]**
- Why I Want to F... Ronald Reagan. Unicorn: 1968. One of 250. Card covers. *(Lewton)* **£130 [≃$249]**
- The Wind from Nowhere. New York: Berkley, 1962. Wrappers (slightly rubbed). His 1st book. *(Moorhouse)* **£20 [≃$38]**

Banks, Iain

- The Bridge. London: Macmillan, 1986. Dustwrapper. Signed by the author and inscribed. *(Michael Johnson)* **£30 [≃$57]**
- The Bridge. 1986. Dustwrapper. Signed by the author. *(First Issues)* **£30 [≃$57]**
- Canal Dreams. London: 1989. Dustwrapper. *(Ellis)* **£15 [≃$28]**
- Cleaning Up. Birmingham: BSF, 1987. Wrappers. Signed by the author. *(Michael Johnson)* **£20 [≃$38]**
- Cleaning Up. BSFG, 1987. Card covers. *(Lewton)* **£15 [≃$28]**
- Consider Phlebas. Macmillan, 1987. Uncorrected proof copy. Wrappers. Inscribed by the author. *(David Rees)* **£45 [≃$86]**
- Consider Phlebas. London: Macmillan, 1987. Dustwrapper. Signed by the author. *(Michael Johnson)* **£25 [≃$47]**

- Consider Phlebas. London: Macmillan, 1987. Dustwrapper. *(Michael Johnson)* **£13 [≃$24]**
- Espedair Street. London: Macmillan, 1987. Uncorrected proof copy. Yellow wrappers, creases to rear corner. Signed by the author. *(Michael Johnson)* **£20 [≃$38]**
- Espedair Street. London: Macmillan, 1987. Dustwrapper. *(Michael Johnson)* **£12 [≃$23]**
- The Player of Games. Macmillan, 1988. Uncorrected proof copy. Wrappers. Inscribed by the author. *(David Rees)* **£40 [≃$76]**
- Player of Games. London: Macmillan, 1988. One of 201 signed. Russet cloth. Slipcase. *(Michael Johnson)* **£65 [≃$124]**
- The State of the Art. Connecticut: 1989. One of 400 signed by the author and illustrator, Arnie Fenner. Dustwrapper. Slipcase. *(David Rees)* **£40 [≃$76]**
- The State of the Art. Connecticut: 1989. Dustwrapper. Signed by the author. *(David Rees)* **£20 [≃$38]**
- The State of the Art. Connecticut: Ziesing, 1989. 1st trade edition. Dust- wrapper. Signed by the author. *(Moorhouse)* **£18 [≃$34]**
- Walking on Glass. London: Macmillan, 1985. Uncorrected proof copy. Wrappers. Signed by the author. *(David Rees)* **£45 [≃$86]**
- Walking on Glass. London: Macmillan, 1985. Clipped dustwrapper. Signed by the author. *(Paul Brown)* **£25 [≃$47]**
- Walking on Glass. London: 1985. Dustwrapper. Signed by the author. *(Buckley)* **£35 [≃$67]**
- Walking on Glass. London: Macmillan, 1985. Dustwrapper. Signed by the author. *(Michael Johnson)* **£30 [≃$57]**
- Walking on Glass. London: Macmillan, 1985. Dustwrapper. *(Lewton)* **£13.50 [≃$26]**
- Walking on Glass. Boston: Houghton Mifflin, (1986). 1st American edition. Proof copy. *(Lopez)* **$35 [≃£18]**
- The Wasp Factory. London: Macmillan, 1984. 1st issue. Dustwrapper. His 1st book. *(Sklaroff)* **£70 [≃$134]**
- The Wasp Factory. London: Macmillan, 1984. Dustwrapper. Signed by the author. *(Michael Johnson)* **£70 [≃$134]**
- The Wasp Factory. London: Macmillan, 1984. Dustwrapper. Signed by the author. *(Moorhouse)* **£55 [≃$105]**
- The Wasp Factory. London: Macmillan, 1984. Price-clipped dustwrapper. *(Alphabet)* **$125 [≃£65]**
- The Wasp Factory. London: Macmillan, 1984. Dustwrapper. *(Paul Brown)* **£35 [≃$67]**
- The Wasp Factory. London: Macmillan, 1984. Dustwrapper. Signed by the author. *(Lewton)* **£60 [≃$115]**

Banks, Lynne Reid

- The L-Shaped Room. London: 1960. Spine ends slightly bruised. Dustwrapper (very slightly rubbed, a few small nicks). Her 1st book. *(Ellis)* **£45 [≃$86]**
- The L-Shaped Room. London: Chatto & Windus, 1960. Price-clipped dustwrapper. *(Sklaroff)* **£35 [≃$67]**

Banville, John

- The Book of Evidence. Secker & Warburg, 1989. Dustwrapper. *(David Rees)* **£18 [≃$34]**
- Long Lankin. London: 1970. Uncorrected proof copy. Wrappers. *(Edrich)* **£60 [≃$115]**

Barker, A.L.

- Apology for a Hero. London: Hogarth, 1950. Dustwrapper. *(Lewton)* **£17.50 [≃$34]**

Barker, Clive

- The Damnation Game. London: Weidenfeld & Nicolson, 1985. Dustwrapper. Signed by the author. *(Lewton)* **£35 [≃$67]**
- The Great and Secret Show. London: Collins, 1989. One of 500 signed. Slipcase. *(Michael Johnson)* **£120 [≃$230]**
- Inhuman Condition. New York: Poseidon, 1987. Dustwrapper. *(Michael Johnson)* **£10 [≃$19]**
- Weaveworld. London: Collins, 1987. Uncorrected proof copy. Wrappers. Signed by the author. *(David Rees)* **£50 [≃$95]**
- Weaveworld. London: Collins, 1987. Special Advance Reader's Sample. Wrappers. *(Michael Johnson)* **£35 [≃$67]**

Barker, George

- Alanna Autumnal. London: 1933. Top edge dusty. Dustwrapper (grubby, spotted on the spine, with a number of short tears). *(Blakeney)* **£45 [≃$86]**
- At Thurgarton Church. Trigram Press: 1969. One of 100 signed. *(Words Etcetera)* **£25 [≃$47]**
- Calamiterror. London: 1937. Corners very slightly bumped. Dustwrapper (spine darkened, very slightly rubbed at extremities). *(Blakeney)* **£35 [≃$67]**
- Calamiterror. London: 1937. Dustwrapper (a trifle browned and creased on spine). *(Words Etcetera)* **£40 [≃$76]**

- The Dead Seagull. London: John Lehmann, 1950. Dustwrapper (slightly chipped). *(Clearwater)* **£25 [≃$47]**
- The Dead Seagull. London: MacGibbon & Kee, 1965. New preface for this edition. Dustwrapper. Signed by the author. *(Hazeldene)* **£35 [≃$67]**
- Janus. London: Faber, 1935. Some spotting on edges. Cloth dusty. *(Halsey)* **£25 [≃$47]**
- Janus. London: 1935. Edges foxed. Dustwrapper (slightly rubbed, slightly frayed, one nick, head of spine internally repaired). *(Ellis)* **£60 [≃$115]**
- Janus. London: 1935. Foredge very slightly spotted. Dustwrapper (spine darkened, tape reinforcement at top of spine). *(Blakeney)* **£45 [≃$86]**
- Lament and Triumph. London: Faber, 1940. Proof copy. *(Halsey)* **£15 [≃$28]**
- Poems. London: 1935. Boards a little bowed. Cloth just bubbling at top edge. Dustwrapper (lightly rubbed). *(Blakeney)* **£20 [≃$38]**
- Poems. London: Faber, [1935]. Dustwrapper (lightly used). *(Dermont)* **$75 [≃£39]**
- Sacred and Secular Elegies. New Directions, CT: 1943. Wrappers. Dustwrapper. *(Polyanthos)* **$20 [≃£10]**
- Selected Poems. New York: 1941. Dustwrapper (a few tiny chips at head of spine). *(Words Etcetera)* **£40 [≃$76]**
- Thirty Preliminary Poems. Parton Press: 1933. Integral dustwrapper (head of spine very slightly chipped). *(David Rees)* **£60 [≃$115]**
- The True Confessions. London: The Parton Press, 1957. Dustwrapper (spine darkened). *(Woolmer)* **$35 [≃£18]**

Barnard, Robert

- Death on the High C's. London: Collins Crime Club, 1977. Dustwrapper (several nicks and short closed tears). *(Mordida)* **$50 [≃£26]**
- Sheer Torture. London: Collins, 1981. Dustwrapper. *(Janus)* **$35 [≃£18]**

Barnes, Djuna

- The Book of Repulsive Women. New York: Bruno Chap Books, 1915. Wrappers (light soiling, some curling, two small nicks at lower edges). *(Any Amount)* **£95 [≃$182]**
- Nightwood. London: 1936. Endsheets a little spotted with some signs of damp. Cloth somewhat bubbled. Dustwrapper (chipped & dusty, small scratch to spine). *(Blakeney)* **£45 [≃$86]**
- Nightwood. London: Faber, 1936. *(Alphabet)* **$50 [≃£26]**

Barnes, Julian

- Before She Met Me. London: Cape, 1982. Dustwrapper. Signed by the author. *(Georges)* **£45 [≃$86]**
- Before She Met Me. London: Cape, 1982. Price-clipped dustwrapper. Signed by the author. *(David Rees)* **£20 [≃$38]**
- Duffy. By Dan Kavanagh. London: Cape, 1980. Price-clipped dustwrapper. Signed by the author as Kavanagh. *(David Rees)* **£35 [≃$67]**
- Fiddle City. By Dan Kavanagh. London: Cape, 1981. Dustwrapper. Signed by the author. *(David Rees)* **£45 [≃$86]**
- Fiddle City. By Dan Kavanagh. London: Cape, 1981. Dustwrapper. *(Moorhouse)* **£45 [≃$86]**
- Flaubert's Parrot. London: Cape, 1984. Dustwrapper. Signed by the author. *(David Rees)* **£120 [≃$230]**
- Flaubert's Parrot. London: 1984. Dustwrapper. Wraparound. Signed presentation copy. *(Egret)* **£110 [≃$211]**
- Flaubert's Parrot. London: 1984. Dustwrapper. Signed by the author. *(Egret)* **£105 [≃$201]**
- Flaubert's Parrot. New York: Knopf, 1985. Dustwrapper. *(Antic Hay)* **$35 [≃£18]**
- Flaubert's Parrot. New York: Knopf, 1985. 1st American edition. Dustwrapper. *(Michael Johnson)* **£35 [≃$67]**
- Going to the Dogs. By Dan Kavanagh. Viking: 1987. Dustwrapper. Signed by the author. *(David Rees)* **£20 [≃$38]**
- A History of the World in 10 1/2 Chapters. London: Cape, 1989. Uncorrected proof copy. Printed wrappers. *(David Rees)* **£30 [≃$57]**
- History of the World in 10 1/2 Chapters. Cape, 1989. Dustwrapper. Signed by the author. *(Michael Johnson)* **£28 [≃$53]**
- A History of the World in 10 1/2 Chapters. London: Cape, 1989. Dustwrapper. Signed by the author. *(David Rees)* **£20 [≃$38]**
- The History of the World in 10 1/2 Chapters. London: 1989. Uncorrected proof copy. Wrappers. Signed by the author. *(First Issues)* **£55 [≃$105]**
- A History of the World in 10 1/2 Chapters. London: 1989. Uncorrected proof copy. *(Egret)* **£50 [≃$95]**
- A History of the World in 10 1/2 Chapters. London: 1989. Dustwrapper. *(Egret)* **£25 [≃$47]**
- Metroland. London: Cape, 1980. Price-clipped dustwrapper. Signed by the author.

His 1st book. *(David Rees)* **£40 [≃$76]**

- Metroland. London: Cape, 1980. Dustwrapper. Signed by the author. *(Michael Johnson)* **£50 [≃$95]**
- Metroland. London: 1980. Dustwrapper. Signed by the author. *(Egret)* **£60 [≃$115]**
- Putting the Boot In. By Dan Kavanagh. London: Cape, 1985. Uncorrected proof copy. Printed wrappers. *(David Rees)* **£30 [≃$57]**
- Putting the Boot In. By Dan Kavanagh. London: Cape, 1985. Dustwrapper. Signed by the author. *(Michael Johnson)* **£22 [≃$42]**
- Staring at the Sun. London: Cape, 1986. Dustwrapper. Signed by the author. *(Michael Johnson)* **£25 [≃$47]**
- Staring at the Sun. London: 1986. Dustwrapper. Signed by the author. *(First Issues)* **£25 [≃$47]**

Barney, Natalie Clifford

- Je Me Souviens. Sansot: 1910. Wrappers (neat crease on top corner). Published anonymously. *(Any Amount)* **£60 [≃$115]**

Barstow, Stan

- A Kind of Loving. London: Michael Joseph, 1960. Dustwrapper (slight abrasion on spine panel). *(Dyke)* **£25 [≃$47]**
- A Kind of Loving. London: Michael Joseph, 1960. Dustwrapper. *(Glyn's)* **£20 [≃$38]**

Barth, John

- Chimera. New York: 1972. Dustwrapper (tiny edge stain). Signed by the author. *(Polyanthos)* **$30 [≃£15]**
- Chimera. New York: Random House, 1972. One of 300 signed by the author. Cardboard slipcase. *(Heritage)* **$85 [≃£44]**
- Chimera. New York: Random House, [1972]. Dustwrapper. *(Houle)* **$45 [≃£23]**
- Chimera. London: 1976. 1st English edition. Dustwrapper. *(Words Etcetera)* **£20 [≃$38]**
- Don't Count On It. Northridge, California: Lord John, 1984. One of 150 signed by the author. *(Heritage)* **$100 [≃£52]**
- The End of the Road. London: Secker, 1962. 1st UK edition. Small stain to foredge. Dustwrapper (closed tear). *(Paul Brown)* **£25 [≃$47]**
- The End of the Road. London: 1962. 1st British edition. Dustwrapper (some browning). *(Pettler & Liebermann)* **$75 [≃£39]**
- The Floating Opera. London: 1968. Dustwrapper. Author's signed presentation. *(Buckley)* **£55 [≃$105]**
- Giles Goat-Boy. Garden City: Doubleday, 1966. Uncorrected proof copy. Spine creased. *(Lopez)* **$200 [≃£104]**
- Giles Goat-Boy or, The Revised New Syllabus. Garden City: Doubleday, 1966. Dustwrapper. Inscribed by the author. *(Heritage)* **$75 [≃£39]**
- Giles Goat-Boy. London: Secker & Warburg, 1966. Price-clipped dustwrapper. *(Sklaroff)* **£21 [≃$40]**
- Letters. A Novel. New York: Putnam, [1979]. Uncorrected proof copy. Printed wrappers (lightly used). *(Dermont)* **$75 [≃£39]**
- Letters. New York: 1979. Proof copy. Wrappers. Signed by the author. *(Polyanthos)* **$45 [≃£23]**
- Lost in the Funhouse. New York: 1968. Dustwrapper (tiny nick side of spine). Publisher's presentation stamp. Signed by the author. *(Polyanthos)* **$45 [≃£23]**
- Sabbatical. New York: 1982. Dustwrapper. Proof dustwrapper. Signed by the author. *(Polyanthos)* **$40 [≃£20]**
- The Sot-Weed Factor. Garden City: 1960. Dustwrapper (a bit chipped, some internal tape reinforcement). *(Pettler & Liebermann)* **$225 [≃£117]**
- The Sot-Weed Factor. New York: Doubleday, 1960. Dustwrapper (crease on back panel). Signed by the author. *(Nouveau)* **$200 [≃£104]**
- The Sot-Weed Factor. London: 1961. 1st British edition. Some browning and foxing to page edges. Dustwrapper. *(Pettler & Liebermann)* **$50 [≃£26]**

Barthelme, Donald

- Amateurs. London: 1977. Tiny label removed. Dustwrapper. *(Polyanthos)* **$25 [≃£13]**
- City Life. New York: 1970. Dustwrapper. *(Polyanthos)* **$20 [≃£10]**
- City Life. New York: FSG, (1970). Dustwrapper. Signed by the author. *(Lopez)* **$55 [≃£28]**
- Come Back, Dr Caligari. Boston: 1964. Dustwrapper (slightly chipped at spine). Signed by the author. *(Buckley)* **£55 [≃$105]**
- Come Back, Dr. Caligari. Boston: 1964. Dustwrapper (some internal paper tape reinforcements). His 1st book. *(Pettler & Liebermann)* **$75 [≃£39]**
- Come Back, Dr. Caligari. Eyre & Spottiswoode, 1966. 1st English edition. Front endpaper slightly scuffed. Top corners slightly bumped. Dustwrapper (slightly browned, small closed tear at foot of spine

repaired internally). His 1st book. *(Virgo)* **£40 [≃$76]**

- Come Back, Dr Caligari. London: 1966. 1st UK edition. Dustwrapper. *(Buckley)* **£30 [≃$57]**
- The Dead Father. New York: FSG, (1975). Dustwrapper. Signed by the author. *(Lopez)* **$45 [≃£23]**
- The Dead Father. New York: 1975. Dustwrapper. *(Polyanthos)* **$20 [≃£10]**
- The Dead Father. New York: Farrar Straus & Giroux, (1975). Dustwrapper. Signed by the author. *(Lopez)* **$50 [≃£26]**
- Great Days. New York: 1979. Dustwrapper. *(Polyanthos)* **$20 [≃£10]**
- Guilty Pleasures. New York: FSG, (1974). Dustwrapper. Signed by the author. *(Lopez)* **$55 [≃£28]**
- Sadness. New York: FSG, (1972). Dustwrapper. Signed by the author. *(Lopez)* **$55 [≃£28]**
- Sixty Stories. New York: (1981). Dustwrapper. *(Polyanthos)* **$25 [≃£13]**
- Sixty Stories. New York: 1981. One of 500 signed. Box. *(Polyanthos)* **$65 [≃£33]**
- Snow White. New York: Atheneum, 1967. Dustwrapper. *(Alphabet)* **$100 [≃£52]**
- Snow White. New York: 1967. Dustwrapper. Signed by the author. *(Polyanthos)* **$65 [≃£33]**
- Snow White. New York: 1967. Name. Dustwrapper. *(Pettler & Liebermann)* **$65 [≃£33]**
- Unspeakable Practices, Unnatural Acts. London: 1969. 1st English edition. Dustwrapper. *(Words Etcetera)* **£25 [≃$47]**

Barthelme, Frederick

- Rangoon. New York: Winter House, 1970. Dustwrapper (lightly chipped). His 1st book. *(Nouveau)* **$45 [≃£23]**

Bass, Rick

- The Deer Pasture. College Station: Texas A & M, 1985. Dustwrapper. Signed by the author. His 1st book. *(Michael Johnson)* **£30 [≃$57]**
- The Deer Pasture. Texas: A & M UP, 1985. Price-clipped dustwrapper. Signed by the author. His 1st book. *(Polyanthos)* **$35 [≃£18]**
- The Deer Pasture. Texas: A & M UP, 1985. Price-clipped dustwrapper. Signed by the author and illustrator Elizabeth Hughes. His 1st book. *(Polyanthos)* **$40 [≃£20]**
- Oil Notes. Boston: 1989. Dustwrapper. Signed by the author. *(Polyanthos)* **$35 [≃£18]**
- The Watch. New York: 1989. Dustwrapper. Signed by the author. *(Polyanthos)* **$35 [≃£18]**
- The Watch. New York: Norton, 1989. Dustwrapper. *(Michael Johnson)* **£20 [≃$38]**
- Wild to the Heart. Harrisburg: Stackpole, 1987. Dustwrapper. Signed by the author. *(Michael Johnson)* **£25 [≃$47]**
- Wild to the Heart. PA: (1987). Dustwrapper. Signed by the author. *(Polyanthos)* **$35 [≃£18]**

Bates, H.E.

- The Black Boxer. London: 1932. Dustwrapper (rubbed, frayed, lower panel torn and creased). *(Ellis)* **£65 [≃$124]**
- The Last Bread. London: 1926. Some usual foxing. Wrappers (slightly rubbed). His 1st book. *(Ellis)* **£120 [≃$230]**
- The Modern Short Story. London: 1941. Bottom corner of lower cover very slightly bruised. Dustwrapper (slightly rubbed, slightly frayed, two nicks). *(Ellis)* **£70 [≃$134]**

Bax, Martin

- The Hospital Ship. London: Cape, 1976. Dustwrapper. Signed by the author. *(Hazeldene)* **£18 [≃$34]**

Baxter, Glen

- Atlas. London: Cape, 1982. No dustwrapper issued. *(Hazeldene)* **£12 [≃$23]**

Beach, Sylvia

- Shakespeare and Company. New York: Harcourt, Brace, [ca 1959]. Edges of pages and cover slightly browned. Cover very slightly marked. Dustwrapper (very small repaired nicks on spine). *(Virgo)* **£35 [≃$67]**
- Ulysses in Paris. New York: Harcourt Brace, [ca 1956]. Head of spine slightly chipped, lower edges slightly shelf worn. Tissue dustwrapper (torn but complete). *(Virgo)* **£60 [≃$115]**

Beagle, Peter

- A Fine and Private Place. New York: Viking, 1960. Dustwrapper (edge tears and small chips). His 1st book. *(Nouveau)* **$55 [≃£28]**

Bear, Greg

- Blood Music. London: Gollancz, 1986. 1st British edition. Dustwrapper. *(Michael Johnson)* **£15 [≃$28]**

- Eon. New York: Bluejay, 1985. Uncorrected proof copy. Wrappers. *(Michael Johnson)* **£45 [≃$86]**
- Eon. London: Gollancz, 1986. 1st British edition. Dustwrapper. *(Michael Johnson)* **£15 [≃$28]**
- Hegira. London: Seven House, 1988. 1st British edition. 1st hardbound edition. Dustwrapper. *(Michael Johnson)* **£14 [≃$26]**
- Infinity Concerto. London: Century, 1988. 1st hardbound edition. Dustwrapper. *(Michael Johnson)* **£30 [≃$57]**

Beaton, George

- See Brennan, Gerald.

Beckett, Samuel

- All Strange Away. New York: Gotham Book Mart, 1976. One of 200 signed by Becket and the illustrator, Edward Gorey. Quarter leather. Box. *(Polyanthos)* **$450 [≃£234]**
- All That Fall. New York: Grove Press, 1957. Dustwrapper (slightly chipped). *(Words Etcetera)* **£45 [≃$86]**
- All that Fall. New York: Grove Press, (1957). Neat name. Dustwrapper (minimal edge rubbing). *(Polyanthos)* **$30 [≃£15]**
- All that Fall. London: 1957. Wrappers. *(McCann)* **£30 [≃$57]**
- All That Fall. London: 1957. Wrappers. *(Sclanders)* **£35 [≃$67]**
- All That Fall. London: 1957. Wrappers. *(Edrich)* **£15 [≃$28]**
- (Translates) An Anthology of Mexican Poetry. Bloomington: Indiana UP, 1958. Dustwrapper (slightly creased, a few slits and tears). *(Words Etcetera)* **£40 [≃$76]**
- As No Other Dare Fail. For Samuel Beckett on his 80th Birthday by his Friends and Admirers. 1986. One of 50 numbered. *(Edrich)* **£100 [≃$191]**
- Avigdor Arikha Dessins. Jerusalem: 1967. *(Whiteson)* **£70 [≃$134]**
- Beginning to End. New York: Gotham Book Mart, 1988. Drawings by Edward Gorey. One of 300 signed by author and illustrator. No dustwrapper issued. *(Moorhouse)* **£185 [≃$355]**
- Catastrophe. A Broadside. [No date given by bookseller]. One of 100 signed. *(First Issues)* **£125 [≃$239]**
- Catastrophe. California: 1983. One of 100 signed. Broadsheet. *(David Rees)* **£145 [≃$278]**
- Catastrophe. N.p.: 1983. One of 100, signed. Broadside. *(Blakeney)* **£150 [≃$287]**
- Collected Shorter Prose. 1945-1980. London: 1984. Dustwrapper. *(Edrich)* **£10 [≃$19]**
- Come and Go, A Dramaticule. London: 1967. Trade edition. Wrappers price-clipped. *(Blakeney)* **£12.50 [≃$24]**
- Comment C'Est. Paris: Les Editions de Minuit, 1961. Wrappers. *(Edrich)* **£25 [≃$47]**
- Company. New York: Grove Press, 1980. Dustwrapper. *(Polyanthos)* **$15 [≃£7]**
- The Complete Dramatic Works. London: 1968. Dustwrapper. Signed by the author. *(Sclanders)* **£125 [≃$239]**
- Disjecta. Introduction by R. Cohn. London: 1983. Stiff wrappers. *(Edrich)* **£8.50 [≃$17]**
- (Translates) The Drunken Boat by Arthur Rimbaud. 1976. One of 100 signed by Beckett. *(Ellis)* **£225 [≃$431]**
- Drunken Boat. Reading: 1976. One of 200 (of 300) unsigned. Folio. *(Words Etcetera)* **£65 [≃$124]**
- Drunken Boat. A Translation of Arthur Rimbaud's Poem Le Bateau Ivre. Reading: Whiteknights Press, 1976. One of 300. *(Woolmer)* **$85 [≃£44]**
- Endgame. London: Faber, 1958. Dustwrapper. *(Lewton)* **£16.50 [≃$32]**
- Endgame, followed by Act Without Words. London: 1958. Endpapers very slightly spotted. Dustwrapper. *(Blakeney)* **£65 [≃$124]**
- Endgame. London: 1958. Dustwrapper (very slightly rubbed, two very small nicks). *(Ellis)* **£50 [≃$95]**
- Ends and Odds. London: Faber, 1977. Dustwrapper. *(Dyke)* **£10 [≃$19]**
- First Love and Other Shorts. New York: Grove Press, 1974. Dustwrapper. *(Polyanthos)* **$20 [≃£10]**
- Footfalls. London: Faber, 1976. Proof copy. Wrappers. *(Words Etcetera)* **£50 [≃$95]**
- Footfalls. London: 1976. Inscription on endpaper. Wrappers. *(Edrich)* **£8 [≃$15]**
- For To End Yet Again & Other Fizzles. London: 1976. The casebound issue. Dustwrapper (slightly creased at top of spine). *(Blakeney)* **£20 [≃$38]**
- From an Abandoned Work. London: 1958. Wrappers slightly faded at spine & very slightly rubbed. *(Blakeney)* **£30 [≃$57]**
- From An Abandoned Work. London: 1958. Wrappers. *(Edrich)* **£15 [≃$28]**
- Guillaume Apollinaire. Zone. Dublin: Dolmen Press; London: Calder & Boyars, 1972. One of 250 signed by Beckett. Slipcase (slightly rubbed and worn). *(Moorhouse)* **£235 [≃$451]**

- Happy Days. New York: Grove Press, Evergreen Original, 1961. Wrappers. *(Polyanthos)* **$15 [≃£7]**
- Happy Days. USA: An Evergreen Original, 1961. Wrappers. *(Edrich)* **£20 [≃$38]**
- Happy Days. London: 1962. Dustwrapper (unfaded, unrubbed). *(Blakeney)* **£45 [≃$86]**
- Ill Seen Ill Said. Northridge: Lord John Press, 1982. One of 299 signed. Quarter leather and marbled boards. *(Moorhouse)* **£175 [≃$335]**
- Ill Seen; Ill Said. London: 1972. The casebound issue. Trace of erasure to front free endpaper. Dustwrapper (very lightly rubbed, spine slightly faded). *(Blakeney)* **£15 [≃$28]**
- Imagination Dead Imagine. London: Calder & Boyars, (1965). One of 100 signed. Slipcase. *(Lopez)* **$375 [≃£195]**
- Krapp's Last Tape & Embers. London: 1959. Wrappers. *(Buckley)* **£35 [≃$67]**
- Krapp's Last Tape & Embers. London: 1959. Wrappers (quarter inch tear to front). *(Blakeney)* **£30 [≃$57]**
- Lessness. London: Calder & Boyars, [1970]. 1st English edition. Stiff wrappers. Inscribed by the author. *(Heritage)* **$150 [≃£78]**
- The Lost Ones. New York: Grove Press, 1972. Wrappers. *(Polyanthos)* **$15 [≃£7]**
- The Lost Ones. London: Calder & Boyars, [1972]. One of 100 signed by the author. Vellum backed cloth, a.e.g. (spine sl darkened). Slipcase. *(Heritage)* **$200 [≃£104]**
- The Lost Ones. London: Calder & Boyars, 1972. One of 100 signed. Quarter calf. Slipcase. *(Words Etcetera)* **£250 [≃$479]**
- Malone Dies. New York: Grove Press, 1956. 1st edition in English. Casebound issue. One of 500 numbered. No dustwrapper issued. *(Blakeney)* **£125 [≃$239]**
- Malone Dies. New York: Grove Press, 1958. One of 500. Cellophane dustwrapper (little torn rear panel). *(Words Etcetera)* **£110 [≃$211]**
- (Translates) La Manivelle / The Old Tune. By Robert Pinget. Paris: 1960. Wrappers. *(Words Etcetera)* **£30 [≃$57]**
- Mercier and Camier. London: 1974. Dustwrapper. *(Edrich)* **£12 [≃$23]**
- Mercier et Camier. Paris: Editions de Minuit, 1970. One of 92 on special paper. Precedes the British and American editions. Wrappers, unopened. *(Moorhouse)* **£65 [≃$124]**
- Molloy. Paris: 1951. Wrappers, unopened. *(Words Etcetera)* **£110 [≃$211]**
- Molloy. Paris: Olympia Press, 1951. Wrappers (slightly rubbed and chipped around edges). *(Virgo)* **£80 [≃$153]**
- Molloy. Paris: Olympia Press, 1955. Wrappers. *(Sclanders)* **£50 [≃$95]**
- Molloy. Paris: Olympia Press, 1955. Thin card wrappers (slightly rubbed and chipped around edges). *(Virgo)* **£80 [≃$153]**
- Molloy. Paris: Olympia, (1955). 1st English language edition. Slight foxing, mostly to foredge. Wrappers. Dustwrapper (lightly chipped and rubbed). Label signed by the author laid in. *(Lopez)* **$225 [≃£117]**
- Molloy, Malone Dies, The Unnameable. Paris: Olympia Press, 1959. 1st complete edition of the trilogy. Wrappers. *(Buckley)* **£35 [≃$67]**
- Molloy, Malone Dies, The Unnameable. New York: Grove Press: 1959. 1st American edition. Dustwrapper. *(Words Etcetera)* **£55 [≃$105]**
- More Pricks Than Kicks. Special Edition for Scholars. Second Edition [actually 3rd edn]. London: 1966. One of 100. Wrappers slightly spotted. *(Blakeney)* **£40 [≃$76]**
- More Pricks Than Kicks. London: Calder & Boyars, 1970. One of 100, signed. Quarter calf. Slipcase. *(Words Etcetera)* **£300 [≃$575]**
- Murphy. New York: Grove Press, [1957]. Dustwrapper (lightly used). *(Dermont)* **$125 [≃£65]**
- Murphy. 1957. 1st American edition. Dustwrapper. *(Words Etcetera)* **£55 [≃$105]**
- No's Knife. London: Calder & Boyars, 1967. One of 100, signed. Full cream calf gilt (small mark on lower cover). Slipcase. Quarter calf called for in colophon. *(Words Etcetera)* **£275 [≃$527]**
- Not I. London: Faber, 1973. Wrappers. *(Virgo)* **£10 [≃$19]**
- Not I. London: Faber, [1973]. 1st English edition. Wrappers. Signed by the author. *(Heritage)* **$150 [≃£78]**
- Oh Les Beaux Jours. Paris: 1963. One of 412. Wrappers. *(Words Etcetera)* **£65 [≃$124]**
- Oh Les Beaux Jours. Paris: 1963. One of 412. Wrappers. *(Buckley)* **£50 [≃$95]**
- Our Exagmination Round His Factification For Incamination Of Work in Progress. London: [1936]. 1st English edition from French sheets. Dustwrapper (sunned at spine & at extremities). *(Blakeney)* **£125 [≃$239]**
- Poemes. Paris: 1968. One of 550 (of 762) numbered. Wrappers, unopened. *(Edrich)* **£45 [≃$86]**
- Poems in English. New York: Grove Press, 1963. Price-clipped dustwrapper. *(Polyanthos)* **$20 [≃£10]**

- Proust. London: Dolphin Books, 1931. Dustwrapper (slightly chipped). Publisher's 4-page pamphlet advertising Proust's works loosely inserted. *(Edrich)* **£85 [≃$163]**
- Proust. London: Dolphin Books, 1931. Head and edge of spine rubbed. *(Edrich)* **£25 [≃$47]**
- Proust. London: 1931. Spine browned, slight wear at head. *(Sclanders)* **£25 [≃$47]**
- Proust. London: Chatto, 1931. Decorated boards. Dustwrapper (dull and slightly torn). *(Whiteson)* **£110 [≃$211]**
- Proust / Three Dialogues. With Georges Duthuit. London: John Calder, [1965]. One of 100 signed. Vellum and decorative cloth, a.e.g. Slipcase. *(Antic Hay)* **$350 [≃£182]**
- Stories and Texts for Nothing. New York: Grove Press, 1967. 1st US edition. Dustwrapper. *(Moorhouse)* **£18 [≃$34]**
- Texts for Nothing. London: 1974. Dustwrapper. *(Edrich)* **£12 [≃$23]**
- That Time. London: 1976. Wrappers. *(Buckley)* **£10 [≃$19]**
- That Time. London: 1976. Wrappers. *(Edrich)* **£8 [≃$15]**
- Three Occasional Pieces. London: 1982. Wrappers. *(Edrich)* **£6 [≃$11]**
- Three Occasional Pieces. London: 1982. Wrappers. *(Buckley)* **£20 [≃$38]**
- Three Occasional Pieces. London: 1982. Wrappers. *(Blakeney)* **£10 [≃$19]**
- Waiting for Godot. London: 1956. Endpapers tanned. Dustwrapper (very slightly nicked, spine browned). *(Sclanders)* **£50 [≃$95]**
- Waiting for Godot. Revised and Unexpurgated Edition. London: 1965. Single biro mark on fly leaf. Dustwrapper. *(Words Etcetera)* **£65 [≃$124]**
- Waiting for Godot. London: Faber, 1965. 2nd, unexpurgated edition. Dustwrapper. *(Moorhouse)* **£45 [≃$86]**
- Watt. Paris: Olympia Press, 1953. One of 1100 (of 1125). Wrappers (spine ends slightly chipped). *(Moorhouse)* **£175 [≃$335]**
- Watt. Paris: Olympia Press, 1958. 1st trade edition. Dustwrapper (slightly rubbed, one closed tear). *(Buckley)* **£50 [≃$95]**
- Watt. Paris: Olympia Press, 1958. 1st trade edition. Spine very slightly bumped. Dustwrapper (minimal wear). *(Sclanders)* **£50 [≃$95]**
- Without Words [in] Live New Departures Programme, 1964. Wrappers. *(Words Etcetera)* **£45 [≃$86]**
- Zone. London: Dolmen Press / Calder, 1972. One of 250 signed. Morocco backed cloth. Slipcase (couple of rub marks on spine). *(Words Etcetera)* **£185 [≃$355]**

Beckett, Samuel, MacGowran, Jack & Gorey, Edward

- Beginning to End. Illustrated by Edward Gorey. New York: 1989. One of 300 signed by Beckett & Gorey. Boards. With the prospectus. *(Blakeney)* **£150 [≃$287]**

Beebe, Lucius Morris

- Fallen Stars. Boston: Cronhill, [1921]. Boards, paper label. *(Houle)* **$150 [≃£78]**

Behan, Brendan

- Borstal Boy. London: 1958. Dustwrapper (two minute nicks). *(Egret)* **£25 [≃$47]**
- Borstal Boy. London: Hutchinson, 1958. Uncorrected proof copy on proof paper. Wrappers (slightly faded). *(Whiteson)* **£35 [≃$67]**
- Brendan Behan's Island. London: Hutchinson, 1962. Dustwrapper. *(Lewton)* **£12.50 [≃$24]**
- The Hostage. London: Methuen, [1958]. Dustwrapper (some creases rear panel). Author's signed presentation inscription. *(Dermont)* **$150 [≃£78]**
- The Quare Fellow. London: Methuen, 1956. Dustwrapper. *(Lewton)* **£30 [≃$57]**

Bell, Clive

- Proust. London: Hogarth Press, 1928. *(Clearwater)* **£40 [≃$76]**

Bell, Julian

- Winter Movement and Other Poems. London: Chatto, 1930. Small stain on cloth at rear. Spine label slightly chipped, slight bruise on foredge. Inscription on fly. *(Halsey)* **£40 [≃$76]**
- Winter Movement and Other Poems. London: Chatto & Windus, 1930. Partly uncut. Dustwrapper (dusty, slightly rubbed at top edge). "Office production copy" sticker. *(Woolmer)* **$135 [≃£70]**

Béllamy, Francis Rufus

- Atta. New York: A.A. Wyn, [1953]. Dustwrapper (slightly soiled). *(Dermont)* **$35 [≃£18]**

Bellow, Saul

- The Adventures of Augie March. New York: Viking, 1953. Dustwrapper. *(Michael Johnson)* **£75 [≃$143]**

- The Adventures of Augie March. New York: 1953. 1st issue. One corner creased. Spine sunned, extremities little rubbed, covers slightly edge sunned. 1st issue dustwrapper (spine extremities little chipped, one small edge chip, slightly rubbed). *(Polyanthos)* **$50 [≃£26]**
- The Adventures of Augie March. New York: Viking, 1953. 2nd iss, with Wolff imprint and top edge unstained. 1st issue dustwrapper, with no reviews. Price-clipped dustwrapper (few edge tears). *(Chapel Hill)* **$60 [≃£31]**
- The Adventures of Augie March. London: 1954. Very slightly cocked. Dustwrapper (a little frayed at extremities). *(Blakeney)* **£55 [≃$105]**
- Dangling Man. New York: 1944. His 1st book. *(Pettler & Liebermann)* **$90 [≃£46]**
- Dangling Man. London: 1946. 1st English edition. Dustwrapper. His 1st book. *(Georges)* **£140 [≃$268]**
- The Dean's December. New York: (1982). 1st Harper & Row edition. One of 500 signed. Slipcase. *(King)* **$75 [≃£39]**
- The Dean's December. New York: 1982. One of 500 signed. Acetate dustwrapper. Box. *(Polyanthos)* **$75 [≃£39]**
- Henderson the Rain King. New York: 1959. Dustwrapper (spine chipped). *(Pettler & Liebermann)* **$75 [≃£39]**
- Henderson the Rain King. New York: 1959. Dustwrapper (slight shallow spine chips). *(Pettler & Liebermann)* **$90 [≃£46]**
- Henderson the Rain King. London: Weidenfeld, 1959. Dustwrapper. *(Dyke)* **£30 [≃$57]**
- Henderson the Rain King. London: Weidenfeld & Nicolson, (1959). 1st English edition. Dustwrapper. *(Limestone Hills)* **$75 [≃£39]**
- Herzog. New York: Viking, 1964. Price-clipped dustwrapper (minor rubbing at extremities). *(Nouveau)* **$40 [≃£20]**
- Him With His Foot in His Mouth and Other Stories. New York: Harper & Row, [1984]. Dustwrapper. Signed by the author. *(Antic Hay)* **$75 [≃£39]**
- Humboldt's Gift. New York: Viking Press, 1975. The true 1st edition. Head and tail bands. Dustwrapper. *(Hazeldene)* **£25 [≃$47]**
- More Die of Heart-Break. London: 1987. Uncorrected proof copy. Wrappers. *(First Issues)* **£25 [≃$47]**
- Mr. Sammler's Planet. New York: Viking, [1970]. Advance review copy with slip. Dustwrapper. Signed by the author. *(Antic Hay)* **$150 [≃£78]**
- Seize the Day. London: 1957. Spine lettering very slightly dull. Dustwrapper (with one short tear). *(Blakeney)* **£55 [≃$105]**
- Seize the Day. London: 1957. Price-clipped dustwrapper (slightly frayed, a few nicks). *(Ellis)* **£60 [≃$115]**

Bemelmans, Ludwig

- My War with the United States. New York: Viking, 1937. Dustwrapper (one short tear). *(Alphabet)* **$175 [≃£91]**

Benchley, Peter

- Jaws. London: 1974. Dustwrapper. *(Words Etcetera)* **£35 [≃$67]**
- Jaws. London: 1974. Dustwrapper. *(Egret)* **£35 [≃$67]**

Benedictus, David

- This Animal is Mischievous. London: 1965. Dustwrapper. *(First Issues)* **£10 [≃$19]**
- You're a Big Boy Now. London: 1963. Dustwrapper. *(First Issues)* **£10 [≃$19]**

Benet, Stephen Vincent

- America. New York: Farrar & Rinehart, [1944]. Dustwrapper (nick to top of spine). *(Houle)* **$55 [≃£28]**
- Selected Works. New York: Farrar & Rinehart, 1942. 2 vols. Minor wear. No dustwrappers issued. Signed by the author. *(Antic Hay)* **$85 [≃£44]**

Benn, Tony

- Arguments for Socialism. London: 1949. Some underlining on 2 pages. Dustwrapper. Signed by the author and inscribed. *(Roberts)* **£8.50 [≃$17]**

Bennett, Alan, Cook, Peter, et al.

- Beyond the Fringe. London: 1964. Inscription. Dustwrapper (slightly nicked). *(McCann)* **£24 [≃$46]**

Bentley, E.C.

- Trent's Last Case. London: Nelson, (1913). Edges tanned, spine darkened. *(Hazeldene)* **£35 [≃$67]**

Berger, John

- G. London: Weidenfeld & Nicolson, 1972. Price-clipped dustwrapper. *(Sklaroff)* **£25 [≃$47]**

Berger, Thomas

- Arthur Rex. Delacorte: 1978. Advance Uncorrected proof copy. Wrappers. *(Nouveau)* **$65 [≃£33]**

- Being Invisible. Boston: Little, Brown, 1987. Advance Uncorrected proof copy. Wrappers. *(Nouveau)* **$65 [≃£33]**
- Being Invisible. Boston: 1987. Dustwrapper. Signed by the author. *(Polyanthos)* **$35 [≃£18]**
- Crazy in Berlin. New York: (1958). Extremities very slightly rubbed. Dustwrapper (two half-inch pieces missing, very slight chipping tears and rubbing but both panels complete). Signed presentation copy from the author with 15-line ALS. His 1st book. *(Polyanthos)* **$100 [≃£52]**
- Killing Time. New York: 1967. Dustwrapper (little edge rubbed). Signed by the author. *(Polyanthos)* **$35 [≃£18]**
- Little Big Man. New York: Dial, 1964. Inscription. Price-clipped dustwrapper. *(Lopez)* **$50 [≃£26]**
- Reinhart's Women. New York: 1981. Dustwrapper. Signed by the author. *(Polyanthos)* **$35 [≃£18]**
- Sneaky People. New York: 1975. Price-clipped dustwrapper. Signed by the author. *(Polyanthos)* **$35 [≃£18]**
- Vital Parts. New York: 1970. Dustwrapper. Signed by the author. *(Polyanthos)* **$35 [≃£18]**
- Who is Teddy Villanova? London: 1977. Dustwrapper. Signed by the author. *(Polyanthos)* **$35 [≃£18]**

Berkeley, Anthony

- Dead Mrs. Stratton. Garden City: Doubleday Crime Club, 1933. 1st American edition. Dust- wrapper. *(Mordida)* **$175 [≃£91]**
- The Layton Court Mystery. Garden City: Doubleday Crime Club, 1929. 1st American edition. Dustwrapper (some tiny chips at foot of spine). *(Mordida)* **$400 [≃£208]**
- Malice Aforethought. By Francis Iles. New York: Harper, 1931. 1st American edition. Edges foxed. Dustwrapper (several short closed tears, wear and chips at corners, minor wear spine ends). *(Mordida)* **$175 [≃£91]**
- The Piccadilly Murder. Garden City: Doubleday Crime Club, 1930. 1st American edition. Small spot on bottom edge. Dustwrapper (tiny wear at spine ends and a few nicks). *(Mordida)* **$200 [≃£104]**
- The Poisoned Chocolates Case. Garden City: Doubleday Crime Club, 1929. 1st American edition. Edges darkened. Dustwrapper (spine slightly faded, several short closed tears, tiny wear at spine ends). *(Mordida)* **$100 [≃£52]**
- The Wychford Poisoning Case. Garden City: Doubleday Crime Club, 1930. 1st American edition. Top edge slightly darkened. Dustwrapper (slight wear at top of spine corner). *(Mordida)* **$250 [≃£130]**

Berlin, Sven

- I am Lazarus. Galley, 1961. Dustwrapper. Signed presentation copy. *(Sklaroff)* **£40 [≃$76]**

Berry, Wendell

- The Broken Ground. London: Cape, 1966. 1st UK edition. Dustwrapper. *(Halsey)* **£22 [≃$42]**
- The Broken Ground. London: 1966. Tiny edge tear title. Name. Dustwrapper. Author's signed presentation copy. *(Polyanthos)* **$75 [≃£39]**
- The Hidden Wound. Boston: 1970. Dustwrapper. Author's inscription. *(Between the Covers)* **$85 [≃£44]**
- The Long-Legged House. New York: Harcourt Brace & World, (1969). Endpapers discoloured under dustwrapper flaps. Dustwrapper. Inscribed by the author. *(Lopez)* **$85 [≃£44]**

Berryman, John

- Berryman's Sonnets. New York: (1967). Covers warped. Dustwrapper. *(Woolmer)* **$35 [≃£18]**
- The Dispossessed. New York: Sloane, (1948). Dustwrapper (very slight wear at edges). *(Woolmer)* **$350 [≃£182]**
- The Dream Songs. New York: Farrar Straus & Giroux, [1969]. Price-clipped dustwrapper. *(Antic Hay)* **$45 [≃£23]**
- His Toy, His Dream, His Rest. 308 Dream Songs. New York: (1968). Dustwrapper. *(Woolmer)* **$35 [≃£18]**
- His Toy, His Dream, His Rest. London: 1969. Advance copy. Publisher's wrappers. *(Blakeney)* **£15 [≃$28]**
- Homage to Mistress Bradstreet. New York: 1956. Dustwrapper (tiny chip top of spine). *(Polyanthos)* **$100 [≃£52]**
- Homage to Mistress Bradstreet. New York: (1956). Dustwrapper. *(Woolmer)* **$150 [≃£78]**
- Homage to Mistress Bradstreet. London: 1959. Dustwrapper. *(Egret)* **£40 [≃$76]**
- Love & Fame. New York: Farrar, Straus & Giroux, 1970. One of 250 signed. Slipcase. *(Houle)* **$95 [≃£49]**
- Poems. New Directions, CT: The Poet of the Month, (1942). Wrappers. Dustwrapper (spine minimally sunned). His 1st book. *(Polyanthos)* **$50 [≃£26]**

- 77 Dream Songs. London: 1964. Dustwrapper. *(Egret)* **£30 [≃$57]**
- Stephen Crane. New York: Sloane, (1950). Dustwrapper. *(Woolmer)* **$125 [≃£65]**
- Stephen Crane. New York: Sloane, (1950). Dustwrapper (slight loss at spine extremities and some other light wear). *(Between the Covers)* **$100 [≃£52]**
- Stefanik, Ernest C., Jr.: John Berryman A Descriptive Bibliography. Univ of Pittsburgh Press: 1974. No dustwrapper issued. *(Woolmer)* **$25 [≃£13]**

Betjeman, John

- Altar and Pew. London: 1959. Wrappers. *(Words Etcetera)* **£10.50 [≃$21]**
- Antiquarian Prejudice. London: Hogarth Press, 1939. Small hole in flyleaf. Wrappers. *(Buckley)* **£17 [≃$32]**
- Church Poems. London: 1980. 1st (withdrawn) issue, with 2 poems printed incompletely. Dustwrapper (slightly faded). *(Clearwater)* **£40 [≃$76]**
- Church Poems. London: Murray, 1980. 1st (withdrawn) issue. Dustwrapper. *(David Rees)* **£20 [≃$38]**
- Collected Poems. London: 1958. Dustwrapper. *(Words Etcetera)* **£25 [≃$47]**
- Continual Dew. London: Murray, 1937. Cloth very slightly dull. Dustwrapper (dull, slightly rubbed). *(Whiteson)* **£70 [≃$134]**
- Continual Dew. London: Murray, 1937. Dustwrapper. *(Lewton)* **£90 [≃$172]**
- First and Last Loves. London: 1952. Foredge lightly foxed. Dustwrapper (slightly foxed, slightly frayed, small closed tear, piece missing from head of spine). *(Ellis)* **£60 [≃$115]**
- Ghastly Good Taste. London: Chapman & Hall, 1933. Erratum slip. Slight foxing. Some rubbing and uneven fading of covers, linen spine faded and slightly bumped, label complete. *(Tiger Books)* **£80 [≃$153]**
- Ghastly Good Taste. London: Chapman & Hall, 1933. Boards lightly used, small chip spine label (extra label at rear). *(Between the Covers)* **$250 [≃£130]**
- Ghastly Good Taste. London: Blond, 1970. One of 200 signed. Very tiny scuff at foot of spine. Slipcase. *(Virgo)* **£95 [≃$182]**
- Ground Plan to Skyline. By Richard M. Farran [pseudonym]. London: Newman Neame, 1960. Wrappers. *(Moorhouse)* **£22 [≃$42]**
- High and Low. London: 1966. Dustwrapper (slightly rubbed). *(Buckley)* **£12 [≃$23]**
- High and Low. London: 1966. Dustwrapper. *(Words Etcetera)* **£15 [≃$28]**
- Lord Mount Prospect. Edinburgh: Tragara Press, 1981. 1st separate edition. One of 95. Wrappers. *(Waterfield's)* **£30 [≃$57]**
- New Bats in Old Belfries. London: 1945. Inscription. Dustwrapper (rubbed, chipped, spine tanned). *(Ellis)* **£25 [≃$47]**
- A Nip in the Air. London: 1974. Dustwrapper. *(Words Etcetera)* **£12.50 [≃$24]**
- A Nip in the Air. London: Murray, 1974. One of 175 signed. Glassine dustwrapper. *(Georges)* **£75 [≃$143]**
- A Pictorial History of English Architecture. London: 1972. Dustwrapper. *(Words Etcetera)* **£20 [≃$38]**
- Summoned by Bells. London: 1960. Dustwrapper. *(Words Etcetera)* **£10.50 [≃$21]**
- Summoned by Bells. London: 1960. Dustwrapper. *(Buckley)* **£18 [≃$34]**
- Vintage London. London: 1942. Dustwrapper (some rubbing). *(Roberts)* **£18 [≃$34]**
- A Wembley Lad: The Crem. Poem of the Month Club. Signed by the author with alterations in his hand *(Whiteson)* **£25 [≃$47]**

Beynon, John

- Pseudonym used by John Wyndham, q.v.

Big Sky

- Big Sky. Editor Bill Berkson. 1976. Nos. 1-10, all published. *(Blakeney)* **£95 [≃$182]**

Birdwell, Cleo

- Pseudonym used by Don De Lillo, q.v.

Bishop, Elizabeth

- The Diary of 'Helena Morley'. London: 1957. Dustwrapper. *(Egret)* **£40 [≃$76]**
- Questions of Travel. New York: Farrar, (1965). Dustwrapper. *(Woolmer)* **$40 [≃£20]**

Bishop, John Peale

- Green Fruit. Boston: Sherman, French & Co, 1917. 1st edn. 8vo. Cloth and boards. His 1st book. *(Black Sun)* **$200 [≃£104]**
- Minute Particulars. New York: The Alcestis Press, 1935. One of 135 signed. Printed wrappers. Tissue overlay. *(Black Sun)* **$150 [≃£78]**

Bissondath, Neil

- Digging up the Mountains. Toronto: Macmillan, 1985. Dustwrapper. His 1st book. *(Alphabet)* **$40 [≃£20]**

- Digging up the Mountains. London: Deutsch, 1986. Dustwrapper. His 1st book. *(Moorhouse)* **£8 [≃$15]**
- Digging up the Mountains. New York: 1986. Dustwrapper. His 1st book. *(Buckley)* **£20 [≃$38]**
- Digging up the Mountains. New York: Viking, [1986]. Uncorrected proof copy. Printed wrappers. *(Alphabet)* **$55 [≃£28]**

Blackburn, Paul

- Gin. Four Journal Pieces. Mt. Horeb, Wisconsin: The Perishable Press, (1970). One of 135. Vellum backed marbled paper boards. *(Black Sun)* **$250 [≃£130]**

Blackburn, Thomas

- The Outer Darkness. Hand & Flower Press: 1951. Stiff wrappers. His 1st book. *(Buckley)* **£12 [≃$23]**

Blaisdell, Anne

- Pseudonym used by Elizabeth Linington, q.v.

Blake, Nicholas

- Pseudonym used by C. Day-Lewis, q.v.

Blatty, William Peter

- The Exorcist. New York: Harper & Row, [1971]. Advance Reading Copy. Wrappers (light wear). *(Dermont)* **$35 [≃£18]**
- The Exorcist. London: 1971. Dustwrapper (slightly rubbed). *(Ellis)* **£25 [≃$47]**

Blaylock, James P.

- Digging Leviathan. Bath: Morrigan, 1988. One of 310 signed. Slipcase. *(Michael Johnson)* **£45 [≃$86]**
- Digging Leviathan. Bath: Morrigan, 1988. 1st trade hardbound edition. Dustwrapper. *(Michael Johnson)* **£16 [≃$30]**
- Homounculus. Bath: Morrigan, 1988. One of 310 signed. Slipcase. *(Michael Johnson)* **£50 [≃$95]**

Bleasdale, Alan

- Who's Been Sleeping in My Bed. London: Hutchinson, 1977. Uncorrected proof copy. Slightly thumbed. Wrappers. *(Ash)* **£25 [≃$47]**

Bleeck, Oliver

- Pseudonym used by Ross Thomas, q.v.

Blish, James

- Mission to the Heart Stars. London: Faber, 1965. Dustwrapper (slightly worn). *(Sklaroff)* **£20 [≃$38]**

Blixen, Karen

- See Dinesen, Isak.

Bloch, Robert

- The Opener of the Way. Sauk City: Arkham House, 1945. Dustwrapper (slight rubbing, light soiling at edges). Author's inscription. His 1st book. *(Houle)* **$225 [≃£117]**

Blochman, Lawrence G.

- Clues for Dr. Coffee. Phila: Lippincott, 1964. Dustwrapper. *(Mordida)* **$45 [≃£23]**

Block, Lawrence

- Deadly Honeymoon. New York: Macmillan, 1967. Price-clipped dustwrapper. *(Mordida)* **$45 [≃£23]**
- Ronald Rabbit is a Dirty Old Man. New York: Bernard Geis Associates, 1971. Damp staining on top edge. Dustwrapper (internal damp stain, several short closed tears, wear at corners). Signed by the author. *(Mordida)* **$35 [≃£18]**
- Such Men are Dangerous. By Paul Kavanagh. New York: Macmillan, 1969. Price-clipped dustwrapper. *(Mordida)* **$35 [≃£18]**
- Such Men are Dangerous. By Paul Kavanagh. New York: Macmillan, 1969. Dustwrapper. *(Janus)* **$45 [≃£23]**

Bly, Robert

- In the Month of May. New York: Red Ozier Press, (1985). One of 140 signed. Wrappers. *(Houle)* **$65 [≃£33]**

Bogan, Louise

- Body of this Death. New York: 1923. Boards, uncut, very slightly soiled. Her 1st book. *(Polyanthos)* **$75 [≃£39]**

Boucher, Anthony

- The Case of the Baker Street Irregulars. New York: Simon, 1940. Price-clipped dustwrapper (lightly worn, small chip back panel, clipped rear flap). Publisher's card laid in. *(Janus)* **$200 [≃£104]**
- The Case of the Crumpled Knave. New York: Simon, 1939. Dustwrapper (chipped). *(Janus)* **$100 [≃£52]**
- The Case of the Seven of Calvary. New York: Simon, 1937. Tiny nick at foot of spine. Dustwrapper (light wear, minor wear along edges). *(Janus)* **$200 [≃£104]**
- The Case of the Seven of Calvary. New York: Simon & Schuster, 1937. Dustwrapper (wear and chips at corners). *(Mordida)* **$200 [≃£104]**

- The Marble Forest. By Theo Durrant. New York: Knopf, 1951. Dustwrapper (spine sunned). *(Janus)* **$50 [≃£26]**
- Nine Times Nine. By H.H. Holmes. New York: Duell, 1940. Dustwrapper (spine ends chipped). *(Janus)* **$300 [≃£156]**
- Rocket to the Morgue. By H.H. Holmes. New York: Duell, 1947. Dustwrapper (spine sunned). *(Janus)* **$300 [≃£156]**

Bourjailey, Vance

- The End of My Life. New York: Scribners, 1947. Dustwrapper. His 1st book. *(Between the Covers)* **$150 [≃£78]**

Bowen, Elizabeth

- Bowen's Court. London: 1942. Very slightly cocked, 2 corners bumped. Dustwrapper (chipped & torn, spine faded). Author's presentation inscription signed Bitha. *(Blakeney)* **£125 [≃$239]**
- The Death of the Heart. London: Gollancz, 1938. Dustwrapper (moderate edgewear, spine browned, front panel faded). *(Antic Hay)* **$75 [≃£39]**
- Encounters. London: 1923. Blue cloth gilt, fine. Her 1st book. *(Egret)* **£95 [≃$182]**
- Eva Trout. London: 1969. Dustwrapper. *(Words Etcetera)* **£10.50 [≃$21]**
- (Edits) The Faber Book of Modern Stories. London: 1937. Dustwrapper (slightly chipped and used). *(Words Etcetera)* **£30 [≃$57]**
- The Heat of the Day. London: 1949. One corner lightly bumped. Author's presentation inscription, signed Bitha. *(Blakeney)* **£50 [≃$95]**
- Pictures and Conversations. London: 1975. Dustwrapper. *(Words Etcetera)* **£12.50 [≃$24]**
- Selected Stories. Dublin & London: Hour Glass Library, 1946. Paper browned. Wrappers. Dustwrapper (rubbed, spine darkened). *(Blakeney)* **£15 [≃$28]**
- Seven Winters. London: 1943. Dustwrapper. *(Words Etcetera)* **£22 [≃$42]**
- A World of Love. London: Cape, 1955. Dustwrapper. *(Lewton)* **£6.90 [≃$13]**

Bowen, Marjorie

- The Rocklitz. By George Preedy [pseud.]. London: 1933. Faint offsetting to endpapers. Dustwrapper. *(Blakeney)* **£35 [≃$67]**

Bowles, Paul

- Call at Corazon. London: Owen, 1985. Price-clipped dustwrapper. *(Alphabet)* **$30 [≃£15]**
- The Delicate Prey and Other Stories. New York: 1950. Dustwrapper (chipped, worn and sunned). *(King)* **$35 [≃£18]**
- A Hundred Camels in the Courtyard. San Francisco: City Lights, (1962). Wrappers (scrape across part of rear wrapper). *(Between the Covers)* **$40 [≃£20]**
- Let It Come Down. New York: (1952). Cloth backed boards (very slight cover discolouration). Dustwrapper (slightly frayed and torn). *(King)* **$50 [≃£26]**
- Let It Come Down. Santa Barbara: Black Sparrow Press, 1980. Limited edition. Cloth backed boards. Signed by the author. *(Heritage)* **$60 [≃£31]**
- Let It Come Down. Santa Barbara: Black Sparrow Press, 1980. One of 350 signed. Acetate dustwrapper. *(Antic Hay)* **$50 [≃£26]**
- Let It Come Down. Santa Barbara: Black Sparrow, 1980. One of 350 signed. Glassine dustwrapper. *(Polyanthos)* **$45 [≃£23]**
- A Little Stone. London: Lehmann, 1950. Dustwrapper (two small pieces scuffed from lower spine). *(Halsey)* **£25 [≃$47]**
- A Little Stone. London: John Lehmann, 1950. 1st edition. Dustwrapper. *(Alphabet)* **$125 [≃£65]**
- A Little Stone. London: Lehmann, (1950). 1st issue, in light green cloth. dustwrapper. Signed by the author. *(Lopez)* **$250 [≃£130]**
- A Little Stone. London: Lehmann, (1950). 1st issue, in light green cloth. Dustwrapper. *(Lopez)* **$125 [≃£65]**
- Midnight Mass. Santa Barbara: Black Sparrow Press, 1981. Limited edition. Cloth backed boards. Signed by the author. *(Heritage)* **$85 [≃£44]**
- Next to Nothing. Kathmandu: Starstreams, 1976. One of 500 numbered. Wrappers. *(Lopez)* **$85 [≃£44]**
- Scenes. Los Angeles: Black Sparrow Press, 1968. One of 250 in wrappers signed. Edges very slightly faded. *(Woolmer)* **$175 [≃£91]**
- The Sheltering Sky. New York: New Directions, (1949). Advance review copy. Dustwrapper. Signed by the author. *(Lopez)* **$750 [≃£390]**
- The Spider's House. New York: 1955. One corner slightly worn. Dustwrapper (price-clipped, rubbed, somewhat frayed). *(Blakeney)* **£85 [≃$163]**
- The Spider's House. Santa Barbara: Black Sparrow Press, 1982. Limited edition. Cloth backed boards. Signed by the author. *(Heritage)* **$60 [≃£31]**
- The Thicket of Spring. Los Angeles: Black

Sparrow Press, 1972. One of 200 hardcover signed. Acetate dustwrapper. *(Houle)* **$95 [≃£49]**

- Things Gone and Things Still Here. Santa Barbara: Black Sparrow Press, 1977. One of 250 hardcover signed. Acetate dustwrapper. *(Houle)* **$95 [≃£49]**
- Things Gone and Things Still Here. Santa Barbara: Black Sparrow Press, 1977. One of 250 signed. *(Heritage)* **$100 [≃£52]**
- The Time of Friendship and Other Stories. New York: 1967. Neat name. Very slightly edge sunned. Price-clipped dustwrapper (tiny tear mended, spine a little sunned). *(Polyanthos)* **$30 [≃£15]**
- The Time of Friendship. New York: Holt Rinehart Winston, (1967). Advance review copy. Dustwrapper. Review slip, photo, and promotional material laid in. *(Lopez)* **$85 [≃£44]**
- Two Poems. New York: The Modern Editions Press, [1933]. Leaves partially browned. Wrappers (partially browned, restored at margins). His 1st book. *(Moorhouse)* **£450 [≃$863]**
- Up Above the World. London: 1967. Dustwrapper (slightly rubbed). *(First Issues)* **£45 [≃$86]**
- Up Above the World. New York: Simon & Schuster, [1966]. Dustwrapper. *(Antic Hay)* **$50 [≃£26]**
- Yallah. New York: McDowell Obolensky, (1957). Two creases on front endpaper, one on half-title. Dustwrapper (lamination not peeling off). *(Lopez)* **$175 [≃£91]**
- Yallah. New York: McDowell, (1957). Price-clipped dustwrapper (undelaminated). *(Between the Covers)* **$250 [≃£130]**

Box, Edgar

- Pseudonym used by Gore Vidal, q.v.

Boyd, William

- Brazzaville Beach. London: London Limited Editions, 1990. One of 150 signed. Cellophane dustwrapper. *(Words Etcetera)* **£35 [≃$67]**
- A Good Man in Africa. London: 1981. Dustwrapper. Author's presentation copy. *(Egret)* **£300 [≃$575]**
- A Good Man in Africa. London: Hamish Hamilton, 1981. Price-clipped dustwrapper. His 1st book. *(Moorhouse)* **£250 [≃$479]**
- A Good Man in Africa. New York: Morrow, 1982. 1st American edition. Dustwrapper. *(Dyke)* **£50 [≃$95]**
- An Ice Cream War. London: Hamilton, 1982. Dustwrapper. Signed by the author (1983). *(David Rees)* **£30 [≃$57]**
- An Ice Cream War. London: Hamilton, 1982. Dustwrapper. *(Dyke)* **£20 [≃$38]**
- An Ice Cream War. London: 1983. Dustwrapper. Author's presentation copy. *(Egret)* **£45 [≃$86]**
- The New Confessions. London: Hamilton, 1987. Dustwrapper. Signed by the author. *(Dyke)* **£25 [≃$47]**
- The New Confessions. New York: Ultramarine, 1988. One of 99. Quarter leather. No dustwrapper issued. *(Michael Johnson)* **£128 [≃$245]**
- The New Confessions. New York: Morrow, 1988. 1st American edition. Advance reading copy. Pictorial wrappers. *(Michael Johnson)* **£28 [≃$53]**
- On the Yankee Station. London: 1981. Price-clipped dustwrapper. Author's presentation copy. *(Egret)* **£250 [≃$479]**
- On the Yankee Station. London: 1981. Dustwrapper. *(Moorhouse)* **£250 [≃$479]**
- On the Yankee Station. New York: Morrow, 1984. 1st US edition (with 2 stories not in the UK edition). Dustwrapper. *(Moorhouse)* **£18 [≃$34]**
- On the Yankee Station. New York: Morrow, 1984. 1st American edition, with 2 extra stories. Dustwrapper. *(Dyke)* **£25 [≃$47]**
- School Ties. London: 1985. Dustwrapper. *(Words Etcetera)* **£45 [≃$86]**
- Stars and Bars. London: Hamilton, 1984. Dustwrapper. Signed by the author. *(Dyke)* **£30 [≃$57]**
- Stars and Bars. London: 1984. Dustwrapper. Author's presentation copy. *(Egret)* **£40 [≃$76]**
- Stars & Bars. London: Hamilton, 1984. Bump on front cover causing scratch. Dustwrapper. *(Alphabet)* **$15 [≃£7]**

Boyer, Rick

- Billingsgate Shoal. Boston: Houghton, 1982. Dustwrapper. *(Janus)* **$45 [≃£23]**
- Billingsgate Shoal. Boston: Houghton, 1982. Dustwrapper. Signed by the author. *(Janus)* **$65 [≃£33]**

Boyle, Kay

- Wedding Day and Other Stories. London: 1932. Dustwrapper (chipped, nicked, lacks pieces along top edge). Author's 1st book. *(Ellis)* **£30 [≃$57]**

Boyle, T. Coraghessan

- Descent of Man. Boston: Atlantic Monthly

Press, [1979]. Dustwrapper (lightly used, one small edge tear). His 1st book. *(Dermont)* **$75 [≃£39]**

Bradbury, Malcolm

- Eating People Is Wrong. London: 1959. Dustwrapper (lightly rubbed & soiled, a little faded at spine). His 1st book. *(Blakeney)* **£65 [≃$124]**
- Eating People is Wrong. London: 1959. Faint evidence of bookplate removal. Dust- wrapper (slightly rubbed, spine slightly faded). His 1st book. *(Ellis)* **£80 [≃$153]**
- Eating People is Wrong. London: Secker & Warburg, 1959. Dustwrapper (spine slightly rubbed and chipped). His 1st book. *(Sotheran's)* **£98 [≃$188]**
- The History Man. London: Secker & Warburg, 1975. Dustwrapper. Signed by the author. *(Virgo)* **£60 [≃$115]**
- The History Man. London: Secker & Warburg, 1975. Dustwrapper. *(Lewton)* **£25 [≃$47]**
- The History Man. London: Secker & Warburg, 1975. Inscription on fly. Dustwrapper. *(Ash)* **£50 [≃$95]**
- The History Man. Boston: 1976. 1st American edition. Dustwrapper. Signed by the author. *(First Issues)* **£25 [≃$47]**
- Mensonge. London: Deutsch, 1987. Dustwrapper. Signed by the author. *(Lewton)* **£10 [≃$19]**
- No, Not Bloomsbury. London: Deutsch, 1987. Dustwrapper. *(Lewton)* **£7.50 [≃$15]**
- Phogey. London: Parrish, 1960. Dustwrapper (small closed tear). *(Lewton)* **£15 [≃$28]**
- Phogey! London: 1960. Price-clipped dustwrapper (very slightly rubbed). Signed by the author. *(Ellis)* **£40 [≃$76]**
- Rates of Exchange. London: S & W, 1983. Dustwrapper. *(Lewton)* **£7.50 [≃$15]**
- Rates of Exchange. London: Secker & Warburg, 1983. Dustwrapper. Signed by the author. *(Virgo)* **£25 [≃$47]**
- Who Do You Think You Are. London: Secker & Warburg, 1976. Dustwrapper. *(Virgo)* **£20 [≃$38]**

Bradbury, Ray

- Beyond 1984: Remembrance of Things Future. Targ Editions: [1979]. One of 300 signed. Dustwrapper. *(Dermont)* **$45 [≃£23]**
- Dandelion Wine. London: 1957. Dustwrapper (head of spine slightly chipped). Signed by the author. *(Sclanders)* **£65 [≃$124]**
- Dandelion Wine. London: 1957. Dustwrapper. Signed presentation slip from the author. *(Polyanthos)* **$95 [≃£49]**
- Dark Carnival. London: Hamish Hamilton, 1948. 1st English edition. Spine slightly cocked. Dustwrapper (few small chips). His 1st book. *(Nouveau)* **$225 [≃£117]**
- Death Has Lost Its Charm for Me. Lord John Press: 1987. One of 150 signed. *(Nouveau)* **$50 [≃£26]**
- The Dragon. New York: 1988. One of 300 signed. Wrappers. Dustwrapper. *(Polyanthos)* **$25 [≃£13]**
- Fahrenheit 451. New York: Ballantine, (1953). Some foxing to page edges. Some rubbing to bottom of boards. Dustwrapper (some spine fading). *(Between the Covers)* **$375 [≃£195]**
- Fahrenheit 451. London: 1954. *(Roberts)* **£45 [≃$86]**
- Fahrenheit 451. London: 1954. Top edges slightly dusty. Dustwrapper (partly sunned, two closed tears, a few signs of wear). *(Sclanders)* **£85 [≃$163]**
- The Golden Apples of the Sun. Garden City: Doubleday, 1953. Rubber stamp on front fly. Dustwrapper (light spotting on spine, quarter inch loss foot of spine, tiny chip). Author's inscription. *(Between the Covers)* **$175 [≃£91]**
- The Golden Apples of the Sun. London: Hart Davis, 1953. Dustwrapper. *(David Rees)* **£50 [≃$95]**
- The Golden Apples of the Sun. London: Hart Davis, 1953. Endpapers tanned, edges spotty, slight fading to spine ends and lower edges. Dustwrapper (torn with loss). *(Hazeldene)* **£40 [≃$76]**
- The Halloween Tree. London: Hart Davis, MacGibbon, 1972. 1st British edition. Dustwrapper. *(Ash)* **£20 [≃$38]**
- The Haunted Computer & the Android Pope. London: Granada, 1981. Dustwrapper. *(Lewton)* **£7.50 [≃$15]**
- The Illustrated Man. London: Hart Davis, 1952. Dustwrapper. Signed by the author. *(Dyke)* **£90 [≃$172]**
- The Last Circus and the Electrocution. Northridge: Lord John Press, 1980. One of 100 signed by Bradbury, Nolan, & Mubnaini. Slipcase. *(Antic Hay)* **$100 [≃£52]**
- Long After Midnight. New York: 1976. Spine extremities very slightly bumped. Dust- wrapper. Signed by the author. *(Polyanthos)* **$30 [≃£15]**
- Martian Chronicles. Garden City: Doubleday, 1950. Cloth soiled and faded,

extremities worn. Dustwrapper (chipped, spine joints tape repaired). Inscribed by the author. *(Heritage)* **$150 [≃£78]**

- The Mummies of Guanajuato. New York: Abrams, 1978. Dustwrapper. Bookplate signed by the author. *(Polyanthos)* **$25 [≃£13]**
- "The Poet Considers His Resources". Northridge: Lord John Press, 1979. One of 200 signed. Broadside. *(Antic Hay)* **$40 [≃£20]**
- The Silver Locusts. London: Hart Davis, 1951. 1st British edition of The Martian Chronicles. Edges slightly spotted. Dustwrapper (very slightly marked and nicked). *(Ash)* **£75 [≃$143]**
- The Silver Locusts. London: 1951. Slight offsetting to endpapers. Dustwrapper (slightly chipped). *(Buckley)* **£30 [≃$57]**
- The Silver Locusts. London: Hart-Davis, 1951. Very slight stain to foredge. Spine slightly faded. Dustwrapper. *(Whiteson)* **£50 [≃$95]**

Bragg, Melvyn

- For Want of a Nail. London: 1965. Dustwrapper. Author's presentation copy. His 1st book. *(Egret)* **£50 [≃$95]**
- For Want of a Nail. London: Secker, 1965. Dustwrapper. His 1st book. *(Any Amount)* **£2.50 [≃$5]**
- The Second Inheritance. London: 1966. Dustwrapper (stained and darkened). *(Buckley)* **£8 [≃$15]**

Braine, John

- Room at the Top. London: Eyre & Spottiswoode, 1957. Dustwrapper (chipped and repaired). His 1st book. *(Sklaroff)* **£42 [≃$80]**

Bramah, Ernest

- The Specimen Case. London: Hodder & Stoughton, 1924. Dustwrapper (1/4 inch chip at lower rear spine corner). *(Alphabet)* **$275 [≃£143]**

Brautigan, Richard

- A Confederate General from Big Sur. New York: 1964. Dustwrapper (small piece of rear flyleaf missing). *(Pettler & Liebermann)* **$85 [≃£44]**
- Dreaming of Babylon. London: 1978. 1st English edition. Dustwrapper. *(Words Etcetera)* **£20 [≃$38]**
- (Contributes to) Four New Poets. Edited by L.W. Hedley. San Francisco: Inferno Press Editions, 1957. Wrappers (spine worn, few spots to covers). *(Pettler & Liebermann)* **$175 [≃£91]**
- The Hawkline Monster. New York: 1974. Price-clipped dustwrapper. *(Pettler & Liebermann)* **$15 [≃£7]**
- Loading Mercury with a Pitchfork. New York: Simon & Schuster, [1976]. Remainder mark lower edge. Dustwrapper (lightly used). Signed by the author. *(Antic Hay)* **$285 [≃£148]**
- Rommel Drives on Deep into Egypt. New York: 1970. Dustwrapper. *(Pettler & Liebermann)* **$60 [≃£31]**
- So the Wind Won't Blow It All Away. [New York]: Delacorte / Lawrence, [1982]. Uncorrected proof copy. Wrappers (some soil). *(Antic Hay)* **$45 [≃£23]**
- So the Wind Won't Blow It All Away. New York: 1982. Remainder spray. Price-clipped dustwrapper. *(Pettler & Liebermann)* **$30 [≃£15]**
- So the Wind Won't Blow It All Away. London: Cape, 1983. Uncorrected proof copy. Wrappers. *(First Issues)* **£15 [≃$28]**
- Sombrero Fallout. London: 1977. 1st English edition. Dustwrapper. *(Words Etcetera)* **£20 [≃$38]**
- The Tokyo-Montana Express. New York: Targ Editions, (1979). One of 350 signed. Glassine dustwrapper. *(Houle)* **$150 [≃£78]**
- The Tokyo-Montana Express. [New York]: Delacorte / Lawrence, [1980]. Advance reading copy from the uncorrected proofs. Wrappers (minor soil). *(Antic Hay)* **$50 [≃£26]**
- The Tokyo-Montana Express. New York: 1980. Advance reading copy from uncorrected proofs. Printed wrappers. *(Pettler & Liebermann)* **$50 [≃£26]**
- The Tokyo-Montana Express. New York: 1980. Dustwrapper. *(Pettler & Liebermann)* **$22.50 [≃£11]**
- The Tokyo-Montana Express. London: Cape, 1981. Dustwrapper. *(Hazeldene)* **£15 [≃$28]**
- Trout Fishing in America. San Francisco: Four Seas, 1967. Hinge cracked, some stress lines on spine. *(Between the Covers)* **$65 [≃£33]**
- Willard and his Bowling Trophies. New York: Simon & Schuster, 1975. Edges spotted. Dustwrapper. *(Hazeldene)* **£15 [≃$28]**
- Willard and his Bowling Trophies. New York: 1975. Remainder stamp. Dustwrapper. *(Pettler & Liebermann)* **$20 [≃£10]**

Brennan, Gerald

- Jack Robinson. A Picaresque Novel by George Beaton. London: 1933. AL inserted. *(Roberts)* **£25 [≃$47]**

Brent-Dyer, E.M.

- The Chalet Book for Girls. London: Chambers, 1947. Pictorial boards (slightly rubbed). *(Green Meadow)* **£55 [≃$105]**
- The Chalet School Wins the trick. London: Chambers, [n.d.] Dustwrapper. *(Green Meadow)* **£65 [≃$124]**
- Chudleigh Hold. London: Chambers, 1954. Dustwrapper. *(Green Meadow)* **£65 [≃$124]**
- The Coming of Age at the Chalet School. London: Chambers, 1958. Dustwrapper (slightly torn). *(Green Meadow)* **£55 [≃$105]**
- The Feud in the Chalet School. London: Chambers, [n.d.]. Dustwrapper. *(Green Meadow)* **£65 [≃$124]**
- The Feud in the Fifth Remove. London: Girl's Own Paper Office. Dustwrapper. *(Green Meadow)* **£45 [≃$86]**
- A Genius at the Chalet School. London: Chambers, 1956. Dustwrapper (torn). *(Green Meadow)* **£40 [≃$76]**
- Janie Steps In. London: Chambers, 1953. Dustwrapper (slightly worn). *(Green Meadow)* **£27.50 [≃$53]**
- Kennelmaid Nan. London: Lutterworth, 1954. Dustwrapper (worn). *(Green Meadow)* **£45 [≃$86]**
- Lavender Laughs in the Chalet School. London: Chambers, 1943. Dustwrapper (torn). *(Green Meadow)* **£35 [≃$67]**
- A Leader in the Chalet School. London: Chambers, 1961. Dustwrapper. *(Green Meadow)* **£40 [≃$76]**
- Shocks for the Chalet School. London: Chambers, 1952. *(Green Meadow)* **£35 [≃$67]**
- Theodora and the Chalet School. London: Chambers, 1959. Dustwrapper. *(Green Meadow)* **£55 [≃$105]**
- Theodora and the Chalet School. London: Chambers, 1959. Dustwrapper (repaired). *(Green Meadow)* **£45 [≃$86]**
- The Third Chalet Book for Girls. London: Chambers, 1949. *(Green Meadow)* **£55 [≃$105]**
- A Thrilling Term at Janeways. London: Nelson, [n.d.]. Pictorial cloth. *(Green Meadow)* **£30 [≃$57]**
- Top Secret. London: Chambers, 1955. Dustwrapper. *(Green Meadow)* **£65 [≃$124]**
- Trials for the Chalet School. London: Chambers, 1959. *(Green Meadow)* **£40 [≃$76]**

Brock, Edwin

- The Portraits and the Poses. London: 1973. Dustwrapper. *(Buckley)* **£19 [≃$36]**

Brooke, Jocelyn

- The Elements of Death. Hand & Flower Press: 1952. Stiff wrappers. *(Buckley)* **£20 [≃$38]**
- A Mine of Serpents. London: Bodley Head, 1949. Spine titling a touch dull. Dustwrapper (slightly nicked). Signed presentation inscription from the author(1960). *(Ash)* **£100 [≃$191]**

Brooke, Rupert

- Lithuania. London: 1935. Wrappers. *(Words Etcetera)* **£25 [≃$47]**
- (Contributes to) New Numbers. Volume I. Number 4. Gloucester: privately printed, 1914. Grey-blue wrappers (restored, some slight stains). Brooke, Abercrombie, Drinkwater, Gibson. *(Ash)* **£100 [≃$191]**
- Twenty Poems. London: 1935. Wrappers. *(Words Etcetera)* **£25 [≃$47]**
- See also the companion IRBP volume Literature.

Brookner, Anita

- Family and Friends. London: Cape, 1985. Uncorrected proof copy. Wrappers. *(Nouveau)* **$75 [≃£39]**
- Family and Friends. London: Cape, 1985. Dustwrapper. *(Lewton)* **£15 [≃$28]**
- A Friend from England. London: Cape, 1987. Dustwrapper. Signed by the author. *(Lewton)* **£16 [≃$30]**
- Hotel du Lac. London: 1984. Uncorrected proof copy. Wrappers (edges very slightly rubbed). *(Ellis)* **£60 [≃$115]**
- Hotel du Lac. London: Cape, 1984. Dustwrapper (slight creasing in laminate). Signed by the author. *(Moorhouse)* **£45 [≃$86]**
- Hotel du Lac. London: Cape, 1984. Dustwrapper. *(Lewton)* **£45 [≃$86]**
- Hotel du Lac. London: Cape, 1984. Dustwrapper. *(Limestone Hills)* **$115 [≃£59]**
- Hotel du Lac. New York: Pantheon, (1984). 1st American edition. Uncorrected proof copy. *(Lopez)* **$45 [≃£23]**
- Ingres. The Masters, No. 16. Knowledge Publications: 1965. Wrappers. Her first separately published work. *(David Rees)* **£20 [≃$38]**
- J.A. Dominique Ingres. Knowledge Publications: 1967. Wrappers. Signed by the author. *(Moorhouse)* **£25 [≃$47]**

- Jacques-Louis David. Knowledge Publications: 1967. Wrappers. Signed by the author. *(Moorhouse)* **£25 [≃$47]**
- Jacques-Louis David: A Personal Interpretation. London: OUP for the British Academy, 1974. Wrappers, faint trace of price sticker on upper wrapper. *(Blakeney)* **£50 [≃$95]**
- Jacques-Louis David: A Personal Interpretation. OUP: 1974. Wrappers. *(Nouveau)* **$75 [≃£39]**
- Latecomers. London: Cape, 1988. Price-clipped dustwrapper. *(David Rees)* **£10 [≃$19]**
- Lewis Percy. London: Cape, 1989. Uncorrected proof copy. Wrappers. *(David Rees)* **£6 [≃$11]**
- Lewis Percy. London: Cape, 1989. Dustwrapper. *(Lewton)* **£8.50 [≃$17]**
- A Misalliance. London: 1986. Uncorrected proof copy. Wrappers. *(First Issues)* **£15 [≃$28]**
- A Misalliance. London: Cape, [1986]. Dustwrapper. *(Antic Hay)* **$20 [≃£10]**
- A Misalliance. London: Cape, 1986. Dustwrapper. *(Lewton)* **£12.50 [≃$24]**
- Providence. London: Cape, 1982. Dustwrapper. Signed by the author. *(Moorhouse)* **£40 [≃$76]**
- Providence. London: Cape, 1982. Dustwrapper. *(David Rees)* **£25 [≃$47]**
- A Start in Life. London: Cape, 1981. Dustwrapper. *(Lewton)* **£75 [≃$143]**
- Watteau. London: Hamlyn, 1967. Dustwrapper. Signed by the author. Copyright date is given as 1967, BL Catalogue gives the date 1971. *(Moorhouse)* **£50 [≃$95]**

Brooks, Gwendolyn

- Annie Allen. New York: Harper, (1949). Dustwrapper (very slight loss to crown, light rubbing). Author's inscription. *(Between the Covers)* **$300 [≃£156]**

Brooks, Louise

- Lulu in Hollywood. New York: Knopf, 1982. Slight bump at base of front board. Dustwrapper. *(Between the Covers)* **$50 [≃£26]**

Brophy, Brigid

- The Finishing Touch. London: S & W, 1963. Dustwrapper. *(Lewton)* **£6 [≃$11]**
- The Finishing Touch. London: Secker & Warburg, 1963. Dustwrapper. Signed and inscribed by the author (1988). *(David Rees)* **£8 [≃$15]**
- Hackenfeller's Ape. London: Hart Davis, 1953. Slight edge staining. Dustwrapper (chipped). *(Paul Brown)* **£25 [≃$47]**

Brown, Bob

- Let There Be Beer. New York: 1932. Dustwrapper (slightly soiled, missing a strip at foot of lower panel). *(Blakeney)* **£85 [≃$163]**

Brown, Frederic

- The Shaggy Dog and Other Stories. London: Bloodhound Special, 1964. Dustwrapper. *(Sclanders)* **£60 [≃$115]**

Brown, Fredric

- The Five-Day Nightmare. New York: Dutton, 1962. Dustwrapper (touch of wear, spine very slightly sunned). *(Janus)* **$200 [≃£104]**
- Knock Three-One-Two. New York: Dutton, 1959. Dustwrapper (light wear head of spine). *(Janus)* **$125 [≃£65]**
- The Lenient Beast. New York: Dutton, 1956. Some scraping to boards. Dustwrapper. *(Janus)* **$175 [≃£91]**

Brown, George Mackay

- Christmas Poems. Oxford: Perpetua Press, 1984. One of 100 signed by author, artist (John Lawrence), and printer. *(Waterfield's)* **£15 [≃$28]**
- Christmas Stories. Oxford: Perpetua Press, 1985. One of 150 signed by author, artist (John Lawrence), and printer. *(Waterfield's)* **£20 [≃$38]**
- The Five Voyages of Arnor. Duval: 1966. One of 100. Wrappers. *(David Rees)* **£25 [≃$47]**
- Greenove. London: 1972. Dustwrapper. *(Words Etcetera)* **£15 [≃$28]**
- Keepers of the House. Illustrated by Gillian Martin. Old Stile Press: 1986. One of 225 signed by author and artist. Slipcase. *(Words Etcetera)* **£45 [≃$86]**
- Keepers of the House. Illustrated by Gillian Martin. Old Stile Press: (1986). One of 225 signed by author and artist. *(Waterfield's)* **£30 [≃$57]**
- Loaves and Fishes. London: 1959. Dustwrapper (slightly used). His 1st book. *(Words Etcetera)* **£35 [≃$67]**
- Loaves and Fishes. London: Hogarth Press, 1959. Dustwrapper (slightly torn). His 1st collection. *(David Rees)* **£40 [≃$76]**
- Magnus. London: 1973. Dustwrapper. *(Words Etcetera)* **£15 [≃$28]**

- The Sun's Net. London: 1976. Dustwrapper. *(Words Etcetera)* **£15 [≃$28]**

Brown, Harry

- The End of a Decade. New Directions: Poet of the Month, 1940. Wrappers. His 1st book. *(Any Amount)* **£16 [≃$30]**

Brown, Larry

- Dirty Work. Chapel Hill: Algonquin, 1989. Dustwrapper. Signed by the author. *(Michael Johnson)* **£25 [≃$47]**
- Facing the Music. Chapel Hill: Algonquin, 1988. Dustwrapper. *(Michael Johnson)* **£20 [≃$38]**

Brown, Rosellen

- Some Deaths in the Delta. Univ Mass Press: 1970. Price-clipped dustwrapper. Signed by the author. Her 1st book. *(Nouveau)* **$60 [≃£31]**

Browne, Howard

- Return of Tharn. Providence: Grandon, 1956. Bookplate. Dustwrapper (spine slightly darkened). Inscribed by Browne. *(Mordida)* **$250 [≃£130]**
- Warrior of the Dawn. Chicago: Reilly & Lee, 1943. Bookplate. Dustwrapper (chipped, spine slightly faded, wear at corners and along edges). Inscribed by Browne. *(Mordida)* **$150 [≃£78]**

Bryan, Michael

- Pseudonym used by Brian Moore, q.v.

Buckeridge, Anthony

- Jennings Abounding. London: Collins, 1967. Dustwrapper (very slightly chipped). *(Green Meadow)* **£25 [≃$47]**
- Take Jennings for Instance. London: Collins, 1958. Dustwrapper. *(Green Meadow)* **£25 [≃$47]**
- Trust Jennings. London: Collins, 1969. Endpapers marked from sellotape strip. Dustwrapper. *(Green Meadow)* **£25 [≃$47]**

Bukowski, Charles

- At Terror Street and Agony Way. LA: Black Sparrow, 1968. One of 800 (of 875) in wrappers. Oversize wrappers slightly curled. *(Lopez)* **$135 [≃£70]**
- Cold Dogs in the Courtyard. Chicago: Literary Times, 1965. One of 500. Wrappers (faintly soiled). *(Any Amount)* **£28 [≃$53]**
- The Days Run Away Like Wild Horses Over the Hills. Santa Barbara: Black Sparrow, 1969. One of 250 signed. Acetate dustwrapper. *(Any Amount)* **£45 [≃$86]**
- Poems Written before Jumping Out of an 8 Story Window. Berkeley: [1968]. Softbound original. Wrappers. *(Pettler & Liebermann)* **$85 [≃£44]**

Bunting, Basil

- Briggflatts; a New Long Poem [in] Poetry Chicago Vol 107, No 4, Jan 1966. Wrappers. *(Words Etcetera)* **£40 [≃$76]**
- Briggflatts. Fulcrum: 1966. 1st trade edition (ie '2nd edition entirely reset'). Wrappers (slightly mottled as usual). *(Halsey)* **£15 [≃$28]**
- Collected Poems. Fulcrum: 1968. Dustwrapper (very slightly rubbed). *(Halsey)* **£30 [≃$57]**
- Loquitur. London: Fulcrum Press, (1965). One of 1000. *(Polyanthos)* **$35 [≃£18]**
- Loquitur. London: Fulcrum Press, (1965). Top edge darkened. Plastic jacket (soiled). *(Woolmer)* **$75 [≃£39]**
- The Spoils. Morden Tower Book Room: 1965. Wrappers. *(Buckley)* **£35 [≃$67]**
- Two Poems. Brighton: 1967. One of 250. Wrappers. *(Words Etcetera)* **£20 [≃$38]**

Bunting, Josiah

- The Lionheads. New York: Braziller, (1972). Dustwrapper. Signed by the author. *(Lopez)* **$85 [≃£44]**

Burgess, Anthony

- Any Old Iron. London: Hutchinson, 1989. Dustwrapper. Signed by the author. *(Tiger Books)* **£20 [≃$38]**
- Beds in the East. London: Heinemann, 1959. Dustwrapper (slightly chipped). *(Limestone Hills)* **$110 [≃£57]**
- Blooms of Dublin. London: 1987. Wrappers. *(Buckley)* **£10 [≃$19]**
- A Clockwork Orange. London: 1962. Black cloth. Dustwrapper (one very small repair). *(Georges)* **£550 [≃$1,055]**
- A Clockwork Orange. London: Heinemann, 1962. 1st issue, in black cloth. Dustwrapper (one small repair). *(Dyke)* **£300 [≃$575]**
- A Clockwork Orange. London: 1962. Probable 2nd issue, in purple (rather than black) boards. Small mark on front free endpaper. One corner bumped. Dustwrapper (lightly frayed) price-clipped by publisher, a sticker has been peeled off the front flap. *(Blakeney)* **£175 [≃$335]**
- A Clockwork Orange. London: 1962. Dustwrapper (some wear to extremities of

corners, one closed tear at head of upper panel). *(Words Etcetera)* **£400 [≃$767]**

- A Clockwork Orange. New York: 1963. 1st American edition. Dustwrapper (spine faded). Signed by the author (1989). *(Georges)* **£160 [≃$307]**
- A Clockwork Orange. New York: Norton, (1963). 1st US edition. Price-clipped dustwrapper. *(Between the Covers)* **$250 [≃£130]**
- The Clockwork Testament or Enderby's End. London: 1974. Dustwrapper. *(Roberts)* **£8.50 [≃$17]**
- Devil of a State. London: 1961. Dustwrapper (two small closed tears). *(Buckley)* **£35 [≃$67]**
- Devil of a State. London: 1961. Dustwrapper. *(First Issues)* **£40 [≃$76]**
- The Doctor is Sick. London: Heinemann, 1960. Dustwrapper. *(David Rees)* **£90 [≃$172]**
- The Doctor is Sick. New York: Norton, [1960]. 1st American edition. Review slip. Dustwrapper (some darkening spine). *(Antic Hay)* **$75 [≃£39]**
- Earthly Powers. London: Hutchinson, 1980. Dustwrapper. *(Hazeldene)* **£25 [≃$47]**
- The End of the World News. London: Hutchinson, 1982. Dustwrapper. Signed by the author. *(Marlborough B'shop)* **£18 [≃$34]**
- The End of the World News. London: Hutchinson,, 1982. Dustwrapper. Signed by the author. *(Whiteson)* **£30 [≃$57]**
- The End of the World News. New York: 1983. Dustwrapper. Signed by the author. *(Polyanthos)* **$40 [≃£20]**
- Enderby Outside. London: 1968. Uncorrected proof copy. *(Buckley)* **£55 [≃$105]**
- Enderby Outside. London: 1968. Slight erasure mark on endpapers. Dustwrapper. *(Buckley)* **£35 [≃$67]**
- Enderby Outside. London: 1968. Dustwrapper. *(Words Etcetera)* **£28 [≃$53]**
- Enderby's Dark Lady. London: Hutchinson, 1984. Uncorrected proof copy. Wrappers. *(Whiteson)* **£28 [≃$53]**
- Enderby's Dark Lady. London: Hutchinson, 1984. Dustwrapper. Signed by the author. *(Moorhouse)* **£15 [≃$28]**
- Enderby's Dark Lady. London: Hutchinson, 1984. Dustwrapper. Inscribed by the author. *(David Rees)* **£25 [≃$47]**
- The Enemy in the Blanket. London: 1958. Top edge sunned, endsheets a little spotted. One corner worn. Dustwrapper (slightly spotted, wear to two corners, spine undiscoloured). *(Blakeney)* **£40 [≃$76]**
- Ernest Hemingway and his World. London: 1978. Dustwrapper. Author's inscription. *(Buckley)* **£30 [≃$57]**
- The Eve of Saint Venus. London: Sidgwick & Jackson, [1964]. 1st English edition. Dustwrapper (small abrasion). *(Antic Hay)* **$45 [≃£23]**
- Honey for the Bears. London: 1963. Slightly cocked. Dustwrapper (rubbed, nicked). *(Ellis)* **£45 [≃$86]**
- Honey for the Bears. London: Heinemann, 1963. Dustwrapper (internally repaired). *(Limestone Hills)* **$65 [≃£33]**
- Inside Mr Enderby. By Joseph Kell. London: Heinemann, 1963. Dustwrapper (spine slightly browned). *(David Rees)* **£125 [≃$239]**
- Joysprick. London: Deutsch, 1973. Dustwrapper. *(David Rees)* **£40 [≃$76]**
- Joysprick. London: Deutsch, 1973. Dustwrapper. *(Alphabet)* **$75 [≃£39]**
- The Kingdom of the Wicked. London: 1985. Advance uncorrected proof copy. Author's inscription. *(Buckley)* **£25 [≃$47]**
- The Kingdom of the Wicked. London: Hutchinson, 1985. Dustwrapper. Signed by the author. *(Marlborough B'shop)* **£14 [≃$26]**
- The Kingdom of the Wicked. New York: (1985). Dustwrapper. Signed by the author. *(Polyanthos)* **$35 [≃£18]**
- Language Made Plain. London: 1964. Name on fly. Dustwrapper. *(Words Etcetera)* **£90 [≃$172]**
- Language Made Plain. London: 1964. Dustwrapper (slightly frayed, nicked, tanned in patches). *(Ellis)* **£65 [≃$124]**
- Language Made Plain. London: The English Universities Press, 1964. Name on endpaper. Price-clipped dustwrapper (slightly soiled and nicked). Signed by the author. *(Moorhouse)* **£75 [≃$143]**
- The Long Day Wanes; a Malayan Trilogy. New York: Norton and Company, 1965. Review slip. Dustwrapper (long closed tear, barely visible, on upper panel). *(Words Etcetera)* **£48 [≃$92]**
- MF. London: 1971. Dustwrapper (one small tear). *(Words Etcetera)* **£18 [≃$34]**
- Napoleon Symphony. London: 1974. Dustwrapper. *(Ellis)* **£35 [≃$67]**
- 1985. London: 1979. Uncorrected proof copy. Wrappers. *(First Issues)* **£45 [≃$86]**
- Nothing Like the Sun. London: Heinemann, 1964. Dustwrapper. *(Limestone Hills)* **$80 [≃£41]**

- Obscenity & the Arts. Valletta: Malta Library Assoc, 1973. Pictorial wrappers. *(Alphabet)* **$25 [≃£13]**
- Obscenity and the Arts. Malta: Malta Library Association, 1973. Wrappers. *(Moorhouse)* **£35 [≃$67]**
- Obscenity and the Arts. Valetta, Malta: 1973. Wrappers. *(Words Etcetera)* **£50 [≃$95]**
- One Hand Clapping. New York: Knopf, 1972. 1st American edition. Review slip. Dust- wrapper. *(Antic Hay)* **$50 [≃£26]**
- The Pianoplayers. London: 1986. Uncorrected proof copy. Wrappers. *(First Issues)* **£25 [≃$47]**
- The Right to an Answer. London: Heinemann, 1960. Name on endpaper. Dustwrapper (slightly chipped and soiled). *(Virgo)* **£55 [≃$105]**
- Time for a Tiger. London: Heinemann, 1956. His 1st book. *(Sklaroff)* **£20 [≃$38]**
- Tremor of Intent. London: 1966. Dustwrapper (slightly rubbed). *(Buckley)* **£30 [≃$57]**
- Tremor of Intent. New York: Norton, [1966]. 1st American edition. Price-clipped dustwrapper (minor wear). *(Antic Hay)* **$35 [≃£18]**
- Urgent Copy. London: Cape, 1968. Dustwrapper. *(Moorhouse)* **£25 [≃$47]**
- Urgent Copy. New York: (1968). Dustwrapper (very slightly edge rubbed). *(Polyanthos)* **$25 [≃£13]**
- A Vision of Battlements. New York: (1965). Dustwrapper (spine slightly sunned, two small edge tears, few tiny edge chips). *(Polyanthos)* **$35 [≃£18]**
- The Wanting Seed. London: Heinemann, 1962. Dustwrapper (two small internal repairs). *(Dyke)* **£65 [≃$124]**
- The Worm and the Ring. London: Heinemann, 1961. Dustwrapper. Suppressed. *(Whiteson)* **£700 [≃$1,343]**

Burke, James Lee

- The Lost Get-Back Boogie. Baton Rouge: Louisiana State University, 1986. Price-clipped dustwrapper. *(Mordida)* **$65 [≃£33]**
- The Lost Get-Back Boogie. Baton Rouge: LSU Press, 1986. Price-clipped dustwrapper. *(Janus)* **$65 [≃£33]**
- The Neon Rain. New York: Holt, 1987. Dustwrapper. *(Michael Johnson)* **£28 [≃$53]**

Burke, Jonathan

- The Dark Gateway. London: Panther Books, [1954]. Dustwrapper. *(Dermont)* **$35 [≃£18]**

Burman, Ben Lucien

- Steamboat Round the Bend. New York: Farrar & Rinehart, (1933). Dustwrapper (slight soiling). *(Houle)* **$150 [≃£78]**

Burnett, W.R.

- The Giant Swing. New York: 1932. Dustwrapper. *(Pettler & Liebermann)* **$90 [≃£46]**
- Iron Man. New York: Dial, 1930. Dustwrapper (spine a bit worn). *(Alphabet)* **$50 [≃£26]**

Burns, Rex

- The Alvarez Journal. New York: Harper, 1975. Dustwrapper. *(Janus)* **$35 [≃£18]**

Burroughs, William S.

- Ah Pook is Here. London: Calder, 1979. Dustwrapper. *(Hazeldene)* **£20 [≃$38]**
- Ali's Smile. Naked Scientology. Bonn: Expanded Media Editions, 1978. Wrappers. *(Polyanthos)* **$20 [≃£10]**
- Blade Runner: A Movie. Berkely: Blue Wind, 1978. 1st trade edition. Pictorial wrappers. Inscribed on title. *(Alphabet)* **$60 [≃£31]**
- The Cat Inside. Drawings by Brion Gysin. New York: Grenfell Press, 1986. One of 183 signed by both. Quarter vellum. No dustwrapper issued. *(Polyanthos)* **$375 [≃£195]**
- Cities of the Red Night. New York: Holt, 1981. 1st trade edition. Dustwrapper (two short closed tears). *(Alphabet)* **$20 [≃£10]**
- Cobble Stone Gardens. New York: 1976. Pictorial wrappers. *(Polyanthos)* **$20 [≃£10]**
- Exterminator! New York: Viking, (1973). Small inscription on half-title. Dustwrapper. *(Lopez)* **$30 [≃£15]**
- The Four Horsemen of the Apocalypse. Bonn: Expanded Media Editions, (1979). Pictorial wrappers. *(Polyanthos)* **$20 [≃£10]**
- Junkie. By William Lee [pseudonym]. New York: Ace-Double D-15, 1953. Wrappers (slight wear to spine ends, slightly rubbed). His 1st book. *(Sclanders)* **£75 [≃$143]**
- Junkie. By William Lee [pseudonym]. New York: Ace Original, (1953). Pictorial wrappers (crease lower front wrapper). His 1st book. *(Polyanthos)* **$125 [≃£65]**
- The Last Words of Dutch Schultz. New York: 1975. Dustwrapper. *(Polyanthos)* **$20 [≃£10]**
- The Naked Lunch. Paris: Olympia Press, 1959. Wrappers, New Franc price on rear wrapper, white portion of spine browned. Author's inscription. *(Alphabet)* **$400 [≃£208]**

- The Naked Lunch. Paris: Olympia, (1959). The correct 1st edition. Short inscription and date. Wrappers. Dustwrapper (light wear at head). *(Lopez)* **$285 [≃£148]**
- The Naked Lunch. Paris: Olympia, (1959). The correct 1st edition. Wrappers (price in New Francs rubber-stamped on rear cover). *(Lopez)* **$125 [≃£65]**
- The Naked Lunch. Paris: Olympia Press, 1959. Name on endpaper. Wrappers (spine slightly creased, slight soiling to inside rear cover and rear endpaper). Dustwrapper (spine repaired internally, small losses at top of front panel and head of spine). *(Sclanders)* **£80 [≃$153]**
- Nova Express. New York: Grove Press, 1964. Dustwrapper. *(Alphabet)* **$40 [≃£20]**
- Nova Express. New York: Grove, (1964). 1st American edition. Dustwrapper. *(Lopez)* **$35 [≃£18]**
- Nova Express. New York: Grove Press, [1964]. Dustwrapper. *(Chapel Hill)* **$55 [≃£28]**
- The Place of Dead Roads. New York: Holt, Rinehart & Winston, 1983. Dustwrapper. Author's inscription. *(Alphabet)* **$85 [≃£44]**
- The Place of Dead Roads. New York: (1984). Dustwrapper. *(Woolmer)* **$25 [≃£13]**
- Port of Saints. Berkley: Blue Wind, 1980. Pictorial wrappers. *(Polyanthos)* **$15 [≃£7]**
- Queer. New York: Viking, 1985. Dustwrapper. *(Alphabet)* **$20 [≃£10]**
- Queer. New York: 1985. Dustwrapper. *(Polyanthos)* **$20 [≃£10]**
- Queer. London: Picador, 1985. Uncorrected proof copy. Wrappers. *(David Rees)* **£12 [≃$23]**
- Roosevelt after Inauguration and Other Atrocities. San Francisco: City Lights, (1978). Pictorial wrappers. *(Polyanthos)* **$20 [≃£10]**
- Sidetripping. New York: Derbi Books, (1975). Wrappers. *(Polyanthos)* **$25 [≃£13]**
- Sidetripping. Photographs by Charles Gatewood. New York: Derbibooks, 1975. Wrappers. Signed by both. *(Between the Covers)* **$135 [≃£70]**
- The Soft Machine. New York: Grove Press, 1966. Dustwrapper (two small nicks). *(Alphabet)* **$35 [≃£18]**
- The Soft Machine. New York: Grove Press, 1966. Dustwrapper. *(Polyanthos)* **$25 [≃£13]**
- The Soft Machine. London: 1968. 1st English edition. Dustwrapper. *(Alphabet)* **£12.50 [≃$24]**
- The Ticket that Exploded. Paris: Olympia, (1962). The correct 1st edition. Wrappers. Dustwrapper (minute wear). Signed by the author. *(Lopez)* **$275 [≃£143]**
- Time. New York: C Press, 1965. One of 100 (this unnumbered) signed by author & artist. 4 drawings by Brian Gysin. Wrappers. *(Any Amount)* **£85 [≃$163]**

Burton, Miles

- Heir to Lucifer. London: Collins Crime Club, 1947. Dustwrapper (tiny wear base of spine). *(Mordida)* **$65 [≃£33]**

Butts, Mary

- Armed with Madness. London: Wishart, 1928. One of 100. Buckram slightly faded at spine, slightly handled, one corner bumped. *(Clearwater)* **£150 [≃$287]**
- Speed the Plough & Other Stories. London: Chapman, 1923. Yellow buckram binding state. Dustwrapper (spine a bit darkened). Her 1st book. *(Any Amount)* **£170 [≃$326]**

Byatt, A.S.

- Possession. London: 1990. Uncorrected proof copy. Wrappers. Signed by the author. *(Egret)* **£45 [≃$86]**
- Possession. London: 1990. Dustwrapper. Signed by the author. *(Egret)* **£25 [≃$47]**
- Still Life. London: 1985. Dustwrapper. Signed by the author. *(Egret)* **£30 [≃$57]**
- Still Life. London: Chatto, 1985. Dustwrapper. Author's signed dated inscription. *(Paul Brown)* **£20 [≃$38]**
- The Virgin in the Garden. London: 1978. Dustwrapper. Signed by the author. *(Egret)* **£45 [≃$86]**
- The Virgin in the Garden. London: Chatto, 1978. Spine bumped. Dustwrapper. Author's signed inscription. *(Paul Brown)* **£25 [≃$47]**
- Wordsworth and Coleridge in their Time. London: Nelson, [n.d.]. Price-clipped dustwrapper. *(Moorhouse)* **£12 [≃$23]**

Byron, Robert

- The Station. London: 1928. Dustwrapper. *(Words Etcetera)* **£65 [≃$124]**

Byron, Robert & Sykes, Christopher

- Innocence and Design. By Richard Waughburton [pseud.]. London: 1935. Dustwrapper (worn and torn). *(Words Etcetera)* **£225 [≃$431]**

Cage, John

- How to Improve the World. Something Else Press: 1967. Wrappers. *(Any Amount)* **£10 [≃$19]**

Cain, James M.

- Love's Lovely Counterfeit. New York: Knopf, 1942. Last page of text roughly opened. Dustwrapper (spine slightly darkened, some very slight soiling). Signed by the author (apparently contemporaneously). *(Between the Covers)* **$500 [≃£260]**
- The Magician's Wife. New York: Dial, 1965. Price-clipped dustwrapper (slightly rubbed). *(Alphabet)* **$25 [≃£13]**
- The Moth. New York: Knopf, 1948. Dustwrapper (slightly worn). *(Whiteson)* **£30 [≃$57]**
- Rainbow's End. New York: Mason / Charter, 1975. Endpaper excised. Dustwrapper. Inscribed by the author. *(Heritage)* **$125 [≃£65]**
- Three of a Kind. New York: Knopf, 1943. Dustwrapper (minor chipping top of spine). *(Janus)* **$185 [≃£96]**

Caldwell, Erskine

- American Earth. New York: 1931. Spine and top edge of rear cover lightly sunned. Bookplate signed by the author. *(Polyanthos)* **$45 [≃£23]**
- Jackpot. Collected Short Stories. London: Falcon Press, 1952. 1st English edition. Dustwrapper. *(Limestone Hills)* **$50 [≃£26]**
- Journeyman. New York: Viking, 1938. 1st trade edition. Price-clipped dustwrapper. *(Nouveau)* **$65 [≃£33]**
- Kneel to the Rising Sun and Other Stories. New York: Viking, 1935. One of 300 signed by the author. Slipcase. *(Heritage)* **$175 [≃£91]**
- Kneel to the Rising Sun and Other Stories. New York: Viking, 1935. One of 300 signed. Slipcase. *(Bromer)* **$275 [≃£143]**
- Kneel to the Rising Sun and Other Stories. New York: Viking, 1935. One of 300 signed by the author. *(Heritage)* **$150 [≃£78]**
- A Place Called Estherville. New York: Duell, Sloan & Pearce, [1948]. Dustwrapper (few short tears, small nick). *(Antic Hay)* **$35 [≃£18]**
- Poor Fool. New York: Rariora Press, 1930. One of 1000. *(Bromer)* **$225 [≃£117]**
- Southways. New York: Viking, 1938. Dustwrapper. Inscribed by the author. *(Bromer)* **$275 [≃£143]**
- Trouble in July. New York: Duell, Sloan and Pearce, [1940]. Price-clipped dust- wrapper. *(Chapel Hill)* **$45 [≃£23]**

Calisher, Hortense

- In the Absence of Angels. Boston: 1951. Dustwrapper. Signed by the author. Her 1st book. *(Polyanthos)* **$50 [≃£26]**

Callaghan, Morley

- Strange Fugitive. New York: 1928. Cloth a little edge rubbed. His 1st book. *(Polyanthos)* **$50 [≃£26]**

Calvino, Italo

- Adam, One Afternoon. London: Collins, 1957. Dustwrapper (foxed, slightly torn). *(Moorhouse)* **£30 [≃$57]**
- The Baron in the Trees. New York: RH, (1959). Dustwrapper (spine slightly darkened, couple of small pieces missing from upper edge of front panel). *(Lopez)* **$65 [≃£33]**
- Cosmicomics. London: Cape, 1969. 1st UK edition. Dustwrapper. *(Any Amount)* **£20 [≃$38]**
- The Silent Mr. Palomar. Targ Editions: 1981. Dustwrapper. *(Nouveau)* **$100 [≃£52]**

Campbell, John W.

- Cloak of Aesir. Chicago: Shasta, [1952]. Dustwrapper (lightly used). Signed by the author. *(Dermont)* **$125 [≃£65]**

Campbell, R.T.

- Unholy Dying. London: John Westhouse, 1945. Dustwrapper (chipped and soiled). *(Limestone Hills)* **$65 [≃£33]**

Campbell, Roy

- The Flaming Terrapin. New York: 1924. Extremities very slightly rubbed. His 1st book. *(Polyanthos)* **$45 [≃£23]**
- Flowering Reeds. London: 1933. One of 69 specially bound and signed. Two-tone brown cloth gilt (upper cover very slightly marked). Glassine dustwrapper. *(Words Etcetera)* **£135 [≃$259]**
- Flowering Reeds. Boriswood, 1933. Dustwrapper. *(Words Etcetera)* **£20 [≃$38]**
- The Georgiad. London: Boriswood, 1931. Dustwrapper. *(Polyanthos)* **$45 [≃£23]**
- Lorca. Cambridge: 1952. Dustwrapper (slightly sunned). *(David Rees)* **£20 [≃$38]**
- Mithraic Emblems. Boriswood: 1936. Dustwrapper (stained & frayed). *(Tiger Books)* **£25 [≃$47]**
- Poems. Paris: Hours Press, 1930. One of 200 signed. Some spotting to prelims. Leather and decorated boards (spine slightly rubbed with small chip at head, couple of small marks on boards). *(Patterson)* **£100 [≃$191]**
- Sons of the Mistral. London: 1941. Dustwrapper. *(Buckley)* **£20 [≃$38]**

- Talking Bronco. London: Faber, 1946. Text slightly browned. Dustwrapper (closed tears). *(Tiger Books)* **£15 [≃$28]**
- Talking Bronco. London: 1946. Dustwrapper (slightly frayed). *(Roberts)* **£12.50 [≃$24]**

Canin, James M.

- Galatea. New York: Knopf, 1953. Dustwrapper (slightly chipped). *(Limestone Hills)* **$45 [≃£23]**

Cannan, Joanna

- Poisonous Relations. New York: Morrow, 1950. 1st American edition. Published in England as "Murder Included". Dustwrapper (couple of short closed tears). *(Mordida)* **$37.50 [≃£19]**

Cannell, Dorothy

- The Thin Woman. New York: St. Martin's Press, 1984. Uncorrected proof copy. Wrappers. *(Mordida)* **$45 [≃£23]**

Capote, Truman

- Answered Prayers. New York: Random House, [1987]. 1st American edition (British edition precedes). Dustwrapper. *(Chapel Hill)* **$35 [≃£18]**
- Breakfast at Tiffany's. London: 1958. 1st English edition. Very slight foxing. Dustwrapper. *(Roberts)* **£35 [≃$67]**
- Breakfast at Tiffany's London: 1958. Small spot on foredge. Dustwrapper (several internally repaired nicks, a few small stains). *(Ellis)* **£45 [≃$86]**
- Breakfast at Tiffany's. London: Hamish Hamilton, 1958. 1st English edition. Dustwrapper (small internal repair). *(Limestone Hills)* **$65 [≃£33]**
- The Grass Harp: A Play. New York: 1952. Dustwrapper (very shallow chipping top edge). *(Pettler & Liebermann)* **$200 [≃£104]**
- In Cold Blood. New York: Random House, [1965]. 1st trade edition. Dustwrapper. *(Houle)* **$125 [≃£65]**
- Local Color. London: 1950. One of 200 specially bound (this copy out of series). Some wear at spine ends. *(Sclanders)* **£90 [≃$172]**
- The Muses are Heard. London: 1957. Dustwrapper (slightly nicked at top). *(Buckley)* **£20 [≃$38]**
- Other Voices, Other Rooms. New York: Random House, 1948. Dustwrapper. His 1st book. *(Nouveau)* **$175 [≃£91]**
- Other Voices Other Rooms. London: 1948. 1st English edition. Some foxing of edges. Dustwrapper (slightly rubbed). *(Roberts)* **£12.50 [≃$24]**
- Other Voices, Other Rooms. Franklin Center: 1979. Franklin Library signed edition. Leatherette. *(Pettler & Liebermann)* **$125 [≃£65]**
- The Thanksgiving Visitor. New York: 1967. Bookplate. Slipcase. No dustwrapper issued. *(Pettler & Liebermann)* **$45 [≃£23]**
- A Tree of Night and Other Stories. 1950. Spine badly faded, covers marked. Dustwrapper (chipped, browned and torn). *(Words Etcetera)* **£40 [≃$76]**

Carey, Peter

- Bliss. London: Faber, 1981. 1st British edition. Signed by the author. *(Michael Johnson)* **£30 [≃$57]**
- Bliss. London: Faber, 1981. 1st British edition. Dustwrapper. *(Michael Johnson)* **£20 [≃$38]**
- Bliss. London: Faber, 1981. Dustwrapper. *(Lewton)* **£18.50 [≃$36]**
- The Fat Man in History. London: Faber, 1980. 1st British edition. Dustwrapper. Signed by the author. *(Michael Johnson)* **£32 [≃$61]**
- The Fat Man in History. London: Faber, 1980. 1st British edition. Dustwrapper. *(Michael Johnson)* **£20 [≃$38]**
- The Fat Man in History. London: 1980. Dustwrapper. *(First Issues)* **£25 [≃$47]**
- Illywhacker. London: Faber, 1985. Uncorrected proof copy. Wrappers. *(David Rees)* **£30 [≃$57]**
- Illywhacker. London: Faber, 1985. Dustwrapper. *(Lewton)* **£17.50 [≃$34]**
- Oscar & Lucinda. London: Faber, 1988. Dustwrapper. *(Lewton)* **£18.50 [≃$36]**
- Oscar and Lucinda. London: Faber, 1988. 1st British edition. Dustwrapper. Signed by the author. *(Michael Johnson)* **£36 [≃$69]**
- Oscar and Lucinda. London: Faber, 1988. Dustwrapper. *(Words Etcetera)* **£35 [≃$67]**
- Oscar and Lucinda. New York: Harper & Row, 1988. Advance reading copy. Illustrated wrappers. *(Moorhouse)* **£35 [≃$67]**
- Oscar and Lucinda. New York: Harper & Row, 1988. 1st American edition. Dustwrapper. The 1st printing was withdrawn from sale. *(Michael Johnson)* **£40 [≃$76]**

Carnevali, Emanuel

- A Hurried Man. Paris: Contact Press, 1925. Wrappers, largely unopened (very slightly dust soiled). *(Words Etcetera)* **£125 [≃$239]**

Carr, John Dickson

- Behind the Crimson Blind. By Carter Dickson. New York: Morrow, 1952. Numbers on endpaper. Dustwrapper. *(Janus)* **$95 [≃£49]**
- The Cavalier's Cup. By Carter Dickson. New York: Morrow, 1953. Dustwrapper. *(Mordida)* **$85 [≃£44]**
- Death in Five Boxes. By Carter Dickson. New York: Morrow, 1938. Small label removed from front endpaper. Dustwrapper (slight interior tape marks, several short closed tears, wear and chips at top corners of spine). *(Mordida)* **$300 [≃£156]**
- Death Turns the Tables. New York: Harper, 1941. Bookplate. Dustwrapper (several tiny closed tears, tiny wear at top of spine). *(Mordida)* **$400 [≃£208]**
- The Emperor's Snuff Box. New York: Harper, 1942. Bookseller's stamp on pastedown. Price- clipped dustwrapper (small chip at top of front panel, several short closed tears). *(Mordida)* **$350 [≃£182]**
- The Four False Weapons. New York: Harper, 1937. Price-clipped dustwrapper (tiny nicks and tears at spine ends, spine slightly faded, tiny wear at corners, small piece missing at lower corner of back panel). *(Mordida)* **$400 [≃£208]**
- The Ghost's High Noon. New York: Harper & Row, 1969. Dustwrapper. Inscribed by the author. *(Mordida)* **$200 [≃£104]**
- He Who Whispers. New York: Harper, 1946. Dustwrapper (several tiny tears). *(Mordida)* **$60 [≃£31]**
- The Hungry Goblin. New York: Harper & Row, 1972. Dustwrapper (tiny tears, scrape at top of spine). *(Mordida)* **$35 [≃£18]**
- The Murder of Sir Edmund Godfrey. New York: Harper, 1936. Edges spotted and darkened. Dustwrapper (spine slightly faded, several short closed tears with small interior tape mends, a small hole on back panel, slight wear at corners). *(Mordida)* **$450 [≃£234]**
- Nine - and Death Makes Ten. By Carter Dickson. New York: Morrow, 1940. Dustwrapper (tiny closed tears at spine ends, very small hole back panel). *(Mordida)* **$350 [≃£182]**
- Seeing is Believing. By Carter Dickson. New York: Morrow, 1941. Advance reading copy. Wrappers. Dustwrapper. Custom made box. *(Mordida)* **$400 [≃£208]**
- Till Death Do Us Part. New York: Harper, 1944. Dustwrapper (minor restoration at foot of spine, small internal tape repair, several tiny closed tears). Signed by the author. *(Mordida)* **$250 [≃£130]**
- The Witch of the Low Tide. London: Hamish Hamilton, 1961. 1st English edition. Dust- wrapper (slightly chipped). *(Limestone Hills)* **$45 [≃£23]**

Carroll, Jim

- The Basketball Diaries Age 13 to 15. Bolinas: Tombouctou, Lamplighter, 1978. The correct 1st edition. Printed wrappers, card covers, spine a bit creased. *(Alphabet)* **$50 [≃£26]**

Carter, Angela

- Black Venus's Tale. London: 1980. Spiral binding. Signed by the author. *(Buckley)* **£30 [≃$57]**
- Black Venus. London: Chatto & Windus, (1985). Dustwrapper. *(Lopez)* **$40 [≃£20]**
- Fireworks. London: 1974. Dustwrapper. *(First Issues)* **£20 [≃$38]**
- Fireworks. London: Quartet, 1974. Dustwrapper. *(Moorhouse)* **£25 [≃$47]**
- Heroes and Villains. London: 1969. Dustwrapper. *(First Issues)* **£65 [≃$124]**
- The Infernal Desire Machines of Doctor Hoffman. London: Hart-Davis, 1972. Dust- wrapper. Signed by the author. *(Ash)* **£50 [≃$95]**
- The Infernal Desire Machines of Doctor Hoffman. London: Hart-Davis, 1972. Dust- wrapper. Signed by the author. *(David Rees)* **£20 [≃$38]**
- The Infernal Desire Machines of Doctor Hoffman. London: Hart-Davis, 1972. Dust- wrapper. *(Limestone Hills)* **$55 [≃£28]**
- Nights at the Circus. London: Chatto & Windus, 1984. Dustwrapper. *(Lewton)* **£7.50 [≃$15]**
- The Sadeian Woman. London: Virago, 1979. The simultaneous casebound issue. Dust- wrapper. *(Moorhouse)* **£45 [≃$86]**
- Saints and Strangers. US: 1986. 1st US edition. Dustwrapper. *(Words Etcetera)* **£12 [≃$23]**
- Shadow Dance. London: Heinemann, 1966. Small abrasion on front free endpaper. Dustwrapper (spine slightly sunned). *(Moorhouse)* **£120 [≃$230]**
- The War of Dreams. New York: 1974. 1st US edition of The Infernal Desire Machines ... . Dustwrapper. *(Words Etcetera)* **£10 [≃$19]**

Carver, Raymond

- At Night the Salmon Move. SB: Capra, 1976. One of 1000 (of 1100) in wrappers. *(Lopez)* **$100 [≃£52]**

- Cathedral. New York: Knopf, 1983. Uncorrected proof copy. Wrappers. *(Lopez)* **$125 [≃£65]**
- Cathedral. New York: Knopf, 1983. Review copy. Price-clipped dustwrapper. *(Lopez)* **$50 [≃£26]**
- Cathedral. New York: 1983. Dustwrapper. *(Polyanthos)* **$20 [≃£10]**
- Cathedral. London: Collins, 1984. Dustwrapper. *(Moorhouse)* **£18 [≃$34]**
- Distress Sale. A Broadside. Illustrated by James Silke. One of 150 signed by both. *(Polyanthos)* **$45 [≃£23]**
- Early for the Dance. Concord: Ewert, 1986. One of 36 (of 136) hardcover, numbered with Roman numerals, signed. No dustwrapper issued. *(Lopez)* **$225 [≃£117]**
- Elephant and Other Stories. London: Collins Harvill: 1988. Dustwrapper. Not published in the US. *(Nouveau)* **$60 [≃£31]**
- Elephant and Other Stories. London: 1988. Dustwrapper. *(Polyanthos)* **$50 [≃£26]**
- Fires. SB: Capra, 1983. One of 250 signed. Original acetate dustwrapper. *(Lopez)* **$125 [≃£65]**
- Fires. London: 1985. Dustwrapper. *(Polyanthos)* **$45 [≃£23]**
- Glimpses. Northampton, MA: Basement Press, 1985. One of 15 numbered copies and two printer's proofs, of which this is one. Cloth, paper label. *(Lopez)* **$1,500 [≃£781]**
- His Bathrobe Pockets Stuffed with Notes. (Elmwood: Raven, 1988). One of 50 (of 70) numbered and signed. *(Lopez)* **$175 [≃£91]**
- If It Please You. Northridge: Lord John, 1984. One of 200 (of 226) signed. No dustwrapper issued. *(Moorhouse)* **£85 [≃$163]**
- In a Marine Light. London: 1987. Dustwrapper. Review slip and publisher's release laid-in. *(Polyanthos)* **$45 [≃£23]**
- In a Marine Light. London: Collins, 1987. Dustwrapper. *(Moorhouse)* **£16 [≃$30]**
- Music. (Concord: Ewert, 1987). One of 26 (of 136) lettered and signed. *(Lopez)* **$225 [≃£117]**
- A New Path to the Waterfall. New York: Atlantic, (1989). Uncorrected proof copy. Wrappers. *(Lopez)* **$125 [≃£65]**
- New Path to the Waterfall. New York: Atlantic, 1989. One of 200 signed by Tess Gallagher. Slipcase. *(Michael Johnson)* **£80 [≃$153]**
- The Painter & The Fish. Ewert: 1988. One of 74 numbered copies signed by the author and by the illustrator Mary Azarian. Wrappers. *(Nouveau)* **$110 [≃£57]**
- The Painter & The Fish. Ewert: 1988. One of 26 lettered copies, signed by the author & by the illustrator Mary Azarian. Paper and cloth over boards. *(Nouveau)* **$225 [≃£117]**
- The Painter and the Fish. Concord: Ewert, 1988. One of 26 (of 100) hardcover, lettered and signed by the author and artist (Mary Azarian). *(Lopez)* **$285 [≃£148]**
- The Pheasant. Worcester: Metacomb Press, 1982. One of 150 signed. Wrappers. *(Words Etcetera)* **£85 [≃$163]**
- Put Yourself in My Shoes. Santa Barbara: 1974. Wrappers. *(Pettler & Liebermann)* **$125 [≃£65]**
- Put Yourself in My Shoes. SB: Capra, 1974. One of 500 in wrappers. *(Lopez)* **$125 [≃£65]**
- The Toes. Ewert: 1988. One of 26 lettered copies. Wrappers. *(Nouveau)* **$135 [≃£70]**
- Ultramarine. New York: RH, (1986). Advance review copy. Dustwrapper. promotional sheet laid in. *(Lopez)* **$50 [≃£26]**
- Ultramarine. New York: RH, (1986). Dustwrapper. *(Lopez)* **$35 [≃£18]**
- Where I'm Calling From. Franklin Center, PA: Franklin Library, 1988. Leather, a.e.g., upper corners slightly bumped. Signed by the author. *(Lopez)* **$250 [≃£130]**
- Where I'm Calling From. New York: Atlantic Monthly Press, 1988. Dustwrapper. *(Michael Johnson)* **£30 [≃$57]**
- Where I'm Calling From. New York: Atlantic Monthly Press, 1988. Dustwrapper. *(Moorhouse)* **£25 [≃$47]**
- Where Water Comes Together with Other Water. New York: RH, (1985). Dustwrapper. *(Lopez)* **$50 [≃£26]**
- Will You Please Be Quiet, Please? New York: McGraw-Hill, (1976). Dustwrapper (one tiny tear on rear panel). Inscribed by the author (1981). *(Lopez)* **$500 [≃£260]**
- Winter Insomnia. (Santa Cruz): Kayak, (1970). Wrappers. *(Lopez)* **$100 [≃£52]**
- Winter Insomnia. (Santa Cruz: Kayak, 1970). Signed by the author. *(Lopez)* **$200 [≃£104]**
- Winter Insomnia. Santa Cruz: 1970. Said to be one of 1000. Wrappers. His 1st regularly published book. *(Pettler & Liebermann)* **$125 [≃£65]**
- Winter Insomnia. Santa Cruz: Kayak Books, 1970. One of 1000. Green and yellow wrappers. His 1st regularly published book. *(Moorhouse)* **£125 [≃$239]**

Carvic, Heron

- Picture Miss Seeton. London: Bles, 1968.

Compliments slip laid in. Stain from paper clip on f.e.p. Dustwrapper (lightly soiled). *(Mordida)* **$85 [≃£44]**

Cary, Joyce

- The African Witch. London: 1936. Dustwrapper (somewhat faded, internally strengthened, a few nicks). *(Words Etcetera)* **£30 [≃$57]**
- An American Visitor. London: Benn, 1933. Slightly marked. *(Edrich)* **£30 [≃$57]**
- Except the Lord. London: 1953. Dustwrapper. *(Buckley)* **£15 [≃$28]**
- Power in Men. London: 1939. No dustwrapper issued. *(Ellis)* **£35 [≃$67]**

Casey, John

- An American Romance. New York: Atheneum, 1977. Dustwrapper. Inscribed by the author. His 1st book. *(Lopez)* **$85 [≃£44]**

Castaneda, Carlos

- The Teachings of Don Juan. Berkeley: 1968. Price-clipped dustwrapper (lightly worn). His 1st book. *(Lopez)* **$100 [≃£52]**

Caterpillar

- Caterpillar. Edited by Clayton Eshleman. 1967-73. Issues 1-20, all published. Includes the suppressed issue 2. *(Blakeney)* **£200 [≃$383]**

Cather, Willa

- A Lost Lady. New York: 1923. One of 200 signed. Cloth backed boards (spine sunned, wear to extremities). Spare label present. *(King)* **$150 [≃£78]**
- Lucy Gayheart. New York: Knopf, 1935. One of 749 signed. Buckram, t.e.g. (spine fading). *(Houle)* **$275 [≃£143]**
- Lucy Gayheart. New York: Knopf, 1935. 1st trade edition. Dustwrapper. *(Houle)* **$175 [≃£91]**
- The Professor's House. New York: Knopf, 1925. One of 40 signed. Spine slightly darkened. *(Lopez)* **$1,250 [≃£651]**
- Shadows on the Rock. New York: Knopf, 1931. No spine fade. Earliest dustwrapper (several small chips). *(Antic Hay)* **$75 [≃£39]**

Caudwell, Sarah

- The Shortest Way to Hades. London: Collins, 1984. Dustwrapper. Signed by the author. *(Limestone Hills)* **$55 [≃£28]**
- The Shortest Way to Hades. London: Collins Crime Club, 1984. Dustwrapper. *(Mordida)* **$45 [≃£23]**
- The Sirens Sang of Murder. London: Collins Crime Club, 1989. Dustwrapper. *(Mordida)* **$30 [≃£15]**

Causley, Charles

- Farewell, Aggie Weston. Hand & Flower Press: 1951. Wrappers. His 1st book. *(Buckley)* **£20 [≃$38]**

Caute, David

- At Fever Pitch. London: 1959. Edges very lightly spotted. Dustwrapper (slightly rubbed, spine slightly faded). His 1st book. *(Ellis)* **£25 [≃$47]**

Cecil, Henry

- The Painswick Line. London: Chapman & Hall, 1951. Dustwrapper (slightly nicked, internally repaired). *(Limestone Hills)* **$45 [≃£23]**

Celine, Louis-Ferdinand

- Death on the Instalment Plan. Translated by John Marks. London: 1938. Dustwrapper (slightly rubbed on the spine & nicked at extremities). *(Blakeney)* **£175 [≃$335]**

Chabon, Michael

- The Mysteries of Pittsburgh. New York: 1988. Dustwrapper. Signed by the author. His 1st book. *(Polyanthos)* **$35 [≃£18]**

Chandler, Raymond

- The Big Sleep. Black Widow Thriller Edition, 1945. Spine a trifle discoloured. Inscribed by the author (1949). *(Words Etcetera)* **£900 [≃$1,727]**
- Farewell, My Lovely. New York: Knopf, 1940. Stamp on front pastedown and endpaper, bookplate. Dustwrapper (taped). *(Janus)* **$500 [≃£260]**
- Five Sinister Characters. New York: Avon, 1945. Paperback original. Date on title, pages browning. *(Janus)* **$185 [≃£96]**
- Five Sinister Characters. New York: Avon Book Company, 1945. Browned. Wrappers. *(Words Etcetera)* **£65 [≃$124]**
- The High Window. New York: Knopf, 1942. Dustwrapper (small chip top of spine, slight rubbing at edges). *(Houle)* **$850 [≃£442]**
- The Lady in the Lake. New York: Knopf, 1943. Covers slightly dull and marked. dustwrapper (worn, parts missing). *(Whiteson)* **£350 [≃$671]**
- The Lady in the Lake. New York: Knopf, 1943. Dustwrapper (lightly chipped). *(Janus)* **$750 [≃£390]**

- The Lady in the Lake. Black Widow Thriller Edition, 1945. Dustwrapper (slightly rubbed). Inscribed by the author (1950). *(Words Etcetera)* **£950 [≃$1,823]**
- The Lady in the Lake. Melbourne: 1946. 1st Australian edition. Dustwrapper (chipped). *(Pettler & Liebermann)* **$80 [≃£41]**
- The Little Sister. Boston: 1949. Dustwrapper (chipped). *(Pettler & Liebermann)* **$125 [≃£65]**
- The Little Sister. Boston: Houghton, 1949. 1st US edition. Dustwrapper (chipped, taped). *(Janus)* **$150 [≃£78]**
- The Long Good-Bye. London: Hamish Hamilton, 1953. 1st edition (precedes American edition of 1954). Dustwrapper (chipped, internally repaired). *(Limestone Hills)* **$165 [≃£85]**
- The Long Goodbye. London: 1953. 1st English edition (precedes the American edition). Dustwrapper (slightly frayed). *(Roberts)* **£20 [≃$38]**
- The Long Goodbye. London: 1953. Very slight offsetting to endpapers. Boards a touch marked. Dustwrapper (rubbed & creased, chipped at base of spine). *(Blakeney)* **£50 [≃$95]**
- Playback. London: 1958. 1st British edition (precedes US edition). Dustwrapper (small chip spine top). *(Pettler & Liebermann)* **$50 [≃£26]**
- Playback. London: 1958. Dustwrapper (very slightly frayed, one nick). *(Ellis)* **£50 [≃$95]**
- Playback. London: 1958. Dustwrapper. *(Roberts)* **£30 [≃$57]**
- Playback. London: Hamish Hamilton, 1958. 1st edition (precedes American edition). Dustwrapper (minutely chipped). *(Limestone Hills)* **$85 [≃£44]**
- Playback. London: Hamish Hamilton, 1958. 1st English edition. Little marked. *(Whiteson)* **£15 [≃$28]**
- Playback. London: Hamish Hamilton, 1958. 1st edition (precedes US edition). Dustwrapper (torn and repaired). *(Whiteson)* **£25 [≃$47]**
- Playback. Boston: Houghton Mifflin, 1958. 1st American edition. Dustwrapper (several tiny tears, rubbing and wear at spine ends and corners, wear along folds). *(Mordida)* **$75 [≃£39]**
- Red Wind. Cleveland: 1946. Dustwrapper (slightly chipped). *(Buckley)* **£45 [≃$86]**
- Red Wind. Cleveland: World, 1946. Minor bump. Dustwrapper. *(Janus)* **$75 [≃£39]**
- The Second Chandler Omnibus. London: Hamish Hamilton, 1962. Price-clipped dustwrapper (tiny tears at spine ends). *(Mordida)* **$90 [≃£46]**
- The Simple Art of Murder. London: 1950. Tail of spine slightly faded. Dustwrapper (rubbed, frayed, nicked, repaired, lacks piece at base of spine). *(Ellis)* **£40 [≃$76]**
- Spanish Blood. Cleveland: World, 1946. Dustwrapper. *(Limestone Hills)* **$60 [≃£31]**
- Spanish Blood. Cleveland: World, 1946. Dustwrapper. *(Janus)* **$50 [≃£26]**
- Raymond Chandler. Descriptive Bibliography by M.J. Bruccoli. Pittsburgh UP: 1979. No dustwrapper issued. *(Woolmer)* **$25 [≃£13]**

Channon, Sir Henry 'Chips'

- Diaries. London: Weidenfeld & Nicolson, 1967. Dustwrapper (slightly nicked and chipped). *(Virgo)* **£40 [≃$76]**

Chappell, Fred

- I Am One of You Forever. Baton Rouge: LSU, 1985. Advance review copy. Dustwrapper (small surface scrape mid-spine). Signed by the author. *(Lopez)* **$50 [≃£26]**

Charteris, Hugo

- A Share of the World. London: Collins, 1953. Dustwrapper. *(Sklaroff)* **£30 [≃$57]**

Charyn, Jerome

- Once Upon a Drosky. New York: 1964. Dustwrapper. Signed presentation copy from the author. Signed publicity photo laid in. His 1st book. *(Polyanthos)* **$55 [≃£28]**

Chase, J. Hadley

- No Orchids for Miss Blandish. London: Jarrolds, [1939]. Slight foxing. Binding dull and discoloured, edges rubbed. *(Whiteson)* **£20 [≃$38]**

Chatwin, Bruce

- In Patagonia. London: Cape, 1977. Price-clipped dustwrapper. *(Moorhouse)* **£180 [≃$345]**
- On the Black Hill. London: Cape, 1982. Dustwrapper. *(Dyke)* **£25 [≃$47]**
- On the Black Hill. London: Cape, 1982. Dustwrapper. *(Ash)* **£30 [≃$57]**
- On the Black Hill. New York: Viking, (1983). 1st American edition. Uncorrected proof copy. *(Lopez)* **$85 [≃£44]**
- The Songlines. London: Cape, 1987. Uncorrected proof copy. Final pages slightly creased. Wrappers. *(David Rees)* **£50 [≃$95]**

- The Songlines. London: 1987. Uncorrected proof copy. Wrappers. *(Words Etcetera)* **£125 [≃$239]**
- The Songlines. London: London Limited Editions, 1987. One of 150 signed. Tissue dustwrapper. *(Any Amount)* **£125 [≃$239]**
- The Songlines. London: Cape, 1987. Dustwrapper. *(Lewton)* **£30 [≃$57]**
- The Songlines. London: Cape, 1987. Dustwrapper. *(Limestone Hills)* **$95 [≃£49]**
- The Songlines. Franklin Center: Franklin Library, 1987. "Apparently the correct first (American) edition". Leather gilt. Signed by the author. *(Lopez)* **$250 [≃£130]**
- Utz. London: Cape, 1988. Dustwrapper. *(Dyke)* **£15 [≃$28]**
- Utz. New York: Viking, (1988). 1st American edition. Uncorrected proof copy. Wrappers. *(Lopez)* **$75 [≃£39]**
- The Viceroy of Ouidah. London: Cape, 1980. Uncorrected proof copy. Wrappers. *(David Rees)* **£55 [≃$105]**
- The Viceroy of Ouidah. London: Cape, 1980. Dustwrapper. *(Dyke)* **£30 [≃$57]**
- What Am I Doing Here. London: Cape, 1989. Uncorrected proof copy. Wrappers, front panel creased. *(Limestone Hills)* **$85 [≃£44]**
- What Am I Doing Here. London: Cape, 1989. Dustwrapper. *(Limestone Hills)* **$75 [≃£39]**
- What Am I Doing Here. London: Cape, 1989. Dustwrapper (slightly rubbed). *(David Rees)* **£30 [≃$57]**

Chatwin, Bruce & Theroux, Paul

- Patagonia Revisited. London: Russell, 1985. One of 250 signed by both. Tissue dustwrapper. *(Any Amount)* **£120 [≃$230]**

Cheever, John

- The Brigadier and the Golf Widow. New York: H&R, (1964). One of an unspecified number of copies signed by the author on a tipped in sheet before title. Erasure mark on free endpaper and small rubber stamp there. Dustwrapper. *(Lopez)* **$165 [≃£85]**
- The Day the Pig Fell into the Well. Northridge: Lord John Press, 1978. 1st edition thus. One of 275 signed. *(Houle)* **$125 [≃£65]**
- Falconer. New York: Knopf, 1977. Price-clipped dustwrapper. Signed by the author. *(Lopez)* **$125 [≃£65]**
- The Leaves, the Lion-Fish, and the Bear. Los Angeles: Sylvester & Orphanos, 1980. One of 300 signed. *(Houle)* **$135 [≃£70]**
- The Stories. New York: 1978. Dustwrapper (lower spine minimally rubbed). Signed presentation from the author (1979). *(Polyanthos)* **$100 [≃£52]**
- The Uncollected Stories of John Cheever 1930-1981. Chicago: 1988. Advance excerpt (the book was subsequently enjoined from publication). Wrappers. *(David Rees)* **£25 [≃$47]**
- The Wapshot Chronicle. London: Gollancz, 1957. 1st English edition. Dustwrapper. *(Limestone Hills)* **$85 [≃£44]**
- The Wapshot Chronicle. 1957. Dustwrapper (trifle nicked, browned on spine). *(Words Etcetera)* **£35 [≃$67]**
- The Wapshot Chronicle. New York: Harper, (1964). Some damp spotting to binding. Price-clipped dustwrapper (tape repaired). Author's brief inscription. *(Between the Covers)* **$85 [≃£44]**
- The World of Apples. New York: Knopf, 1973. Dustwrapper. *(Limestone Hills)* **$60 [≃£31]**

Chimera

- Chimera. A Literary Quarterly. NJ: Spring 1942 - Summer 1947. 20 issues. Complete run. Wrappers. The three Richard Eberhardt contributions are signed by him. *(Polyanthos)* **$200 [≃£104]**

Christie, Agatha

- After the Funeral. London: Collins, 1953. Dustwrapper. *(Sklaroff)* **£20 [≃$38]**
- Akhnaton: A Play in Three Acts. New York: Dodd, 1973. 1st US edition. Dustwrapper. *(Janus)* **$30 [≃£15]**
- An Autobiography. London: Collins, 1977. Uncorrected advance proofs. Printed wrappers. *(Sklaroff)* **£35 [≃$67]**
- By the Pricking of My Thumbs. London: Collins, 1968. 1st English edition. Name. Dustwrapper (short tear). *(Antic Hay)* **$40 [≃£20]**
- By the Pricking of my Thumbs. London: 1968. Dustwrapper. *(Roberts)* **£13.50 [≃$26]**
- By the Pricking of my Thumbs. London: Collins, 1968. Dustwrapper. *(Sklaroff)* **£8 [≃$15]**
- A Caribbean Mystery. London: Collins, 1964. Uncorrected proof copy. Red wrappers with paper label, publication date in ink. *(Alphabet)* **$125 [≃£65]**
- Cat Among the Pigeons. London: Collins, 1959. Dustwrapper. *(Alphabet)* **$25 [≃£13]**
- Cat Among the Pigeons. London: Collins, [1959]. Some foxing endpapers. Dustwrapper

(few small nicks, moderate wear and browning). *(Antic Hay)* **$40 [≃£20]**

- Curtains. Poirot's Last Case. London: Collins Crime Club, 1975. Dustwrapper. *(Marlborough B'shop)* **£9 [≃$17]**
- Death Comes as the End. London: Collins, 1945. Dustwrapper. *(Limestone Hills)* **$175 [≃£91]**
- Death on the Nile. New York: Dodd Mead, 1938. 1st American edition. Dustwrapper (worn). *(Alphabet)* **$55 [≃£28]**
- Destination Unknown. London: Collins, 1954. Dustwrapper. *(Limestone Hills)* **$50 [≃£26]**
- Elephants Can Remember. London: 1972. Proof copy. Canvas backed paper wrappers (spine a little shaken). *(Words Etcetera)* **£75 [≃$143]**
- Elephants Can Remember. London: Collins Crime Club, 1972. Price-clipped dustwrapper. *(Mordida)* **$20 [≃£10]**
- Elephants Can Remember. London: 1972. Price-clipped dustwrapper. *(Buckley)* **£12 [≃$23]**
- Endless Night. London: 1967. Dustwrapper. *(Buckley)* **£15 [≃$28]**
- Evil Under the Sun. London: 1941. Dustwrapper (price-clipped, slightly frayed and rubbed, speckled with what appears to be coffee). *(Blakeney)* **£95 [≃$182]**
- Evil Under the Sun. New York: Dodd, Mead, 1941. 1st American edition. Dustwrapper (chips to lower spine & lower corner of upper wrapper). *(Houle)* **$175 [≃£91]**
- 4.50 from Paddington. London: Collins, 1957. Dustwrapper. *(Janus)* **$45 [≃£23]**
- 4.50 from Paddington. London: 1957. Minimal foxing. Dustwrapper. *(Roberts)* **£12.50 [≃$24]**
- 4-50 from Paddington. London: Collins, [1957]. 1st English edition. Ink inscription. Dustwrapper (moderate soil). *(Antic Hay)* **$50 [≃£26]**
- Hercule Poirot's Christmas. London: 1939. Spine faded. *(Roberts)* **£30 [≃$57]**
- Hickory Dickory Dock. London: 1955. Dustwrapper (spine very slightly faded). *(Ellis)* **£25 [≃$47]**
- Hickory Dickory Dock. London: Collins Crime Club, 1955. Dustwrapper. *(Lewton)* **£20 [≃$38]**
- The Hound of Death & Other Stories. London: 1933. Edges slightly foxed. *(Buckley)* **£30 [≃$57]**
- The Hound of Death. London: Odhams, 1933. Dustwrapper (strengthened). *(Sklaroff)* **£50 [≃$95]**
- The Labours of Hercules. London: Collins, 1947. Faded. *(Tiger Books)* **£30 [≃$57]**
- The Mirror Crack'd from Side to Side. London: Collins, [1962]. 1st English edition. Dustwrapper (minor wear and soil). *(Antic Hay)* **$50 [≃£26]**
- The Mirror Crack'd from Side to Side. London: 1962. Dustwrapper (slightly chipped). *(Buckley)* **£12 [≃$23]**
- The Mirror Crack'd From Side to Side. London: Collins, 1962. Dustwrapper. *(Alphabet)* **$25 [≃£13]**
- Miss Marple's Final Cases. London: (1979). Uncorrected proof copy. Wrappers (creased). *(Ellis)* **£25 [≃$47]**
- The Moving Finger. New York: 1942. Precedes the UK edition. Dustwrapper (edges and spine ends chipped). *(Words Etcetera)* **£90 [≃$172]**
- Mrs. McGinty's Dead. London: Collins, 1952. Dustwrapper (slightly chipped). *(Limestone Hills)* **$55 [≃£28]**
- Mrs. McGinty's Dead. London: Collins Crime Club, 1952. Dustwrapper. *(Lewton)* **£30 [≃$57]**
- A Murder is Announced. London: Collins, 1950. Spine faded. *(Sklaroff)* **£10 [≃$19]**
- Nemesis. London: Collins, 1971. Dustwrapper (spine panel worn). *(Sklaroff)* **£10 [≃$19]**
- Nemesis. New York: Dodd, Mead, [1971]. 1st American edition. Dustwrapper (slight rubbing). *(Chapel Hill)* **$30 [≃£15]**
- The Pale Horse. London: Collins, 1961. Dustwrapper (very slightly worn). *(Sklaroff)* **£15 [≃$28]**
- Passenger to Frankfurt: An Extravaganza. London: Collins, 1970. Dustwrapper with no price on front flap. *(Janus)* **$25 [≃£13]**
- A Pocket Full of Rye. London: 1953. Edges foxed. Dustwrapper (nicked, small piece missing head of spine). *(Ellis)* **£25 [≃$47]**
- A Pocket Full of Rye. London: Collins, 1953. Dustwrapper (worn, chipped, some loss at spine ends). *(Glyn's)* **£15 [≃$28]**
- A Pocket Full of Rye. London: Collins Crime Club, 1953. Dustwrapper (chipped). *(Marlborough B'shop)* **£8 [≃$15]**
- Poirot's Last Case. Collins, 1975. Uncorrected proof copy. Wrappers with label. *(David Rees)* **£25 [≃$47]**
- The Secret of Chimneys. London: John Lane; The Bodley Head, 1925. Bookplate. *(Alphabet)* **$275 [≃£143]**
- Sparkling Cyanide. London: 1945. Top edge

slightly dusty. Ownership inscription on pastedown. Dustwrapper (slightly rubbed, torn and creased). *(Blakeney)* **£45 [≃$86]**
- Star Over Bethlehem & Other Stories. London: Collins, 1963. Dustwrapper (very slightly rubbed). *(Whiteson)* **£16 [≃$30]**
- Taken at the Flood. London: Collins, 1948. Dustwrapper (internally repaired, slightly worn at spine extremities). *(Limestone Hills)* **$85 [≃£44]**
- There is a Tide. New York: 1948. 1st US edition of Taken at the Flood. Dustwrapper (trifle creased). *(Words Etcetera)* **£30 [≃$57]**
- They Came to Baghdad. London: 1951. Dustwrapper (dusty, slightly torn). *(Clearwater)* **£35 [≃$67]**
- They Came to Baghdad. London: 1951. Dustwrapper. *(Roberts)* **£28 [≃$53]**
- They Do It with Mirrors. London: 1952. Dustwrapper (slightly chipped and rubbed). *(Clearwater)* **£25 [≃$47]**
- Third Girl. London: 1966. Dustwrapper (slightly rubbed). *(Buckley)* **£10 [≃$19]**
- Towards Zero. London: Collins Crime Club, 1944. Dustwrapper. *(Lewton)* **£120 [≃$230]**
- The Underdog. A Story. With Blackman's Wood by E. Phillips Oppenheim. London: Reader's Library, 1929. Dustwrapper (rubbed and chipped at corners, 1/2 inch loss at top of spine, couple of short closed tears). *(First Issues)* **£100 [≃$191]**
- Why Didn't They Ask Evans? London: 1934. Covers a bit marked. *(Words Etcetera)* **£25 [≃$47]**

Christopher, John (C.S. Youd)
- The Death of Grass. London: Michael Joseph, 1956. Dustwrapper (slightly dusty). His 1st book. *(Clearwater)* **£35 [≃$67]**
- The Death of Grass. London: Michael Joseph, 1956. Dustwrapper. *(Sklaroff)* **£35 [≃$67]**

Churchill, Sir Winston Spencer
- Blood Sweat and Tears. Toronto: 1942. 1st Canadian edition. Boards unevenly faded. Dustwrapper (chipped & torn). *(Blakeney)* **£20 [≃$38]**
- A History of the English Speaking Peoples. New York: 1956-58. Presentation edition, not for sale. 4 vols. Dustwrappers (spines slightly sunned, few tiny edge tears, slightly rubbed). *(Polyanthos)* **$95 [≃£49]**
- Into Battle. London: 1941. Dustwrapper (little worn). *(Blakeney)* **£20 [≃$38]**
- The Second World War. London: (1948-54). 6 vols. Some edges a little spotted. One or two corners bumped. Dustwrappers (some a little torn). *(Bow Windows)* **£40 [≃$76]**
- The Second World War: and, An Epilogue ... London: Cassell, (1959). 1st edition thus. Dustwrapper. *(Houle)* **$150 [≃£78]**
- A Speech by the Prime Minister: Aug. 20th 1940. Wrappers (slight foxing on cover). Specially made case. *(Whiteson)* **£140 [≃$268]**

Ciardi, John
- Homeward to America. New York: 1940. Dustwrapper (three tiny edge tears, little edge rubbed). Bookplate signed by the author. His 1st book. *(Polyanthos)* **$75 [≃£39]**

Clampitt, Amy
- Westward. New York: Knopf, 1990. Uncorrected proof copy. *(Lopez)* **$35 [≃£18]**

Clancy, Tom
- Clear and Present Danger. New York: Putnam, 1989. Uncorrected proof copy. Wrappers. *(Mordida)* **$50 [≃£26]**

Clark, Thomas (Tom)
- Airplanes. Essex (UK): 1966. Pictorial stapled wrappers. Signed presentation copy from the author. *(Polyanthos)* **$45 [≃£23]**

Clark, Walter Van Tilburg
- The City of Trembling Leaves. New York: 1945. Dustwrapper. *(Pettler & Liebermann)* **$50 [≃£26]**

Clarke, Arthur C.
- The Challenge of the Sea. New York: HRW, (1960). Small patch of offsetting to front fly. Dustwrapper (extremities slightly chipped. *(Between the Covers)* **$65 [≃£33]**
- Dolphin Island. London: Gollancz, 1963. 1st British edition. Name on endpaper. Dustwrapper (slightly rubbed). *(Dyke)* **£30 [≃$57]**
- The Fountains of Paradise. London: Gollancz, 1979. Dustwrapper. *(Sklaroff)* **£35 [≃$67]**
- Imperial Earth. London: Gollancz, 1975. Dustwrapper (one short tear). *(Dyke)* **£25 [≃$47]**
- The Sands of Mars. London: Sidgwick & Jackson, 1951. Erased inscription on endpaper. Foredge of binding rasped. *(Sklaroff)* **£36 [≃$69]**
- The Songs of Distant Earth. London: Grafton, 1986. Dustwrapper. Signed by the author. *(Dyke)* **£25 [≃$47]**

- 2010: Odyssey Two. New York: Ballantine, [1982]. Price-clipped dustwrapper. *(Antic Hay)* **$15 [≃£7]**
- 2010: Odyssey Two. New York: Ballantine, 1982. Uncorrected proof copy. Wrappers. *(Nouveau)* **$75 [≃£39]**

Clarke, Lindsay

- The Chymical Wedding. London: 1989. Dustwrapper. Signed by the author. *(First Issues)* **£20 [≃$38]**
- The Chymical Wedding. London: Cape, 1989. Dustwrapper. Publicity bookmark. *(Paul Brown)* **£15 [≃$28]**
- The Chymical Wedding. New York: Knopf, 1989. Uncorrected proof copy. Wrappers. *(Lopez)* **$45 [≃£23]**
- Sunday Whiteman. London: Cape, 1987. Dustwrapper. *(David Rees)* **£30 [≃$57]**

Clouston, J. Storer

- Carrington's Cases. London: 1920. *(Words Etcetera)* **£85 [≃$163]**
- Count Bunker. London: 1906. Some foxing. *(Words Etcetera)* **£28 [≃$53]**
- The Lunatic in Charge. London: 1926. *(Words Etcetera)* **£35 [≃$67]**

Coetzee, J.M.

- Life & Times of Michael K. London: 1983. Dustwrapper. *(Buckley)* **£30 [≃$57]**

Coffey, Brian

- Pseudonym used by Dean Koontz, q.v.

Cohen, Leonard

- Book of Mercy. New York: Villard Books, 1984. 1st American edition. Uncorrected proof copy. Printed wrappers. *(Alphabet)* **$65 [≃£33]**
- The Energy of Slaves. London: Cape, 1972. Wrappers issue. *(Halsey)* **£5 [≃$9]**
- The Favorite Game. New York: Viking, [1963]. 1st American edition. Uncorrected galley proofs in tall blue ring bound wrappers. *(Alphabet)* **$550 [≃£286]**
- Let Us Compare Mythologies. Montreal: McGill Poetry Series, 1956. Dustwrapper. Signed by the author and dated a month after publication. His 1st book. *(Alphabet)* **$800 [≃£416]**
- Let Us Compare Mythologies. Montreal: McGill Poetry Series, Contact Press, 1956. Dustwrapper (a few chips at spine). Author's presentation inscription dated "May 1956". His 1st book. *(Alphabet)* **$800 [≃£416]**
- Parasites of Heaven. Toronto: McClelland, 1966. Wrappers. *(Any Amount)* **£15 [≃$28]**

Cole, Henri

- The Marble Queen. New York: Atheneum, 1986. Dustwrapper. Inscribed by author. His 1st book. *(Woolmer)* **$35 [≃£18]**

Colegate, Isabel

- A Man of Power. London: 1960. Corners missing from two pages not affecting text. Dustwrapper (slightly creased and torn). *(First Issues)* **£35 [≃$67]**

Collier, John

- His Monkey Wife or Married to a Chimp. New York: Appleton, 1931. 1st American edition. Dustwrapper (two tiny tears). His 1st book. *(Alphabet)* **$225 [≃£117]**

Comment

- Comment. Edited by Sheila Macleod and Victor B. Neuburg. Vol I, 1 to Vol III, 58 (December 1935 - January 1937). All published. Wrappers, staples rusty. *(Patterson)* **£250 [≃$479]**

Compton-Burnett, Ivy

- Brothers and Sisters. London: 1929. Dustwrapper (just a little sunned on spine). *(Words Etcetera)* **£225 [≃$431]**
- Darkness and Day. London: 1951. Dustwrapper (minimal foxing). *(Roberts)* **£12.50 [≃$24]**
- A Father & His Fate. London: 1957. Dustwrapper. *(Buckley)* **£12 [≃$23]**
- The First and the Last. London: 1971. Review slip. Dustwrapper. *(Roberts)* **£10 [≃$19]**
- Men and Wives. London: 1931. Inscription on fly. *(Words Etcetera)* **£30 [≃$57]**
- The Mighty and their Fall. London: 1961. Review slip. dustwrapper. *(Roberts)* **£14 [≃$26]**
- Mother and Son. London: 1955. Slight foxing at foredge. *(Roberts)* **£12.50 [≃$24]**
- Mother and Son. London: 1955. Slight foxing. Spine ends slightly bruised, one corner slightly bumped. Dustwrapper (very slightly rubbed, head of spine slightly creased). Inscribed by the author (February 1955). *(Ellis)* **£100 [≃$191]**
- The Present and the Past. London: 1953. Slight foxing at foredge. Dustwrapper. *(Roberts)* **£12.50 [≃$24]**
- Two Worlds and their Ways. London: 1949. Dustwrapper. *(Roberts)* **£13.50 [≃$26]**
- Two Worlds and Their Ways. London: 1949. Edges foxed. Dustwrapper (rubbed, tanned). *(Ellis)* **£20 [≃$38]**

- [Collected Works]. London: Gollancz, 1972. One of 500 sets. 19 vols. Silk bookmarkers. Dustwrappers. 4 slipcases. *(Houle)* **$350 [≃£182]**

Condon, Richard

- The Abandoned Woman. New York: Dial, [1977]. Price-clipped dustwrapper. Signed by the author and dated. *(Antic Hay)* **$45 [≃£23]**
- And Then We Moved to Rossenarra. New York: Dial, 1973. Dustwrapper. Signed by the author and dated. *(Antic Hay)* **$40 [≃£20]**
- Arigato. New York: Dial, 1972. Uncorrected proof copy. Wrappers (some soil). Signed by the author and dated. *(Antic Hay)* **$75 [≃£39]**
- The Entwining. New York: Marek, [1980]. Dustwrapper. Signed by the author and dated. *(Antic Hay)* **$45 [≃£23]**
- The Manchurian Candidate. New York: McGraw-Hill, [1959]. Small ink name. Dustwrapper (moderate wear). Signed by the author (1990). *(Antic Hay)* **$100 [≃£52]**

Connolly, Cyril

- The Missing Diplomats. London: Queen Anne Press, 1952. Wrappers (front cover slightly stained). *(Buckley)* **£25 [≃$47]**
- The Modern Movement. London: 1965. Dustwrapper. Author's presentation inscription signed "Cyril". *(Words Etcetera)* **£225 [≃$431]**
- The Modern Movement. London: Deutsch & Hamilton, 1965. Dustwrapper (very slightly yellowed). *(Virgo)* **£50 [≃$95]**
- The Modern Movement. London: 1965. Dustwrapper. *(Georges)* **£40 [≃$76]**
- One Hundred Modern Books 1880-1950. Catalogue of an Exhibition held at the University of Texas at Austin in 1971. USA: 1971. *(Edrich)* **£25 [≃$47]**
- Previous Convictions. London: 1963. Dustwrapper. *(Words Etcetera)* **£40 [≃$76]**
- The Rock Pool. Paris: Obelisk Press, 1936. Partly unopened. Wrappers (slightly dull). Specially made case. His 1st book. *(Whiteson)* **£140 [≃$268]**
- The Rock Pool. Paris: Obelisk Press, 1936. Half leather, t.e.g., original wrappers bound in at end. *(Edrich)* **£150 [≃$287]**
- The Rock Pool. New York: Scribners, 1936. 1st American edition. Page edges very slightly browned. Covers soiled. *(Virgo)* **£120 [≃$230]**
- The Rock Pool. London: Hamish Hamilton, 1947. 1st UK edition. Dustwrapper (minor nicks). *(Any Amount)* **£20 [≃$38]**
- The Rock Pool. London: Hamish Hamilton, 1947. 1st British edition. Slightly turned. Dustwrapper (slightly rubbed). *(Ash)* **£25 [≃$47]**
- The Unquiet Grave. By Palinurus. London: Horizon, 1944. One of 1000. Wrappers over card covers (slightly soiled, small splits at spine ends). *(Virgo)* **£60 [≃$115]**
- The Unquiet Grave. London: Hamilton, 1945. 1st public edition (revised). Dustwrapper (torn with loss). *(Hazeldene)* **£20 [≃$38]**

Connolly, Joseph

- Collecting Modern First Editions. London: 1977. Dustwrapper. *(Words Etcetera)* **£35 [≃$67]**
- Modern First Editions. London: 1984. Dustwrapper. *(Words Etcetera)* **£25 [≃$47]**

Conrad, Joseph

- See the companion IRBP volume Literature.

Conroy, Frank

- Stop-Time. New York: Viking, (1967). Small rubber stamp on half-title. Dustwrapper. Inscribed by the author. *(Lopez)* **$125 [≃£65]**
- Stop-Time. New York: 1967. Dustwrapper. His 1st book. *(Pettler & Liebermann)* **$45 [≃£23]**
- Stop-Time. London: Bodley Head, 1968. 1st English edition. Dustwrapper. *(Lopez)* **$50 [≃£26]**

Conroy, Jack

- A World to Win. New York: Covici Friede, 1935. Price-clipped dustwrapper (spine lightly browned). *(Alphabet)* **$65 [≃£33]**

Conroy, Pat

- The Great Santini. Boston: HM Co, 1976. Dustwrapper. Signed by the author. *(Between the Covers)* **$100 [≃£52]**
- The Prince of Tides. Boston: HM Co, 1986. Dustwrapper. Signed by the author. *(Between the Covers)* **$65 [≃£33]**

Constantine, K.C.

- The Rocksburg Railroad Murders. New York: Saturday Review Press, 1972. Price-clipped dustwrapper. *(Mordida)* **$250 [≃£130]**

Contemporary Poetry and Prose

- Contemporary Poetry and Prose. Edited by

Roger Roughton. 10 issues in 9 (May 1936 - Autumn 1937). Complete set. Some light foxing. *(Patterson)* **£175 [≃$335]**

Conway, James

- The Big Easy. Boston: HM Co, 1970. Dustwrapper. Author's inscription. *(Between the Covers)* **$125 [≃£65]**

Cook, Robin

- The Crust on its Uppers. London: Hutchinson, 1962. Proof copy. Wrappers. His 1st book. *(Any Amount)* **£75 [≃$143]**

Cooper, William

- Scenes from Married Life. London: Macmillan, 1961. Dustwrapper. Author's presentation inscription dated 13 Jan 1961 signed Harry [Hoff, his real name]. *(Alphabet)* **$125 [≃£65]**

Coover, Robert

- In Bed One Night and Other Brief Encounters. Prov.: 1983. One of 1200. Wrappers. Signed by the author. *(Polyanthos)* **$25 [≃£13]**
- A Night at the Movies. New York: 1987. Dustwrapper. Signed by the author (1987). *(Polyanthos)* **$35 [≃£18]**
- The Origin of the Brunists. New York: 1966. Dustwrapper. Signed by the author with 15-word ALS. *(Polyanthos)* **$125 [≃£65]**
- The Origin of the Brunists. New York: Putnam, [1966]. Dustwrapper (few nicks). His 1st book. *(Houle)* **$150 [≃£78]**
- Origin of the Brunists. New York: 1966. Price-clipped dustwrapper (slightly chipped). Signed by the author and dated. His 1st book. *(Pettler & Liebermann)* **$95 [≃£49]**
- The Origin of the Brunists. London: Barker, 1967. Price-clipped dustwrapper. His 1st book. *(Sklaroff)* **£45 [≃$86]**
- A Political Fable. New York: (1980). Dustwrapper. Signed by the author. *(Polyanthos)* **$25 [≃£13]**
- Pricksongs and Descants. New York: 1969. Dustwrapper. Signed by the author. *(Polyanthos)* **$40 [≃£20]**
- The Public Burning. New York: 1977. Dustwrapper. Signed by the author. Publicity photo signed laid in. *(Polyanthos)* **$40 [≃£20]**
- Spanking the Maid. Bloomfield Hills: 1981. One of XCV signed and with a page of MS. *(Pettler & Liebermann)* **$100 [≃£52]**
- A Theological Position: Plays. New York: Dutton, 1972. Clothbound issue. Bookplate. Dustwrapper. *(Alphabet)* **$85 [≃£44]**
- The Universal Baseball Association, Inc. New York: 1968. Dustwrapper (two tiny snags). Signed by the author. *(Polyanthos)* **$75 [≃£39]**
- The Universal Basketball Association Inc. London: Hart Davis, 1970. 1st English edition. Dustwrapper (short wrinkled tear at rear foredge corner). *(Alphabet)* **$45 [≃£23]**

Cope, Wendy

- Across the City. Berkhampstead: Priapus Poets, 1980. Wrappers. Her 1st book. *(Blakeney)* **£95 [≃$182]**
- Does She Like Word-Games? Anvil Press: 1989. One of about 500, signed, for subscribers only. Wrappers. *(David Rees)* **£20 [≃$38]**
- From a Colour Chart of House Paints. Priapus: 1986. One of 100 signed. Wrappers. *(David Rees)* **£20 [≃$38]**
- Making Cocoa for Kingsley Amis. London: Faber, 1985. Advance excerpt, with an extra poem. Wrappers. *(David Rees)* **£35 [≃$67]**
- Making Cocoa for Kingsley Amis. London: Faber, 1986. Uncorrected proof copy. Wrappers. *(David Rees)* **£30 [≃$57]**
- Men and their Boring Arguments. Winchester: Wykeham Press, 1988. One of 10 (of 500) signed and with an additional holograph poem. *(David Rees)* **£120 [≃$230]**
- Men and their Boring Arguments. Winchester: Wykeham Press, 1988. One of 500. Wrappers. *(Moorhouse)* **£15 [≃$28]**

Cortazar, Julio

- Hopscotch. London: Collins, 1967. 1st English edition. Dustwrapper. *(Nouveau)* **$65 [≃£33]**

Corvo, Baron (Fr. Rolfe)

- Amico di Sandro. Privately Printed (Curwen Press), 1951. One of 150 (this unnumbered). Proof copy. Wrappers. *(Any Amount)* **£100 [≃$191]**
- The Cardinal Prefect of Propaganda. London: Nicholas Vane, 1957. One of 250. No dustwrapper issued. *(Any Amount)* **£90 [≃$172]**
- Chronicles of the House of Borgia. London: 1901. Bookplate. Fine. Slipcase (rubbed). *(Ellis)* **£250 [≃$479]**
- Collected Poems. London: Woolf, 1974. One of 200. Slipcase. *(Words Etcetera)* **£75 [≃$143]**
- The Desire and Pursuit of the Whole. London: 1934. Name. Dent top edge upper cover, one corner slightly bumped.

Dustwrapper (spine slightly faded). *(Ellis)* **£85 [≃$163]**

- The Desire and Pursuit of the Whole. London: Cassell, 1934. 1st issue, in viridian cloth. Slight browning of pages and endpapers, slight foxing. Dustwrapper (slightly nicked and chipped at edges and spine). *(Virgo)* **£125 [≃$239]**
- Don Renato. Edited by Cecil Woolf. London: 1963. One of 200. Illustrated buckram gilt. Slipcase. *(Words Etcetera)* **£75 [≃$143]**
- Don Renato. London: Chatto & Windus, 1963. 1st published edition. Dustwrapper. *(Alphabet)* **$45 [≃£23]**
- Hubert's Arthur. London: 1935. Spine slightly sunned. *(Polyanthos)* **$75 [≃£39]**
- Hubert's Arthur. London: Cassell, 1935. 1st issue in correct binding (Woolf B16). Pages slightly browned, prelims very slightly foxed. Dustwrapper (2 very small closed tears, corners very slightly chafed, very small mark front panel). *(Virgo)* **£90 [≃$172]**
- The Letters of Baron Corvo to Kenneth Grahame. Tragara Press for The Peacocks Press: 1962. One of 40. Wrappers. *(Words Etcetera)* **£125 [≃$239]**
- Letters to Grant Richards. Peacocks Press (printed by Guido Morris): [n.d.]. One of 200. *(Any Amount)* **£120 [≃$230]**
- Letters to Grant Richards. The Peacocks Press: 1952. One of 200. Presentation inscription. *(First Issues)* **£135 [≃$259]**
- (Translates) The Songs of Meleager. London: First Edition Club, [1937]. *(Clearwater)* **£80 [≃$153]**
- Nicholas Crabbe. London: Chatto & Windus, 1960. One of 215. Slipcase. *(Virgo)* **£80 [≃$153]**
- (Translates) The Rubaiyat of Umar Khaiyam. London: John Lane, (1924). One of 750 issued in the 1st binding. *(Woolmer)* **$125 [≃£65]**
- Without Prejudice. London: Allen Lane, Privately Printed, 1963. One of 600. Dustwrapper. *(Words Etcetera)* **£125 [≃$239]**
- Without Prejudice; One Hundred Letters from Baron Corvo to John Lane. London: Allen Lane, 1963. One of 600. Dustwrapper. *(Words Etcetera)* **£150 [≃$287]**

Coterie

- Coterie. London: 1919-22. 7 issues in 6, all published. Wrapper of issue 1 backed and restitched, a little dusty throughout. *(Blakeney)* **£100 [≃$191]**

Coxe, George Harmon

- The Camera Clue. New York: Knopf, 1937. Dustwrapper (corners chipped, wear at spine ends). *(Mordida)* **$50 [≃£26]**

Coxe, Louis O.

- The Sea Faring and Other Poems. New York: Henry Holt, [1947]. Dustwrapper (edge worn, spine darkened with two small inside tape repairs). His 1st book. *(Dermont)* **$40 [≃£20]**

Cozzens, James Gould

- By Love Possessed. New York: Harcourt, Brace, [1957]. 2nd state, with pp 173-174 and pp 301-302 cancels to correct transposed lines. Dustwrapper. *(Antic Hay)* **$35 [≃£18]**

Crawley, Rayburn

- Chattering Gods. New York: Harper & Row, 1931. Dustwrapper (slightly used). *(Dermont)* **$40 [≃£20]**

Creeley, Robert

- Away. Santa Barbara: Black Sparrow, 1976. One of 500. Glassine dustwrapper. Signed by the author. *(Polyanthos)* **$30 [≃£15]**
- The Charm. SF: 1969. Wrappers. Signed by the author. *(Polyanthos)* **$25 [≃£13]**
- A Form of Women. New York: Jargon Books, 1959. Wrappers. Signed by the author. *(Polyanthos)* **$50 [≃£26]**
- A Form of Women. New York: Jargon / Corinth, 1959. Pictorial wrappers (slightly soiled). Inscribed. *(Alphabet)* **$85 [≃£44]**
- Le Fou. Poems. Columbus: The Golden Goose Press, 1952. One of 500. Hand-decorated wrappers. His 1st book. *(Dermont)* **$550 [≃£286]**
- Le Fou. Poems. Columbus: The Golden Goose Press, 1952. One of 500. Hand-decorated wrappers (tanned at edges, slight dust soiling). His 1st book. *(Dermont)* **$350 [≃£182]**
- The Island. New York: Scribner's, 1961. 1st issue (precedes hardbound issues). Wrappers. *(Alphabet)* **$30 [≃£15]**
- 1,2,3,4,5,6,7,8,9,0. Berkeley: Shambala, 1971. One of 200 signed by author and illustrator Arthur Okamura. Dustwrapper. *(Any Amount)* **£25 [≃$47]**
- (Contributes to) Origin II, Summer, 1951. Covers coffee stained. Author's inscription. His 1st book length selection. *(Alphabet)* **$65 [≃£33]**
- Pieces. Black Sparrow Press: 1968. One of 250 signed. Wrappers. *(Words Etcetera)* **£40 [≃$76]**

- Pieces. New York: 1969. Dustwrapper. Signed by the author. *(Polyanthos)* **$25 [≃£13]**

Crews, Harry

- Car. London: Secker & Warburg, (1973). 1st English edition. Dustwrapper. *(Lopez)* **$45 [≃£23]**
- A Childhood. New York: H&R, (1978). Uncorrected proof copy. Wrappers. *(Lopez)* **$125 [≃£65]**
- A Childhood. New York: H&R, (1978). Dustwrapper (two tears rear panel). *(Lopez)* **$30 [≃£15]**
- Florida Frenzy. Gainesville: Florida UP, (1982). Wrappers. Inscribed by the author. *(Lopez)* **$45 [≃£23]**
- The Gospel Singer. New York: Morrow, 1968. Residue from small label on front endpaper. Dustwrapper. Signed by the author. His 1st book. *(Lopez)* **$500 [≃£260]**
- The Gospel Singer. New York: William Morrow, 1968. Dustwrapper (small tear in rear panel). His 1st book. *(Alphabet)* **$550 [≃£286]**
- The Hawk is Dying. New York: Knopf, 1973. Dustwrapper (small faint stains at corners of flaps). *(Lopez)* **$45 [≃£23]**
- The Hawk is Dying. London: Secker & Warburg, 1974. 1st English edition. Dustwrapper. *(Lopez)* **$50 [≃£26]**
- Naked in Garden Hills. New York: Morrow, 1969. 1st issue dustwrapper, with reviews of The Gospel Singer on rear. *(Lopez)* **$150 [≃£78]**
- Naked in Garden Hills. New York: Morrow, 1969. Dustwrapper. *(Dermont)* **$125 [≃£65]**
- Naked in the Garden Hills. New York: Morrow, 1969. Paper boards rubbed on bottom edge. Dustwrapper. *(Alphabet)* **$110 [≃£57]**
- 2 by Crews. Lord John Press: 1984. One of 200 signed. Cloth. No dustwrapper issued. *(Dermont)* **$50 [≃£26]**

Crisp, Quentin

- All This and Bevin Too. Poems. Illustrated by Mervyn Peake. London: Nicholson & Watson, 1943. Printed wrappers (some foxing, slightly marked and rubbed, split along spine). *(Dalian)* **£250 [≃$479]**
- Colour in Display. London: Blandford Press, 1937. Folding chart at rear. Dust- wrapper (foxed, lacks portion at top of spine). His 1st book (preceded by a collaboration with Albert Stuart). *(Moorhouse)* **£15 [≃$28]**
- The Naked Civil Servant. London: 1968. Head of spine slightly bumped. Dustwrapper (lightly worn). *(Sclanders)* **£25 [≃$47]**

Crispin, Edmund

- Dead and Dumb. Phila: Lippincott, 1947. 1st American edition (published in England as "Swan Song'). Dustwrapper (back panel slightly soiled). *(Mordida)* **$50 [≃£26]**
- Swan Song. London: Gollancz, 1947. Dustwrapper (slightly chipped). *(Limestone Hills)* **$75 [≃£39]**

Crofts, Freeman Wills

- Death of a Train. London: Hodder & Stoughton, 1946. Dustwrapper (slightly wrinkled, minor internal reinforcement). *(Limestone Hills)* **$85 [≃£44]**
- Enemy Unseen. London: Hodder & Stoughton, 1945. Gift inscription. Dustwrapper (lightly chipped). *(Limestone Hills)* **$75 [≃£39]**
- French Strikes Oil. London: Hodder & Stoughton, 1952. Dustwrapper (slightly chipped and faded). *(Limestone Hills)* **$75 [≃£39]**
- Murderers Make Mistakes. London: Hodder & Stoughton, 1947. Dustwrapper (slightly chipped and soiled, internally repaired). *(Limestone Hills)* **$95 [≃£49]**
- Sudden Death. London: Collins, 1932. Spine faded. *(Limestone Hills)* **$50 [≃£26]**

Crompton, Richmal

- Naomi Godstone. London: Newnes. Dustwrapper. *(Green Meadow)* **£25 [≃$47]**
- William and the Artist's Model. London: 1956. Wrappers. Price-clipped dustwrapper. *(Ellis)* **£35 [≃$67]**
- William & The Masked Ranger. London: Newnes, 1966. Dustwrapper (slightly chipped). *(Green Meadow)* **£45 [≃$86]**
- William and the Pop Singers. London: Newnes, 1965. Dustwrapper. *(Green Meadow)* **£65 [≃$124]**
- William and the Space Animal. London: Newnes, 1956. Dustwrapper. *(Green Meadow)* **£55 [≃$105]**

Crosby, Caresse

- The Passionate Years. New York: 1953. Dustwrapper (somewhat soiled). Signed by the author. *(Words Etcetera)* **£25 [≃$47]**

Crowley, Aleister

- The City of God. A Rhapsody. O.T.O.: 1943. One of 200 signed. Wrappers. *(Any Amount)* **£135 [≃$259]**

- The Stratagem. London: Mandrake Press, (1935). Short wormhole at upper hinge. Dustwrapper (slightly soiled). *(Any Amount)* **£35 [≃$67]**
- Cammell, C.R.: Aleister Crowley. London: Richards Press, 1951. Dustwrapper. *(Any Amount)* **£28 [≃$53]**

Crowley, John

- The Deep. London: NEL, (1977). 1st English edition. Paper yellowed. Dustwrapper. *(Lopez)* **$50 [≃£26]**
- Engine Summer. London: Gollancz, 1980. 1st English edition. Dustwrapper. Signed by the author. *(Lopez)* **$45 [≃£23]**
- Little, Big. New York: Bantam, (1981). Wrappers. Signed by the author. *(Lopez)* **$55 [≃£28]**

Crumley, James

- Dancing Bear. New York: RH, (1983). Dustwrapper. *(Lopez)* **$65 [≃£33]**
- The Last Good Kiss. New York: Random House, 1978. Dustwrapper. *(Mordida)* **$35 [≃£18]**
- The Last Good Kiss. New York: RH, (1978). Remainder stamp. Dustwrapper. Signed by the author. *(Lopez)* **$45 [≃£23]**
- The Muddy Fork. Northridge: Lord John Press, 1984. One of 200 signed. No dustwrapper issued. *(Mordida)* **$75 [≃£39]**
- One to Count Cadence. New York: 1969. Dustwrapper. Signed by the author. His 1st book. *(Pettler & Liebermann)* **$250 [≃£130]**
- One to Count Cadence. New York: Random House, 1969. Dustwrapper. Signed by the author. *(Mordida)* **$250 [≃£130]**
- The Pigeon Shoot. Santa Barbara: Neville, 1987. Acetate dustwrapper. *(Mordida)* **$75 [≃£39]**
- Whores. Missoula: Dennis McMillan Publications, 1988. One of 475 signed. Dustwrapper. *(Mordida)* **$100 [≃£52]**

Cummings, E.E.

- C I O P W. New York: Covici Friede, 1931. One of 391 signed. Bookplate. *(Bromer)* **$750 [≃£390]**
- The Enormous Room. New York: 1922. 1st issue. Endpapers browned. *(Buckley)* **£65 [≃$124]**
- The Enormous Room. New York: Boni & Liveright, 1922. 1st issue of page 219. Slight offsetting to endpapers. Dustwrapper (1 1/2 x 1 inch chip at rear foredge corner). His 1st book. *(Alphabet)* **$625 [≃£325]**
- Fairy Tales. New York: 1965. Dustwrapper. *(Words Etcetera)* **£20 [≃$38]**
- A Miscellany. New York: The Argophile Press, 1958. One of 75 signed by the author. Glassine dustwrapper (barely chipped). *(Heritage)* **$350 [≃£182]**
- 95 Poems. New York: Harcourt, Brace, [1958]. 1st trade edition. Evidence of small label removal rear pastedown. Dustwrapper (minor soil). *(Antic Hay)* **$75 [≃£39]**
- No Thanks. New York: The Golden Eagle Press, [1935]. One of 90 signed by the author. Minor rubbing spine ends and corners. *(Heritage)* **$375 [≃£195]**
- 1/20. London: Contemporary Poetry and Prose Editions, 1936. Paper boards a little rubbed & dusty. *(Blakeney)* **£95 [≃$182]**
- 73 Poems. New York: Harcourt, 1962. Dustwrapper (backstrip slightly faded). *(Nouveau)* **$75 [≃£39]**
- Six Nonlectures. Cambridge: Harvard UP, 1953. One of 350 signed by the author. Few pencil marks. Dustwrapper (2 x 1 inch piece chipped from lower panel). *(Heritage)* **$200 [≃£104]**
- Tulips and Chimneys. New York: Thomas Seltzer, 1923. Spine faintly foxed. *(Bromer)* **$300 [≃£156]**

Cunard, Nancy

- Outlaws; Poems. 1921. Name on fly. Boards, spine a little browned, spine title label chipped. *(Words Etcetera)* **£85 [≃$163]**
- Parallax. Hogarth Press: 1925. Prize label on pastedown, name on endpaper. Covers soiled, mark at foot of front cover, slightly loose. *(Virgo)* **£200 [≃$383]**
- Releve Into Maquis. The Grasshopper Press, 1944. One of 250. Single leaf, folded. *(David Rees)* **£25 [≃$47]**
- Sublunary. London: Hodder & Stoughton, 1923. Some foxing mostly on edges and prelims. Spine and top front edge of cover slightly faded. *(Virgo)* **£120 [≃$230]**
- These Were the Hours. Southern Illinois UP: [1969]. Dustwrapper. *(Clearwater)* **£24 [≃$46]**
- Those Were the Hours. Southern Illinois UP: 1969. Dustwrapper. *(Any Amount)* **£18 [≃$34]**

D., H.

- See Doolittle, Hilda ('H.D.').

Dahl, Roald

- The BFG. Illustrated by Quentin Blake. New York: 1982. One of 300 signed by author and artist. Slipcase. *(Words Etcetera)* **£85 [≃$163]**

- Charlie and the Chocolate Factory. New York: Knopf, 1964. 1st edition. Covers little dull, corners slightly rubbed. Author's signature on slip inserted. *(Whiteson)* **£50 [≃$95]**
- Charlie and the Great Glass Elevator. London: Allen & Unwin, 1973. Glazed pictorial boards (touch of wear to spine). *(Green Meadow)* **£30 [≃$57]**
- The Gremlins. From the Walt Disney Production. A Royal Air Force Story. New York: Random House, (1943). Extremities slightly worn, foot of spine frayed. Dustwrapper (defective). Signed and dated (1943) inscription and drawing by the author. His 1st book. *(Bromer)* **$650 [≃£338]**
- Kiss, Kiss. New York: Knopf, 1960. 1st American edition. Dustwrapper (minor wear and soil). *(Antic Hay)* **$45 [≃£23]**
- The Magic Finger. London: 1968. 1st English edition. Pictorial boards a little dusty. No dustwrapper issued. *(Blakeney)* **£25 [≃$47]**
- My Uncle Oswald. London: Michael Joseph, 1979. Dustwrapper. *(Lewton)* **£7.50 [≃$15]**
- Over to You. 10 Stories of Flyers. London: 1946. Spine faded, some minor marks. *(Roberts)* **£50 [≃$95]**
- Over to You. London: 1946. Small patch of fading base of spine. Dustwrapper (top edge slightly frayed, small internal repairs, small nick bottom edge). *(Ellis)* **£120 [≃$230]**
- Over to You. London: Hamish Hamilton, 1946. *(Green Meadow)* **£75 [≃$143]**
- Someone Like You. London: 1961. Revised and expanded edition. Dustwrapper (discreetly reinforced at top folds & base of spine). *(Blakeney)* **£30 [≃$57]**
- Some Time Never. New York: Scribner, 1948. 1st US edition. Dustwrapper (worn and chipped). *(Marlborough B'shop)* **£36 [≃$69]**
- Sometime Never: A Fable for Supermen. New York: Scribners, 1948. 1st edition (precedes UK edition). Dustwrapper (worn and chipped with some loss). *(Moorhouse)* **£40 [≃$76]**
- Sometime Never. London: 1949. Dustwrapper (frayed, chipped, spine slightly faded). *(Ellis)* **£85 [≃$163]**
- Switch Bitch. London: Michael Joseph, 1974. Dustwrapper. *(Lewton)* **£12.50 [≃$24]**
- Tales of the Unexpected. London: 1979. Price-clipped dustwrapper (top of spine just a little rubbed). *(Blakeney)* **£20 [≃$38]**
- Tales of the Unexpected. London: 1979. Dustwrapper. *(Lewton)* **£10 [≃$19]**
- The Wonderful Story of Henry Sugar and Six More. London: Cape, 1977. Dustwrapper. *(Green Meadow)* **£25 [≃$47]**

Dahlberg, Edward

- Bottom Dogs. Introduction by D.H. Lawrence. Putnam: 1929. One of 520. Covers very slightly marked. His 1st book. *(Clearwater)* **£40 [≃$76]**
- The Sorrows of Priapus. Norfolk: New Directions, (1957). Dustwrapper (very slight rubbing). *(Between the Covers)* **$40 [≃£20]**

Daumal, Rene

- A Night of Serious Drinking. Boulder: Shambala, 1979. Price-clipped dustwrapper. *(Alphabet)* **$40 [≃£20]**

Davie, Donald

- Purity of Diction in English Verse. London: 1952. Dustwrapper. Inscribed by the author (1952). His 1st book. *(Clearwater)* **£75 [≃$143]**

Davies, Hugh Sykes

- Petron. London: Dent, 1935. Dustwrapper (rubbed, short tear top of spine). *(Halsey)* **£20 [≃$38]**

Davies, Hunter

- Here We Go, Round the Mulberry Bush. London: 1965. Dustwrapper (slightly soiled). His 1st book. *(Words Etcetera)* **£40 [≃$76]**

Davies, Robertson

- At My Heart's Core. Toronto: Clarke, 1950. Simultaneous paperback issue. Dustwrapper (slight stain edge of front panel). *(Between the Covers)* **$75 [≃£39]**
- The Diary of Samuel Marchbanks. Toronto: Clarke Irwin, 1947. This copy with cancel title, dark red cloth, and no notice to the reader tipped in. Dustwrapper (small chip rear panel). *(Alphabet)* **$125 [≃£65]**
- Leaven of Malice. 1955. Dustwrapper. *(Words Etcetera)* **£150 [≃$287]**
- The Lyre of Orpheus. Toronto: Macmillan, 1988. Precedes the US edition. Dustwrapper. *(Alphabet)* **$30 [≃£15]**
- The Lyre of Orpheus. Pennsylvania: The Franklin Library, 1988. Limitation unspecified. Leather. Signed by the author. Precedes the trade edition. *(Moorhouse)* **£30 [≃$57]**
- The Manticore. Toronto: Macmillan, 1972. Correct 1st edition. Dustwrapper (edge worn, some internal repairs). *(Alphabet)* **$25 [≃£13]**
- The Manticore. Toronto: Macmillan, 1972.

Correct 1st edition. Dustwrapper (slight edge wear at spine top). *(Alphabet)* **$75 [≃£39]**

- The Manticore. New York: Viking, (1972). Advance reading copy. Wrappers. Inscribed by the author. *(Lopez)* **$100 [≃£52]**
- The Manticore. New York: Viking, (1972). Advance reading copy. Wrappers (one small bump). *(Lopez)* **$55 [≃£28]**
- A Mixture of Frailties. New York: Scribner, (1958). 1st American edition. Dustwrapper. Signed by the author. *(Lopez)* **$125 [≃£65]**
- One Half of Robertson Davies. Toronto: Macmillan, 1977. Dustwrapper (edge worn at spine). *(Alphabet)* **$25 [≃£13]**
- Question Time. Toronto: Macmillan, 1975. Trade wrappers (black portions of covers a bit rubbed). *(Alphabet)* **$40 [≃£20]**
- The Rebel Angels. Macmillan of Canada, 1981. Dustwrapper. *(Words Etcetera)* **£65 [≃$124]**
- The Rebel Angels. Toronto: Macmillan, 1981. Dustwrapper (slightly rubbed). *(Alphabet)* **$35 [≃£18]**
- Samuel Marchbanks Almanac. Toronto: M&S, 1967. Dustwrapper. *(Alphabet)* **$75 [≃£39]**
- Stephen Leacock. Toronto: Canadian Writers 7, 1970. Paper browned. Wrappers, price on front wrapper blotted out in ink. *(Blakeney)* **£20 [≃$38]**
- Table Talk of Samuel Marchbanks. Toronto: Clarke Irwin, 1949. Dustwrapper (one tiny nick at foot of spine). *(Alphabet)* **$150 [≃£78]**
- Table Talk of Samuel Marchbanks. Toronto: Clarke Irwin, 1949. Bookplate removed. Dustwrapper (two tiny nicks). Signed by Davies. *(Alphabet)* **$125 [≃£65]**
- Table Talk of Samuel Marchbanks. Toronto: Clarke Irwin, 1949. Inscription on fly. Dustwrapper (two tiny nicks). *(Alphabet)* **$75 [≃£39]**
- (Contributes to) Twice Have The Trumpets Sounded. Toronto: Clarke Irwin, 1954. Dustwrapper. *(Alphabet)* **$45 [≃£23]**
- A Voice from the Attic. New York: Knopf, 1960. 1st American edition. Dustwrapper (from the Canadian edition - perhaps supplied). Inscribed by the author. *(Lopez)* **$100 [≃£52]**
- World of Wonders. New York: Viking, 1975. 1st American edition. Advance reading copy. *(Alphabet)* **$85 [≃£44]**
- World of Wonders. New York: Viking, (1976). Advance reading copy. This copy bound upside down. Inscribed by the author. *(Lopez)* **$40 [≃£20]**
- World of Wonders. Toronto: Macmillan, 1975. Correct 1st edition. Dustwrapper (slight edge wear top of spine). *(Alphabet)* **$75 [≃£39]**
- World of Wonders. London: W.H. Allen, 1977. 1st English edition. Dustwrapper. Inscribed by the author. *(Lopez)* **$65 [≃£33]**

Day-Lewis, Cecil

- Beechen Vigil and Other Poems. London: Fortune Press, 1925. Wrappers very slightly frayed. His 1st book. *(Edrich)* **£200 [≃$383]**
- Beechen Vigil. London: Fortune Press, 1925. Signed on half-title. Wrappers (slightly curled and chipped at edges). His 1st book. *(Any Amount)* **£95 [≃$182]**
- The Buried Day. London: 1960. Dustwrapper (slightly chipped). *(Buckley)* **£12 [≃$23]**
- The Buried Day. London: Chatto & Windus, 1960. Dustwrapper. *(Limestone Hills)* **$50 [≃£26]**
- Christmas Eve. London: Faber, Ariel Poems, 1954. Wrappers, envelope. *(Edrich)* **£8 [≃$15]**
- Collected Poems 1929-1936. London: Hogarth Press, 1948. Dustwrapper. *(Edrich)* **£16 [≃$30]**
- Collected Poems 1929-36. London: Hogarth Press, 1948. Revised edition. Dustwrapper (slightly chipped). *(Buckley)* **£25 [≃$47]**
- Country Comets. London: 1928. 1st issue. *(Edrich)* **£30 [≃$57]**
- Country Comets. London: 1928. Boards unevenly faded, browned at spine. Original unprinted glassine. His 1st book. *(Blakeney)* **£15 [≃$28]**
- Country Comets. London: 1928. 2nd issue. *(Edrich)* **£10 [≃$19]**
- Country Comets. London: 1928. Spine sunned. *(Buckley)* **£30 [≃$57]**
- Country Comets. London: Hopkinson, 1928. Boards slightly rubbed, wear on foredge. *(Halsey)* **£18 [≃$34]**
- The Magnetic Mountain. London: Hogarth Press, 1933. *(Edrich)* **£26.50 [≃$51]**
- The Morning After Death. By Nicholas Blake. London: 1966. Uncorrected proof copy. Wrappers. *(Edrich)* **£12 [≃$23]**
- Noah and the Waters. London: Hogarth Press, 1936. One of 100 signed. Covers and endpapers very browned. *(Woolmer)* **$125 [≃£65]**
- Noah and the Waters. Hogarth Press, 1936. 1st unlimited edition. Dustwrapper (edges slightly darkened, front hinge strengthened).

(Virgo) **£25 [≃$47]**

- Noah and the Waters. London: Hogarth Press, 1936. dustwrapper. *(Edrich)* **£20 [≃$38]**
- Noah and the Waters. London: Hogarth Press, 1936. Dustwrapper (slight darkening at edges, front hinge strengthened). *(Virgo)* **£25 [≃$47]**
- Overtures to Death and Other Poems. London: 1938. Spine a little sunned. *(Edrich)* **£10 [≃$19]**
- Poems in Wartime. London: 1940. One of 250 numbered. Wrappers (a little sunned around edges). *(Edrich)* **£30 [≃$57]**
- A Question of Proof. By Nicholas Blake. London: 1935. Covers sunned, spine slightly marked. *(Edrich)* **£25 [≃$47]**
- Selected Poems. London: Hogarth Press, 1940. Dustwrapper (spine slightly sunned). *(Buckley)* **£25 [≃$47]**
- Ten Singers. London: 1925. Stiff wrappers. *(Edrich)* **£30 [≃$57]**
- Transitional Poem. London: Hogarth Press, 1929. Tip of spine rubbed. *(Edrich)* **£36.50 [≃$71]**
- World Over All. London: Cape, 1943. Dustwrapper (slightly discoloured). *(Whiteson)* **£18 [≃$34]**

Deighton, Len

- Action Cook Book. London: Cape, 1965. Pictorial boards. *(Sklaroff)* **£45 [≃$86]**
- (Introduces) The Adventures of the Priory School; a Facsimile of the Original Sherlock Holmes Manuscript. Santa Barbara: Santa Teresa Press, 1985. One of 350 signed by Deighton. Dustwrapper. *(Words Etcetera)* **£45 [≃$86]**
- Airshipwreck. London: Cape, 1978. Dustwrapper. *(Lewton)* **£12.50 [≃$24]**
- Berlin Game. London: 1983. Dustwrapper. *(Marlborough B'shop)* **£16 [≃$30]**
- Berlin Game. New York: Knopf, 1985. 1st US edition. One corner bumped. Dustwrapper. Signed by the author. *(Moorhouse)* **£25 [≃$47]**
- Billion Dollar Brain. London: Cape, 1966. 1st English edition. Dustwrapper (several nicks and short closed tears, scrape on front panel, creases on inner flaps). *(Mordida)* **$65 [≃£33]**
- Billion Dollar Brain. London: Cape, 1966. Dustwrapper. *(Glyn's)* **£25 [≃$47]**
- Billion-Dollar Brain. London: Cape, 1966. 1st British edition. Dustwrapper (slightly worn). *(Ash)* **£25 [≃$47]**
- Close Up. London: Cape, 1972. Dustwrapper (worn at extremities). *(Marlborough B'shop)* **£12 [≃$23]**
- Continental Dossier. London: Michael Joseph, 1968. Pictorial boards. *(Lewton)* **£12.50 [≃$24]**
- The Egypt Flight: LZ 127 Graf Zeppelin. By Cyril Deighton [ie Len Deighton] and Fred Blau. US: Germany Philatelic Soc, 1981. One of 500. Card covers. *(Lewton)* **£65 [≃$124]**
- An Expensive Place to Die. London: Cape, 1967. Dustwrapper (slight chipping). Includes "Top Secret Document". *(Marlborough B'shop)* **£40 [≃$76]**
- Expensive Place to Die. London: Cape, 1967. With docket. Dustwrapper. *(Lewton)* **£30 [≃$57]**
- Funeral In Berlin. London: Cape, 1964. Price-clipped dustwrapper. *(Alphabet)* **$65 [≃£33]**
- Funeral in Berlin. London: Cape, 1964. Price-clipped dustwrapper. *(Alphabet)* **$125 [≃£65]**
- Horse Under Water. London: 1963. *(Roberts)* **£30 [≃$57]**
- Horse Under Water. New York: 1968. 1st US edition. Price-clipped dustwrapper (slightly rubbed, one small chip). Author's signed presentation to his bibliographer E.M. Oliver. *(Moorhouse)* **£55 [≃$105]**
- Introduction to The Adventures of The Priory School. Santa Barbara: Santa Teresa Press, 1985. One of 25 printed for copyright purposes. Wrappers. *(Mordida)* **$250 [≃£130]**
- The Ipcress File. New York: Simon and Schuster, 1963. 1st American edition. Dustwrapper. *(Mordida)* **$150 [≃£78]**
- London Dossier. London: Cape, 1967. Dustwrapper. *(Lewton)* **£30 [≃$57]**
- London Dossier. London: Cape, 1967. Dustwrapper. *(Lewton)* **£27.50 [≃$53]**
- London Match. London: Hutchinson, 1985. Uncorrected proof copy. Wrappers. *(Limestone Hills)* **$45 [≃£23]**
- London Match. London: Hutchinson, 1985. Dustwrapper. Signed by the author. *(Marlborough B'shop)* **£37.50 [≃$72]**
- Mexico Set. London: Hutchinson, 1984. Dustwrapper. Signed by the author. *(Marlborough B'shop)* **£37.50 [≃$72]**
- Mexico Set. New York: Knopf, 1985. 1st US edition. Dustwrapper. Signed by the author. *(Moorhouse)* **£35 [≃$67]**
- The Orient Flight: LZ 127 Graf Zeppelin. By Cyril Deighton [ie Len Deighton] and Fred

Blau. US: Germany Philatelic Soc, 1980. One of 1000. Boards. *(Lewton)* **£65 [≃$124]**
- Ou Est le Garlic. London: Penguin, (1965). Wrappers. *(Limestone Hills)* **$45 [≃£23]**
- Ou Est Le Garlic. Penguin: 1965. Wrappers. *(Lewton)* **£15 [≃$28]**
- Spy Line. London: Hutchinson, 1989. Dustwrapper. *(Limestone Hills)* **$40 [≃£20]**
- Spy Sinker. New York: Harper, 1990. 1st US edition. Advance review copy. Wrappers with no spine crease. *(Janus)* **$45 [≃£23]**
- XPD. New York: Knopf, 1981. 1st US edition. Price-clipped dustwrapper. Signed by the author. *(Moorhouse)* **£35 [≃$67]**

de la Mare, Walter
- See the companion IRBP volume Literature.

Delaney, Shelagh
- A Taste of Honey. London: 1959. Wrappers (slightly rubbed). *(McCann)* **£20 [≃$38]**

Delbanco, Nicholas
- The Martlet's Tale. Phila: Lippincott, [1966]. Dustwrapper. His 1st book. *(Dermont)* **$30 [≃£15]**

De Lillo, Don
- Amazons. By Cleo Birdwell [pseudonym]. New York: 1980. Proof copy. Wrappers. Signed presentation copy from the author. *(Polyanthos)* **$35 [≃£18]**
- End Zone. New York: Houghton, 1972. Dustwrapper (slight edge wear). *(Michael Johnson)* **£37.50 [≃$72]**
- End Zone. London: Deutsch, 1974. 1st British edition. Name inscription. Dustwrapper. *(Michael Johnson)* **£16 [≃$30]**
- Great Jones Street. New York: 1973. Dustwrapper. *(Michael Johnson)* **£30 [≃$57]**
- Great Jones Street. London: 1974. Dustwrapper. *(First Issues)* **£35 [≃$67]**
- Libra. New York: 1988. Advance Reading Copy. Wrappers. Signed by the author. *(Polyanthos)* **$45 [≃£23]**
- Libra. New York: Viking, (1988). Advance reading copy. Wrappers. Author's inscription. *(Between the Covers)* **$85 [≃£44]**
- The Names. New York: 1982. Dustwrapper. Wraparound band. Signed by the author. *(Polyanthos)* **$35 [≃£18]**
- The Names. New York: Knopf, 1982. Dustwrapper. *(Michael Johnson)* **£24 [≃$46]**
- Players. New York: 1977. Dustwrapper. *(Michael Johnson)* **£24 [≃$46]**
- Ratner's Star. New York: Knopf, 1976. Dustwrapper. *(Michael Johnson)* **£26 [≃$49]**
- Running Dog. New York: Knopf, 1978. Dustwrapper. Signed by the author. *(Between the Covers)* **$85 [≃£44]**
- White Noise. New York: Viking, 1985. Dustwrapper. *(Michael Johnson)* **£22 [≃$42]**

Dell, Floyd
- Intellectual Vagabondage: An Apology for the Intelligentsia. New York: Doran, [1926]. Dustwrapper (moderate soil). *(Antic Hay)* **$50 [≃£26]**

Del Vecchio, John M.
- The 13th Valley. New York: 1982. Dustwrapper (two tiny nicks at spine extremities). His 1st book. *(Polyanthos)* **$30 [≃£15]**

Demijohn, Thom
- Black-Alice. Garden City: Doubleday, 1968. Dustwrapper (internally reinforced chip). *(Between the Covers)* **$45 [≃£23]**

Derleth, August
- Mr. Fairlie's Final Journey. Mycroft & Moran: 1968. Dustwrapper. *(Dermont)* **$35 [≃£18]**
- Travellers by Night. Arkham House: 1967. Dustwrapper. *(Dermont)* **$35 [≃£18]**
- Walden West. US: Sloan, 1961. Dustwrapper. Signed by the author. *(Lewton)* **£19 [≃$36]**

Desai, Anita
- Games at Twilight & Other Stories. London: Heinemann, 1978. Dustwrapper. *(Paul Brown)* **£20 [≃$38]**

De Teran, Lisa St. Aubin
- The Black Idol. London: Cape, 1988. Uncorrected proof copy. Wrappers. *(Michael Johnson)* **£10 [≃$19]**
- The High Place. London: Cape, 1985. Dustwrapper. *(Michael Johnson)* **£12 [≃$23]**
- Keepers of the House. London: Cape, 1982. Dustwrapper. *(Michael Johnson)* **£25 [≃$47]**
- Keepers of the House. London: 1982. Dustwrapper. Her 1st book. *(Buckley)* **£40 [≃$76]**
- The Slow Train to Milan. London: Cape, 1983. Dustwrapper. *(Michael Johnson)* **£18 [≃$34]**
- The Tiger. London: Cape, 1984. Dustwrapper. *(Michael Johnson)* **£14 [≃$26]**

Devlin, Denis
- The Heavenly Foreigner. Dublin: Dolmen

Press, 1967. One of 1000, signed by the editor Brian Coffey. Spine slightly bumped. Tiny stain on foredge. Dustwrapper (price-clipped, very lightly rubbed). *(Blakeney)* **£75 [≃$143]**

- Intercessions. The Europa Press: 1937. One of 300 numbered, this out of series. Spine lettering just flaking. Dustwrapper (minimally rubbed at spine, a single nick, one short tear). His 1st book. *(Blakeney)* **£75 [≃$143]**

De Vries, Peter

- Comfort Me With Apples. Boston: Little, Brown, 1956. Dustwrapper. *(Nouveau)* **$45 [≃£23]**

Dexter, Colin

- The Dead of Jericho. 1981. Dustwrapper. 15-word inscription by the author. *(McCann)* **£36 [≃$69]**
- Last Bus to Woodstock. 1975. Pages browned as usual. Dustwrapper (slightly nipped, spine slightly scratched). 18-word inscription by the author. His 1st book. *(McCann)* **£85 [≃$163]**

Dick, Philip K.

- Flow My Tears, the Policeman Said. Garden City: Doubleday Doran, 1974. Remainder spray bottom edge of pages. Dustwrapper (very slightly rubbed). *(Lopez)* **$50 [≃£26]**
- Galactic Pot-Boiler. London: Gollancz, 1970. Uncorrected proof copy. Printed wrappers. *(Sklaroff)* **£30 [≃$57]**
- The Variable Man and Other Stories. US: Ace Books, 1957. Wrappers. *(Words Etcetera)* **£30 [≃$57]**

Dickey, James

- Alnilam. Garden City: 1987. Advance uncorrected proof. Wrappers. Author's inscription. *(Pettler & Liebermann)* **$45 [≃£23]**
- Deliverance. Boston: 1970. Spine extremities very slightly bumped. Dustwrapper (spine extremities very slightly rubbed). Signed presentation copy from the author . *(Polyanthos)* **$50 [≃£26]**
- Deliverance. Boston: Houghton, Mifflin, 1970. Dustwrapper. Signed by the author. *(Chapel Hill)* **$75 [≃£39]**
- The Zodiac. Garden City: Doubleday, 1976. Signed limited edition. Dustwrapper. Slipcase. *(Antic Hay)* **$75 [≃£39]**

Dickinson, Peter

- The Glass-Sided Ant's Nest. New York: Harper & Row, 1968. 1st American edition. Dustwrapper. *(Mordida)* **$50 [≃£26]**

Dickson, Carter

- Lord of the Sorcerers. London: Heinemann, 1946. 1st English edition. Dustwrapper (missing one small chip from middle of spine and front panel). *(Limestone Hills)* **$65 [≃£33]**
- Pseudonym used by John Dickson Carr, q.v.

Didion, Joan

- Run, River. London: 1964. 1st English edition. Dustwrapper. Author's 1st book. *(Words Etcetera)* **£55 [≃$105]**
- Slouching Towards Bethlehem. New York: 1968. Tiny sticker on endpaper. Dustwrapper. *(Pettler & Liebermann)* **$75 [≃£39]**
- Slouching Towards Bethlehem. London: 1969. 1st English edition. Dustwrapper. *(Words Etcetera)* **£45 [≃$86]**

Dillon, Ellis

- Death in the Quadrangle. London: Faber, 1956. Dustwrapper. *(Janus)* **$45 [≃£23]**

Dillon, George

- Boy in the Wind. New York: Viking, 1927. Dustwrapper (some darkening of spine, small nicks along edge). His 1st book. *(Antic Hay)* **$75 [≃£39]**

Dinesen, Isak

- Anecdotes of Destiny. 1958. Dustwrapper (a few small chips). Signed by the author using both names, Isak Dinesen and Karen Blixen, dated 14-10-58 (the day after publication). *(Words Etcetera)* **£650 [≃$1,247]**
- The Angelic Avengers. By Pierre Andrezel [pseudonym]. New York: Random, (1947). Dustwrapper (slight rubbing extremities). *(Between the Covers)* **$65 [≃£33]**
- The Angelic Avengers. By Pierre Andrezel [pseudonym]. New York: 1947. Spine extremities minimally rubbed. Dustwrapper (half-inch missing top panel, edges very slightly rubbed). *(Polyanthos)* **$25 [≃£13]**
- Daguerrotypes and Other Essays. Univ of Chicago Press: 1979. Dustwrapper. *(Words Etcetera)* **£8.50 [≃$17]**
- Last Tales. New York: Random House, [1957]. 1st edition. Some discoloration endpapers. Price-clipped dustwrapper. *(Antic Hay)* **$25 [≃£13]**
- Last Tales. Putnam, 1957. Dustwrapper (torn). *(Whiteson)* **£20 [≃$38]**
- Last Tales. London: 1957. Dustwrapper. *(Roberts)* **£15 [≃$28]**
- Last Tales. London: 1957. Dustwrapper. *(Words Etcetera)* **£16 [≃$30]**

- On Mottoes of My Life. Copenhagen: 1962. Boards. *(Polyanthos)* **$20 [≃£10]**
- Out of Africa. Putnam, 1937. 1st edition in English (published simultaneously with the edition in Danish). Edges and prelims spotted. Slightly cocked. Dustwrapper (somewhat rubbed and worn). *(Ash)* **£125 [≃$239]**
- Out of Africa. New York: Random House, [1938]. Dustwrapper. *(Houle)* **$225 [≃£117]**
- Out of Africa. New York: Random House, 1938. 1st US edition. Dustwrapper (chipped). *(Nouveau)* **$60 [≃£31]**
- Seven Gothic Tales. Harrison Smith: 1934. 1st US edition. Name. Dustwrapper. Her 1st book. *(Nouveau)* **$125 [≃£65]**
- Seven Gothic Tales. London: 1934. Front endpaper slightly stained. Dustwrapper (worn, chipped, internally reinforced). Her 1st book. *(Clearwater)* **£50 [≃$95]**
- Seven Gothic Tales. New York: Harrison Smith and Robert Haas, 1934. Dustwrapper. Fine. *(Chapel Hill)* **$250 [≃£130]**
- Shadows on the Grass. London: 1960. Dustwrapper (very lightly rubbed & darkened at the spine, two short tears at foot). *(Blakeney)* **£10 [≃$19]**

Disch, Thomas M.

- Camp Concentration. London: 1968. Dustwrapper (very slightly rubbed). *(Ellis)* **£100 [≃$191]**
- Camp Concentration. London: 1968. Dustwrapper. *(Egret)* **£80 [≃$153]**
- Echo Round His Bones. Berkeley Medallion: 1967. The true 1st edition. Wrappers. Edges stained red. *(Blakeney)* **£20 [≃$38]**
- On Wings of Song. London: 1979. Dustwrapper. *(Egret)* **£25 [≃$47]**
- On Wings of Song. London: Gollancz, 1979. Dustwrapper. *(Blakeney)* **£9.50 [≃$19]**
- 334. London: McGibbon & Kee, 1972. Dustwrapper. *(Sklaroff)* **£75 [≃$143]**

Disch, Thomas M. & Sladek, John T.

- Black Alice. London: 1969. Embossed owner's stamp on title. Dustwrapper (lightly scratched, very slightly faded at the spine). *(Blakeney)* **£30 [≃$57]**

Dobyns, Stephen

- A Man of Little Evils. New York: Atheneum, 1973. Dustwrapper (short crease on inner flap). *(Mordida)* **$75 [≃£39]**

Doctorow, E.L.

- Billy Bathgate. New York: Random House, (1989). Uncorrected proof copy. Wrappers. *(Lopez)* **$65 [≃£33]**
- The Book of Daniel. New York: Random House, 1971. Dustwrapper. *(Nouveau)* **$50 [≃£26]**
- The Book of Daniel. New York: Random House, 1971. Dustwrapper (red spine lettering faded). *(Alphabet)* **$25 [≃£13]**
- Book of Daniel. London: Macmillan, 1972. 1st British edition. Name. Dustwrapper. *(Michael Johnson)* **£10 [≃$19]**
- Drinks before Dinner. New York: Random House, [1979]. Dustwrapper. Signed by the author. *(Antic Hay)* **$85 [≃£44]**
- Lives of the Poets. New York: Random House, 1984. Dustwrapper. Signed by the author. *(Michael Johnson)* **£20 [≃$38]**
- Lives of the Poets. New York: Random House, 1984. One of 350 signed. Cloth. Slipcase (small mark bottom edge). *(Alphabet)* **$75 [≃£39]**
- Loon Lake. New York: 1980. Dustwrapper. Signed presentation copy from the author. *(Polyanthos)* **$35 [≃£18]**
- Loon Lake. New York: 1980. Dustwrapper. Signed by the author. *(Polyanthos)* **$25 [≃£13]**
- Loon Lake. New York: Random House, [1980]. One of 350 signed. Slipcase, original shrink-wrap, unopened. *(Antic Hay)* **$85 [≃£44]**
- Ragtime. New York: Random, 1975. One of a limited number for presentation. Specially bound boards (some wear base of spine). Acetate protector. Author's signed presentation. *(Michael Johnson)* **£37 [≃$71]**
- Ragtime. New York: Random, [1975]. Special Edition "For friends of the author and publisher' (2000). Acetate dustwrapper. *(Antic Hay)* **$50 [≃£26]**
- Ragtime. New York: Random House, 1975. Price-clipped dustwrapper. Signed by the author. *(Lopez)* **$75 [≃£39]**
- Ragtime. New York: Random, 1975. Dustwrapper. Author's signed presentation. *(Michael Johnson)* **£28 [≃$53]**
- Ragtime. London: Macmillan, 1976. 1st British edition. Dustwrapper. Signed by the author. *(Michael Johnson)* **£25 [≃$47]**
- Welcome to Hard Times. New York: S&S, 1960. Pages yellowing as usual. Dustwrapper (minimal rubbing and soiling). Signed by the author. His 1st book. *(Lopez)* **$225 [≃£117]**
- World's Fair. London: Joseph, 1986. 1st British edition. Dustwrapper. Signed by the author. *(Michael Johnson)* **£20 [≃$38]**

Doig, Ivan

- This House of Sky. New York: 1978. Dustwrapper (small chip at rear, one short tape repair). His 1st book.
(Pettler & Liebermann) **$35 [≃£18]**

Donleavy, J.P.

- Are You Listening Rabbi Low. Viking Press: 1987. Dustwrapper. *(Edrich)* **£8 [≃$15]**
- De Alfonce Tennis. London: Weidenfeld & Nicolson, 1984. Dustwrapper.
(Lewton) **£4.50 [≃$9]**
- A Fairy Tale of New York. New York: Delacorte / Seymour Lawrence, (1973). Dustwrapper (small nick).
(Houle) **$35 [≃£18]**
- Fairy Tales of New York. New York: Random House, [1961]. Dustwrapper.
(Houle) **$65 [≃£33]**
- The Ginger Man. Paris: Olympia Press, (1955). Wrappers. His 1st book.
(Edrich) **£150 [≃$287]**
- The Ginger Man. Paris: Olympia Press, (1955). Wrappers. His 1st book.
(Virgo) **£200 [≃$383]**
- The Ginger Man. London: Neville Spearman, (1956). 1st English edition. Dustwrapper (few nicks).
(Houle) **$125 [≃£65]**
- The Ginger Man. Paris: Olympia Press, 1958. 1st hardback edition. Dustwrapper.
(Virgo) **£75 [≃$143]**
- The Ginger Man. Paris: Olympia Press, 1958. Dustwrapper. *(Edrich)* **£12 [≃$23]**
- The Ginger Man. Paris: Olympia Press, 1958. 1st unexpurgated (hardback) edition. Dustwrapper. *(Any Amount)* **£18 [≃$34]**
- The Ginger Man. Paris: Olympia Press, 1958. 1st hardback, Olympia edition. Dustwrapper (one short tear).
(Blakeney) **£15 [≃$28]**
- The Ginger Man. Paris: Olympia Press, 1958. 1st unexpurgated hardbound edition. Dustwrapper. *(Nouveau)* **$150 [≃£78]**
- Meet My Maker the Mad Molecule. London: Bodley Head, 1965. Dustwrapper.
(Marlborough B'shop) **£15 [≃$28]**
- Meet My Maker, the Mad Molecule. London: 1965. Dustwrapper (two tiny tears).
(Polyanthos) **$20 [≃£10]**
- The Onion Eaters. London: Eyre & Spottiswoode, 1971. Dustwrapper.
(Paul Brown) **£15 [≃$28]**
- The Onion Eaters. London: Eyre & Spottiswoode, 1971. Dustwrapper.
(Lewton) **£6.50 [≃$13]**
- A Singular Man. London: 1964. Inscription on endpaper. dustwrapper.
(Edrich) **£8 [≃$15]**
- What They Did in Dublin with Ginger Man. London: 1961. Dustwrapper.
(Edrich) **£6.50 [≃$13]**

Donoso, Jose

- The Obscene Bird of Night. New York: 1973. Name. Dustwrapper.
(Polyanthos) **$30 [≃£15]**

Doolittle, Hilda ('H.D.')

- By Avon River. New York: Macmillan, 1949. Dustwrapper. *(Lopez)* **$55 [≃£28]**
- Heliodora & Other Poems. London: Cape, 1924. Slight foxing to prelims. Quarter cloth & decorated paper boards.
(Alphabet) **$75 [≃£39]**
- Sea Garden. London: New Poetry Series, 1916. Marginal waterstain to a few pages. Paper over boards (spine sunned, covers waterstained). Her 1st book.
(King) **$125 [≃£65]**

Dorn, Edward

- Gunslinger, Book II. Los Angeles: Black Sparrow, 1969. One of 250 signed by the author. Acetate dustwrapper.
(Lopez) **$40 [≃£20]**
- The Newly Fallen. New York: Totem, (1961). Wrappers. *(Lopez)* **$30 [≃£15]**

Dos Passos, John

- Adventures of a Young Man. Constable, 1939. Top edge marked. Dustwrapper (slightly worn). *(Glyn's)* **£30 [≃$57]**
- 1919. New York: Harcourt, Brace, [1932]. Small ink name. Dustwrapper (chip at head of spine affecting some type).
(Antic Hay) **$125 [≃£65]**
- Orient Express. London: 1928. Cover slightly waterstained. Dustwrapper (faintly used).
(Buckley) **£50 [≃$95]**
- A Pushcart at the Curb. New York: Doran, 1922. Dustwrapper (a few chips).
(Nouveau) **$330 [≃£171]**

Douglas, Alfred

- The True History of Shakespeare's Sonnets. London: Secker, 1933. Dustwrapper.
(Any Amount) **£30 [≃$57]**

Douglas, Norman

- Birds and Beasts of the Greek Anthology. London: Chapman & Hall, 1928. 1st trade edition. 1st issue, in fawn cloth. Endpapers slightly browned, foredge spotted. Dustwrapper (slightly soiled, spine browned and slightly scratched and internally repaired). *(Virgo)* **£50 [≃$95]**

- Birds and Beasts of the Greek Anthology. London: Chapman & Hall, 1928. 1st British and 1st trade edition. 1st issue, in the fawn coloured primary binding. Unopened. Dustwrapper (slightly darkened, small hole). *(Ash)* **£75 [≃$143]**
- D.H. Lawrence and Maurice Magnus. Privately Printed: 1924. Wrappers (little dull). *(Whiteson)* **£22 [≃$42]**
- Experiments. London: Chapman & Hall, 1925. 1st trade edition. Dustwrapper (spine browned, corners and spine ends frayed). *(Virgo)* **£35 [≃$67]**
- Footnote on Capri. London: Sidgwick and Jackson, 1952. Dustwrapper (corners and spine extremities slightly chipped, small scratch front panel, back panel slightly soiled). *(Virgo)* **£25 [≃$47]**
- How About Europe. Florence: 1929. One of 550 signed. Edges and endpapers very slightly browned. Unopened. Dustwrapper (spine faded, head of spine and corners very slightly nicked). *(Virgo)* **£95 [≃$182]**
- In the Beginning. London: 1928. Dustwrapper (slightly browned and rubbed). *(Buckley)* **£35 [≃$67]**
- London Street Games. London: St Catherine Press, 1916. Foredge slightly foxed. Buckram, t.e.g. *(Buckley)* **£110 [≃$211]**
- London Street Games. London: St. Catherine Press, 1916. Buckram, t.e.g. Author's presentation copy. *(Whiteson)* **£80 [≃$153]**
- Looking Back. London: 1933. One of 500 (of 535) signed. 2 vols. Cloth backed boards (minor soil, covers a bit bowed). Dustwrappers (soiled, worn, chipped). *(King)* **$75 [≃£39]**
- Looking Back. London: Chatto & Windus, 1933. One of 535 signed. 2 vols. Endpapers browned and foxed, foredges spotted. *(Virgo)* **£165 [≃$316]**
- Nerinda. Florence: Orioli, 1929. One of 475 signed. Name and address on endpaper. Unopened. New slipcase with original title laid on. *(Virgo)* **£70 [≃$134]**
- Paneros. Florence: Orioli, [ca 1931]. One of 250 signed by the author. Dustwrapper (1 inch chip lower panel). Cardboard box. *(Heritage)* **$200 [≃£104]**
- Siren Land. London: Dent, 1911. Inscription on fly. Mild foxing of edges. Dustwrapper (lower panel slightly imperfect). *(Ash)* **£350 [≃$671]**
- South Wind. London: Secker, [1922]. One of 125 signed by the author. Partly unopened. Spine tips very slightly rubbed. *(Heritage)* **$125 [≃£65]**
- Unprofessional Tales. By Normyx. London: 1901. Inscription. Lacks rear endpaper. Staining on two pages. Edges spotted. Orange pictorial covers (rubbed and scratched, spine tanned and scuffed at ends). His 1st book. *(Ellis)* **£200 [≃$383]**

Drabble, Margaret

- The Garrick Year. London: 1964. Uncorrected proof copy. Signed by the author. *(Egret)* **£35 [≃$67]**
- Hassan's Tower. Los Angeles: 1980. One of 300 (of 330) signed. *(David Rees)* **£50 [≃$95]**
- Jerusalem the Golden. London: Weidenfeld & Nicolson, 1967. Dustwrapper (small chip). *(Alphabet)* **$45 [≃£23]**
- The Middle Ground. London: 1980. Dustwrapper. Signed by the author. *(Egret)* **£20 [≃$38]**
- A Natural Curiosity. London: London Limited, 1989. One of 150 signed. Marbled paper and cloth over boards. Dustwrapper. *(Nouveau)* **$110 [≃£57]**
- The Radiant Way. London: 1987. Dustwrapper. Signed by the author. *(Egret)* **£15 [≃$28]**
- The Realms of Gold. London: 1975. Advance proof copy. *(Buckley)* **£15 [≃$28]**
- The Waterfall. London: 1969. Dustwrapper (small internal stain). *(Alphabet)* **$30 [≃£15]**
- The Waterfall. London: 1969. Review slip inserted. Dustwrapper. *(Moorhouse)* **£12 [≃$23]**

Dreiser, Theodore

- An American Tragedy. New York: 1925. One of 795 signed by the author. 2 vols. Spines very slightly soiled. *(Ellis)* **£180 [≃$345]**
- Epitaph. A Poem. Decorations by Robert Fawcett. New York: Heron Press, 1929. One of 200 signed. Decorated leather (rear hinge reglued). *(Black Sun)* **$225 [≃£117]**
- Epitaph. A Poem. Decorations by Robert Fawcett. New York: Heron Press, 1929. One of 200 (of 1100) signed. Decorated leather (slight rubbing to spine). Later slipcase, with original label. *(Houle)* **$200 [≃£104]**
- Free & Other Stories. New York: Boni & Liveright, 1918. Dustwrapper. *(Dermont)* **$135 [≃£70]**
- Moods. New York: Boni & Liveright, 1928. 1st trade edition. Dustwrapper. *(Dermont)* **$100 [≃£52]**

Dudek, Louis

- The Transparent Sea. Toronto: Contact Press, 1956. Name. Wrappers. *(Alphabet)* **$110 [≃£57]**

Duff, Charles

- Anthropological Report on a London Suburb. London: Grayson & Grayson, 1935. Dustwrapper (slightly spotted). *(Patterson)* **£25 [≃$47]**

Duffy, Maureen

- The Venus Touch. London: Weidenfeld, 1971. One of 500 signed. Dustwrapper. *(Hazeldene)* **£25 [≃$47]**

Du Maurier, Daphne

- Frenchman's Creek. London: 1941. Dustwrapper (just a trifle faded on spine). *(Words Etcetera)* **£50 [≃$95]**
- Rebecca. 1938. Extreme lower edge of upper cover showing signs of damp marking. Dustwrapper (little faded on spine, four closed tears around hinges with spine and on lower panel, one or two nicks on corners). *(Words Etcetera)* **£150 [≃$287]**
- Rebecca. New York: 1938. Spine a little sunned with very small tear. Signed by the author. *(Polyanthos)* **$100 [≃£52]**
- Rebecca. London: Gollancz, 1938. Covers rubbed. *(Limestone Hills)* **$55 [≃£28]**

Duncan, Robert

- Medieval Scenes. San Francisco: The Centaur Press, 1950. One of 250 signed. Slight fading to edges of wrappers. *(Alphabet)* **$275 [≃£143]**
- Poems 1948-49. Berkeley: Berkeley Miscellany Editions, [1949]. One of 400 with the expurgated text. Printed wrappers. *(Alphabet)* **$75 [≃£39]**

Dunn, Douglas

- The Happier Life. London: Faber, 1972. Dustwrapper. Signed by the author. *(Lewton)* **£25 [≃$47]**

Dunn, Nell

- Poor Cow. London: 1967. Dustwrapper. *(Words Etcetera)* **£20 [≃$38]**
- Up the Junction. London: 1963. Dustwrapper. *(Words Etcetera)* **£25 [≃$47]**

Dunsany, Edward Plunkett, Lord

- Alexander & Three Small Plays. London: Putnam's, 1925. *(Georges)* **£18 [≃$34]**
- The Blessing of Pan. London: Putnam's, 1927. *(Georges)* **£25 [≃$47]**
- The Book of Wonder. London: Heinemann, 1912. Lacks front free endpaper. Boards soiled and a little rubbed, front hinge weak. *(Georges)* **£25 [≃$47]**
- The Charwoman's Shadow. London: Putnam's, 1926. *(Georges)* **£25 [≃$47]**
- The Chronicles of Rodriguez. London: 1922. One of 500 signed. Frontis signed by Sime. Vellum spine, t.e.g. *(Polyanthos)* **$250 [≃£130]**
- The Chronicles of Rodriguez. London: Putnam's, 1922. One of 500, signed by author and artist (S.H. Sime). Quarter vellum (very slightly soiled), t.e.g., partly unopened. *(Georges)* **£175 [≃$335]**
- The Curse of the Wise Woman. London: Heinemann, 1933. Covers very slightly marked. *(Georges)* **£20 [≃$38]**
- The Donnellan Lectures 1943. London: Heinemann, 1945. Dustwrapper. *(Georges)* **£20 [≃$38]**
- A Dreamer's Tales. London: George Allen & Sons, 1910. Later issue, with gilt top edges. Spine slightly sunned. *(Georges)* **£50 [≃$95]**
- Fifty-One Tales. London: Elkin Mathews, 1915. Covers and edges rather browned. *(Georges)* **£30 [≃$57]**
- Five Plays. London: Grant Richards, 1914. T.e.g. Covers a little faded. *(Georges)* **£15 [≃$28]**
- The Gods of Pegana. London: Elkin Mathews, 1905. Slight spotting in text. A few pages carelessly opened. His 1st book. *(Georges)* **£100 [≃$191]**
- The Gods of Pegana. London: Elkin Mathews, 1905. Slight foxing, mainly to endpapers. Slightly rubbed. *(Sklaroff)* **£75 [≃$143]**
- Guerilla. London: Heinemann, 1944. *(Georges)* **£15 [≃$28]**
- His Fellow Men. London: 1952. Edges foxed. Dustwrapper (slightly rubbed, a few small nicks). Signed by the author and inscribed (1953). *(Ellis)* **£45 [≃$86]**
- His Fellow Men. London: Jarrolds, 1952. Dustwrapper. *(Georges)* **£15 [≃$28]**
- If I Were Dictator. London: Methuen, 1934. Spine slightly faded. *(Georges)* **£18 [≃$34]**
- A Journey. London: Macdonald, [1943]. One of 250, initialled by the author. Dark blue leather, t.e.g. *(Georges)* **£35 [≃$67]**
- The King of Elfland's Daughter. London: 1924. One of 250 signed. Frontis signed by Sime. Vellum spine, t.e.g. *(Polyanthos)* **$250 [≃£130]**

- The King of Elfland's Daughter. London: Putnam's, 1924. One of 250, signed by the author & artist (S.H. Sime). Some foxing spots, mostly at edges. Quarter vellum, t.e.g., partly unopened. Dustwrapper (slightly frayed). *(Georges)* **£200 [≃$383]**
- The Little Tale of Smethers and Other Stories. London: Jarrolds, 1952. Dustwrapper. *(Georges)* **£15 [≃$28]**
- Mr Jorkens Remembers Africa. London: Heinemann, 1934. Spine very slightly soiled. *(Georges)* **£20 [≃$38]**
- My Ireland. London: Jarrolds, 1937. Dustwrapper. Signed by the author. ALS by Dunsany loosely inserted. *(Georges)* **£30 [≃$57]**
- A Night at an Inn. New York: The Sunwise Turn Inc, 1916. Blue wrappers. Signed by the author. *(Georges)* **£50 [≃$95]**
- The Odes of Horace. Translated by Lord Dunsany. London: Heinemann, 1947. Dustwrapper (frayed). *(Georges)* **£15 [≃$28]**
- The Old Folk of the Centuries. London: 1930. One of 100 signed. Dustwrapper (slightly rubbed, some loss head of spine). *(Ellis)* **£100 [≃$191]**
- The Old Folk of the Centuries. London: Elkin Mathews & Marrot, 1930. One of 900. Dustwrapper. *(Georges)* **£18 [≃$34]**
- Patches of Sunlight. London: Heinemann, 1938. Tiny mark on cover. *(Georges)* **£18 [≃$34]**
- Plays for Earth and Air. London: Heinemann, 1937. *(Georges)* **£15 [≃$28]**
- Plays of God and Men. London: Fisher Unwin, 1917. 1st London edition (Dublin edition precedes). Spine a trifle soiled. *(Georges)* **£30 [≃$57]**
- Plays of Near & Far. London: Putnam's, 1922. One of 500. Cover a trifle soiled. *(Georges)* **£20 [≃$38]**
- Rory and Bran. London: Heinemann, 1936. *(Georges)* **£18 [≃$34]**
- Rory and Bran. London: Heinemann, 1936. Dustwrapper (slightly chipped). *(Ash)* **£50 [≃$95]**
- Seven Modern Comedies. London: Putnam's, 1928. One of 250. Covers a trifle soiled, a few pages carelessly opened. *(Georges)* **£18 [≃$34]**
- The Story of Mona Sheehy. London: 1939. Dustwrapper (slightly rubbed). *(Buckley)* **£30 [≃$57]**
- The Story of Mona Sheehy. London: Heinemann, 1939. *(Georges)* **£20 [≃$38]**
- The Strange Journey of Colonel Polders. London: Jarrolds, 1950. *(Georges)* **£15 [≃$28]**
- The Strange Journeys of Colonel Polders. London: Jarrolds, 1950. Slight bruise to spine. Dustwrapper (very slightly rubbed). *(Ash)* **£50 [≃$95]**
- The Sword of Welleran and Other Stories. London: George Allen & Sons, 1908. Possibly later issue, without gilt top edge. Bookplate. Photograph pasted to endpaper. Spine dull. *(Georges)* **£50 [≃$95]**
- Tales of Three Hemispheres. London: Fisher Unwin, 1920. 1st English edition (the Boston edition 1919 precedes). *(Georges)* **£25 [≃$47]**
- Tales of Three Hemispheres. London: 1920. 1st issue. Protective cloth wrapper, half leather box. Signed by the author with his autograph correction in Table of Contents. *(Polyanthos)* **$125 [≃£65]**
- Tales of War. Dublin: The Talbot Press; London: Fisher Unwin, 1918. Some gilt chipped from the word 'Tales' on spine. Dustwrapper (torn). *(Georges)* **£35 [≃$67]**
- Tales of Wonder. London: Elkin Mathews, 1916. Buckram backed boards, a little soiled, corners slightly rubbed. *(Georges)* **£35 [≃$67]**
- Time and the Gods. London: Heinemann, 1906. Some foxing to outer edges. *(Georges)* **£75 [≃$143]**
- To Awaken Pegasus and Other Poems. Oxford: George Ronald, 1949. Dustwrapper. *(Georges)* **£15 [≃$28]**
- To Awaken Pegasus. London: 1949. Dustwrapper. *(Buckley)* **£20 [≃$38]**
- The Travel Tales of Mr Joseph Jorkens. London: Putnam's, 1931. *(Georges)* **£25 [≃$47]**
- Unhappy Far-Off Things. London: Elkin Mathews, 1919. Spine slightly sunned, boards a trifle dusty. *(Georges)* **£25 [≃$47]**
- Unhappy Far-Off Things. Boston: 1919. 1st American edition. Dustwrapper (missing tiny piece at top of spine, a few short tears). *(Blakeney)* **£30 [≃$57]**
- Wandering Songs. London: Hutchinson, [1943]. Dustwrapper (slightly torn). *(Georges)* **£18 [≃$34]**
- War Poems. London: Hutchinson, [1941]. Dustwrapper (torn). *(Georges)* **£20 [≃$38]**
- The Year. London: Jarrolds, 1946. Dustwrapper (slightly sunned). *(Georges)* **£20 [≃$38]**

Durrant, Theo

- Pseudonym used by Anthony Boucher, q.v.

Durrell, Lawrence

- The Alexandria Quartet. London: Faber, 1962. 1st 1-volume edition. Dustwrapper. *(Dyke)* **£50 [≃$95]**
- The Alexandria Quartet. London: Faber, 1962. 1st collected edition. One of 500 signed by the author. Cloth, t.e.g. Slipcase. *(Sotheran's)* **£398 [≃$764]**
- Balthazar. London: 1958. Advance proof copy. Edges slightly spotted. *(Buckley)* **£60 [≃$115]**
- The Cherries [in] Masterpieces of Thrills. Edited by John Gawsworth. London: Daily Express, [1936]. Decorated boards (lightly worn). *(Patterson)* **£35 [≃$67]**
- Clea. London: 1960. Dustwrapper (slightly rubbed). *(Buckley)* **£30 [≃$57]**
- Esprit de Corps. London: 1957. Dustwrapper. *(Buckley)* **£17 [≃$32]**
- An Irish Faustus. London: Faber, 1963. Dustwrapper. *(Lewton)* **£10 [≃$19]**
- Mountolive. London: 1958. Dustwrapper (head of spine slightly frayed). *(Ellis)* **£70 [≃$134]**
- A Private Country. London: Faber, 1943. Upper cover slightly creased. Dustwrapper (much torn, tanned). *(Hazeldene)* **£50 [≃$95]**
- The Red Limbo Lingo. London: Faber, 1971. One of 200 (of 1200) signed. Slipcase. *(Virgo)* **£85 [≃$163]**
- The Red Limbo Lingo; A Poetry Notebook. London: Faber, 1971. One of 1200. Glassine dustwrapper. Slipcase. *(Hadley)* **£30 [≃$57]**
- Sappho. A Play in Verse. London: Faber, 1950. Dustwrapper (minimal rubbing of edges). *(Woolmer)* **$50 [≃£26]**
- Sauve Qui Peut. London: 1966. Dustwrapper. *(Buckley)* **£12 [≃$23]**
- The Tree of Idleness. London: 1955. Dustwrapper (small loss top of spine). *(Buckley)* **£24 [≃$46]**
- Tunc. London: Faber, 1968. Dustwrapper. *(Tiger Books)* **£15 [≃$28]**

Dwyer, K.R.

- Pseudonym used by Dean Koontz, q.v.

Dyment, Clifford

- First Day. London: 1935. Dustwrapper (edges slightly worn). His 1st book. *(Buckley)* **£20 [≃$38]**

Eastlake, William

- The Bamboo Bed. New York: Simon & Schuster, (1969). Dustwrapper. *(Houle)* **$75 [≃£39]**

Eberhart, Richard

- Burr Oaks. London: Chatto & Windus, 1947. Dustwrapper. Signed by the author. *(Antic Hay)* **$125 [≃£65]**
- An Herb Basket. Cummington, Mass.: The Cummington Press, 1950. One of 155. Wrappers. Signed by the author and dated. *(Black Sun)* **$350 [≃£182]**

Eco, Umberto

- The Name of the Rose. New York: Harcourt, Brace Jovanovich, 1983. 1st American edition. Dustwrapper. *(Mordida)* **$50 [≃£26]**

Egan, Lesley

- Pseudonym used by Elizabeth Linington, q.v.

Eliot, T.S.

- After Strange Gods. London: Faber, (1934). Tiny library stamp blacked out on dedication page. Dustwrapper (internally repaired, some wear at edges). *(Woolmer)* **$100 [≃£52]**
- After Strange Gods. New York: Harcourt, Brace, (1934). 1st US edition. Spine faded. *(Woolmer)* **$65 [≃£33]**
- (Translates) Anabasis. A Poem by St.-J. Perse. London: Faber, 1930. One of 350 signed. Minor wear spine ends. Dustwrapper. *(Woolmer)* **$300 [≃£156]**
- Andrew Marvell 1621-1678 Tercentenary Tributes. OUP: 1922. Spine and top cover gilt. By Eliot and others. *(Woolmer)* **$35 [≃£18]**
- Andrew Marvell. Tercentenary Tributes. London: 1922. Dustwrapper (some inconsequential soiling to lower panel, 2 closed tears). *(Blakeney)* **£65 [≃$124]**
- Animula. London: Faber, Ariel Poem, 1929. Wrappers very slightly dusty, unchipped. *(Woolmer)* **$35 [≃£18]**
- Ash-Wednesday. New York: Fountain Press; London: Faber, 1930. One of 600 signed, this copy marked "Out of Series". Cloth gilt. *(Black Sun)* **$575 [≃£299]**
- Ash-Wednesday. New York: Fountain Press; London: Faber, 1930. One of 600 signed. Minor wear spine ends, covers a bit darkened. *(Woolmer)* **$350 [≃£182]**
- Ash-Wednesday. New York & London: Fountain Press, 1930. One of 600 signed. T.e.g. Acetate dustwrapper. Box (discoloured and soiled, edges rubbed, traces of removed tape). *(Polyanthos)* **$375 [≃£195]**
- Ash Wednesday. New York: Fountain Press, London: Faber, 1930. One of 600 signed. Slipcase. *(Virgo)* **£350 [≃$671]**

- Ash-Wednesday. London: 1930. Dustwrapper (slightly chipped). *(Words Etcetera)* **£35 [≃$67]**
- British Writers and Their Work 4. Lincoln, Nebraska, 1964. 1st American edition of George Herbert. Wrappers. *(Blakeney)* **£25 [≃$47]**
- Burnt Norton. London: Faber, (1941). Wrappers. *(Woolmer)* **$45 [≃£23]**
- Charles Whibley. A Memoir. London: 1931. 1st issue. Wrappers a little browned and slightly marked. *(Blakeney)* **£15 [≃$28]**
- Charles Whibley A Memoir. London: English Association, 1931. 1st issue, with wrappers. Wrappers darkened. *(Woolmer)* **$100 [≃£52]**
- Charles Whibley, a Memoir. London: The English Association, 1931. Wrappers (browned at edges). *(Clearwater)* **£25 [≃$47]**
- Christmas card for the year 1958, designed for Faber & Faber by Gerald Rose. Signed by T.S. Eliot. *(Moorhouse)* **£75 [≃$143]**
- The Cocktail Party. London: Faber, (1950). Correct reading on page 29. Some fading at edges. Dustwrapper (spine ends worn). *(Woolmer)* **$50 [≃£26]**
- The Cocktail Party. London: 1950. 2nd issue. Dustwrapper (single nick at foot of spine). *(Words Etcetera)* **£10 [≃$19]**
- The Cocktail Party. New York: Harcourt, Brace, (1950). 1st US edition. Dustwrapper (torn). *(Woolmer)* **$25 [≃£13]**
- Collected Poems 1909-1935. London: Faber, (1936). Covers dusty. *(Woolmer)* **$50 [≃£26]**
- Collected Poems. New York: 1936. 1st US edition. 1st issue (grey) dustwrapper. *(Words Etcetera)* **£35 [≃$67]**
- The Confidential Clerk. London: 1954. 1st issue, priced 10/6d. Dustwrapper (very slightly chipped). *(Buckley)* **£15 [≃$28]**
- The Confidential Clerk. London: Faber, (1954). 1st issue dustwrapper. Corrected reading on page 7. Dustwrapper (worn at edges). *(Woolmer)* **$75 [≃£39]**
- The Cultivation of Christmas Trees. London: Faber, 1954. Wrappers. Envelope (slightly torn). *(David Rees)* **£10 [≃$19]**
- The Cultivation of Christmas Trees. London: Faber, Ariel Poem, (1954). Wrappers. *(Woolmer)* **$25 [≃£13]**
- Dante. London: Faber, (1929). One of 125 signed. Edges slightly faded. Tissue dustwrapper. *(Woolmer)* **$800 [≃£416]**
- Dante. London: Faber, (1929). Offsetting to fly leaves. Dustwrapper (some soiling and spine darkening). *(Between the Covers)* **$200 [≃£104]**
- Dante. London: Faber, (1929). Some darkening at edges. *(Woolmer)* **$85 [≃£44]**
- Dante. London: Faber, 1929. Some extremities of boards slightly faded. Dustwrapper (chipped). *(Clearwater)* **£45 [≃$86]**
- The Dry Salvages. London: Faber, 1941. Slight foxing. Wrappers. *(David Rees)* **£15 [≃$28]**
- The Dry Salvages. London: 1941. Wrappers (cover browned at edges, very small crease). *(Roberts)* **£12.50 [≃$24]**
- The Dry Salvages. London: 1941. Wrappers slightly lightened at edges. *(Buckley)* **£15 [≃$28]**
- East Coker. London: Faber, (1940). 1st Faber edition. Wrappers (darkened at edges, few nicks bottom edge). *(Woolmer)* **$45 [≃£23]**
- The Elder Statesman. London: 1959. Dustwrapper. *(Words Etcetera)* **£10 [≃$19]**
- The Elder Statesman. New York: Farrar, Straus & Giroux, [1959]. 1st edition. Dustwrapper (minor wear). *(Antic Hay)* **$30 [≃£15]**
- The Elder Statesman. London: 1959. Dustwrapper (slightly rubbed). *(Buckley)* **£25 [≃$47]**
- The Elder Statesman. New York: 1959. Dustwrapper. *(Polyanthos)* **$25 [≃£13]**
- Elizabethan Essays. London: Faber, 1934. 1st issue binding. Half-title tipped in. Some foxing of prelims. *(Woolmer)* **$85 [≃£44]**
- Essays Ancient and Modern. London: Faber, (1936). Spine darkened, some rubbing at outer hinges. *(Woolmer)* **$35 [≃£18]**
- Ezra Pound, his Metric and Poetry. New York: 1917. Spine and edges slightly sunned. Faint damp staining lower edges including prelims. Leather and cloth folder. *(Polyanthos)* **$350 [≃£182]**
- Ezra Pound His Metric and Poetry. New York: Knopf, 1917. Boards slightly faded at spine, no edge wear. Dustwrapper (separated at spine). *(Woolmer)* **$300 [≃£156]**
- The Family Reunion. London: 1939. Dustwrapper (slightly browned). *(Words Etcetera)* **£40 [≃$76]**
- The Family Reunion. London: Faber, (1939). Darkened at edges. 1st issue dustwrapper (spine darkened). *(Woolmer)* **$85 [≃£44]**
- The Film of Murder in the Cathedral. New York: Harcourt, Brace, (1952). 1st US edition. Remainder binding. Dustwrapper (worn at edges). *(Woolmer)* **$35 [≃£18]**
- For Lancelot Andrewes. London: Faber &

Gwyer, 1928. Dustwrapper (one small tear in lower panel). *(Moorhouse)* **£80 [≃$53]**
- For Lancelot Andrewes. London: Faber & Gwyer, (1928). Uncut, partly unopened. Spine faded. *(Woolmer)* **$60 [≃£31]**
- Four Quartets. New York: Harcourt, Brace, (1943). Dustwrapper (minimal wear at edges). *(Woolmer)* **$500 [≃£260]**
- Four Quartets. New York: Harcourt, Brace, (1943). Copy without "first american edition" on copyright page. Price-clipped dustwrapper. *(Woolmer)* **$100 [≃£52]**
- Four Quartets. New York: HB, (1943). 2nd impression. Small owner name and date. Dustwrapper (small piece missing from upper edge rear panel). *(Lopez)* **$65 [≃£33]**
- Four Quartets. London: Faber, 1944. 1st collected UK edn. Endpapers very slightly spotted. Dustwrapper (browned, two edge tears, top of spine frayed). *(Virgo)* **£30 [≃$57]**
- From Poe to Valery. New York: 1948. Paper boards a little bumped with a couple of negligible scratches. *(Blakeney)* **£35 [≃$67]**
- From Poe to Valery. New York: Harcourt, Brace, (1948). One of 1500. Tiny nick at foot of spine. *(Woolmer)* **$40 [≃£20]**
- The Frontiers of Criticism. University of Minnesota: (1956). Wrappers. *(Woolmer)* **$25 [≃£13]**
- The Frontiers of Criticism. University of Minnesota: 1956. Wrappers. Compliments / review slip laid in. *(Blakeney)* **£35 [≃$67]**
- The Hollow Men. Oxford: School of Art Press, 1964. Covers very slightly marked. *(Waterfield's)* **£75 [≃$143]**
- The Hollow Men. Oxford: School of Art Press, 1964. 1st separate English edition. Cloth covers slightly darkened at edges. *(Woolmer)* **$350 [≃£182]**
- Homage to John Dryden. London: Hogarth Press, 1924. Wrappers (spine worn, covers dusty). *(Woolmer)* **$100 [≃£52]**
- (Introduces) Intimate Journals by Charles Baudelaire. Translated by Christopher Isherwood. London: 1930. No dustwrapper issued. *(Blakeney)* **£35 [≃$67]**
- John Dryden. New York: Holliday, 1932. Page edges slightly browned. Lower front corner bumped, spine faded and slightly rubbed at ends. *(Virgo)* **£25 [≃$47]**
- Journey of the Magi. London: Faber & Gwyer, Ariel Poem, (1927). Wrappers (soiled). *(Woolmer)* **$45 [≃£23]**
- Knowledge and Experience in the Philosophy of F.H. Bradley. London: 1964. Dustwrapper (slightly marked and rubbed). *(Clearwater)* **£20 [≃$38]**
- Later Poems 1925-1935. London: Faber, (1941). Dustwrapper. *(Woolmer)* **$50 [≃£26]**
- The Literature of Politics. London: Conservative Political Centre, (1955). Wrappers. *(Woolmer)* **$50 [≃£26]**
- Little Gidding. London: 1942. 1st issue, stitched not stapled. Wrappers very slightly creased. *(Blakeney)* **£20 [≃$38]**
- Little Gidding. London: Faber, 1942. Wrappers (slightly sunned). *(David Rees)* **£14 [≃$26]**
- Little Gidding. London: 1942. Wrappers. *(Roberts)* **£12.50 [≃$24]**
- Little Gidding. London: Faber, (1942). Stapled issue. Wrappers faded at spine. *(Woolmer)* **$50 [≃£26]**
- Little Gidding. London: Faber, 1942. 1st English edition. Stapled issue. Signed by the author. *(First Issues)* **£95 [≃$182]**
- Marina. London: Faber, 1930. One of 400 signed. Light shelfwear at edges. *(Woolmer)* **$250 [≃£130]**
- Marina. London: Faber, Ariel Poem, 1930. Wrappers lightly faded at edges. *(Woolmer)* **$35 [≃£18]**
- Milton, London: Geoffrey Cumberledge, 1947. Wrappers little darkened at edges. *(Woolmer)* **$125 [≃£65]**
- The Music of Poetry. Glasgow: 1942. Wrappers. *(Clearwater)* **£30 [≃$57]**
- The Music of Poetry. Glasgow: UP, 1942. Printed wrappers. *(Polyanthos)* **$45 [≃£23]**
- Notes towards the Definition of Culture. London: Faber, (1948). Edges faded. Dustwrapper. *(Woolmer)* **$75 [≃£39]**
- Old Possum's Book of Practical Cats. London: Faber, (1939). Endpapers foxed. Covers a little faded. Dustwrapper. *(Woolmer)* **$250 [≃£130]**
- Old Possum's Book of Practical Cats. London: Faber, 1939. Dustwrapper (slight rubbing and stain rear panel). *(Lewton)* **£160 [≃$307]**
- Old Possum's Book of Practical Cats. New York: Harcourt, Brace, (1939). 1st US edition. Rust mark on title & half-title. Dustwrapper. *(Woolmer)* **$125 [≃£65]**
- On Poetry & Poets. London: 1957. Dustwrapper (slightly chipped, faint ring stain rear panel). *(Buckley)* **£18 [≃$34]**
- On Poetry and Poets. London: Faber, (1957). Dustwrapper (some wear at edges). *(Woolmer)* **$50 [≃£26]**
- Order of Service in Memory of T.S. Eliot, February, 1965. Wrappers (a little browned and creased). *(Words Etcetera)* **£12.50 [≃$24]**

- Poems. New York: Knopf, 1920. 1st US edition of Ara Vos Prec. "About the author" clipped from dustwrapper and laid in. *(Woolmer)* **$150 [≃£78]**
- Poems. New York: Knopf, 1920. 1st American edition. Boards slightly rubbed, three small stains to upper panel. *(First Issues)* **£85 [≃$163]**
- Poems 1909-1925. London: 1925. One of 85 signed. White buckram (spine and top edge of upper panel a little browned). *(Words Etcetera)* **£985 [≃$1,891]**
- Poems 1909-1925. London: Faber & Gwyer, 1925. Stain on half-title. Minor rubbing spine ends. *(Woolmer)* **$85 [≃£44]**
- Poems 1909-1925. London: 1925. Covers browned. *(Words Etcetera)* **£30 [≃$57]**
- Poems Written in Early Youth. London: Faber, (1967). 1st trade edition. *(Woolmer)* **$50 [≃£26]**
- Poems Written in Early Youth. London: Faber, 1967. 1st trade edition. Dustwrapper. *(Limestone Hills)* **$45 [≃£23]**
- Poems Written in Early Youth. New York: FS&G, (1967). 1st US edition. Dustwrapper. *(Woolmer)* **$35 [≃£18]**
- Poetry and Drama. Harvard: UP, 1951. *(Woolmer)* **$35 [≃£18]**
- Poetry and Drama. London: Faber, 1951. Dustwrapper (slightly sunned). *(David Rees)* **£10 [≃$19]**
- Poetry and Drama. London: Faber, 1951. 1st English edition. Dustwrapper. *(Virgo)* **£40 [≃$76]**
- Points of View. London: 1941. Ownership signature. Dustwrapper (spine darkened and rubbed). *(First Issues)* **£10 [≃$19]**
- Points of View. London: Faber, (1941). Covers dull, light wear at edges. *(Woolmer)* **$35 [≃£18]**
- Prufrock and Other Observations. London: The Egoist Ltd, 1917. Wrappers (little darkened, minute wear at spine ends). *(Woolmer)* **$2,500 [≃£1,302]**
- Religious Drama: Mediaeval and Modern. New York: House of Books, 1954. One of 300 (326) signed. *(Woolmer)* **$350 [≃£182]**
- The Rock. London: 1934. Dustwrapper (trifle soiled). *(Words Etcetera)* **£28 [≃$53]**
- The Rock. London: Faber, (1934). One of 1000 issued in boards. Spine darkened. *(Woolmer)* **$125 [≃£65]**
- The Rock. London: 1934. Spine and edges browned. *(Buckley)* **£12 [≃$23]**
- The Sacred Wood. London: Methuen, 1920. Name on endpaper. 2nd issue dustwrapper, with sub-title on front panel (small chips from corners and spine ends, spine faded). *(Virgo)* **£100 [≃$191]**
- Selected Essays 1917-1932. London: Faber, (1932). Spine faded, slight trace of dampness at bottom edge. *(Woolmer)* **$100 [≃£52]**
- Selected Poems. Penguin Books: (1948). Paperback original. Some rubbing at spine. *(Woolmer)* **$25 [≃£13]**
- Selected Poems. London: Faber, 1954. 1st Faber edition. 1st casebound edition. Some soiling to front endpapers. Dustwrapper (little rubbed & chipped, top of spine crudely repaired). *(Blakeney)* **£20 [≃$38]**
- Shakespeare and the Stoicism of Seneca. London: OUP, 1927. Wrappers. *(Woolmer)* **$150 [≃£78]**
- A Song for Simeon. London: Faber & Gwyer, Ariel Poem, 1928. Spine chipped, wrappers loose. *(Woolmer)* **$35 [≃£18]**
- The Song of the Jellicles. Music by Dorothy Howell. London: 1953. 1st separate edition. Wrappers slightly creased with 1/- overstamp as issued. *(Blakeney)* **£25 [≃$47]**
- Sweeney Agonistes. London: Faber, 1932. Endpapers lightly foxed. Small chip to top of spine. Price-clipped dustwrapper (small chip at head of spine). *(Nouveau)* **$125 [≃£65]**
- Sweeney Agonistes. London: Faber, (1932). 1st issue binding. Spine darkened, covers dusty. *(Woolmer)* **$85 [≃£44]**
- Sweeney Agonistes. London: Faber, (1932). 1st issue binding. Dustwrapper (some soiling, repair at top of spine). *(Woolmer)* **$175 [≃£91]**
- Thoughts after Lambeth. London: Criterion Miscellany, 1931. Wrappers, slightly rubbed at foredges. *(Clearwater)* **£25 [≃$47]**
- Thoughts After Lambeth. London: Faber, (1931). Wrappers, partly unopened. *(Woolmer)* **$45 [≃£23]**
- The Three Voices of Poetry. Cambridge: UP, 1953. Wrappers. *(Woolmer)* **$45 [≃£23]**
- The Three Voices of Poetry. NBL & CUP, 1953. Wrappers. *(Lewton)* **£10 [≃$19]**
- To Criticize the Critic and Other Writings. New York: FS&G, (1965). 1st US edition. Dustwrapper. *(Woolmer)* **$35 [≃£18]**
- To Criticize the Critic. London: 1965. Dustwrapper. *(Buckley)* **£20 [≃$38]**
- Triumphal March. London: Faber, 1931. One of 300 signed. Boards just a bit darkened. *(Woolmer)* **$300 [≃£156]**
- The Undergraduate Poems. Cambridge: The Harvard Advocate, (1949). Wrappers very slightly faded. *(Woolmer)* **$125 [≃£65]**

- The Undergraduate Poems. Cambridge, Mass: 1949. Unauthorized. Grey wrappers (slightly soiled, lower cover slightly scuffed). *(Virgo)* **£100 [≃$191]**
- The Use of Poetry & the Use of Criticism. London: 1933. Uncut. *(Buckley)* **£25 [≃$47]**
- The Use of Poetry & The Use of Criticism. London: Faber, 1933. Dustwrapper (spine sunned). *(Lewton)* **£44 [≃$84]**
- The Use of Poetry and the Use of Criticism. London: Faber, (1933). Endpapers a bit foxed. Unopened. *(Woolmer)* **$75 [≃£39]**
- The Use of Poetry and the Use of Criticism. Harvard: UP, 1933. 1st US edition. Spine darkened. *(Woolmer)* **$50 [≃£26]**
- The Value and Use of Cathedrals in England To-day. [Chichester: 1952]. Wrappers (slightly dusty). *(Clearwater)* **£35 [≃$67]**
- The Waste Land. Richmond: Hogarth Press, 1923. 1st English edition. Boards (spine faded, minor shelfwear at edges). With Gallup's 1st state label (no priority). *(Woolmer)* **$1,000 [≃£520]**
- The Waste Land. A Facsimile and Transcript. London: Faber, [1971]. One of 500. Original box. *(Woolmer)* **$85 [≃£44]**
- The Waste Land. A Facsimile and Transcript. London: Faber, [1971]. 1st trade edition. Dustwrapper. *(Woolmer)* **$35 [≃£18]**
- The Waste Land. A Facsimile and Transcript ... New York: HBJ, (1971). 1st US edition. Dustwrapper. *(Woolmer)* **$35 [≃£18]**

Ellin, Stanley

- Mystery Stories. New York: Simon and Schuster, 1956. Pages darkened. Dustwrapper (short crease-tear on front panel). *(Mordida)* **$65 [≃£33]**

Ellis, Alice Thomas

- The Birds of the Air. London: Duckworth, 1980. Dustwrapper. Inscribed by the author. *(Lewton)* **£30 [≃$57]**
- The Birds of the Air. London: Duckworth, 1980. Dustwrapper. *(Lewton)* **£20 [≃$38]**
- The Clothes in the Wardrobe. London: 1987. Dustwrapper. *(Words Etcetera)* **£12.50 [≃$24]**
- Home Life. London: Duckworth, 1986. Dustwrapper. *(Lewton)* **£8.50 [≃$17]**
- The Other Side of the Fire. London: 1983. Dustwrapper. *(Words Etcetera)* **£15 [≃$28]**
- The Sin Eater. London: Duckworth, 1977. dustwrapper (one small nick). Her 1st book. *(Moorhouse)* **£30 [≃$57]**
- The Sin Eater. London: Duckworth, 1977. Dustwrapper. *(David Rees)* **£30 [≃$57]**
- The Skeleton in the Cupboard. London: Duckworth, 1988. Dustwrapper. Signed by the author. *(David Rees)* **£16 [≃$30]**
- The 27th Kingdom. London: 1982. Dustwrapper. *(Words Etcetera)* **£18 [≃$34]**
- Unexplained Laughter. London: 1985. Dustwrapper. *(Words Etcetera)* **£15 [≃$28]**

Ellis, Havelock

- The Revaluation of Obscenity. Paris: Hours Press, 1931. One of 200 signed. Partly unopened. Endpapers browned. Half leather. Corners and edges rubbed, boards slightly soiled. *(Virgo)* **£40 [≃$76]**

Ellis, Royston

- Jiving to Gyp. Scorpion Press: 1959. Wrappers. Author's 1st book. *(Any Amount)* **£14 [≃$26]**

Ellison, Ralph

- The Invisible Man. New York: Random House, [1952]. Ink presentation on endpaper. Some browning to two pages from clipping laid in. Dustwrapper (moderate wear). His 1st book. *(Antic Hay)* **$150 [≃£78]**

Ellroy, James

- Brown's Requiem. London: Allison & Busby, 1984. 1st hardcover edition. Dustwrapper. Signed by the author and inscribed. His 1st book. *(Michael Johnson)* **£50 [≃$95]**
- Clandestine. London: Allison & Busby, 1984. 1st hardcover edition. Dustwrapper. *(Michael Johnson)* **£40 [≃$76]**

Empson, William

- Poems. London: 1935. Spine slightly bumped. Dustwrapper (shelfworn, slightly torn), His 1st book. *(Buckley)* **£35 [≃$67]**
- (Contributes to) Shakespeare Survey. Brendin Publishing Co: [1937]. Wrappers, staples rusted. *(Moorhouse)* **£75 [≃$143]**
- Some Versions of Pastoral. London: 1935. Dustwrapper. *(Clearwater)* **£30 [≃$57]**

Enright, D.J.

- The Laughing Hyena. London: 1953. Dustwrapper. His 1st book. *(Buckley)* **£30 [≃$57]**
- Selected Poems. London: 1968. Dustwrapper. *(Buckley)* **£12 [≃$23]**

Epilogue: a Critical Summary

- See Riding, Laura.

Erdrich, Louise

- Baptism of Fire. New York: Harper & Row, 1989. Dustwrapper. *(Michael Johnson)* **£20 [≃$38]**
- The Beet Queen. New York: 1986. Dustwrapper. *(Words Etcetera)* **£35 [≃$67]**
- The Beet Queen. New York: Holt, 1986. Dustwrapper. *(Michael Johnson)* **£24 [≃$46]**
- Jacklight. New York: HRW, (1984). Wrappers (minimal rubbing). Signed by the author. Her 1st book. *(Lopez)* **$150 [≃£78]**
- Love Medicine. New York: 1984. Dustwrapper. *(Words Etcetera)* **£80 [≃$153]**
- Love Medicine. New York: 1984. Dustwrapper. *(Michael Johnson)* **£150 [≃$287]**
- Tracks. New York: 1988. Dustwrapper. *(Words Etcetera)* **£25 [≃$47]**

Erickson, Stephen

- Days Between Stations. New York: Poseidon, 1985. Dustwrapper. *(Michael Johnson)* **£18 [≃$34]**
- Rubicon Beach. New York: Poseidon, 1986. Dustwrapper (remainder mark). *(Michael Johnson)* **£25 [≃$47]**

Estleman, Loren D.

- The Hider. Garden City: Doubleday, 1978. Dustwrapper. *(Mordida)* **$75 [≃£39]**
- The Wolfer. London: Robert Hale, 1983. 1st hardcover edition. Dustwrapper. Signed by the author. *(Mordida)* **$65 [≃£33]**

Evans, John

- Halo for Satan. Indianapolis: Bobbs-Merrill, 1948. Dustwrapper (spine ends chipped and frayed, several short closed tears). *(Mordida)* **$145 [≃£75]**
- Halo in Blood. Indianapolis: Bobbs-Merrill, 1946. Flawed rear pastedown. Dustwrapper (spine ends frayed and chipped, wear at corners and folds). *(Mordida)* **$115 [≃£59]**

Everson, William

- Tendril in the Mesh. [Aromas, CA]: Cayucos Books, 1973. One of 250 numbered. Leather backed patterned boards. No dustwrapper issued. *(Antic Hay)* **$125 [≃£65]**

Ewart, Gavin

- Alphabet Soup. Sycamore Broadsheet: 1971. *(Edrich)* **£5 [≃$9]**
- The Gavin Ewart Show. Trigram Press: 1971. Wrappers. Poetry Society wraparound. *(Edrich)* **£12 [≃$23]**
- An Imaginary Love Affair. Belfast: Ulsterman, 1974. Wrappers. Signed by the author. *(Hazeldene)* **£15 [≃$28]**
- Poems and Songs. London: Fortune Press, Fortune Poets Series, (1939). Dustwrapper. His 1st book. *(Edrich)* **£50 [≃$95]**
- Poems and Songs. London: Fortune Press, Fortune Poets Series, 1939. Name on endpaper. Covers a little damp mottled and slightly worn. *(Edrich)* **£16 [≃$30]**
- A Question Partly Answered. Sceptre Press: 1976. One of 50 signed. Card wrappers. *(Hazeldene)* **£15 [≃$28]**
- Twelve Apostles. Belfast: Ulsterman, 1970. Wrappers. Signed and corrected by the author. *(Hazeldene)* **£15 [≃$28]**
- Two Children. Keepsake Press: 1966. One of 175 signed. Wrappers (slightly faded). *(Any Amount)* **£14 [≃$26]**

Exley, Frederick

- A Fan's Notes. New York: H&R, (1968). Dustwrapper. Signed by the author. *(Lopez)* **$125 [≃£65]**
- A Fan's Notes. New York: H&R, (1968). Dustwrapper. *(Lopez)* **$50 [≃£26]**
- A Fan's Notes. New York: Harper, 1968. Uncorrected proof copy. Wrappers. His 1st book. *(Nouveau)* **$150 [≃£78]**

Exupery, Antoine de Saint

- The Little Prince. New York: 1943. One of 525 signed. Dustwrapper (spine ends chipped, one or two other small closed tears). *(Words Etcetera)* **£1,100 [≃$2,111]**

Fairlie, Gerald

- Captain Bulldog Drummond. London: Hodder & Stoughton, 1945. Dustwrapper. *(Ash)* **£25 [≃$47]**

Fante, John

- Dago Red. New York: 1940. Dustwrapper (bit of shallow chipping along top edge). *(Pettler & Liebermann)* **$200 [≃£104]**

Farina, Richard

- Been Down So Long It Looks Like Up to Me. New York: 1966. Dustwrapper. His 1st book. *(Pettler & Liebermann)* **$75 [≃£39]**
- Long Time Coming and a Long Time Gone. New York: 1969. Price-clipped dustwrapper. *(Pettler & Liebermann)* **$25 [≃£13]**

Farran, Richard M.

- Pseudonym used by John Betjeman, q.v.

Farrell, J.G.

- A Girl in the Head. London: 1967. Dustwrapper. *(First Issues)* **£75 [≃$143]**
- A Girl in the Head. London: Cape, 1967. Price-clipped dustwrapper (top of spine a little rubbed). *(Alphabet)* **$100 [≃£52]**
- A Girl in the Head. New York: Harper, 1967. 1st American edition. Dustwrapper. *(First Issues)* **£30 [≃$57]**
- The Singapore Grip. London: Weidenfeld & Nicolson, 1978. 1st English edition. Dustwrapper. *(Limestone Hills)* **$50 [≃£26]**
- The Singapore Grip. London: Weidenfeld & Nicolson, 1978. Dustwrapper. *(Lewton)* **£10 [≃$19]**
- Troubles. London: Cape, 1970. Dustwrapper. *(Lewton)* **£35 [≃$67]**

Farrell, James T.

- The Collected Poems. New York: Fleet, [1965]. Dustwrapper. Signed by the author. *(Antic Hay)* **$75 [≃£39]**
- The Fate of Writing in America. New York: New Directions, [1946]. Stapled wrappers (some dust soiling). *(Dermont)* **$10 [≃£5]**
- Judith and Other Stories. Garden City: Doubleday, [1973]. Dustwrapper (short tear). Signed by the author. *(Antic Hay)* **$75 [≃£39]**
- Judith. Athens, Ohio: Duane Schneider Press, 1969. One of 300 signed. Printed wrappers (edges lightly faded). *(Antic Hay)* **$85 [≃£44]**
- A Misunderstanding. New York: House of Books, 1949. Out of series, unsigned. *(Dermont)* **$20 [≃£10]**
- A Misunderstanding. New York: House of Books, 1949. One of 300 signed. Dustwrapper. *(Dermont)* **$60 [≃£31]**
- A Misunderstanding. New York: House of Books, 1949. One of 300 signed. Glassine dustwrapper. *(Antic Hay)* **$85 [≃£44]**
- A Note on Literary Criticism. New York: Vanguard, [1936]. Minor browning rear endpaper. Dustwrapper (few tears, minor soil). Author's signed presentation (1936). *(Antic Hay)* **$225 [≃£117]**
- Young Lonigan. New York: 1932. Author's presentation inscription laid in. His 1st book. *(Polyanthos)* **$75 [≃£39]**

Farrell, M.J.

- Loving Without Tears. London: 1951. Minor abrasions to extremities. Dustwrapper (chipped). *(Egret)* **£40 [≃$76]**

Faulkner, William

- Absalom, Absalom! New York: Random House, 1936. Folding map. Usual very slight cracking to hinges. Dustwrapper (small chip at head of spine). *(Chapel Hill)* **$325 [≃£169]**
- Absalom, Absalom! New York: Random House, 1936. Slight wear to hinges. Dustwrapper (somewhat rubbed, some edgewear). Author's signed inscription dated November 1936. *(Chapel Hill)* **$9,000 [≃£4,687]**
- Absalom, Absalom! New York: Random House, 1936. One of 300 signed by the author. Half buckram, t.e.g., others uncut (cover edges darkened). Slipcase. *(Heritage)* **$1,500 [≃£781]**
- As I Lay Dying. New York: Jonathan Cape & Harrison Smith, (1930). 1st state, with dropped "I" on page 11 and top edge stained dark brown. Dustwrapper, pristine. *(Chapel Hill)* **$6,000 [≃£3,125]**
- Collected Stories. New York: Random House, 1950. 1st issue, with 2-colour title & top edge stained grey. Small bookplate. 1st issue dustwrapper, not price-clipped (two 1/4 inch tears at foot of spine). *(Alphabet)* **$275 [≃£143]**
- Collected Stories. New York: 1950. Book Club issue, tiny dot on rear cover, top edge unstained. Stated first printing. Price- clipped dustwrapper (1/4 inch tear). *(Alphabet)* **$45 [≃£23]**
- Dr Martino. London: Chatto & Windus, 1934. Spine faded. *(Tiger Books)* **£30 [≃$57]**
- A Fable. New York: Random House, (1954). Dustwrapper (half-inch clean tear at top of rear panel). Author's signed inscription dated September 1954. *(Chapel Hill)* **$9,000 [≃£4,687]**
- A Fable. New York: (1954). One of 1000 signed. Slipcase. *(Black Sun)* **$450 [≃£234]**
- A Fable. New York: 1954. Dustwrapper (slightly frayed and soiled). *(King)* **$45 [≃£23]**
- A Fable. New York: Random House, 1954. One of 1000 signed. Tissue dustwrapper. Slipcase. *(Nouveau)* **$750 [≃£390]**
- A Fable. New York: Random House, [1954]. One of 1000 signed. Slipcase (minor scuffing). *(Antic Hay)* **$500 [≃£260]**
- A Fable. London: 1955. Dustwrapper (slightly chipped). *(Buckley)* **£25 [≃$47]**
- A Fable. London: Chatto & Windus, 1955. 1st English edition. *(Limestone Hills)* **$30 [≃£15]**
- Faulkner's County. Tales of Yaknapatawpha County. London: Chatto & Windus, 1955. 1st

English edition. Dustwrapper.
(Limestone Hills) **$45 [≃£23]**

- Flags in the Dust. New York: Random House, [1973]. Dustwrapper. *(Dermont)* **$50 [≃£26]**
- Go Down Moses. New York: Random, (1942). Variant red cloth (very slight puckering). Dustwrapper. *(Between the Covers)* **$1,000 [≃£520]**
- Go Down, Moses: and Other Stories. New York: Random House, [1942]. 1st issue, with top edge stained red. Dustwrapper (few nicks). *(Houle)* **$425 [≃£221]**
- The Hamlet. New York: Random House, 1940. 1st issue dustwrapper without reviews on rear panel (three 1/4 inch tears, edges lightly rubbed). *(Alphabet)* **$450 [≃£234]**
- Idyll in the Desert. New York: 1931. One of 400 signed by the author. Decorated boards. *(Black Sun)* **$850 [≃£442]**
- Intruder in the Dust. New York: (1948). Two corners bumped. Dustwrapper (bumped with slight tear). *(King)* **$100 [≃£52]**
- Intruder in the Dust. New York: Random House, (1948). Dustwrapper. *(Houle)* **$350 [≃£182]**
- Intruder in the Dust. New York: Random House, [1948]. Dustwrapper. *(Chapel Hill)* **$225 [≃£117]**
- Intruder in the Dust. London: 1949. 1st English edition. Endpapers and edges foxed. Extremities and spine sunned, foot of spine very faded. Dustwrapper (chipped and frayed). *(King)* **$65 [≃£33]**
- Jealosy and Episode [sic]. Faulkner Studies: 1955. One of 500. Cloth over boards, two small light spots on front. *(Nouveau)* **$350 [≃£182]**
- Knight's Gambit. New York: (1949). Dustwrapper (frayed, slightly creased). *(King)* **$150 [≃£78]**
- Knight's Gambit. London: Chatto & Windus, 1951. 1st English edition. Dustwrapper (missing 3/4 inch from head of spine). *(Limestone Hills)* **$65 [≃£33]**
- Knight's Gambit. London: 1951. Spine slightly bumped. Dustwrapper (chipped). *(Buckley)* **£28 [≃$53]**
- Light in August. New York: Harrison Smith and Robert Haas, [1932]. Some offsetting to endpapers. Dustwrapper (spine sunned, few small edge chips). *(Chapel Hill)* **$400 [≃£208]**
- The Mansion. New York: 1959. Dustwrapper. *(Polyanthos)* **$50 [≃£26]**
- The Mansion. New York: Random House, 1959. Dustwrapper. *(Nouveau)* **$75 [≃£39]**
- The Mansion. New York: (1959). One of 500 signed. Name and date on half-title. Glassine dustwrapper (slightly used). *(King)* **$400 [≃£208]**
- The Mansion. New York: (1959). Price-clipped dustwrapper (spine slightly sunned). *(King)* **$100 [≃£52]**
- The Mansion. London: Chatto & Windus, 1961. 1st English edition. Dustwrapper. *(Nouveau)* **$65 [≃£33]**
- The Marble Faun. Boston: The Four Seas Company, [1924]. Slight split along one inch of rear bottom edge of spine. Signed and dated (30 December 1924) presentation inscription by the author. His 1st book. *(Black Sun)* **$17,500 [≃£9,114]**
- The Marionettes. A Play. [The University of Virginia: 1975]. One of 100. Unbound sheets, in cardboard sleeve and matching slipcase, as issued. *(Black Sun)* **$325 [≃£169]**
- Mosquitoes. London: Chatto & Windus, 1964. 1st English edition. Dustwrapper (back panel lightly soiled). *(Limestone Hills)* **$85 [≃£44]**
- New Orleans Sketches. London: 1958. Spine slightly dull. Dustwrapper (dusty & spotted, chipped at spine ends). *(Blakeney)* **£15 [≃$28]**
- Notes on a Horsethief. Greenville, Mississippi: The Levee Press, [1950]. One of 975 signed by the author. *(Black Sun)* **$700 [≃£364]**
- Pylon. New York: 1935. Some spotting throughout, spine quite badly mottled with lettering slightly flaked. Dustwrapper (lightly rubbed & frayed). *(Blakeney)* **£150 [≃$287]**
- Pylon. New York: Smith & Haas, 1935. 1st trade edition. Front hinge partly wormed, spine a bit spotted. *(Alphabet)* **$45 [≃£23]**
- Pylon. New York: 1935. One of 310 signed by the author. Cloth backed boards. *(Black Sun)* **$600 [≃£312]**
- The Reivers. New York: Random House, 1962. 1st issue. Dustwrapper. *(Nouveau)* **$55 [≃£28]**
- The Reivers. New York: Random House, [1962]. One of 500 signed by the author. Light wear to extremities. *(Heritage)* **$500 [≃£260]**
- Requiem for a Nun. New York: Random House, (1951). One of 750 signed. Acetate dustwrapper. *(Houle)* **$865 [≃£455]**
- Requiem for a Nun. New York: Random House, 1951. Dustwrapper (minor rubbing and chipping). *(Nouveau)* **$85 [≃£44]**
- Requiem for a Nun. New York: Random House, [1951]. Dustwrapper (usual

discoloration of spine). *(Antic Hay)* **$150 [≃£78]**

- Requiem for a Nun. New York: Random House, [1951]. Erasure from front endpaper, very faint tape marks. Dustwrapper. *(Chapel Hill)* **$150 [≃£78]**
- Requiem for a Nun. New York: Random House, [195]. Dustwrapper (spine slightly sunned). *(Dermont)* **$150 [≃£78]**
- Salmagundi ... And a Poem by Ernest M. Hemingway. Milwaukee: The Casanova Press, 1932. One of 525. Portrait. Wrappers (spine soiled). Dustwrapper (chipped and spotted). *(King)* **$450 [≃£234]**
- Sanctuary. New York: Cape & Smith, (1931). Dustwrapper (couple of small chips at head of spine, slight scratch front panel). *(Between the Covers)* **$1,250 [≃£651]**
- Sanctuary. London: Chatto, 1931. 1st English edition. Rose cloth, stamped in black on spine, no advertisements. Dustwrapper (a touch darkened on spine with two small closed nicks to upper panel). *(First Issues)* **£200 [≃$383]**
- Sanctuary. London: Chatto, 1931. Edges tanned. Spine gilt rubbed, spine darkened and marked. *(Hazeldene)* **£35 [≃$67]**
- Sartoris. New York: Harcourt, Brace, [1929]. Dustwrapper (small spot at foot of rear panel, small chip at head of spine). *(Chapel Hill)* **$3,600 [≃£1,875]**
- Sartoris. New York: Harcourt Brace, 1929. Dustwrapper (thumb size light stain to rear lower edge, narrow 1/8 inch chip along top of spine). *(Alphabet)* **$2,000 [≃£1,041]**
- Sartoris. London: Chatto & Windus, 1932. 1st English edition. Spine lettering faded. *(Limestone Hills)* **$95 [≃£49]**
- Selected Letters. London: Scolar Press, 1977. Dustwrapper. *(Words Etcetera)* **£28 [≃$53]**
- Soldier's Pay. London: Chatto & Windus, 1930. Cloth slightly faded at spine, top edge slightly mottled. *(Moorhouse)* **£40 [≃$76]**
- A Sorority Pledge. Northport: The Seajay Press, 1983. One of 100 (of 126). Wrappers (top cover just a touch dusty). *(Woolmer)* **$150 [≃£78]**
- The Sound & The Fury. New York: Cape & Smith, 1929. Spine browned, rear hinge repaired. *(Alphabet)* **$175 [≃£91]**
- The Sound and the Fury. London: Chatto, 1931. Edges and endpapers tanned. *(Hazeldene)* **£35 [≃$67]**
- These Thirteen. New York: (1931). One of 299 signed. *(Black Sun)* **$1,100 [≃£572]**
- These Thirteen. New York: Cape & Smith, 1931. Spine little sunned, top minimally rubbed. Dustwrapper (spine sunned, slight chipping, a few tiny pieces missing, lined). *(Polyanthos)* **$250 [≃£130]**
- The Town. New York: Random House, [1957]. One of 450 signed by the author. *(Heritage)* **$650 [≃£338]**
- The Town. New York: Random House, 1957. 1st issue. Name on endpaper. Dustwrapper. *(Nouveau)* **$75 [≃£39]**
- The Town. New York: 1957. Dustwrapper (little rubbed, two tiny chips to spine). *(Polyanthos)* **$35 [≃£18]**
- The Town. New York: Random, (1957). Dustwrapper (two small chips). *(Between the Covers)* **$85 [≃£44]**
- The Unvanquished. New York: (1938). One of 250 signed. *(Black Sun)* **$1,200 [≃£625]**
- The Unvanquished. New York: RH, (1938). Dustwrapper (several long tears). *(Lopez)* **$125 [≃£65]**

Fearing, Kenneth

- The Crozart Story. Garden City: Doubleday, 1960. Dustwrapper (minor wear at corners). *(Mordida)* **$65 [≃£33]**

Fenton, James

- Terminal Moraine. London: Secker & Warburg, 1972. Dustwrapper (slightly marked). His 1st collection. *(David Rees)* **£75 [≃$143]**

Ferber, Edna

- Giant. Garden City: Doubleday, 1952. Dustwrapper (few nicks). *(Houle)* **$135 [≃£70]**
- Giant. Garden City: Doubleday, 1952. Price-clipped dustwrapper. Signed by the author on a tipped-in leaf. *(Chapel Hill)* **$75 [≃£39]**
- Saratoga Trunk. New York: Doubleday, 1941. One of 562 signed. Publisher's box. *(Black Sun)* **$150 [≃£78]**
- Saratoga Trunk. Garden City: Doubleday, 1941. 1st trade edition. Dustwrapper (nicks). *(Houle)* **$65 [≃£33]**
- Show Boat. Garden City: Doubleday, Page, 1926. One of 201 signed. Vellum and boards. Slipcase. *(Antic Hay)* **$225 [≃£117]**

Ferguson, Helen

- Pseudonym used by Anna Kavan, q.v.

Ferlinghetti, Lawrence

- After the Cries of the Birds. San Francisco: Dave Haslewood Books, 1967. Wrappers. Author' signed presentation copy. *(Polyanthos)* **$30 [≃£15]**

- Back Roads to Far Places. New York: (1971). Wrappers. Author's signed presentation copy. *(Polyanthos)* **$25 [≃£13]**
- A Coney Island of the Mind. London: 1959. Dustwrapper. *(Words Etcetera)* **£25 [≃$47]**
- Lawrence Ferlinghetti ['I am Waiting']. Verona: Corubolo & Castiglioni, American Authors Series, 1977. One of 30. Wrappers. *(Bromer)* **$250 [≃£130]**

Figes, Eva

- Tragedy and Social Evolution. London: 1976. The casebound edition. Dustwrapper. *(Blakeney)* **£12 [≃$23]**

Findley, Timothy

- The Last of the Crazy People. New York: Meredith, (1967). Dustwrapper (couple of small flaws). *(Between the Covers)* **$45 [≃£23]**
- The Last of the Crazy People. London: Macdonald, 1967. 1st English edition. Dustwrapper. His 1st book. *(Alphabet)* **$35 [≃£18]**

Finlay, Ian Hamilton

- Honey by the Water. LA: Black Sparrow, 1973. One of 200 signed. Glassine dustwrapper. *(Any Amount)* **£40 [≃$76]**
- Honey by the Water. LA: Black Sparrow, 1973. One of 200 signed. Acetate dustwrapper (tiny chip). *(Alphabet)* **$30 [≃£15]**

Finney, Jack

- The Body Snatchers. London: Eyre & Spottiswoode, 1955. Price-clipped dustwrapper (showing signs of wear and creasing but complete). *(Any Amount)* **£100 [≃$191]**

Fisher, Roy

- Collected Poems. Fulcrum Press, 1969. One of 100 signed. *(Words Etcetera)* **£20 [≃$38]**

Fisher, Vardis

- Children of God. New York: 1939. Dustwrapper (slightly frayed and torn). *(King)* **$45 [≃£23]**

Fitzgerald, F. Scott

- Afternoon of an Author. Princeton: University Press, 1957. One of 1500. Dustwrapper (two short closed tears). *(Alphabet)* **$100 [≃£52]**
- Afternoon of an Author. New York: 1957. Name and date. Dustwrapper (chipped). *(Pettler & Liebermann)* **$40 [≃£20]**
- Afternoon of an Author. New York: 1957. Dustwrapper. *(Pettler & Liebermann)* **$60 [≃£31]**
- Afternoon of an Author. New York: Scribner's, [1958]. Dustwrapper. *(Antic Hay)* **$75 [≃£39]**
- All the Sad Young Men. New York: Scribners, 1926. Name. Dustwrapper (chip, head of spine). *(Nouveau)* **$950 [≃£494]**
- The Beautiful and the Damned. New York: Scribners, 1922. Adverts at end. Binding dull, few slight marks. *(Whiteson)* **£75 [≃$143]**
- Fie! Fie! Fi-Fi! A Musical Comedy in Two Acts ... [Cincinnati]: The John Church Co, 1914. Very minor dust soiling. *(Chapel Hill)* **$2,750 [≃£1,432]**
- The Last Tycoon. London: 1949. 1st English edition. Dustwrapper (extremities very slightly rubbed). *(Roberts)* **£20 [≃$38]**
- The Last Tycoon. Grey Walls Press: 1949. Dustwrapper (chipped). *(Buckley)* **£40 [≃$76]**
- The Letters. New York: Scribner's, [1963]. Price-clipped dustwrapper (a few short tears). *(Antic Hay)* **$50 [≃£26]**
- The Notebooks. New York: Harcourt, Brace, Jovanovich; Bruccoli Clark, [1978]. Price-clipped dustwrapper. *(Antic Hay)* **$35 [≃£18]**
- The Pat Hobby Stories. New York: 1962. Price-clipped dustwrapper (slightly chipped). *(Pettler & Liebermann)* **$55 [≃£28]**
- The Pat Hobby Stories. New York: Scribners, [1962]. Dustwrapper. *(Dermont)* **$65 [≃£33]**
- Tales of the Jazz Age. New York: Scribner, 1922. 1st printing, September 1922. Dustwrapper (small chips, stained). *(Houle)* **$850 [≃£442]**
- Tales of the Jazz Age. New York: Scribner, 1922. 1st printing, September 1922. Upper cover slightly rubbed. *(Houle)* **$250 [≃£130]**
- Taps at Reveille. New York: Scribners, 1935. 1st state of text. Dustwrapper (very slightly rubbed). *(Alphabet)* **$950 [≃£494]**
- Taps at Reveille. New York: Scribners, 1935. 1st American edition, only printing, 2nd state. Pages 349-352 cancelled. Green cloth. *(First Issues)* **£65 [≃$124]**
- Taps at Reveille. New York: 1935. 2nd issue. Neat name. Spine slightly spotted. *(Polyanthos)* **$75 [≃£39]**
- Tender is the Night. New York: 1934. Spine sunned, extremities minimally rubbed, cloth edge rubbed. *(Polyanthos)* **$75 [≃£39]**
- Tender is the Night. New York: 1934. 1st

issue. Spine lettering indistinct. *(Buckley)* **£40 [≃$76]**

- The Vegetable. New York: Scribners, 1923. 1st American edition, 1st printing. Gilt title on spine faded. *(First Issues)* **£75 [≃$143]**

Fitzgerald, Penelope

- Offshore. London: 1979. Dustwrapper. Signed by the author. *(Egret)* **£25 [≃$47]**

Fitzgerald, Zelda

- Save Me the Waltz. London: Grey Walls Press, 1953. 1st English edition. Dustwrapper (chipped). *(Limestone Hills)* **$115 [≃£59]**
- Save Me the Waltz. London: Grey Walls, 1953. Dustwrapper. *(Sklaroff)* **£25 [≃$47]**
- Save Me the Waltz. London: Grey Walls, (1953). 1st UK edition. Dustwrapper (very lightly soiled, tiny nick). *(Between the Covers)* **$125 [≃£65]**

Fitzgibbon, Constantine

- When the Kissing Had to Stop. London: Cassell, 1960. 2nd issue, with pages 3/4 suppressed, cancelled and replaced. Dustwrapper. *(Ash)* **£25 [≃$47]**

Fleming, Ian

- The Diamond Smugglers. London: Cape, 1957. This copy has white lettering on spine instead of gilt. Dustwrapper (browned at spine). *(Alphabet)* **$100 [≃£52]**
- The Diamond Smugglers. London: Cape, 1957. Small marks on endpaper. Dustwrapper. *(Lewton)* **£30 [≃$57]**
- The Diamond Smugglers. London: Cape, 1957. Dustwrapper. *(Limestone Hills)* **$125 [≃£65]**
- Diamonds Are Forever. London: Cape, 1956. Dustwrapper (slight wear at spine top, 1/2 inch closed tear). *(Alphabet)* **$400 [≃£208]**
- Diamonds Are Forever. London: Cape, 1956. Edges slightly darkened. Dustwrapper (short closed tear and crease at top of spine, minor rubbing spine, back panel slightly soiled). *(Mordida)* **$450 [≃£234]**
- (Contributes) "Foreign News" to The Kemsley Manual of Journalism. London: Cassell, 1950. Spine very faded. *(Glyn's)* **£25 [≃$47]**
- From Russia, with Love. London: Cape, 1957. Dustwrapper (slightly worn and repaired). *(Ash)* **£100 [≃$191]**
- Gilt Edged Bonds. New York: 1961. Dustwrapper (slight stain rear panel). *(Words Etcetera)* **£48 [≃$92]**
- Goldfinger. London: Cape, 1959. Dustwrapper. *(Limestone Hills)* **$175 [≃£91]**
- Goldfinger. London: Cape, 1959. Dustwrapper. *(Lewton)* **£60 [≃$115]**
- Goldfinger. London: Cape, 1959. Label on pastedown. Name on endpaper. Dustwrapper (back panel slightly soiled). *(Mordida)* **$250 [≃£130]**
- Live and Let Die. London: Cape, 1954. Name on endpaper. Price-clipped dustwrapper (minor fraying head of spine). *(Frew Mackenzie)* **£485 [≃$931]**
- The Man with the Golden Gun. London: 1965. Uncorrected proof copy. Wrappers. *(Ellis)* **£180 [≃$345]**
- The Man with the Golden Gun. London: Cape, 1965. Dustwrapper. *(Lewton)* **£12.50 [≃$23]**
- The Man With the Golden Gun. London: Cape, 1965. Spotting on top edge. Price-clipped dustwrapper. *(Mordida)* **$50 [≃£26]**
- The Man with the Golden Gun. London: Cape, 1965. Dustwrapper. *(Virgo)* **£20 [≃$38]**
- The Man With The Golden Gun. NAL: 1965. 1st US edition. Price-clipped dustwrapper (two short closed tears). *(Nouveau)* **$45 [≃£23]**
- Moonraker. London: 1955. Dustwrapper (spine just a trifle browned). *(Words Etcetera)* **£350 [≃$671]**
- Octopussy and the Living Daylights. London: Cape, 1966. Dustwrapper. *(Mordida)* **$45 [≃£23]**
- Octopussy and the Living Daylights. London: Cape, [1966]. 1st English edition. Price-clipped dustwrapper (minor soil). *(Antic Hay)* **$40 [≃£20]**
- On Her Majesty's Secret Service. London: Cape, [1963]. One of 250 signed by the author. Vellum backed boards, t.e.g. *(Heritage)* **$2,500 [≃£1,302]**
- On Her Majesty's Secret Service. London: cape, 1963. Some spotting on edges. Price-clipped dustwrapper. *(Mordida)* **$75 [≃£39]**
- On Her Majesty's Secret Service. London: (1963). Dustwrapper (slightly worn). *(King)* **$60 [≃£31]**
- (Contributes) The Property of a Lady, in The Ivory Hammer. The Year at Sotheby's. 219th Season 1962-1963. London: Longmans, 1963. Dustwrapper (somewhat worn). *(Limestone Hills)* **$150 [≃£78]**
- The Spy Who Loved Me. London: Cape, 1962. Dustwrapper (stain on rear panel). *(Lewton)* **£19.50 [≃$38]**

- Thrilling Cities. London: 1963. Dustwrapper. *(Blakeney)* **£25 [≃$47]**
- Thrilling Cities. London: Cape, 1963. Dustwrapper. *(Lewton)* **£17.50 [≃$34]**
- Thrilling Cities. New York: New American Library, (1964). 1st American edition. Dustwrapper (few nicks). *(Houle)* **$65 [≃£33]**
- Thunderball. London: 1961. 1st state blind-stamped boards. Dustwrapper (slightly rubbed). *(Buckley)* **£30 [≃$57]**
- Thunderball. London: Cape, [1961]. Small ink name. Dustwrapper. *(Antic Hay)* **$150 [≃£78]**
- Thunderball. London: Cape, 1961. Dustwrapper (slightly nicked). *(Limestone Hills)* **$125 [≃£65]**
- Thunderball. London: Cape, 1961. Dustwrapper. *(Lewton)* **£29 [≃$55]**
- Thunderball. London: Cape, 1961. Slight spotting on top edge. Dustwrapper. *(Mordida)* **$125 [≃£65]**
- Where Shall John Go [in] Horizon: December, 1947. Wrappers. 1st appearance of Fleming under his own name. *(Lewton)* **£17.50 [≃$34]**
- Where Shall John Go? [in] Horizon, December, 1947. Wrappers (dull and worn). His 1st published work. *(Whiteson)* **£40 [≃$76]**
- You Only Live Twice. London: Cape, 1964. Dustwrapper (some tiny nicks). *(Mordida)* **$45 [≃£23]**
- You Only Live Twice. London: 1964. Dustwrapper. *(Roberts)* **£15 [≃$28]**
- You Only Live Twice. London: Cape, 1964. Slightly cocked. Dustwrapper. *(Limestone Hills)* **$75 [≃£39]**
- You Only Live Twice. NAL: 1964. 1st US edition. Dustwrapper. *(Nouveau)* **$50 [≃£26]**

Folder

- Folder. Edited by Daisy Aldan and Richard Miller. 1953-56. Numbers 1-4, all published. *(Blakeney)* **£175 [≃$335]**

Foote, Shelby

- Jordan County. New York: 1954. Dustwrapper. *(Pettler & Liebermann)* **$40 [≃£20]**

Ford, Ford Madox

- See the companion IRBP volume Literature.

Ford, Jesse Hill

- Mountains of Gilead. Boston: 1961. Dustwrapper (a bit chipped). Author's inscription. His 1st book. *(Pettler & Liebermann)* **$50 [≃£26]**

Ford, Leslie

- Old Lover's Ghost. New York: Scribner, 1940. Dustwrapper. *(Janus)* **$45 [≃£23]**

Ford, Richard

- A Piece of My Heart. London: Collins Harvill, 1987. 1st English edition. Dustwrapper. Signed by the author. *(Nouveau)* **$65 [≃£33]**
- A Piece of My Heart. London: Collins Harvill, 1987. 1st English edition. Dustwrapper. Signed by the author. *(Lopez)* **$75 [≃£39]**
- A Piece of My Heart. London: 1987. Author's signed presentation copy. Dustwrapper. *(Polyanthos)* **$60 [≃£31]**
- A Piece of My Heart. London: 1987. Dustwrapper. Signed by the author. *(Polyanthos)* **$50 [≃£26]**
- A Piece of My Heart. New York: H&R, (1976). Upper front corner slightly bumped. Price-clipped dustwrapper. His 1st book. *(Lopez)* **$135 [≃£70]**
- Rock Springs. New York: Atlantic, (1987). Corners bumped. Dustwrapper. Signed by the author. *(Lopez)* **$45 [≃£23]**
- Rock Springs. New York: Atlantic, (1987). Dustwrapper. *(Lopez)* **$25 [≃£13]**
- Rock Springs. New York: Atlantic, 1988. Dustwrapper. *(Michael Johnson)* **£16 [≃$30]**
- Rock Springs. New York: Atlantic, 1988. Dustwrapper. Signed by the author. *(Michael Johnson)* **£25 [≃$47]**
- Rock Springs. London: Collins Harvill, 1988. 1st English edition. Dustwrapper. Signed by the author. *(Lopez)* **$65 [≃£33]**
- Rock Springs. New York: 1987. Dustwrapper. Author's signed presentation copy. *(Polyanthos)* **$40 [≃£20]**
- The Sportswriter. New York: Vintage, 1986. Wrappers. Signed by the author. *(Michael Johnson)* **£45 [≃$86]**
- The Sportswriter. London: Collins Harvill, 1986. Dustwrapper. *(Moorhouse)* **£30 [≃$57]**
- The Ultimate Good Luck. London: Collins Harvill, 1989. dustwrapper. Signed by the author. *(Nouveau)* **$65 [≃£33]**
- The Ultimate Good Luck. Boston: 1981. Dustwrapper. Author's signed presentation copy. *(Polyanthos)* **$55 [≃£28]**
- The Ultimate Good Luck. London: Collins, 1989. 1st English edition. Advance review copy. Dustwrapper. *(Nouveau)* **$60 [≃£31]**

- The Ultimate Good Luck. London: Collins, 1989. 1st UK edition. Advance review copy with slip. Dustwrapper. Signed by the author. *(Between the Covers)* **$100 [≃£52]**
- The Ultimate Good Luck. London: Collins, 1989. Dustwrapper. *(Moorhouse)* **£6 [≃$11]**
- Wildlife. New York: Atlantic, (1990). One of 250 signed. Slipcase. *(Lopez)* **$150 [≃£78]**
- Wildlife. New York: Atlantic, (1990). Dustwrapper. Signed by the author. *(Lopez)* **$35 [≃£18]**

Forester, C.S.

- The Bedchamber Mystery. Toronto: Saunders, 1944. Only edition. Dustwrapper (torn & chipped). *(Clearwater)* **£75 [≃$143]**
- The Commodore. London: Michael Joseph, 1945. Dustwrapper (slightly worn). *(Glyn's)* **£17.50 [≃$34]**
- The Earthly Paradise. London: Michael Joseph, 1940. Price-clipped dustwrapper (slightly frayed). *(Glyn's)* **£15 [≃$28]**
- The Good Shepherd. London: Michael London: Michael Joseph, 1955. Uncorrected proof copy. Very occasional blemish. Dustwrapper (some loss at head of spine). *(Tiger Books)* **£30 [≃$57]**
- The Hornblower Companion. London: Michael Joseph, 1964. Dustwrapper (slightly torn). *(Limestone Hills)* **$125 [≃£65]**
- Lord Nelson. Indianopolis: Bobbs-Merrill, 1929. 1st American edition. Dustwrapper (separating at one foredge, other defects). *(Alphabet)* **$200 [≃£104]**
- Mr Midshipman Hornblower. London: 1950. Dustwrapper (slightly rubbed). *(Buckley)* **£30 [≃$57]**
- Poo-Poo and the Dragons. London: Michael Joseph, 1942. Dustwrapper. *(Green Meadow)* **£145 [≃$278]**
- The Sky & the Forest. London: 1948. Dustwrapper (slightly chipped), Book Society wraparound. *(Buckley)* **£18 [≃$34]**

Form

- Form. Edited by A.O. Spare & Francis Marsden. London: April 1916 - January 1922. 5 issues, all published. Large folio & small folio. Some spotting to the 1st issue. *(Blakeney)* **£675 [≃$1,295]**

Forster, E.M.

- Abinger Harvest. London: Arnold, 1936. Proof copy. Printed wrappers (upper panel slightly creased on leading edge with couple of tiny nicks, foredge slightly dusty). Includes 'A Flood in the Office'. *(First Issues)* **£100 [≃$191]**
- Alexandria: A History and Guide. Alexandria: 1922. Offsetting to endsheets. Spine lettering a little rubbed, two tiny holes in top of front board. Prospectus laid in. No dustwrapper issued. *(Blakeney)* **£225 [≃$431]**
- Billy Budd. With E. Crozier. London: 1951. Wrappers. *(Buckley)* **£15 [≃$28]**
- The Celestial Omnibus. London: Sidgwick & Jackson, 1911. Some foxing. Cloth slightly marked and worn, endpapers splitting at hinges. *(Glyn's)* **£50 [≃$95]**
- The Celestial Omnibus. London: Sidgwick & Jackson, 1911. Cloth little dull. Author's initialled presentation copy. *(Whiteson)* **£90 [≃$172]**
- Commonplace Book. London: Scolar Press, (1978). One of 350. Spine very slightly marked. *(Woolmer)* **$200 [≃£104]**
- England's Pleasant Land. London: Hogarth Press, 1940. Dustwrapper. *(Clearwater)* **£25 [≃$47]**
- A Letter to Madan Blanchard. Hogarth Press: 1931. Wrappers. *(Virgo)* **£20 [≃$38]**
- Nordic Twilight. London: Macmillan, 1940. Printed wrappers. *(Sklaroff)* **£15 [≃$28]**
- Pharos and Pharillon. New York: Knopf, 1923. *(Sklaroff)* **£28 [≃$53]**
- The Story of the Siren. Hogarth Press: 1920. Inner pages browned. Marbled wrappers (evenly faded, chipped). *(McCann)* **£125 [≃$239]**
- Tolstoy's 'War and Peace'. London: BBC, 1942. Wrappers a little marked. *(Glyn's)* **£15 [≃$28]**
- Virginia Woolf. Cambridge: 1942. A little browned. Wrappers. *(Ash)* **£20 [≃$38]**
- Virginia Woolf. Cambridge: UP, 1942. Wrappers (slight soiling). *(Houle)* **$75 [≃£39]**
- What I Believe. London: Hogarth Press, 1939. Wrappers. *(Woolmer)* **$35 [≃£18]**

Forsyth, Frederick

- The Day of the Jackal. London: Hutchinson, 1971. Dustwrapper. *(Lewton)* **£50 [≃$95]**
- The Negotiator. London: London Limited Editions, 1989. One of 50 signed. Glassine dustwrapper. *(Michael Johnson)* **£45 [≃$86]**
- The Negotiator. London: London Limited Editions, 1989. One of 150 signed. Tissue dustwrapper. *(Mordida)* **$150 [≃£78]**
- The Odessa File. London: 1972. Dustwrapper. *(Buckley)* **£15 [≃$28]**
- The Odessa File. London: Hutchinson, 1972. Dustwrapper. *(Lewton)* **£12 [≃$23]**

- The Shepherd. London: Hutchinson, 1975. Dustwrapper. *(Janus)* **$35 [≃£18]**
- The Shepherd. London: Hutchinson, 1975. Dustwrapper. *(Lewton)* **£6.50 [≃$13]**

Fowles, John

- The Aristos. Boston: Little, Brown, 1964. 1st edition (precedes UK edition). Dustwrapper (sunned). *(Michael Johnson)* **£75 [≃$143]**
- The Aristos. Boston: 1964. 1st US edition. Dustwrapper. *(Pettler & Liebermann)* **$85 [≃£44]**
- The Aristos. Boston: Little, Brown, 1964. 1st edition (precedes English edition). Dustwrapper. *(Alphabet)* **$150 [≃£78]**
- The Aristos. London: Cape, 1965. Dustwrapper. Signed by the author. *(Dyke)* **£250 [≃$479]**
- A Brief History of Lyme. Lyme Regis: 1981. Wrappers. Signed by the author. *(David Rees)* **£15 [≃$28]**
- (Translates and adapts) Cinderella by Perrault. London: 1974. Dustwrapper (very slightly browned near edges). *(Buckley)* **£35 [≃$67]**
- Cinderella. London: Cape, 1974. Dustwrapper. *(Lewton)* **£17.50 [≃$34]**
- Cinderella. London: Cape, 1974. Price-clipped dustwrapper. Signed by the author. *(David Rees)* **£20 [≃$38]**
- The Collector. London: Cape, 1963. Uncorrected proof copy. Paint stains on front covers, large ink initial front endpaper, cocked. *(Paul Brown)* **£150 [≃$287]**
- The Collector. London: Cape, 1963. Dustwrapper (one tiny tear). *(Dyke)* **£300 [≃$575]**
- The Collector. Boston: Little, Brown, 1963. 1st American edition. Dustwrapper. *(Georges)* **£150 [≃$287]**
- The Collector. Boston: Little Brown, 1963. 1st US edition. Dustwrapper. *(Lewton)* **£75 [≃$143]**
- The Collector. New York: Franklin Library Limited Edition, 1982. 1st edition thus. Leather. Signed by the author. *(Michael Johnson)* **£50 [≃$95]**
- Daniel Martin. London: Cape, 1977. Dustwrapper (slightly rubbed). Signed by the author. *(Alphabet)* **$85 [≃£44]**
- Daniel Martin. London: Cape, 1977. Faint removal marks to front endpaper. Price-clipped dustwrapper. Signed by the author and dated. *(Paul Brown)* **£35 [≃$67]**
- Daniel Martin. London: Cape, 1977. Dustwrapper. *(Dyke)* **£25 [≃$47]**
- Daniel Martin. London: Cape, 1977. Dustwrapper (slight stain on front panel). *(Sklaroff)* **£25 [≃$47]**
- Daniel Martin. London: Cape, 1977. Dustwrapper. *(Paul Brown)* **£17.50 [≃$34]**
- The Ebony Tower. London: Cape, (1974). Uncorrected proof copy. Name on half title. Slightly oversize proof dustwrapper. *(Lopez)* **$375 [≃£195]**
- The Ebony Tower. London: Cape, 1974. Dustwrapper. Signed by the author. *(Sklaroff)* **£85 [≃$163]**
- The Ebony Tower. London: Cape, 1974. Dustwrapper. *(Dyke)* **£30 [≃$57]**
- The Enigma of Stonehenge. London: Cape, 1980. Dustwrapper. *(Lewton)* **£15 [≃$28]**
- The French Lieutenant's Woman. London: Cape, 1969. Dustwrapper. *(Dyke)* **£80 [≃$153]**
- The French Lieutenant's Woman. London: Cape, 1969. Dustwrapper. *(Lewton)* **£75 [≃$143]**
- The French Lieutenant's Woman. Boston: Little, Brown, 1969. 1st American edition. Dustwrapper. *(Georges)* **£100 [≃$191]**
- Islands. London: Cape, (1978). Dustwrapper. Signed by the author. *(Lopez)* **$85 [≃£44]**
- Islands. London: 1978. Dustwrapper. Signed by the author. *(Words Etcetera)* **£20 [≃$38]**
- Islands. With Fay Godwin. London: Cape, 1978. Price-clipped dustwrapper. *(Sklaroff)* **£25 [≃$47]**
- King's Order for Lyme Siege [and] A Letter from Charles I concerning Lyme. Lyme Regis: 1980. 1st limited and signed edition. One of 100, with 2 holographic corrections by Fowles. Two broadsides. The Letter is unsigned. *(First Issues)* **£75 [≃$143]**
- Lorenzaccio. By Alfred De Musset. Written & Translated by John Fowles. London: [ca 1977?]. Nine typed sheets in an illustrated folder. Signed by the author. *(Alphabet)* **$100 [≃£52]**
- Lyme Regis Museum: Curator's Report: with Notes on Recent Research & New Acquisitions. Lyme Regis: Philpot Museum, 1982. 20-page pamphlet. Signed by the author. *(Alphabet)* **$150 [≃£78]**
- Lyme Regis Museum Curator's Report, 1982. Wrappers. Signed by the author. *(David Rees)* **£12 [≃$23]**
- Lyme Regis Museum Curator's Report, 1983. Wrappers. Signed by the author. *(David Rees)* **£12 [≃$23]**
- Lyme Regis Museum Curator's Report, 1984. Wrappers. Signed by the author.

(David Rees) **£10 [≃$19]**
- Lyme Regis. Three Town Walks. (1983). Wrappers. Signed by the author. *(Lopez)* **$45 [≃£23]**
- A Maggot. London: 1985. One of 500 signed. Glassine dustwrapper. *(Words Etcetera)* **£35 [≃$67]**
- A Maggot. London: 1985. One of 500 signed by the author. Tissue dustwrapper (chipped). *(Ellis)* **£60 [≃$115]**
- A Maggot. London: Cape, 1985. Dustwrapper. Signed by the author. *(Alphabet)* **$75 [≃£39]**
- A Maggot. London: Cape, 1985. Dustwrapper. Signed by the author. *(Dyke)* **£25 [≃$47]**
- A Maggot. Cape, 1985. Price-clipped dustwrapper. *(Paul Brown)* **£12.50 [≃$24]**
- The Magus. Boston: 1965. 1st US edition (precedes UK edition). Dustwrapper (very light foxing). *(Pettler & Liebermann)* **$65 [≃£33]**
- The Magus. London: Cape, 1966. Dustwrapper (somewhat worn). Signed by the author. *(Alphabet)* **$150 [≃£78]**
- The Magus. London: Cape, 1966. Dustwrapper (a little creased at top). *(Dyke)* **£65 [≃$124]**
- The Magus. London: Cape, 1966. Name on endpaper. Front flap only of dustwrapper. *(Sklaroff)* **£40 [≃$76]**
- Mantissa. London: 1982. Uncorrected proof copy. Wrappers. *(Lewton)* **£15 [≃$28]**
- Mantissa. Boston: Little, Brown, [1982]. One of 510 signed. Cloth. Slipcase. original shink-wrap. *(Antic Hay)* **$100 [≃£52]**
- Mantissa. London: Cape, 1982. Price-clipped dustwrapper. Signed by the author. *(Alphabet)* **$85 [≃£44]**
- Mantissa. London: Cape, 1982. Dustwrapper. *(Dyke)* **£12 [≃$23]**
- Mantissa. London: Cape, 1982. Dustwrapper. *(Paul Brown)* **£12.50 [≃$24]**
- Poems. Ecco Press, 1973. Dustwrapper. *(Words Etcetera)* **£25 [≃$47]**
- Poems. Ecco Press: 1973. 1st US edition (not published in England). Dustwrapper. *(Whiteson)* **£25 [≃$47]**
- Poems. Ecco: 1973. Dustwrapper. *(Nouveau)* **$40 [≃£20]**
- Poems. New York: 1973. Dustwrapper. No British edition was published. *(Pettler & Liebermann)* **$50 [≃£26]**
- Shipwreck. London: Cape, 1974. Dustwrapper. *(Lewton)* **£17.50 [≃$34]**
- The Tree. Aurum Press: 1979. Price-clipped dustwrapper (somewhat rubbed, with a nick). *(David Rees)* **£25 [≃$47]**

Frame, Janet
- Owls Do Cry. New York: 1960. Spine extremities minimally rubbed. Price-clipped dustwrapper. *(Polyanthos)* **$45 [≃£23]**

Frame, Ronald
- Winter Journey. London: Bodley Head, 1984. proof copy. Wrappers. His 1st book. *(Paul Brown)* **£15 [≃$28]**
- Winter Journey. London: Bodley Head, 1984. Dustwrapper. *(Paul Brown)* **£12.50 [≃$24]**

Francis, Dick
- Blood Sport. London: Michael Joseph, 1967. dustwrapper. *(Lewton)* **£78 [≃$149]**
- Blood Sport. New York: Harper & Row, 1968. 1st American edition. Dustwrapper. *(Mordida)* **$65 [≃£33]**
- Bonecrack. London: Michael Joseph, 1971. Dustwrapper. *(Mordida)* **$85 [≃£44]**
- Bonecrack. London: Michael Joseph, 1971. Dustwrapper. *(Lewton)* **£20 [≃$38]**
- Bonecrack. London: Michael Joseph, 1971. Dustwrapper. *(Limestone Hills)* **$75 [≃£39]**
- Bone Crack. New York: Harper & Row, 1972. 1st US edition. Dustwrapper. Signed by the author. *(Moorhouse)* **£22 [≃$42]**
- Bonecrack. New York: Harper, 1972. 1st US edition. Dustwrapper (lightly rubbed). *(Nouveau)* **$45 [≃£23]**
- Break In. London: Michael Joseph, 1985. Dustwrapper. Signed by the author. *(Limestone Hills)* **$55 [≃£28]**
- Break In. London: Michael London: Michael Joseph, 1985. 1st UK edition. Dustwrapper. Signed by the author. *(Marlborough B'shop)* **£18 [≃$34]**
- Enquiry. London: Michael Joseph, 1969. Dustwrapper (short closed tear, minor wear at corners and along front panel-flap fold, couple of light creases back panel). *(Mordida)* **$100 [≃£52]**
- Enquiry. London: Michael Joseph, 1969. Dustwrapper. *(Limestone Hills)* **$115 [≃£59]**
- Enquiry. London: Michael Joseph, 1969. Dustwrapper. *(Lewton)* **£45 [≃$86]**
- Flying Finish. London: Michael Joseph, 1966. Dustwrapper (couple of tiny tears, slight rubbing along folds). *(Mordida)* **$185 [≃£96]**
- Forfeit. London: Michael Joseph, 1968. Dustwrapper. *(Limestone Hills)* **$150 [≃£78]**

- Forfeit. New York: Harper, 1969. 1st US edition. Dustwrapper. *(Nouveau)* **$60 [≃£31]**
- Hot Money. New York: Putnam, 1988. One of 250 signed. Slipcase. *(Nouveau)* **$125 [≃£65]**
- In the Frame. London: Michael Joseph, 1976. Dustwrapper. Signed by the author. *(Limestone Hills)* **$95 [≃£49]**
- In the Frame. London: Michael Joseph, 1976. Dustwrapper. Inscribed by the author. *(David Rees)* **£25 [≃$47]**
- Knock Down. London: 1974. Author's presentation copy. *(Whiteson)* **£35 [≃$67]**
- Odds Against. London: Michael Joseph, 1965. Dustwrapper (slightly worn and nicked). *(David Rees)* **£25 [≃$47]**
- Odds Against. London: Michael Joseph, 1965. Dustwrapper. *(Limestone Hills)* **$225 [≃£117]**
- Odds Against. London: Michael Joseph, 1965. Dustwrapper. *(Lewton)* **£70 [≃$134]**
- Proof. London: Michael Joseph, 1984. Dustwrapper. With promotional bag. Signed by the author. *(David Rees)* **£20 [≃$38]**
- Rat Race. London: Michael Joseph, 1970. Untidy marks to prelims, etc. Dustwrapper (heavily chipped). *(Marlborough B'shop)* **£36 [≃$69]**
- Risk. New York: Harper & Row, 1978. 1st US edition. Dustwrapper. Signed by the author. *(Moorhouse)* **£20 [≃$38]**
- Slay-Ride. London: Michael Joseph, 1973. Dustwrapper. *(Ash)* **£20 [≃$38]**
- Slay-Ride. London: Michael Joseph, 1973. Dustwrapper. *(Limestone Hills)* **$55 [≃£28]**
- Slayride. New York: Harper & Row, 1973. 1st US edition. Dustwrapper (slightly rubbed). Signed by the author. *(Moorhouse)* **£20 [≃$38]**
- Smokescreen. London: Michael Joseph, 1972. Dustwrapper. *(Paul Brown)* **£12.50 [≃$24]**
- Smokescreen. London: Michael Joseph, 1972. Dustwrapper. *(Lewton)* **£16 [≃$30]**
- The Sport of Queens. London: 1957. New endpapers. Covers slightly marked. *(Whiteson)* **£70 [≃$134]**
- The Sport of Queens. London: 1957. Ex libris. *(Whiteson)* **£55 [≃$105]**
- The Sport of Queens. New York: 1969. Dustwrapper. *(Polyanthos)* **$150 [≃£78]**
- Trial Run. New York: Harper & Row, 1979. 1st US edition. Dustwrapper. Signed by the author. *(Moorhouse)* **£20 [≃$38]**
- Whip Hand. London: Michael Joseph, 1979. 1st UK edition. Dustwrapper. *(Marlborough B'shop)* **£15 [≃$28]**
- Whip Hand. New York: Harper & Row, 1979. Dustwrapper. Signed by the author. *(Marlborough B'shop)* **£25 [≃$47]**

Francis, Robert

- Stand With Me Here. New York: Macmillan, 1936. Dustwrapper (slightly used with tear). His 1st book. *(Dermont)* **$50 [≃£26]**
- Three Poems. Amherst: &tc Press, [1968]. One of 18. Wrappers. *(Dermont)* **$50 [≃£26]**

Fraser, George Macdonald

- Flashman. London: Jenkins, 1969. Dustwrapper. *(Lewton)* **£35 [≃$67]**
- Flashman. London: Jenkins, 1969. Dustwrapper. *(Marlborough B'shop)* **£30 [≃$57]**

Frayn, Michael

- The Book of Fub. London: Collins, 1963. Dustwrapper. *(Lewton)* **£7.50 [≃$15]**

Freeman, R. Austin

- The Singing Bone. London: Hodder & Stoughton, 1912. *(Tiger Books)* **£30 [≃$57]**

Friedan, Betty

- The Feminine Mystique. London: Gollancz, 1963. Dustwrapper. *(Paul Brown)* **£10 [≃$19]**
- The Feminine Mystique. London: Gollancz, 1963. 1st English edition. Dustwrapper (slightly chipped). *(Limestone Hills)* **$35 [≃£18]**
- The Second Stage. London: Michael Joseph, 1982. Dustwrapper. Inscribed and signed by the author. *(Paul Brown)* **£10 [≃$19]**

Friedberg, Gertrude

- The Revolving Boy. London: Gollancz, 1967. Dustwrapper (with neat patch). *(Sklaroff)* **£35 [≃$67]**

Friedman, Bruce Jay

- Black Angels. London: Cape, 1967. Dustwrapper (spine slightly darkened). *(Paul Brown)* **£15 [≃$28]**

Frost, Robert

- Accidentally on Purpose. 1960. Decorative wrappers. *(Whiteson)* **£25 [≃$47]**
- Away. 1958. Decorative wrappers. *(Whiteson)* **£25 [≃$47]**
- A Boy's Will. London: David Nutt, 1913. 1st issue. Binding A, bronzed brown pebbled cloth, gilt lettering, blind rule border, fine. Original tissue dustwrapper. His 2nd (but 1st

published) book.
(Black Sun) **$3,500 [≃£1,822]**

- A Boy's Will. London: David Nutt, 1913. 2nd issue binding. One of 135 signed. Printed wrappers. His 1st book.
(Polyanthos) **$500 [≃£260]**
- A Further Range. New York: 1936. Dustwrapper (chipped, spine darkened).
(Buckley) **£25 [≃$47]**
- A Further Range. New York: Henry Holt, [ca 1936]. Front cover slightly marked. Dustwrapper (chips at corners, small stain front edge, 1 inch closed tear).
(Virgo) **£30 [≃$57]**
- In the Clearing. New York: Holt, Rinehart & Winston, (1962). One of 1500 signed. Buckram. Slipcase.
(Black Sun) **$250 [≃£130]**
- In the Clearing. New York: 1962. Dustwrapper (tiny tear). *(Polyanthos)* **$20 [≃£10]**
- In the Clearing. New York: Holt, Rinehart & Winston, [1962]. Price-clipped dustwrapper.
(Antic Hay) **$35 [≃£18]**
- In the Clearing. New York: Holt, [1962]. Price-clipped dustwrapper.
(Chapel Hill) **$40 [≃£20]**
- A Masque of Mercy. New York: 1947. One of 751 signed. Tiny area rubbed. Box.
(Polyanthos) **$125 [≃£65]**
- A Masque of Mercy. New York: Henry Holt & Co, (1947). One of 751 signed by the author. Tissue dustwrapper (spine torn). Slipcase. *(Black Sun)* **$225 [≃£117]**
- A Masque of Mercy. New York: Holt, (1947). One of 751 signed. Dustwrapper. Slipcase.
(Houle) **$150 [≃£78]**
- A Masque of Mercy. New York: Holt, [1947]. One of 751 signed. Slipcase (very slightly used). *(Chapel Hill)* **$200 [≃£104]**
- A Masque of Mercy. New York: Holt, [1947]. 1st trade edition. Dustwrapper (moderate sunning of spine). *(Antic Hay)* **$45 [≃£23]**
- A Masque of Reason. New York: (1945). 1st edition. Dustwrapper (slightly worn and nicked). Signed by the author.
(Black Sun) **$275 [≃£143]**
- A Masque of Reason. New York: Holt, [1945]. Tiny pinhole in spine. Dustwrapper.
(Chapel Hill) **$40 [≃£20]**
- New Hampshire. A Poem. New Hampshire: The Dresden Press, 1955. 1st separate edition. One of 750 signed by the author. Prospectus laid in.
(Black Sun) **$250 [≃£130]**
- North of Boston. London: David Nutt, [1914]. 1st issue, binding A. Fine. Cloth case.
(Black Sun) **$2,750 [≃£1,432]**
- One More Brevity. 1953. Decorative wrappers. *(Whiteson)* **£25 [≃$47]**
- The Prophets really Prophesy as Mystics ... 1962. Decorative wrappers.
(Whiteson) **£25 [≃$47]**
- West-Running Brook. New York: Henry Holt, (1928). One of 1000 signed. Slipcase.
(Bromer) **$350 [≃£182]**
- A Witness Tree. New York: Henry Holt, 1942. One of 735 signed. Slipcase (faintly rubbed). *(Bromer)* **$275 [≃£143]**
- A Witness Tree. New York: 1942. Large inscription on fly. Dustwrapper (slightly rubbed). *(Words Etcetera)* **£30 [≃$57]**
- A Witness Tree. New York: Holt, [1942]. Few pencil marks. Price-clipped dustwrapper. *(Chapel Hill)* **$50 [≃£26]**
- A Witness Tree. New York: Holt, [1942]. Price-clipped dustwrapper (edgeworn and rubbed, short tears, small chip to head of spine). *(Antic Hay)* **$45 [≃£23]**

Fry, Roger

- A Sampler of Castile. Hogarth Press: 1923. One of 550. Michael Sadleir's bookplate.
(Black Sun) **$275 [≃£143]**
- A Sampler of Castile. Richmond: Hogarth Press, 1923. One of 550 numbered. Cloth backed boards, a little soiled, one corner knocked. *(Lamb)* **£120 [≃$230]**
- A Sampler of Castile. Richmond: Hogarth Press, 1923. One of 550 (this out of series). Covers slightly soiled, endpapers and edges browned. *(Virgo)* **£200 [≃$383]**
- Transformations. London: 1926. Dustwrapper (a few nicks, spine ends chipped). *(Ellis)* **£120 [≃$230]**

Fugard, Athol

- The Blood Knot. New York: 1964. 1st US edition. Dustwrapper (lightly rubbed, minor chipping top edge). 1st book.
(Pettler & Liebermann) **$125 [≃£65]**

Fuller, John

- Tell It Me Again. London: London Limited, 1988. One of 150 signed.
(Nouveau) **$90 [≃£46]**

Fuller, Roy

- Collected Poems. London: Deutsch, 1962. Dustwrapper (slightly tanned).
(Hazeldene) **£20 [≃$38]**
- A Lost Season. London: Hogarth Press, (1944). Dustwrapper. Signed by the author.
(Woolmer) **$50 [≃£26]**

Gaddis, William

- Jr. New York: 1975. Dustwrapper (slightly worn). Signed by the author. *(King)* **$75 [≃£39]**
- The Recognitions. New York: Harcourt Brace, (1955). Advance reading copy. His 1st book. *(Lopez)* **$550 [≃£286]**

Gallant, Mavis

- The Other Paris: Stories. Boston: Houghton Mifflin, 1956. Very slight foxing to endpapers. Dustwrapper (bit rubbed at spine extremities). Her 1st book. *(Alphabet)* **$150 [≃£78]**

Gallico, Paul

- The Snow Goose. New York: Knopf, 1941. Gift inscription. Dustwrapper (front panel discoloured). *(Chapel Hill)* **$55 [≃£28]**

Galsworthy, John

- See the companion IRBP volume Literature.

Garcia Marquez, Gabriel

- See Marquez, Gabriel Garcia.

Gardner, Erle Stanley

- The Case of the Backward Mule. New York: Morrow, 1946. Dustwrapper (wear at base of spine and corners). *(Mordida)* **$45 [≃£23]**
- The Case of the Careless Kitten. New York: Morrow, 1942. Dustwrapper (spine extremities lightly chipped). *(Janus)* **$100 [≃£52]**
- The Case of the Daring Decoy. New York: Morrow, [1957]. Blind stamp on endpaper. Dustwrapper (a few short tears). *(Antic Hay)* **$25 [≃£13]**
- The Case of the Grinning Gorilla. New York: Morrow, 1952. Dustwrapper. *(Janus)* **$20 [≃£10]**
- The Case of the Reluctant Model. New York: Morrow, [1961]. Dustwrapper. *(Antic Hay)* **$20 [≃£10]**
- The Case of the Rolling Bones. New York: Morrow, 1939. Softbound advance copy. A bit leaned. Bound with the dustwrapper. *(Janus)* **$400 [≃£208]**
- The Case of the Velvet Claws. New York: Morrow, 1933. 2nd printing. Rear hinge cracked. Author's inscription. *(Janus)* **$350 [≃£182]**
- The Case of the Worried Waitress. New York: Morrow, 1966. Small mark on title. Dustwrapper. *(Janus)* **$25 [≃£13]**
- The D.A. Breaks an Egg. New York: Morrow, 1949. Name stamp. Dustwrapper (faint price-change stamp on front flap). *(Janus)* **$65 [≃£33]**
- The D.A. Draws a Circle. New York: Morrow, 1939. Advance softbound copy. A bit leaned. Bound with the dustwrapper. *(Janus)* **$400 [≃£208]**
- Double or Quits. New York: Morrow, 1941. Advance softbound copy. A bit leaned. Archival tape repair to inside of front flap. Bound with the dustwrapper. *(Janus)* **$300 [≃£156]**
- Jason and Medeia. New York: Knopf, 1973. Dustwrapper (two short tears). *(Antic Hay)* **$50 [≃£26]**
- Neighborhood Frontiers. New York: Morrow, 1954. Dustwrapper (slightly rubbed, some nicks and wear at corners). Inscribed by Gardner. *(Mordida)* **$100 [≃£52]**

Gardner, John

- Amber Nine. London: Muller, 1966. Dustwrapper (closed tears). *(Tiger Books)* **£22.50 [≃$44]**
- The Art of Fiction. New York: Knopf, 1984. Uncorrected proof copy. *(Lopez)* **$50 [≃£26]**
- The Art of Living and Other Stories. New York: Knopf, 1981. Advance review copy. Dustwrapper. Signed by the author. *(Lopez)* **$100 [≃£52]**
- The Art of Living and Other Stories. New York: Knopf, 1981. "Internal review copy" slip. Dustwrapper. *(Lopez)* **$45 [≃£23]**
- A Child's Bestiary. New York: Knopf, (1977). Dustwrapper. *(Lopez)* **$45 [≃£23]**
- A Complete State of Death. London: Cape, 1969. Dustwrapper. *(Paul Brown)* **£10 [≃$19]**
- Dragon, Dragon and Other Tales. New York: Knopf, (1975). The "library binding" in decorated boards. No dustwrapper issued. Signed by the author. *(Lopez)* **$85 [≃£44]**
- The Forms of Fiction. By John Gardner and Lennis Dunlap. New York: 1962. Printed boards. Apparently issued without dustwrapper. His 1st book. *(Pettler & Liebermann)* **$100 [≃£52]**
- The Forms of Fiction. By John Gardner and Lennis Dunlap. New York: 1962. Printed boards (light soil). Apparently issued without dustwrapper. His 1st book. *(Pettler & Liebermann)* **$75 [≃£39]**
- Freddy's Book. New York: Knopf, 1980. Advance review copy. Dustwrapper. Slip and promotional photo laid in. Signed by the author. *(Lopez)* **$100 [≃£52]**
- The Gawain-Poet. Cliff Notes: 1967.

Wrappers, small store mark front cover. *(Nouveau)* **$35 [≃£18]**

- Grendel. New York: Knopf, 1971. Advance Review Copy with promotional material laid in. Dustwrapper (spine faded). *(Between the Covers)* **$100 [≃£52]**
- Grendel. New York: Knopf, 1971. Dustwrapper. *(Nouveau)* **$200 [≃£104]**
- Gudgekin the Thistle Girl and Other Tales. New York: Knopf, (1976). Dustwrapper. Signed by the author. *(Lopez)* **$85 [≃£44]**
- In the Suicide Mountains. New York: Knopf, 1977. Uncorrected proof copy. Label removal mark on covers. *(Lopez)* **$125 [≃£65]**
- In the Suicide Mountains. New York: Knopf, 1977. Dustwrapper. Signed by the author. *(Lopez)* **$85 [≃£44]**
- An Invective against Mere Fiction. N.p.: The Southern Review, 1967. Offprint. *(Lopez)* **$450 [≃£234]**
- The King of the Hummingbirds and Other Tales. New York: Knopf, (1977). Dustwrapper. Signed by the author. *(Lopez)* **$85 [≃£44]**
- The King's Indian. New York: Knopf, 1974. Dustwrapper. Signed by the author. *(Lopez)* **$100 [≃£52]**
- The King's Indian. New York: Knopf, 1974. Dustwrapper (spine slightly sunned). *(Lopez)* **$30 [≃£15]**
- The King's Indian. London: Cape, 1975. 1st English edition. Dustwrapper. *(Lopez)* **$30 [≃£15]**
- Le Morte d'Arthur. Cliff Notes: 1967. Wrappers, store stamp and small rub mark on front cover. *(Nouveau)* **$35 [≃£18]**
- The Life & Times of Chaucer. New York: Knopf, 1977. Dustwrapper. Signed by the author. *(Lopez)* **$85 [≃£44]**
- Mickelsson's Ghosts. New York: Knopf, 1982. Dustwrapper. *(Lopez)* **$20 [≃£10]**
- Nickel Mountain. New York: Knopf, 1973. Dustwrapper (two short tears). *(Nouveau)* **$35 [≃£18]**
- Nickel Mountain. New York: Knopf, 1973. Issue with dark orange title page. Dustwrapper. Signed by the author. *(Lopez)* **$85 [≃£44]**
- October Light. New York: 1977. Proof copy. Wrappers (two tiny corner creases). Author's signed presentation copy. *(Polyanthos)* **$125 [≃£65]**
- October Light. New York: Knopf, 1976. Dustwrapper. Signed by the author. *(Lopez)* **$85 [≃£44]**
- October Light. New York: Knopf, 1976. Dustwrapper. Signed by the author. *(Chapel Hill)* **$100 [≃£52]**
- October Light. New York: 1976. Dustwrapper. *(Pettler & Liebermann)* **$25 [≃£13]**
- October Light. London: Cape, 1977. Dustwrapper. *(Lopez)* **$35 [≃£18]**
- On Moral Fiction. New York: Basic Books, (1978). Advance review copy. Dustwrapper (one small hole). Review slip & complimentary card from author laid in. Signed by the author. *(Lopez)* **$150 [≃£78]**
- On Moral Fiction. New York: Basic Books, (1978). Dustwrapper. *(Lopez)* **$30 [≃£15]**
- On Moral Fiction. New York: 1978. Dustwrapper. *(Pettler & Liebermann)* **$30 [≃£15]**
- The Poetry of Chaucer. Carbondale: Southern Illinois University, (1977). Dustwrapper. Signed by the author. *(Lopez)* **$225 [≃£117]**
- The Sunlight Dialogues. New York: Knopf, 1972. Dustwrapper. *(Lopez)* **$65 [≃£33]**
- Vlemk the Box-Painter. Northridge: 1979. One of 300 signed. Dustwrapper. *(Pettler & Liebermann)* **$65 [≃£33]**
- Vlemk the Box Painter. Northridge, CA: Lord John, 1979. Dustwrapper. *(Lopez)* **$20 [≃£10]**

Garner, Alan

- The Guizer. London: Hamish Hamilton, 1975. Dustwrapper. *(Green Meadow)* **£35 [≃$67]**
- The Owl Service. London: Collins, 1967. Dustwrapper (slightly chipped). *(James)* **£85 [≃$163]**

Garner, Hugh

- The Silence on the Shore. Toronto: M&S, 1962. Proof sheets, uncut & untrimmed. Proof jacket, a bit edge worn. *(Alphabet)* **$125 [≃£65]**

Garnett, David

- Aspects of Love. London: 1955. Dustwrapper. *(Words Etcetera)* **£75 [≃$143]**
- Beany-Eye. London: Chatto & Windus, 1935. One of 110 signed. T.e.g. *(Limestone Hills)* **$55 [≃£28]**

Garrett, George

- King of the Mountain. New York: (1957). Extremities very slightly rubbed, spine little chipped, two tiny tears, edges very slightly rubbed. Author's signed presentation copy. His 1st book. *(Polyanthos)* **$50 [≃£26]**

Gascoyne, David

- Holderlins Madness. London: Dent, (1938). Slightly dull. Dustwrapper (dull, slightly worn). *(Whiteson)* **£70 [≃$134]**
- Paris Journal 1937-1939. Enitharmon Press, 1978. One of 75 signed. Cloth backed marbled paper covered boards, t.e.g. Dustwrapper. *(Virgo)* **£30 [≃$57]**
- Poems 1937-1942. London: PL Editions, 1943. Decorated boards little dull, edges slightly rubbed. *(Whiteson)* **£35 [≃$67]**
- Three Poems. London: Enitharmon Press, 1976. One of 126. Wrappers. Signed by the author. *(Woolmer)* **$75 [≃£39]**

Gash, Jonathan

- The Judas Pair. New York: Harper & Row, 1977. 1st American edition. Dustwrapper (several closed tears, rubbing along edges, wear at corners and spine ends). *(Mordida)* **$60 [≃£31]**
- Pearlhanger. London: Collins, 1985. Dustwrapper. Signed by the author. *(Limestone Hills)* **$75 [≃£39]**
- Spend Game. London: Collins, 1980. Dustwrapper. *(Limestone Hills)* **$75 [≃£39]**
- The Very Last Gambado. London: Collins, 1989. Dustwrapper. Signed by the author. *(Limestone Hills)* **$45 [≃£23]**

Gass, William H.

- In the Heart of the Heart of the Country. New York: Harper, 1968. Dustwrapper. *(Nouveau)* **$75 [≃£39]**
- Omensetter's Luck. New York: 1966. Sticker on endpaper. Dustwrapper (slight rubbing). His 1st book. *(Pettler & Liebermann)* **$100 [≃£52]**
- Omensetter's Luck. NAL: 1966. Dustwrapper. His 1st book. *(Nouveau)* **$250 [≃£130]**
- Willie Master's Lonesome Wife. TriQuarterly Supplement Number Two. Northwestern Univ Press: 1968. One of 100 (of 400) signed. Cloth (back cover slightly discoloured). *(King)* **$125 [≃£65]**

Gee, Maggie

- Dying, in Other Words. Brighton: Harvester, 1981. Dustwrapper. Her 1st book. *(Moorhouse)* **£20 [≃$38]**

Gellhorn, Martha

- Pretty Tales for Tired People. London: 1965. Dustwrapper (very slightly rubbed). *(Ellis)* **£40 [≃$76]**

Georgian Poetry ...

- Georgian Poetry 1916-1917 ... see Graves, Robert.

Gerhardi, William

- A Bad End. London: Benn, 1926. One of 265 signed. Wrappers (faintly soiled). *(Ash)* **£20 [≃$38]**

Gibbon, Monk

- For Daws To Peck At. London: Gollancz's New Poetry Series, 1929. Dustwrapper (somewhat sunned at spine). *(Blakeney)* **£35 [≃$67]**

Gibbons, Stella

- Cold Comfort Farm. London: Longmans, Green, 1932. Occasional very slight foxing. Modern morocco gilt. *(Ash)* **£200 [≃$383]**
- The Mountain Beast and Other Poems. London: 1930. Wrappers (spine lightened). Her 1st book. *(First Issues)* **£40 [≃$76]**

Gibson, William

- Neuromancer. London: Gollancz, 1984. Dustwrapper. Signed by the author. *(Michael Johnson)* **£75 [≃$143]**
- Neuromancer. London: 1984. Dustwrapper. *(First Issues)* **£75 [≃$143]**

Gilbert, Michael

- After the Fine Weather. London: Hodder & Stoughton, [1963]. Dustwrapper. *(Limestone Hills)* **$55 [≃£28]**
- The Dust and the Heat. London: Hodder & Stoughton, 1967. Dustwrapper (one small internally closed tear). *(Limestone Hills)* **$40 [≃£20]**
- Game Without Rules. London: Hodder & Stoughton, 1968. 1st English edition. Dustwrapper (one closed tear). *(Limestone Hills)* **$45 [≃£23]**
- The Long Journey Home. London: Hodder & Stoughton, 1985. Dustwrapper. Signed by the author. *(Limestone Hills)* **$35 [≃£18]**
- Paint, Gold and Blood. London: Hodder & Stoughton, 1989. Dustwrapper. Signed by the author. *(Limestone Hills)* **$40 [≃£20]**
- Petrella at Q. London: Hodder & Stoughton, 1977. Dustwrapper. *(Limestone Hills)* **$40 [≃£20]**
- The Wycherley Woman. London: Collins, 1962. 1st English edition. Dustwrapper (slightly chipped). *(Limestone Hills)* **$30 [≃£15]**

Gilliatt, Penelope

- One by One. London: Secker, 1965. Slight edge foxing. Dustwrapper (the odd small closed tear). *(Paul Brown)* **£25 [≃$47]**

Ginsberg, Allen

- Airplane Dreams. San Francisco: City Lights, 1969. Wrappers. Signed by the author. *(Polyanthos)* **$20 [≃£10]**
- Allen Verbatim. New York: McGraw-Hill, [1974]. Dustwrapper (some rubbing, small chip rear panel). Signed by the author. *(Antic Hay)* **$45 [≃£23]**
- Ankor-Wat. [London]: Fulcrum, (1968). Proof copy. Plain white wrappers. *(Lopez)* **$100 [≃£52]**
- Ankor Wat. London: Fulcrum Press, (1968). 1st edition thus. One of 100 signed and with Ginsberg's red chop mark. Dustwrapper. *(Houle)* **$175 [≃£91]**
- Ankor Wat. London: Fulcrum, [1968]. One of 100 signed. Cloth. Dustwrapper. *(Dermont)* **$100 [≃£52]**
- Careless Love. Madison: The Red Ozier Press, 1978. One of 280 signed. Wrappers. *(Alphabet)* **$85 [≃£44]**
- Collected Poems 1947-1980. New York: 1984. Dustwrapper. Signed by the author. *(Polyanthos)* **$50 [≃£26]**
- First Blues. New York: Full Court Press, (1975). One of 100 signed. Dustwrapper. *(Houle)* **$125 [≃£65]**
- The Gates of Wrath. Bolinas: Grey Fox Press, 1972. One of 100 signed. Acetate dustwrapper. *(Houle)* **$150 [≃£78]**
- Howl and Other Poems. San Francisco: City Lights, Pocket Poets Series No. 4, (1956). Neat name. Printed wrappers (little soiled and rubbed). Signed by the author. His 1st book. *(Polyanthos)* **$350 [≃£182]**
- Improvised Poetics. San Francisco: Anonym Editions, 1972. 1st published edition. Wrappers. Signed by the author. *(Alphabet)* **$20 [≃£10]**
- Kaddish & Other Poems. San Francisco: City Lights, 1961. Wrappers. *(Alphabet)* **$22.50 [≃£11]**
- Kaddish and Other Poems 1958-1960. SF: City Lights, (1961). Wrappers. *(Lopez)* **$75 [≃£39]**
- Planet News. San Francisco: City Lights, (1968). One of 500 signed. Slipcase. *(Houle)* **$125 [≃£65]**
- Planet News. San Francisco: City Lights, 1968 [1969]. One of 500 signed. Slipcase (a bit rubbed). *(Alphabet)* **$65 [≃£33]**
- Punk Rock Your My Big Crybaby. Grindstone City: The Alternative Press, 1977. Broadside. *(Lopez)* **$40 [≃£20]**
- Reality Sandwiches. San Francisco: City Lights, 1963. Wrappers. *(Alphabet)* **$17.50 [≃£9]**
- Sad Dust Glories. Berkeley: The Workingman's Press, 1975. Wrappers. Inscribed. *(Alphabet)* **$45 [≃£23]**
- Scrap Leaves: Tasty Scribbles. New York: Poet's Press, [1968]. One of 150 signed. Wrappers. *(Alphabet)* **$110 [≃£57]**
- T.V. Baby Poems. London: Cape Goliard Press, [1967]. One of 100 hardbound signed. Boards. Dustwrapper. *(Antic Hay)* **$100 [≃£52]**
- T.V. Baby Poems. New York: Grossman, 1968. 1st American edition (Cape Goliard edition precedes). Wrappers. Inscribed. *(Alphabet)* **$45 [≃£23]**
- T.V. Baby. Poem. Beach Books: 1968. 4to. Wrappers. Signed by Ginsberg. *(Blakeney)* **£25 [≃$47]**

Godfrey, Dave

- Death Goes Better with Coca-Cola. Toronto: Anansi, 1967. The casebound edition in fabricoid over boards. No dustwrapper issued. *(Alphabet)* **$65 [≃£33]**

Gogarty, Oliver St. John

- Tumbling in the Hay. London: Constable, 1939. *(Any Amount)* **£15 [≃$28]**

Gold, Herbert

- Birth of a Hero. New York: 1951. Spine extremities minimally rubbed. Dustwrapper (little edge worn). Author's signed presentation copy. His 1st book. *(Polyanthos)* **$40 [≃£20]**

Golding, Louis

- Magnolia Street. London: Gollancz, 1932. Dustwrapper (slightly creased and repaired, spine slightly sunned). *(Ash)* **£40 [≃$76]**

Golding, William

- The Brass Butterfly. London: Faber, 1958. Dustwrapper. *(Lewton)* **£110 [≃$211]**
- The Brass Butterfly. London: 1958. Dustwrapper (very slightly nicked). *(Clearwater)* **£90 [≃$172]**
- Close Quarters. London: Faber, 1987. Uncorrected proof copy. Wrappers. *(David Rees)* **£30 [≃$57]**
- Close Quarters. London: 1987. Dustwrapper. *(Roberts)* **£6.25 [≃$13]**

- Darkness Visible. New York: 1979. 1st American edition (precedes the English edition). Dustwrapper. *(First Issues)* **£35 [≃$67]**
- Darkness Visible. London: Faber, 1979. Dustwrapper. Short ALS (33 words) about the book inserted. *(Dyke)* **£50 [≃$95]**
- Darkness Visible. London: Faber, 1979. Dustwrapper. *(Sklaroff)* **£25 [≃$47]**
- Darkness Visible. London: Faber, 1979. Dustwrapper. *(Ash)* **£25 [≃$47]**
- Egyptian Journal. London: Faber, 1985. Dustwrapper. *(Lewton)* **£10 [≃$19]**
- Fire Down Below. London: Faber, 1989. Dustwrapper. Signed by the author. *(Moorhouse)* **£25 [≃$47]**
- Fire Down Below. London: Faber, 1989. Dustwrapper. *(David Rees)* **£10 [≃$19]**
- Free Fall. London: Faber, 1959. Trace of 'Boots' shield upper cover. *(Sklaroff)* **£25 [≃$47]**
- Free Fall. London: Faber, 1959. Dustwrapper (rear panel slightly dusty). *(Lewton)* **£65 [≃$124]**
- Free Fall. London: 1959. Dustwrapper (slightly tanned at extremities, couple of corners slightly rubbed). *(First Issues)* **£50 [≃$95]**
- Free Fall. London: Faber, 1959. Dustwrapper (rear panel slightly dusty). *(Lewton)* **£65 [≃$124]**
- The Inheritors. London: 1955. Dustwrapper (two small abrasions on corners). *(Words Etcetera)* **£85 [≃$163]**
- The Inheritors. London: Faber, 1955. Slightly worn, especially edges of spine. *(Sklaroff)* **£35 [≃$67]**
- Nobel Lecture. Leamington Spa: Sixth Chamber Press, 1984. One of 50 (of 500) signed, bound in goatskin. Slipcase. *(David Rees)* **£275 [≃$527]**
- Nobel Lecture. Leamington Spa: Sixth Chamber Press, 1984. One of 500. Wrappers. Signed by the author on title. *(Moorhouse)* **£55 [≃$105]**
- Nobel Lecture. Leamington Spa: Sixth Chamber Press, 1984. One of 500. Wrappers. *(Moorhouse)* **£20 [≃$38]**
- Nobel Lecture. Sixth Chamber Press: 1984. One of 500 trade copies. Wrappers. Signed by the author. *(First Issues)* **£45 [≃$86]**
- The Paper Men. London: Faber, 1984. Unbound proof signatures. *(David Rees)* **£65 [≃$124]**
- The Paper Men. London: Faber, 1984. Dustwrapper. Inscribed and signed by the author. *(David Rees)* **£95 [≃$182]**
- The Paper Men. London: Faber, 1984. Dustwrapper. Signed by the author. *(Sklaroff)* **£50 [≃$95]**
- The Paper Men. London: Faber, 1984. Dustwrapper. *(Lewton)* **£7.50 [≃$15]**
- Pincher Martin. London: Faber, 1956. Dustwrapper. *(Sklaroff)* **£60 [≃$115]**
- Pincher Martin. London: 1956. Dustwrapper (very chipped). *(Buckley)* **£70 [≃$134]**
- The Pyramid. London: Faber, 1967. Dustwrapper. *(Sklaroff)* **£18 [≃$34]**
- The Pyramid. London: Faber, 1967. Dustwrapper. *(Lewton)* **£22.50 [≃$44]**
- The Pyramid. London: 1967. Dustwrapper. *(Roberts)* **£21 [≃$40]**
- The Pyramid. London: Faber, [1967]. Dustwrapper. *(Dermont)* **$65 [≃£33]**
- Rites of Passage. London: Faber, 1980. Dustwrapper. *(Dyke)* **£20 [≃$38]**
- Rites of Passage. London: Faber, 1980. Dustwrapper. *(Sklaroff)* **£25 [≃$47]**
- Rites of Passage. London: Faber, 1980. Dustwrapper. *(Ash)* **£40 [≃$76]**
- Rites of Passage. Farrar: 1980. Advance Uncorrected proof copy. Wrappers. *(Nouveau)* **$70 [≃£36]**
- (Introduces) A Selection from the Guardian 1980-1981. Edited by W.L. Webb. London: Collins, 1981. Dustwrapper. *(Marlborough B'shop)* **£8 [≃$15]**
- The Spire. London: Faber, 1964. Dustwrapper. *(Alphabet)* **$85 [≃£44]**
- The Spire. London: Faber, 1964. Dustwrapper. *(Lewton)* **£37.50 [≃$72]**
- The Spire. London: Faber, 1964. Dustwrapper. *(Lewton)* **£37.50 [≃$72]**
- The Spire. 1964. 1st American edition. Dustwrapper. *(First Issues)* **£20 [≃$38]**
- The Two Deaths of Christopher Martin. New York: 1956. 1st US edition of Pincher Martin. Name. Dustwrapper (spine and edges sunned, few small edge tears and tiny edge chips). Gorey bookplate signed by the author. *(Polyanthos)* **$75 [≃£39]**

Goldman, William

- The Silent Gondoliers. By S. Morgenstern. New York: Ballantine, [1983]. Uncorrected proof copy. Wrappers. *(Antic Hay)* **$45 [≃£23]**

Goodman, Paul

- The Empire City. Indianapolis: (1959). Neat name. Dustwrapper (tiny tear, spine extremities little rubbed). Signed by the author. *(Polyanthos)* **$65 [≃£33]**

- Stop-Light. 5 Dance Poems. NJ: 5 x 8 Press, 1941. Plain dustwrapper with later printed dustwrapper over. *(Any Amount)* **£25 [≃$47]**

Gordimer, Nadine

- The Conservationist. London: 1974. Dustwrapper. Signed by the author. *(Egret)* **£35 [≃$67]**
- Face to Face. Johannesburg: Silver Leaf Books, 1949. Name on pastedown hidden by flap. Dustwrapper (rather worn and frayed). 1st book. *(Moorhouse)* **£75 [≃$143]**
- A Guest of Honour. London: 1971. Advance uncorrected proof copy. Edges slightly rubbed. *(Buckley)* **£35 [≃$67]**
- A Guest of Honour. London: Cape, (1971). 1st English edition. Uncorrected proof copy. *(Lopez)* **$125 [≃£65]**
- The Lying Days. London: 1953. Dustwrapper (few small closed tears). Signed by the author. *(Egret)* **£65 [≃$124]**
- Not for Publication. London: 1965. Price-clipped dustwrapper (slightly chipped). Signed by the author. *(Egret)* **£20 [≃$38]**
- Selected Stories. London: 1975. Dustwrapper. *(Words Etcetera)* **£20 [≃$38]**
- Six Feet of the Country. New York: S&S, 1956. Top edge of pages slightly spotted. Dustwrapper. *(Lopez)* **$45 [≃£23]**
- The Soft Voice of the Serpent and Other Stories. New York: 1952. Dustwrapper (top sides of spine little torn, little sunned, very small piece missing, tiny chip lower spine, little soiled). *(Polyanthos)* **$45 [≃£23]**
- The Soft Voice of the Serpent. London: 1953. Covers slightly bumped. Dustwrapper (faded, slightly torn). Signed by the author. *(Egret)* **£55 [≃$105]**
- Something Out There. London: 1984. Proof copy. Wrappers. *(Words Etcetera)* **£15 [≃$28]**
- Town and Country Lovers. Los Angeles: 1980. One of 300 (of 330) signed. *(David Rees)* **£60 [≃$115]**
- A World of Strangers. London: 1958. Dustwrapper (torn). *(Words Etcetera)* **£30 [≃$57]**

Gordon, Caroline

- The Garden of Adonis. New York: Scribners, 1937. Slight soiling to spine. Dustwrapper (very lightly rubbed). *(Between the Covers)* **$250 [≃£130]**
- Old Red and Other Stories. New York: 1963. Advance review copy with slip. Dustwrapper. *(Pettler & Liebermann)* **$75 [≃£39]**
- The Women on the Porch. New York: 1944. Usual paper browning. Two pen marks on page edge bottom. Dustwrapper (a bit worn). *(Pettler & Liebermann)* **$85 [≃£44]**
- The Women on the Porch. New York: Scribners, 1944. Dustwrapper (one nearly invisible tear). *(Between the Covers)* **$200 [≃£104]**

Gordon, Rex (S.R. Hough)

- The Time Factor. London: Gibbs & Phillips, 1964. Dustwrapper. *(Sklaroff)* **£25 [≃$47]**

Gores, Joe

- Final Notice. New York: 1973. Dustwrapper. *(Pettler & Liebermann)* **$40 [≃£20]**
- Gone, No Forwarding. New York: 1978. Dustwrapper. *(Pettler & Liebermann)* **$25 [≃£13]**
- A Time of Predators. New York: 1969. Dustwrapper. His 1st book. *(Pettler & Liebermann)* **$100 [≃£52]**

Gosling, Paula

- A Running Duck. London: Macmillan, 1978. Dustwrapper. *(Mordida)* **$60 [≃£31]**

Gottschalk, Laura

- See Riding, Laura.

Grafton, Sue

- "A" is for Alibi. New York: Holt, Rinehart and Winston, 1982. Dustwrapper (short scratch on front panel). Signed by the author. *(Mordida)* **$300 [≃£156]**
- "A" is for Alibi. New York: Holt, 1982. Dustwrapper. Signed by the author. *(Janus)* **$375 [≃£195]**
- A is for Alibi. London: Macmillan, 1986. 1st British edition. Dustwrapper. Signed by the author. *(Michael Johnson)* **£45 [≃$86]**
- "A" is for Alibi. London: Macmillan, 1986. 1st English edition. Dustwrapper. Signed by the author. *(Mordida)* **$85 [≃£44]**
- "B" is for Burglar. New York: Holt, Rinehart and Winston, 1985. Uncorrected proof copy. Wrappers (slightly soiled). *(Mordida)* **$150 [≃£78]**
- "B" is for Burglar. New York: Holt, 1985. Dustwrapper. Signed by the author. *(Janus)* **$150 [≃£78]**
- "B" is for Burglar. London: Macmillan, 1986. 1st English edition. Dustwrapper. *(Mordida)* **$45 [≃£23]**
- "C" is for Corpse. New York: Holt, Rinehart & Winston, 1986. Dustwrapper. *(Mordida)* **$45 [≃£23]**

- "D" is for Deadbeat. New York: Henry Holt, 1987. Dustwrapper. *(Mordida)* **$30 [≃£15]**
- E is for Evidence. New York: Holt, 1988. Dustwrapper. Signed by the author. *(Michael Johnson)* **£20 [≃$38]**
- F is for Fugitive. London: Macmillan, 1989. 1st British edition. Dustwrapper. Signed by the author. *(Michael Johnson)* **£14 [≃$26]**

Graham, Caroline

- The Envy of the Stranger. London: Century, 1984. Slightly leaned. Dustwrapper. *(Janus)* **$45 [≃£23]**
- The Killings at Badger's Drift. London: Century London: Hutchinson, 1987. Dustwrapper. Signed by the author. *(Michael Johnson)* **£36 [≃$69]**
- Murder at Madingley Grange. London: Century Mysterious, 1990. Dustwrapper. Signed by the author. *(Michael Johnson)* **£16 [≃$30]**

Graham, W.S.

- The White Threshold. London: Faber, 1949. Dustwrapper (slightly tanned, top edge chipped). *(Halsey)* **£30 [≃$57]**

Grass, Gunter

- The Flounder. New York: 1978. Dustwrapper. Signed by the author. *(Polyanthos)* **$45 [≃£23]**

Grau, Shirley Ann

- The Black Prince. New York: Knopf, 1955. Name. Dustwrapper. Her 1st book. *(Nouveau)* **$45 [≃£23]**
- The Hard Blue Sky. New York: Knopf, 1958. Dustwrapper (rubbed at extremities, one tear on back panel). *(Nouveau)* **$35 [≃£18]**

Graves, Robert

- Advice from a Mother. Poem of the Month Club. Signed by the author. *(Whiteson)* **£25 [≃$47]**
- Ann at Highwood Hall. London: 1964. Dustwrapper. *(Words Etcetera)* **£48 [≃$92]**
- Antigua Penny Puce. Seizin: 1936. 1st impression with 'ytyle' for 'style' on p 100. Library stamp on pastedown, slight foxing to foredge. Maroon cloth, white spine lettering bright and unchipped. *(First Issues)* **£70 [≃$134]**
- At the Gate. Privately Printed, 1974. One of 500 signed. Dustwrapper (slightly faded). *(Lewton)* **£40 [≃$76]**
- Beyond Giving. Privately Printed: 1969. One of 536 signed by the author. Unopened. Dustwrapper. *(Sotheran's)* **£78 [≃$149]**
- Claudius the God: and his Wife Messalina. New York: Harrison Smith and Robert Haas, 1935. 1st American edition. Dustwrapper. *(Houle)* **$150 [≃£78]**
- Collected Poems. New York: Random House, 1938 [sic]. 1st American edition. Higginson gives date of publication as 1939. Brick red cloth stamped on the spine in black & gilt, spine slightly faded. *(Blakeney)* **£325 [≃$623]**
- Collected Poems. London: 1959. Uncorrected proof copy. Wrappers (a little browned). *(Words Etcetera)* **£30 [≃$57]**
- Contemporary Techniques of Poetry. London: 1925. Wrappers (slightly dull). *(Whiteson)* **£45 [≃$86]**
- Count Belisarius. London: 1938. *(Buckley)* **£12 [≃$23]**
- The English Ballad. London: Benn, 1927. Spare spine label tipped in. *(Halsey)* **£25 [≃$47]**
- Fairies and Fusiliers. London: 1917. Covers slightly marked. Author's signed presentation inscription. *(Words Etcetera)* **£200 [≃$383]**
- The Feather Bed. London: Hogarth Press, 1923. One of 250, signed. Ownership signature and a 42 word comment on 1st page of text. Corners a little bumped, covers very slightly rubbed, backstrip a little chipped. *(Blakeney)* **£225 [≃$431]**
- 5 Pens in Hand. New York: Doubleday, 1958. Dustwrapper (slightly chipped and rubbed). *(Words Etcetera)* **£40 [≃$76]**
- (Contributes to) Georgian Poetry 1916 - 1917. London: Poetry Bookshop, 1917. Offsetting to endpapers. Two corners bumped. Dustwrapper (slightly chipped & torn, internally repaired, spine sunned). *(Blakeney)* **£50 [≃$95]**
- Goodbye to All That. London: Cape, 1929. 1st edition. 2nd issue, with Siegfried Sassoon's poem omitted. Dustwrapper (somewhat worn and chipped). *(David Rees)* **£50 [≃$95]**
- Goodbye to All That. London: 1929. 1st edition, 2nd issue. Dustwrapper (a couple of minute chips). *(Words Etcetera)* **£150 [≃$287]**
- The Green-Sailed Vessel. 1971. Signed limited edition. Dustwrapper. *(Whiteson)* **£45 [≃$86]**
- The Green-Sailed Vessel. Privately Printed: 1971. One of 536 signed by the author. Unopened. Dustwrapper. *(Sotheran's)* **£78 [≃$149]**
- I, Claudius. London: 1934. Minor foxing.

Cloth unevenly sunned. Dustwrapper (some loss to upper front). *(Egret)* **£65 [≃$124]**

- The Isles of Unwisdom. London: 1950. Dustwrapper (small chip extreme head upper panel). *(Words Etcetera)* **£28 [≃$53]**
- Jesus in Rome. With J. Podro. London: Cassell, 1957. Dustwrapper (soiled). *(Virgo)* **£45 [≃$86]**
- Jesus in Rome. With Joshua Podro. London: Cassell, (1957). Dustwrapper. *(Houle)* **$55 [≃£28]**
- Lars Porsena. London: 1972. One of 100 signed. Slipcase. *(Whiteson)* **£55 [≃$105]**
- Lars Porsena. London: 1972. One of 100 signed. Slipcase. *(Georges)* **£50 [≃$95]**
- Lawrence & the Arabs. London: 1927. *(Buckley)* **£20 [≃$38]**
- Lawrence and the Arabs. London: 1927. Dustwrapper (a few small chips and tears). *(Words Etcetera)* **£100 [≃$191]**
- Love Respelt Again. Garden City: Doubleday, (1969). 1st edition thus. One of 1000 signed. Dustwrapper. *(Houle)* **$125 [≃£65]**
- Love Respelt Again. New York: (1969). One of 1000. Dustwrapper (two tiny tears rear panel and tiny area rubbed). Signed by the author. *(Polyanthos)* **$40 [≃£20]**
- Love Respelt Again. New York: Doubleday, [1969]. One of 1000 signed. Dustwrapper. original cardboard mailing box. *(Antic Hay)* **$65 [≃£33]**
- Love Respelt. New York: Doubleday, [1969]. One of 1000 signed. Dustwrapper. *(Dermont)* **$45 [≃£23]**
- Man Does, Woman Is. London: Cassell, (1964). Dustwrapper (slightly soiled). *(Woolmer)* **$45 [≃£23]**
- The Nazarene Gospel Restored. With Joshua Podro. New York: Doubleday, 1954. 1st American edition. Covers slightly soiled at edges. Dustwrapper (corners chipped, top edge frayed). Signed presentation copy from Podro. *(Virgo)* **£120 [≃$230]**
- New Poems. London: Cassell, 1962. 1st printing. Dustwrapper. *(Virgo)* **£15 [≃$28]**
- On English Poetry. London: 1922. Spine slightly rubbed. *(Buckley)* **£30 [≃$57]**
- On English Poetry. London: Heinemann, 1922. Dustwrapper (very slightly rubbed). *(Lewton)* **£75 [≃$143]**
- Poems (1914-1926). London: Heinemann, 1927. Endpapers browned, foredge and first and last few pages spotted. Cover edges slightly rubbed. Dustwrapper (browned, chipped, cracks in folds). *(Virgo)* **£95 [≃$182]**
- Poems 1926-30. London: 1931. 1st issue, with misbound title page. *(Buckley)* **£20 [≃$38]**
- Poems 1929. Hammersmith: Seizin Press, 1929. One of 225 signed. Offsetting to endpapers. Spine a little faded. No dustwrapper issued. *(Blakeney)* **£275 [≃$527]**
- Poems 1968-1970. London: Cassell, 1970. Price-clipped dustwrapper. *(Ash)* **£20 [≃$38]**
- Poetic Unreason and Other Studies. London: 1925. Dustwrapper. *(Georges)* **£60 [≃$115]**
- Poetic Unreason. London: 1925. Covers slightly marked and spotted, foredges slightly foxed. *(Clearwater)* **£40 [≃$76]**
- Proceed, Sergeant Lamb. New York: Random House, (1941). 1st (American) edition. Dustwrapper (small chips). *(Houle)* **$85 [≃£44]**
- Seven Days in New Crete. London: 1949. Dustwrapper (trifle creased and nicked). *(Words Etcetera)* **£30 [≃$57]**
- The Shout. London: Elkin Mathews, Woburn Books, 1929. One of 530 signed. Spine and cover edges slightly browned. Dustwrapper (edges slightly browned, small chips from corners and spine extremities). *(Virgo)* **£180 [≃$345]**
- Steps. London: 1958. Proof copy. *(Buckley)* **£100 [≃$191]**
- Ten Poems More. Paris: Hours Press, 1930. One of 200 signed. Original transparent paper jacket. *(Woolmer)* **$250 [≃£130]**
- Ten Poems More. Paris: Hours Press, 1930. One of 200 signed by the author. Endpapers and half-title very slightly foxed. Morocco backed pictorial boards (spine extremities rubbed, backstrip darkened to black). *(Heritage)* **$450 [≃£234]**
- To Whom Else? Deya, Majorca: The Seizin Press, 1931. One of 200 signed. Tissue wrapper adhering to the boards as is usual, bottom of rear endpaper stuck to inside cover. *(Woolmer)* **$250 [≃£130]**
- To Whom Else? Majorca: Seizin Press, 1931. One of 200 signed. Canvas backed decorated boards. *(Words Etcetera)* **£285 [≃$547]**
- To Whom Else? Seizin Press: 1931. One of 200 signed. Light wear, slight soiling. *(Dermont)* **$375 [≃£195]**
- Watch the Northwind Rise. New York: Creative Age, 1949. 1st edition. Dustwrapper (spine ends worn). *(Antic Hay)* **$35 [≃£18]**
- Watch the Northwind Rise. New York: Creative Age Press, 1949. Dustwrapper (edges chipped). Signed by the author. *(Heritage)* **$150 [≃£78]**

- Whipperginny. London: Heinemann, 1923. Mottled boards (spine strip little worn and dull). *(Whiteson)* **£35 [≃$67]**

Gray, Alasdair

- The Fall of Kelvin Walker. Edinburgh: Canongate, 1985. Dustwrapper. *(First Issues)* **£10 [≃$19]**
- Lanark. Edinburgh: Canongate, 1985. The 'definitive' edition. One of 1000, signed. Dustwrapper. *(Dyke)* **£35 [≃$67]**
- Lanark. New York: 1985. Dustwrapper. *(Polyanthos)* **$30 [≃£15]**
- Lean Tales. With James Kelman and Agnes Owens. London: Cape, 1985. Dustwrapper. Signed by Gray and Kelman. *(David Rees)* **£25 [≃$47]**
- McGrotty and Ludmilla. 1990. Wrappers. Signed by the author. *(David Rees)* **£15 [≃$28]**
- 1982 Janine. London: Cape, 1984. Price-clipped dustwrapper. *(David Rees)* **£6 [≃$11]**
- Old Negatives. London: Cape, 1989. One of 500, numbered dated and signed by the author. Errata sheet. Dustwrapper. *(David Rees)* **£25 [≃$47]**
- Old Negatives. London: Cape, 1989. One of 500 signed. Dustwrapper. *(Michael Johnson)* **£20 [≃$38]**
- Something Leather. Cape, 1990. Uncorrected proof copy. Wrappers (slightly rubbed). *(David Rees)* **£25 [≃$47]**
- Unlikely Stories Mostly. Canongate: 1983. Erratum slip. Dustwrapper. Signed by the author. *(David Rees)* **£65 [≃$124]**
- Unlikely Stories, Mostly. 1983. Dustwrapper. *(Egret)* **£60 [≃$115]**

Green, Henry

- Back. London: 1946. Dustwrapper (chipped, slightly rubbed, slightly tanned, head of spine internally repaired). *(Ellis)* **£45 [≃$86]**
- Back. London: Hogarth Press, 1946. Slightly worn. *(Sklaroff)* **£15 [≃$28]**
- Back. London: Hogarth Press, 1946. Paper darkening. Dustwrapper (some minor wear at edges, slight soiling). *(Woolmer)* **$85 [≃£44]**
- Back. New York: Viking, 1950. 1st US edition. Dustwrapper (little worn). *(Whiteson)* **£30 [≃$57]**
- Blindness. London: Dent, 1926. Some fading at spine ends, small split at head and slight wear at foot. Corners slightly worn. Dustwrapper (worn, lacking pieces from spine and top back panel, repaired internally with paper). *(Virgo)* **£650 [≃$1,247]**
- Doting. London: Hogarth Press, 1952. *(Sklaroff)* **£15 [≃$28]**
- Nothing. London: Hogarth Press, 1950. *(Sklaroff)* **£15 [≃$28]**
- Nothing. London: 1950. Dustwrapper (head of spine chipped). *(Buckley)* **£25 [≃$47]**
- Nothing. London: 1950. Inscription. Dustwrapper (slightly rubbed, spine tanned). *(Ellis)* **£40 [≃$76]**
- Nothing. New York: Viking Press, 1950. Dustwrapper (slightly worn and repaired). *(Sklaroff)* **£15 [≃$28]**
- Nothing. New York: Viking, 1950. 1st US edition. Dustwrapper (slightly chipped). *(Whiteson)* **£45 [≃$86]**

Greene, Graham

- The Basement Room and Other Stories. London: 1935. Spine a little dull. *(Words Etcetera)* **£200 [≃$383]**
- Brighton Rock. London: 1938. Paper browning a little. Slight signs of damp at edges. *(Blakeney)* **£150 [≃$287]**
- Brighton Rock. London: Heinemann, 1938. Covers a little soiled, some browning of pages and endpapers. Spine ends slightly worn. *(Virgo)* **£195 [≃$374]**
- Brighton Rock. London: Heinemann, 1938. Variant binding in dull mauvish cloth (slight wear to edges). *(Whiteson)* **£135 [≃$259]**
- British Dramatists. London: Collins, 1942. Dustwrapper. *(Nouveau)* **$85 [≃£44]**
- British Dramatists. London: Britain in Pictures, 1942. Some shelfwear. Dustwrapper (a bit worn). *(Pettler & Liebermann)* **$55 [≃£28]**
- British Dramatists. London: Britain in Pictures Series, 1942. Dustwrapper. *(Roberts)* **£7.50 [≃$15]**
- A Burnt-Out Case. London: 1961. Uncorrected proof copy. Slight foxing. Wrappers (slightly stained, very slightly rubbed). *(Ellis)* **£150 [≃$287]**
- A Burnt-Out Case. London: Heinemann, (1961). Inscription. Dustwrapper. *(Lopez)* **$50 [≃£26]**
- A Burnt-Out Case. London: Heinemann, 1961. 1st British edition. Price-clipped dustwrapper. *(Ash)* **£50 [≃$95]**
- A Burnt-Out Case. London: Heinemann, 1961. Dustwrapper. *(Lewton)* **£15 [≃$28]**
- The Comedians. New York: Viking Press, Christmas, 1965. One of 500 specially bound for presentation in advance of publication. Green buckram, lettered in gilt on spine on two black panels. *(Georges)* **£200 [≃$383]**

- The Complaisant Lover. New York: Viking, 1961. 1st US edition. Price-clipped dustwrapper (lightly rubbed). *(Nouveau)* **$35 [≃£18]**
- The Confidential Agent. London: 1939. Pages a little spotted, late ownership inscription on front free endpaper. Boards just a little marked. *(Blakeney)* **£200 [≃$383]**
- The Confidential Agent. London: 1939. Corners of upper cover slightly bumped, slightly rubbed and tanned. *(Ellis)* **£180 [≃$345]**
- The Confidential Agent. New York: Viking, 1939. 1st American edition ('September 1939'). Dustwrapper (few nicks). *(Houle)* **$225 [≃£117]**
- Doctor Fischer of Geneva or the Bomb Party. London: Bodley Head, 1980. Dustwrapper. *(Nouveau)* **$25 [≃£13]**
- The End of the Affair. London: Heinemann, 1951. Proof copy. Printed wrappers (slightly cocked, a few notes on lower panel). *(David Rees)* **£175 [≃$335]**
- The End of the Affair. London: Heinemann, [1951]. Price-clipped dustwrapper. *(Chapel Hill)* **$125 [≃£65]**
- The End of the Affair. London: Heinemann, 1951. Dustwrapper (slightly browned and nicked). *(Ash)* **£40 [≃$76]**
- The End of the Affair. New York: Viking, 1951. 1st American edition. Small abraded area on front cover. Dustwrapper (minor edgewear, very small chip foot of spine). *(Chapel Hill)* **$65 [≃£33]**
- England Made Me. London: 1935. Bookseller's sticker partially removed from pastedown. Foredge a little spotted. Boards a little marked, spine slightly faded. *(Blakeney)* **£135 [≃$259]**
- England Made Me. New York: Doubleday, 1935. 1st American edition. Small stamp on endpaper. Short tear to preliminary page. *(First Issues)* **£85 [≃$163]**
- (Contributes) The Gamesters. [In] Public School Verse An Anthology 1921-1922. Edited by Martin Gilkes, Richard Hughes, P.H.B. Lyon. London: 1923. Spine slightly sunned. *(First Issues)* **£65 [≃$124]**
- Getting to Know the General. Toronto: Dennys, 1984. Dustwrapper. *(Sklaroff)* **£18 [≃$34]**
- Getting to Know the General. London: Bodley Head, 1984. Dustwrapper. *(Sklaroff)* **£15 [≃$28]**
- Graham Greene On Film. Collected Film Criticism 1935-1940. New York: 1972. Dustwrapper (top of spine minimally rubbed). *(Polyanthos)* **$30 [≃£15]**
- A Gun for Sale. London: 1936. Label removed from front endpaper. Traces of erasure on half-title. Spine a little faded. *(Blakeney)* **£225 [≃$431]**
- The Heart of the Matter. New York: Viking, 1948. 1st American edition. Dustwrapper. *(Chapel Hill)* **$125 [≃£65]**
- The Honorary Consul. London: Bodley Head, 1973. Dustwrapper. *(Marlborough B'shop)* **£20 [≃$38]**
- How Father Quixote Became a Monsignor. Sylvester & Orphanos: 1980. One of 300 signed. Glassine dustwrapper. *(David Rees)* **£200 [≃$383]**
- How Father Quixote Became a Monsignor. Los Angeles: Sylvester & Orphanos, 1980. One of 330 signed. Acetate dustwrapper. *(Houle)* **$225 [≃£117]**
- The Human Factor. London: Bodley Head, 1978. 1st issue. Dustwrapper. *(Sklaroff)* **£45 [≃$86]**
- In Search of a Character. London: 1961. Uncorrected proof copy. Wrappers (edges very slightly spotted). Dustwrapper (rubbed, frayed). *(Ellis)* **£150 [≃$287]**
- In Search of a Character. London: Bodley Head, 1961. Dustwrapper. *(Dyke)* **£15 [≃$28]**
- In Search of a Character. London: 1961. Dustwrapper. *(Ellis)* **£30 [≃$57]**
- In Search of a Character. London: Bodley Head, 1961. Dustwrapper. *(Ash)* **£30 [≃$57]**
- The Lawless Road. London: Longmans, Green, 1939. Covers and edges rubbed. Front endpaper slightly foxed. Corners slightly knocked. *(Virgo)* **£180 [≃$345]**
- The Little Horse Bus. London: 1952. Binding dull and slightly worn. *(Whiteson)* **£50 [≃$95]**
- Lord Rochester's Monkey. London: Bodley Head, 1974. Publisher's slip inserted. Price-clipped dustwrapper. *(David Rees)* **£20 [≃$38]**
- Loser Takes All. London: Heinemann, 1955. proof copy. Printed wrappers. *(David Rees)* **£225 [≃$431]**
- Loser Takes All. London: Heinemann, 1955. *(Sklaroff)* **£15 [≃$28]**
- The Lost Childhood & Other Essays. London: 1951. Foredge spotted. Dustwrapper (slightly spotted). *(Buckley)* **£45 [≃$86]**
- The Lost Childhood and Other Essays. London: 1951. Foredge spotted. One corner bumped. Dustwrapper (slightly spotted,

internal offsetting at spine, spine a little sunned). *(Blakeney)* **£45 [≃$86]**

- The Lost Childhood and Other Essays. London: Eyre & Spottiswoode, 1951. Dustwrapper (lightly rubbed and chipped). *(Glyn's)* **£32 [≃$61]**
- The Lost Childhood. London: 1951. Dustwrapper. *(Words Etcetera)* **£75 [≃$143]**
- The Man Within. London: 1929. *(Georges)* **£250 [≃$479]**
- The Man Within. Garden City: Doubleday Doran, 1929. 1st American edition. Name. 2nd issue dustwrapper, predominantly green with spine blocked in light green boxes (a few small chips & tears). *(Alphabet)* **$500 [≃£260]**
- May We Borrow Your Husband? London: Bodley Head, 1967. One of 500 signed. Tissue and glassine dustwrappers. *(Georges)* **£125 [≃$239]**
- May We Borrow Your Husband? London: Bodley Head, 1967. Dustwrapper. *(Dyke)* **£20 [≃$38]**
- Monsignor Quixote. Canada: Lester & Orpen Dennys, 1982. 1st edition (precedes both English & American editions). Dustwrapper. *(First Issues)* **£35 [≃$67]**
- Monsignor Quixote. London: 1982. Proof copy. Wrappers. *(Words Etcetera)* **£45 [≃$86]**
- Monsignor Quixote. London: Bodley Head, 1982. Dustwrapper. *(Dyke)* **£15 [≃$28]**
- Monsignor Quixote. New York: Simon and Schuster, [1982]. One of 250 signed. Slipcase, shrink-wrap, unopened. *(Antic Hay)* **$125 [≃£65]**
- Monsignor Quixote. New York: 1982. One of 250 signed. Slipcase. *(Words Etcetera)* **£165 [≃$316]**
- The Name of Action. London: 1930. Foxing quite heavy in parts. Puncture mark to upper cover. *(Ellis)* **£250 [≃$479]**
- 19 Stories. New York: Viking, 1949. 1st American edition. Dustwrapper. Signed by the author. *(Lopez)* **$225 [≃£117]**
- (Edits) The Old School. Essays by Divers Hands. London: Cape, (1934). Some light foxing. 1st impression binding (a bit cocked). *(Woolmer)* **$125 [≃£65]**
- Our Man in Havana. London: Heinemann, [1958]. Price-clipped dustwrapper. *(Antic Hay)* **$60 [≃£31]**
- Our Man in Havana. London: Heinemann, 1958. Price-clipped dustwrapper. *(Ash)* **£50 [≃$95]**
- The Potting Shed. New York: Viking, 1957. 1st US edition (precedes UK edition and differs textually in the third act). Dustwrapper. *(Moorhouse)* **£45 [≃$86]**
- The Power and the Glory. London: 1940. Endpapers browned as always, light spotting to prelims. Initials & bookplate. Ring mark on front board, spine a little dusty. *(Blakeney)* **£125 [≃$239]**
- A Quick Look Behind. Los Angeles: Sylvester & Orphanos, 1983. One of 300 (of 330) signed. Slipcase. *(Moorhouse)* **£135 [≃$259]**
- A Quick Look behind. Sylvester & Orphanos: 1983. One of 300 (of 330) signed. Slipcase. *(David Rees)* **£200 [≃$383]**
- A Quick Look Behind. Los Angeles: Sylvester & Orphanos, 1983. One of 300 (of 330) signed. Slipcase. *(Moorhouse)* **£145 [≃$278]**
- The Quiet American. London: Heinemann, (1956). Uncorrected proof copy. Incorrect date on title. Wrappers. *(Lopez)* **$850 [≃£442]**
- The Quiet American. London: Heinemann, 1956. Proof copy. Printed wrappers. *(David Rees)* **£250 [≃$479]**
- The Quiet American. London: 1955. Inscription. Slightly cocked. Dustwrapper (slightly frayed). *(Blakeney)* **£15 [≃$28]**
- The Quiet American. London: 1955. Dustwrapper, wraparound band, fine. *(Words Etcetera)* **£75 [≃$143]**
- Reflections on Travels with My Aunt. Firsts & Company: 1989. One of 250 signed. Painted papers over gold stamped boards. *(Nouveau)* **$125 [≃£65]**
- Reflections on Travels with my Aunt. New York: 1989. One of 250 signed. *(Polyanthos)* **$125 [≃£65]**
- Reflections on Travels with My Aunt. Firsts & Company: 1989. One of 250 signed. Stiff wrappers. *(Moorhouse)* **£85 [≃$163]**
- The Return of A.J. Raffles. London: Bodley Head, 1975. Semi-stiff wrappers. *(Marlborough B'shop)* **£6.50 [≃$13]**
- A Sort of Life. London: Bodley Head, 1971. Dustwrapper. *(Dyke)* **£18 [≃$34]**
- A Sort of Life. London: Bodley Head, [1971]. Price-clipped dustwrapper (very slight rubbing rear panel). *(Chapel Hill)* **$50 [≃£26]**
- A Sort of Life. London: Bodley Head, 1971. Dustwrapper. *(Marlborough B'shop)* **£17.50 [≃$34]**
- (Edits) The Spy's Bedside Book. London: Hart-Davis, 1957. Dustwrapper (slightly chipped and sunned). *(David Rees)* **£20 [≃$38]**

- (Contributes) 'Stepping Stones' and 'Apologia' [in] Oxford Poetry 1923. New York: 1924. 1st American edition. Dustwrapper. *(First Issues)* **£65 [≃$124]**
- The Tenth Man [in] You Magazine (The Mail Sunday Supplement). London: Associated Newspapers Group, 1985. The true 1st edition. Tiny tear to one wrapper. *(Between the Covers)* **$85 [≃£44]**
- The Tenth Man. London: Bodley Head / Blond, 1985. Dustwrapper. *(Sklaroff)* **£12 [≃$23]**
- The Third Man. New York: Viking, 1950. Precedes the English edition. Dustwrapper (faintly spine sunned). *(Chapel Hill)* **$175 [≃£91]**
- The Third Man. New York: Viking Press, 1950. 1st American edition. Corner of title slightly creased. Dustwrapper (slightly worn, spine faded). *(Virgo)* **£75 [≃$143]**
- The Third Man & The Fallen Idol. London: 1950. Dustwrapper (very slightly chipped). *(Whiteson)* **£110 [≃$211]**
- The Third Man. London: Heinemann, 1950. Dustwrapper (slightly worn and chipped). *(David Rees)* **£35 [≃$67]**
- The Third Man & The Fallen Idol. London: Heinemann, 1950. Dustwrapper. *(Lewton)* **£75 [≃$143]**
- The Third Man and The Fallen Idol. London: 1950. Price-clipped dustwrapper. *(Georges)* **£100 [≃$191]**
- 21 Stories. New York: (1962). Names. Dustwrapper (strengthened internally, little edge rubbed). *(Polyanthos)* **$50 [≃£26]**
- The Virtue of Disloyalty. London: Bodley Head, 1972. One of 300. Wrappers, envelope. *(Georges)* **£250 [≃$479]**
- The Virtue of Disloyalty. London: Bodley Head, 1972. One of 300. Wrappers. *(Moorhouse)* **£200 [≃$383]**
- The Virtue of Disloyalty. Privately Printed: 1972. One of 300. Wrappers. *(Whiteson)* **£150 [≃$287]**
- Ways of Escape. Canada: Dennys, 1980. 1st edition (precedes both English & American editions). One of 97 (of 150) signed and bound in cloth, cloth slipcase (very faint spotting). *(First Issues)* **£300 [≃$575]**
- Ways of Escape. Canada: (1980). The correct 1st edition. Dustwrapper. *(Polyanthos)* **$35 [≃£18]**
- Ways of Escape. Toronto: 1980. 1st Canadian edition (the true 1st, precedes UK and US editions). Dustwrapper. *(Pettler & Liebermann)* **$50 [≃£26]**
- Ways of Escape. New York: 1980. Advance uncorrected proof copy. Wrappers (a little dusty). *(Buckley)* **£40 [≃$76]**
- Why the Epigraph. London: Nonesuch, 1989. One of 950 signed. Glassine dustwrapper. *(Lewton)* **£50 [≃$95]**
- Why the Epigraph? London: Nonesuch Press, 1989. One of 950 signed. Glassine dustwrapper. *(Georges)* **£30 [≃$57]**
- Why the Epigraph? Nonesuch Press, 1989. One of 950 signed. *(Paul Brown)* **£45 [≃$86]**

Greer, Germaine

- Daddy, We Hardly Knew You. London: 1989. Dustwrapper. *(Buckley)* **£10 [≃$19]**
- The Female Eunuch. London: MacGibbon & Kee, 1970. Dustwrapper. *(Ash)* **£40 [≃$76]**
- The Obstacle Race. London: Secker, 1979. Dustwrapper. *(Paul Brown)* **£12.50 [≃$24]**

Gregory, Dick

- From the Back of the Bus. New York: Dutton, 1962. Photo wrappers. His 1st book. *(Alphabet)* **$40 [≃£20]**

Grieve, C.M.

- See MacDiarmid, Hugh.

Grimes, Martha

- The Anodyne Necklace. Boston: Little Brown, 1983. Dustwrapper (tiny wear at spine ends, worn streak front flap fold). *(Mordida)* **$65 [≃£33]**
- The Old Fox Deceiv'd. Boston: Little Brown, 1982. Dustwrapper. *(Mordida)* **$75 [≃£39]**

Gunn, James E.

- This Fortress World. New York: Gnome Press, [1954]. Dustwrapper. *(Dermont)* **$45 [≃£23]**

Gunn, Thom

- Jack Straw's Castle. London: 1976. Proof copy. *(Buckley)* **£25 [≃$47]**
- Moly. London: Faber, 1971. Dustwrapper (slightly soiled). *(Halsey)* **£10 [≃$19]**
- Selected Poems 1950-1975. New York: 1979. Dustwrapper. Signed by the author. *(Polyanthos)* **$30 [≃£15]**
- Songbook. Albondocani: 1973. One of 200 signed by the author and by the illustrator. Marbled wrappers. *(Nouveau)* **$75 [≃£39]**
- The Spell. London: 1973. Single sheet broadside poem. One of 500. *(First Issues)* **£100 [≃$191]**
- Touch. London: Faber, 1967. Price-clipped dustwrapper. Poetry Book Society Bulletin 54 laid in. *(Nouveau)* **$40 [≃£20]**

- Touch. London: 1967. Dustwrapper. *(Egret)* **£20 [≃$38]**

Gurganus, Alan

- Oldest Living Confederate Widow Tells All. New York: Knopf, 1989. Dustwrapper. Signed by the author. *(Lopez)* **$65 [≃£33]**
- Oldest Living Confederate Widow Tells All. New York: Knopf, 1989. Dustwrapper. Signed by the author. *(Michael Johnson)* **£35 [≃$67]**
- Oldest Living Confederate Widow Tells All. New York: Knopf, 1989. Dustwrapper. *(Michael Johnson)* **£25 [≃$47]**

Gysin, Brion

- To Master, A Long Goodnight. New York: Creative Age, [1946]. Dustwrapper (very slightly used). His 1st book. *(Dermont)* **$75 [≃£39]**

Haley, Alex

- Roots. Garden City: Doubleday, 1976. One of 500 signed by the author. Spine extremities rubbed. Slipcase. *(Heritage)* **$275 [≃£143]**
- Roots. New York: Doubleday, 1976. Price-clipped dustwrapper. Signed by the author. *(Nouveau)* **$50 [≃£26]**

Hall, Radclyffe

- The Well of Loneliness. US: 1928. 1st US edition. One of 500. Spine faded. Slipcase (rubbed, splitting). *(Ellis)* **£80 [≃$153]**
- The Well of Loneliness. New York: Covici-Friede, 1928. 1st American edition. 1st "authorized" edition. One of 500. Partly unopened. Plain white translucent dustwrapper. *(Houle)* **$375 [≃£195]**
- The Well of Loneliness. New York: Covivi-Friede, 1929. Victory Edition. One of 225 signed. 2 vols. Partly unopened. Slipcase. *(Houle)* **$600 [≃£312]**

Halsman, Philippe

- Jump Book. New York: 1959. Price-clipped dustwrapper (a bit chipped). *(Pettler & Liebermann)* **$60 [≃£31]**

Hamady, Walter

- Seeds & Chairs. Perishable Press: 1979. One of 200. Wrappers. Dustwrapper. *(Between the Covers)* **$50 [≃£26]**

Hamilton, Patrick

- The Duke in Darkness. A Play in Three Acts. London: Constable, 1943. Wrappers chipped and worn at joints. *(Moorhouse)* **£20 [≃$38]**

Hammett, Dashiell

- The Big Knockover. Edited by Lillian Hellman. New York: Random House, 1966. Price-clipped dustwrapper. *(Dyke)* **£50 [≃$95]**
- The Big Knockover. New York: Random House, [1966]. Dustwrapper (tiny interior repair). *(Antic Hay)* **$75 [≃£39]**
- The Maltese Falcon. New York: Knopf, 1930. *(Houle)* **$950 [≃£494]**
- A Man Named Thin. New York: Ferman Mercury, 1962. *(Janus)* **$75 [≃£39]**
- A Man Named Thin. New York: Joseph W. Ferman, 1962. Wrappers. *(Mordida)* **$85 [≃£44]**
- The Novels. New York: Knopf, 1965. Omnibus edition. Dustwrapper. *(Mordida)* **$45 [≃£23]**
- Red Harvest. London: 1929. 1st US edition. Spine ends snagged. *(Ellis)* **£120 [≃$230]**
- "The Thin Man" in Redbook: December 1933. Some chipping to rear cover. *(Janus)* **$100 [≃£52]**
- The Thin Man. New York: Knopf, 1934. The green covers have the usual blotchy fading, the red and blue colours are bright. Trace of foxing on foredge. Green dustwrapper (spine ends chipped, spine slightly faded, several short closed tears, some wear to front fold). *(Mordida)* **$500 [≃£260]**

Hamnett, Nina

- Laughing Torso. London: 1932. Label removed from half-title. Top edge a little bumped. Dustwrapper (a little frayed at extremities, one or two short tears, some internal strengthening). *(Blakeney)* **£125 [≃$239]**

Hamsun, Knut

- The Ring is Closed. New York: Coward-McCann, 1937. Dustwrapper (small chip and light edge wear at spine top). *(Alphabet)* **$75 [≃£39]**

Hanley, Gerald

- The Year of the Lion. London: 1953. Dustwrapper. *(Edrich)* **£20 [≃$38]**

Hanley, James

- Between the Tides. London: Methuen, 1939. Cover edges slightly faded. Endpapers and edges tanned and spotted. Dustwrapper (torn with loss). *(Hazeldene)* **£40 [≃$76]**
- Crilley and Other Stories. London: 1945. Dustwrapper (soiled). *(Edrich)* **£18 [≃$34]**

Hannah, Barry

- Airships. New York: 1978. Dustwrapper. *(Pettler & Liebermann)* **$60 [≃£31]**
- Boomerang. Ultramarine: 1989. One of 40 signed. Half leather. *(Nouveau)* **$175 [≃£91]**
- Geronimo Rex. New York: Viking, (1972). Small sticker removal mark front pastedown. Dustwrapper. Signed by the author. His 1st book. *(Lopez)* **$150 [≃£78]**
- Geronimo Rex. New York: Viking, (1972). Dustwrapper. *(Lopez)* **$100 [≃£52]**
- Nightwatchmen. New York: 1973. Dustwrapper. *(Pettler & Liebermann)* **$45 [≃£23]**

Hardwick, Elizabeth

- The Simple Truth. New York: Harcourt, Brace, [1955]. Advance reading copy. Spine faded, title in pencil. *(Antic Hay)* **$75 [≃£39]**
- The Simple Truth. New York: Harcourt, Brace, [1955]. Two dustwrappers (both with some wear, few tears outer jacket). *(Antic Hay)* **$65 [≃£33]**

Harris, Max

- The Vegetative Eye. Melbourne: Reed & Harris, 1943. Dustwrapper by Sidney Nolan (a few nicks). *(Any Amount)* **£45 [≃$86]**

Harris, Thomas

- Black Sunday. New York: Putnam, 1975. Dustwrapper. *(Michael Johnson)* **£75 [≃$143]**
- Red Dragon. New York: Putnam, 1981. No remainder mark. Dustwrapper. *(Michael Johnson)* **£36 [≃$69]**
- Red Dragon. London: Bodley Head, 1982. 1st British edition. Dustwrapper. *(Michael Johnson)* **£20 [≃$38]**
- Silence of the Lambs. New York: St Martins, 1988. Dustwrapper. *(Michael Johnson)* **£20 [≃$38]**

Harris, Timothy

- Kronski / McSmash. London: Michael Joseph, 1969. Dustwrapper. His 1st book. *(Any Amount)* **£30 [≃$57]**

Harris, Wilson

- The Eye of the Scarecrow. London: 1965. Dustwrapper (small stain lower panel). *(Ellis)* **£45 [≃$86]**

Harrison, Jim (James)

- Letters to Yesenin. Fremont: Sumac, (1973). One of 1000 in wrappers (slightly rubbed). *(Lopez)* **$150 [≃£78]**
- Locations. New York: 1968. Dustwrapper. *(Pettler & Liebermann)* **$75 [≃£39]**
- Locations. New York: Norton, (1968). Dustwrapper (spine slightly darkened). *(Woolmer)* **$75 [≃£39]**
- Locations. New York: Norton, (1968). Dustwrapper. *(Lopez)* **$125 [≃£65]**
- Plain Song. New York: Norton, (1965). Dustwrapper (very slight wear spine ends). His 1st book. *(Woolmer)* **$115 [≃£59]**
- Wolf. New York: S&S, (1971). Dustwrapper. Inscribed by the author (January, 1972). *(Lopez)* **$125 [≃£65]**
- Wolf. New York: Simon, 1971. Short light line bottom edge. Dustwrapper. Signed by the author. *(Nouveau)* **$60 [≃£31]**
- The Woman Lit by Fireflies. Boston: HM / Seymour Lawrence, 1988. One of 225 signed. Slipcase. *(Lopez)* **$100 [≃£52]**

Harrison, Tony

- Anno Forty Two. Scargill Press: 1987. One of 350. Wrappers. Signed by the author. *(Moorhouse)* **£20 [≃$38]**
- Earthwork. Leeds: Northern House Pamphlet Press, 1964. Wrappers slightly sunned at edges. His 1st book. *(Blakeney)* **£65 [≃$124]**
- Earthworks. By T.W. Harrison. Leeds: Northern House Pamphlets, 1964. Wrappers (small mark on front wrapper). His 1st book. *(Moorhouse)* **£65 [≃$124]**
- Earthworks. Northern House Pamphlet Poets, 1964. Wrappers. His 1st book. *(Any Amount)* **£30 [≃$57]**
- Earthworks. Northern House Pamphlets: 1964. Wrappers. His 1st publication. *(Egret)* **£75 [≃$143]**
- (Contributes to) The Lesser Known Shag. Newcastle: Ultima Thule Bookshop, [ca 1969]. Edited by Tony Jackson & Tom Pickard. Roneoed sheets stapled in decorated card wrappers, slightly dusty and worn at base of spine. *(Blakeney)* **£65 [≃$124]**
- The Loiners. London: 1970. Dustwrapper. *(Egret)* **£75 [≃$143]**
- The Loiners. London: London Magazine Editions, 1970. Dustwrapper (slightly rubbed and worn at extremities). *(Moorhouse)* **£45 [≃$86]**
- Palladas. Anvil Press: 1975. The clothbound issue. Dustwrapper (slightly browned and soiled). *(Moorhouse)* **£35 [≃$67]**
- Ten Sonnets from The School of Eloquence. Anvil Press Poetry: 1987. One of 250 signed. Wrappers. *(Words Etcetera)* **£35 [≃$67]**

Hartley, L.P.

- Eustace & Hilda. London: 1947. Dustwrapper (slightly rubbed). *(Buckley)* **£25 [≃$47]**
- Facial Justice. London: 1960. Dustwrapper. *(Buckley)* **£20 [≃$38]**
- The Hireling. London: 1957. Dustwrapper. *(Words Etcetera)* **£12.50 [≃$24]**
- The Hireling. London: Hamish Hamilton, 1957. Dustwrapper. *(Ash)* **£25 [≃$47]**
- A Perfect Woman. London: 1955. Little shaken. Name on fly. Dustwrapper (trifle nicked). *(Words Etcetera)* **£10 [≃$19]**
- Simonetta Perkins. London: 1925. Some edges slightly rubbed. *(Clearwater)* **£55 [≃$105]**
- The Travelling Grave. London: James Barrie, 1951. Dustwrapper (slightly nicked). *(Moorhouse)* **£25 [≃$47]**

Hartley, Marsden

- Twenty Five Poems. Paris: Contact Press, 1923. Wrappers (a little dust soiled on upper wrapper, couple of small nicks to either side of spine). *(Words Etcetera)* **£185 [≃$355]**
- Twenty-Five Poems. Paris: Contact Editions, (1923). Glassine sleeve (a few nicks and chips). Signed by the author. *(Lopez)* **$1,350 [≃£703]**

Hartnett, Michael

- Anatomy of a Cliche. Dolmen Press: 1968. Wrappers. *(Blakeney)* **£45 [≃$86]**

Hasford, Gustav

- The Short-Timers. New York: 1979. Price-clipped dustwrapper. Author's inscription. His 1st book. *(Pettler & Liebermann)* **$75 [≃£39]**

Hawkes, John

- Second Skin. New Directions: (1964). One of 100 signed. Slipcase. *(Woolmer)* **$150 [≃£78]**

Hazzard, Shirley

- The Evening of the Holiday. London: 1966. Dustwrapper (very slightly rubbed). *(Clearwater)* **£25 [≃$47]**

Heaney, Seamus

- After Summer. Massachusetts & Dublin: 1978. One of 250 signed. Dustwrapper (light ring mark on front panel, spine slightly faded). *(Blakeney)* **£75 [≃$143]**
- Agenda. Seamus Heaney Fiftieth Birthday Issue. Spring, 1989. One of 50 signed. Slipcase. *(Dermont)* **$125 [≃£65]**
- Agenda. Special Issue, Spring, 1989. One of 50 signed. Wrappers. Slipcase. *(Words Etcetera)* **£60 [≃$115]**
- Among Schoolchildren. Belfast: 1983. Wrappers. *(Dyke)* **£15 [≃$28]**
- Among Schoolchildren. Belfast: 1983. One of 1000. Blue wrappers. *(David Rees)* **£12 [≃$23]**
- Among Schoolchildren. Malone Memorial Committee: 1983. One of 1000. Wrappers. *(Buckley)* **£20 [≃$38]**
- Death of a Naturalist. London: 1966. Dustwrapper (very slightly frayed). *(Edrich)* **£180 [≃$345]**
- Death of a Naturalist. London: 1969. 1st paperback edition. *(Buckley)* **£7 [≃$13]**
- Door into the Dark. New York: Oxford, 1969. 1st American edition. Reportedly only 300 copies printed. Dustwrapper (couple of 1/4 inch tears). *(Alphabet)* **$150 [≃£78]**
- Door Into the Dark. London: 1972. 1st paper issue. Wrappers. Signed by the author. *(Edrich)* **£16 [≃$30]**
- Eleven Poems. Belfast: (1965). 1st issue, with device in purple. Wrappers. His 1st book. Author's signed inscription dated 1965. *(Edrich)* **£600 [≃$1,151]**
- Eleven Poems. Belfast: Festival Publications, [1965]. 1st issue. Wrappers. His 1st book. *(Moorhouse)* **£450 [≃$863]**
- Field Work. London: Faber, 1979. Dustwrapper. Signed by the author. *(Any Amount)* **£45 [≃$86]**
- Field Work. London: 1979. Dustwrapper. *(Edrich)* **£25 [≃$47]**
- Field Work. US: 1979. 1st US edition. proof copy. Wrappers. *(Any Amount)* **£60 [≃$115]**
- The Fire Gaze. Cheltenham: Friends of Cheltenham Festival, 1989. Poster. *(Words Etcetera)* **£10 [≃$19]**
- The Fire i' the Flint. British Academy Lecture, 1975. Wrappers. *(Dyke)* **£20 [≃$38]**
- From the Republic of Conscience. Dublin: 1985. Wrappers. *(Dyke)* **£15 [≃$28]**
- From the Republic of Conscience. Dublin: 1985. One of 2000. Wrappers. *(David Rees)* **£12 [≃$23]**
- The Government of the Tongue. London: 1988. Dustwrapper. *(Buckley)* **£10 [≃$19]**
- Hailstones. 1984. One of 500 (of 750) in wrappers. *(Edrich)* **£25 [≃$47]**
- The Haw Lantern. London: Faber, 1987. Uncorrected proof copy. Wrappers. *(Moorhouse)* **£50 [≃$95]**
- The Haw Lantern. New York: 1987. One of 250 signed. Slipcase.

(Words Etcetera) **£85 [≃$163]**

- The Haw Lantern. New York: 1987. One of 250 signed. Slipcase. *(First Issues)* **£100 [≃$191]**
- Hedge School. Vermont: Janus Press, 1979. Wrappers. *(Words Etcetera)* **£285 [≃$547]**
- (Contributor to) Hill Field; Poems and Memoirs for John Montague on his Sixtieth Birthday. Minneapolis: 1989. One of 26 specially bound. Canvas backed marbled paper boards. *(Words Etcetera)* **£125 [≃$239]**
- Land. London: Poem of the Month Club, 1971. Broadside. Signed by Heaney. Very slightly creased. *(Blakeney)* **£35 [≃$67]**
- Land. Poem of the Month Club. Signed by the author. *(Whiteson)* **£25 [≃$47]**
- Land. Poem of the Month: 1971. Single sheet, signed. *(Edrich)* **£30 [≃$57]**
- The Makings of a Music. Liverpool, 1978. Wrappers. *(Dyke)* **£15 [≃$28]**
- The Makings of a Music. Liverpool: 1978. Wrappers. *(David Rees)* **£12 [≃$23]**
- An Open Letter. Field Day Pamphlet No 2, 1983. *(Edrich)* **£25 [≃$47]**
- A Personal Selection. Belfast: 1982. Wrappers. *(Dyke)* **£10 [≃$19]**
- Place and Displacement. Dove Cottage: 1984. Wrappers. *(Egret)* **£25 [≃$47]**
- Place and Displacement. Dove Cottage, 1984. Wrappers. *(Dyke)* **£15 [≃$28]**
- Poem Posters. The Four Elements. By Seamus Heaney, Jenny Joseph, Laurie Lee, Lawrence Sail. Cheltenham Festival: 1989. One of 125 signed by the four authors. Posters laid inside folder. *(Egret)* **£90 [≃$172]**
- Poem Posters. The Four Elements. By Seamus Heaney, Jenny Joseph, Laurie Lee, Lawrence Sail. Cheltenham Festival: 1989. Trade edition (unsigned, without folder). *(Egret)* **£12 [≃$23]**
- Poems 1965-1975. New York: FSG, [1980]. Uncorrected proof copy. Printed wrappers. *(Dermont)* **$100 [≃£52]**
- Poems and Memoir. New York: Limited Editions Club, 1982. One of 2000 signed. Calf gilt. Boxed. *(Polyanthos)* **$250 [≃£130]**
- (Contributes to) Poems for Shakespeare. London: Globe Playhouse Publications, 1978. One of 500 numbered. Wrappers. Signed by Sam Wanamaker. *(Moorhouse)* **£15 [≃$28]**
- Preoccupations. New York: FSG, [1980]. 1st American edition. Uncorrected proof copy. Wrappers. *(Dermont)* **$100 [≃£52]**
- Recent Poetry in Northern Ireland. Grasmere: 1985. Wrappers. Dustwrapper. *(Blakeney)* **£12.50 [≃$24]**
- Selected Poems 1965-1975. London: 1980. Dustwrapper. Signed by the author. *(Edrich)* **£32.50 [≃$63]**
- Selected Poems. London: Faber, 1980. Clothbound. dustwrapper. Signed by the author. *(Moorhouse)* **£45 [≃$86]**
- Skoleradioen. Copenhagen: Denmark Radio, 1977. Wrappers. Author's signed presentation copy. *(Polyanthos)* **$55 [≃£28]**
- Station Island. London: Faber, 1984. Dustwrapper. *(Lewton)* **£17.50 [≃$34]**
- Station Island. London: 1984. Dustwrapper. Signed by the author. *(Edrich)* **£30 [≃$57]**
- Station Island. London: 1984. Dustwrapper. *(Edrich)* **£16.50 [≃$32]**
- Station Island. US: 1985. 1st US edition. Proof copy. Wrappers. *(Words Etcetera)* **£45 [≃$86]**
- Sweeney Astray. Derry: 1983. Dustwrapper. Signed by the author. *(Edrich)* **£40 [≃$76]**
- Sweeney Astray. Derry: 1983. Dustwrapper. *(Edrich)* **£30 [≃$57]**
- Sweeney Astray. Field Day, 1983. Card covers. *(Lewton)* **£12.50 [≃$24]**
- Sweeney Astray. New York: Farrar Straus Giroux, 1984. 1st US edition. One of 350 signed. Slipcase. *(Moorhouse)* **£95 [≃$182]**
- Sweeney Astray. A Version from the Irish. New York: 1984. One of 350 signed. Slipcase. *(First Issues)* **£95 [≃$182]**
- Sweeney Astray. New York: 1984. One of 350 signed. Slipcase. *(David Rees)* **£80 [≃$153]**
- The Tree Clock. Belfast: Linen Hall Library, 1990. One of 100 signed. Slipcase. *(Words Etcetera)* **£150 [≃$287]**
- (Contributes to) Twelve to Twelve. Poets Trust: 1970. Wrappers. *(Moorhouse)* **£10 [≃$19]**
- An Upstairs Outlook. By Seamus Heaney and Michael Longley. Belfast: 1989. One of 500. *(First Issues)* **£25 [≃$47]**
- Verses for a Fordham Commencement. New York: Nadja, 1984. One of 12 sets of page proofs signed by the printers. Foldover case. *(Words Etcetera)* **£385 [≃$739]**

Heard, H.F.

- The Notched Hairpin. New York: Vanguard Press, 1949. Dustwrapper. *(Mordida)* **$65 [≃£33]**
- A Taste for Honey. New York: Vanguard, 1941. Dustwrapper (three quarter inch piece missing at top of spine, chipped corners, several short closed tears). *(Mordida)* **$150 [≃£78]**

Heath-Stubbs, John

- Satires and Epigrams. Turret: 1968. One of 200 signed. Dustwrapper. *(Halsey)* **£25.50 [≃$49]**

Hecht, Ben

- Count Bruga. New York: Boni & Liveright, 1926. Scattered darkening along edge of cloth. Dustwrapper (small chips along the edges). *(Antic Hay)* **$75 [≃£39]**

Heinlein, Robert

- Citizen of the Galaxy. New York: Scribner's, (1957). Review slip. Dustwrapper (lightly chipped). *(Bromer)* **$350 [≃£182]**
- The Green Hills of Earth. London: Sidgwick & Jackson, 1954. Dustwrapper (top third of front panel defective). *(Sklaroff)* **£45 [≃$86]**
- The Man Who Sold the Moon. London: 1953. Dustwrapper (very chipped). *(Buckley)* **£20 [≃$38]**
- The Man Who Sold the World. Sydney: [1950s]. Wrappers almost detached at spine. *(Blakeney)* **£65 [≃$124]**
- Methuselah's Children. New York: Gnome Press, [1958]. 1st issue binding. Paper browned as usual. Dustwrapper. Bookplate signed by the author. *(Polyanthos)* **$200 [≃£104]**
- The Puppet Masters. London: Museum Press, 1953. *(Sklaroff)* **£30 [≃$57]**
- Starman Jones. London: 1954. Ink squiggle on fly. Dustwrapper (very slightly rubbed). *(Blakeney)* **£20 [≃$38]**
- Time for the Stars. New York: Scribner, 1956. Dustwrapper. *(Lewton)* **£35 [≃$67]**

Heller, Joseph

- Catch-22. New York: S&S, 1961. Advance reading copy. Small name on front blank. Wrappers. *(Lopez)* **$575 [≃£299]**
- Catch 22. New York: Simon & Schuster, 1961. Name. Dustwrapper (few short tears). His 1st book. *(Alphabet)* **$500 [≃£260]**
- Catch-22. London: Cape, 1962. 1st UK edition. Name on endpaper. Dustwrapper (soiled and rubbed, spine edges worn). *(Virgo)* **£45 [≃$86]**
- God Knows. London: 1984. Proof copy. Wrappers. *(Polyanthos)* **$45 [≃£23]**
- Good as Gold. New York: S&S, (1979). Dustwrapper. Signed by the author. *(Lopez)* **$35 [≃£18]**
- Good as Gold. New York: Simon & Schuster, 1979. Inscription. Dustwrapper (rubbed, closed tears, piece missing from front flap). *(Tiger Books)* **£20 [≃$38]**

Hellman, Lillian

- Scoundrel Time. Boston: Little, Brown, [1976]. Dustwrapper. Signed by the author. *(Antic Hay)* **$85 [≃£44]**

Helprin, Mark

- A Dove of the East. New York: Knopf, 1975. Dustwrapper. Inscribed by the author. His 1st book. *(Lopez)* **$100 [≃£52]**
- Ellis Island and Other Stories. New York: Delacorte, (1981). Dustwrapper. Inscribed by the author (1981). *(Lopez)* **$75 [≃£39]**
- Refiner's Fire. New York: Knopf, 1977. Dustwrapper (one short tear rear upper edge panel). Inscribed by the author. *(Lopez)* **$85 [≃£44]**

Hemingway, Ernest

- Across the River and Into the Trees. London: 1950. Precedes the US edition. Dustwrapper, fine. *(Polyanthos)* **$250 [≃£130]**
- Across the River and into the Trees. London: Cape, 1950. Precedes the American edition. Slight staining to bottom of boards. *(First Issues)* **£20 [≃$38]**
- Across the River and into the Trees. London: Cape, (1950). 1st English edition (precedes the American edition). Dustwrapper (few nicks, spine sunned). *(Houle)* **$150 [≃£78]**
- Across the River and into the Trees. New York: Scribner's, 1950. 1st American edition. 1st issue dustwrapper, with spine lettered in yellow (slight edgewear). *(Chapel Hill)* **$100 [≃£52]**
- Across the River and Into the Trees. New York: 1950. Name and address. 1st issue dustwrapper (a few small edge tears, edge rubbed). *(Polyanthos)* **$45 [≃£23]**
- (Contributes to) The Best Short Stories of 1923. Boston: Small, Maynard, (1924). Name. Couple of small faint spots to cloth. His 1st book appearance. *(Between the Covers)* **$100 [≃£52]**
- Death in the Afternoon. New York: Scribner, (1932). Short inscription on free endpaper. Slight foxing and darkening of page edges. Dustwrapper. *(Lopez)* **$450 [≃£234]**
- A Divine Gesture. (New York): Aloe Editions, 1974. One of 250. Wrappers. *(Woolmer)* **$75 [≃£39]**
- A Farewell to Arms. New York: Scribner's, 1929. One of 510 signed. Half vellum, unopened. Glassine dustwrapper (two pieces missing from top). Slipcase (lightly worn). *(Chapel Hill)* **$5,000 [≃£2,604]**
- A Farewell to Arms. New York: Scribner, 1929. 1st issue, without legal disclaimer. 1st

issue dustwrapper, with name mispelt "Katharine Barclay" on front flyleaf, (small chip, slight rubbing). *(Houle)* **$750 [≃£390]**

- A Farewell to Arms. New York: Scribner's, 1929. 1st state, without the notice that "none of the characters in this book is a living person". *(Chapel Hill)* **$75 [≃£39]**
- A Farewell to Arms. New York: Scribner, 1929. 1st issue. Name. Spine label cracked. Dustwrapper (rubbed, small chips and tears). *(Alphabet)* **$300 [≃£156]**
- A Farewell to Arms. New York: Scribners, 1929. 2nd printing, with legal disclaimer on page x. Dustwrapper (two 2-inch tears at base of upper panel with some creasing). *(First Issues)* **£150 [≃$287]**
- A Farewell to Arms. New York: Scribners, 1929. Dustwrapper (tiny lateral stain at bottom of spine, slightly rubbed). *(Alphabet)* **$950 [≃£494]**
- Fiesta. London: Cape, 1927. 1st English edition (published in America as The Sun Also Rises). Backstrip and gilt lettering faded, sides slightly faded. *(Limestone Hills)* **$125 [≃£65]**
- For Whom the Bell Tolls. New York: 1940. 1st issue. Usual slight discolouration to endpapers. Dustwrapper (rather chipped). *(King)* **$100 [≃£52]**
- For Whom the Bell Tolls. New York: 1940. Spine little sunned. 1st state dustwrapper (a few tiny edge nicks, edges a little rubbed). *(Polyanthos)* **$200 [≃£104]**
- For Whom the Bell Tolls. New York: Scribners, 1940. 2nd issue dustwrapper (usual darkening). *(Nouveau)* **$100 [≃£52]**
- For Whom the Bell Tolls. New York: Scribner, 1940. Later printing. Dustwrapper (spine extremities chipped). Signed by the author. *(Lopez)* **$1,750 [≃£911]**
- For Whom the Bell Tolls. London: 1941. Dustwrapper (slightly nicked). *(Sclanders)* **£120 [≃$230]**
- The Garden of Eden. New York: Scribner's, 1986. Dustwrapper. *(Antic Hay)* **$25 [≃£13]**
- Hokum. Wellesley Hills: Sans Souci Press, (1978). One of 200 (of 273), this copy unnumbered and marked for review. Dustwrapper. Slipcase. *(Between the Covers)* **$150 [≃£78]**
- In Our Time. New York: Boni & Liveright, 1925. Bookplate. Some wear to spine ends, spine faded. *(Woolmer)* **$150 [≃£78]**
- Islands in the Stream. Collins, 1970. Dustwrapper. *(Paul Brown)* **£10 [≃$19]**
- (Introduces) Kiki's Memoirs. Paris: Black Manikin Press, 1930. 20 illustrations by Kiki (Alice Prin). Paper wrappers, wraparound band, portrait pasted on front cover. *(First Issues)* **£200 [≃$383]**
- (Edits) Men at War; the Best War Stories of all Time. New York: 1942. Dustwrapper (strengthened around flaps). *(Words Etcetera)* **£125 [≃$239]**
- Men Without Women. New York: Scribner's, 1927. *(Chapel Hill)* **$85 [≃£44]**
- A Moveable Feast. New York: Scribner's, [1964]. Price-clipped dustwrapper (tiny rubbed spot). *(Antic Hay)* **$50 [≃£26]**
- A Moveable Feast. London: Cape, 1964. Dustwrapper. *(Paul Brown)* **£20 [≃$38]**
- A Moveable Feast. London: Cape, 1964. 1st English edition. Price-clipped dustwrapper, fine. *(Nouveau)* **$65 [≃£33]**
- The Nick Adams Stories. New York: 1972. Dustwrapper. *(Pettler & Liebermann)* **$60 [≃£31]**
- The Old Man and the Sea. Advance galley proofs for its appearance in Life magazine, September 1, 1952. 16 long galley sheets, folded, lightly aged. With a copy of the issue of Life as published. 1st printing of the novel in any form. *(Chapel Hill)* **$500 [≃£318]**
- The Old Man and the Sea. New York: Scribners, 1952. Price-clipped dustwrapper. *(First Issues)* **£95 [≃$182]**
- The Old Man and the Sea. New York: 1952. Dustwrapper (tiny edge nick rear panel). *(Polyanthos)* **$150 [≃£78]**
- The Old Man and the Sea. New York: Scribners, 1952. Dustwrapper. *(First Issues)* **£75 [≃$143]**
- The Spanish Earth. Cleveland: J.B. Savage, 1938. One of 1000. 2nd issue, with excerpt from Hemingway's telegram printed on back pastedown. *(Bromer)* **$250 [≃£130]**
- The Spanish War. Fact Monograph No 16: July 1938. Wrappers (faded name on upper wrapper). *(Patterson)* **£60 [≃$115]**
- The Sun also Rises. New York: 1926. 1st issue. Spine extremities minimally rubbed, spine label slightly darkened. *(Polyanthos)* **$300 [≃£156]**
- The Sun Also Rises. New York: Scribner's, 1926. 1st state, with "stoppped" on p 181, line 26. Small red mark on bottom edge. *(Chapel Hill)* **$350 [≃£182]**
- To Have & Have Not. New York: Scribners, 1937. Two clippings pasted in, one clumsily removed. Dustwrapper (slight edge wear). *(Alphabet)* **$350 [≃£182]**
- To Have and Have Not. New York: 1937. Dustwrapper (tiny tear), fine. *(Polyanthos)* **$500 [≃£260]**

- To Have and Have Not. New York: Scribners, 1937. Very slightly dull. *(Whiteson)* **£70 [≃$134]**
- Winner Take Nothing. New York: Scribner, 1933. 1st edition ('A'). 1st issue dustwrapper, with quote from Stallings' review of "Death in the Afternoon" on lower wrapper, (small chip to top of spine). *(Houle)* **$550 [≃£286]**
- Winner Take Nothing. New York: Scribners, 1933. 1st American edition. *(First Issues)* **£75 [≃$143]**
- Winner Takes Nothing. New York: 1933. Name and date. 1st issue dustwrapper (very chipped). *(Pettler & Liebermann)* **$75 [≃£39]**
- Winner Take Nothing. New York: Scribner's, 1933. Ring stain on front cover. *(Chapel Hill)* **$75 [≃£39]**

Herbert, Frank

- Dune. London: Gollancz, 1966. Edges tanned. Dustwrapper (slightly rubbed). Nebula Award wraparound band (slightly damaged). *(Hazeldene)* **£45 [≃$86]**

Herbert, James

- The Spear. NEL: 1978. Dustwrapper. *(Lewton)* **£16 [≃$30]**

Herlihy, James Leo

- Midnight Cowboy. New York: 1965. Spine extremities minimally rubbed. Dustwrapper. Author's signed presentation copy. *(Polyanthos)* **$50 [≃£26]**
- The Sleep of Baby Filbertson and Other Stories. New York: 1959. Author's signed presentation copy. His 1st book. *(Polyanthos)* **$40 [≃£20]**

Herr, Michael

- Dispatches. New York: 1977. Dustwrapper. His 1st book. *(Pettler & Liebermann)* **$90 [≃£46]**

Herriot, James

- Vets Might Fly. London: Michael Joseph, 1976. Dustwrapper. Author's presentation copy. *(Limestone Hills)* **$70 [≃£36]**

Hesse, Herman

- Demian. Translated by W.J. Strachan. London: Peter Owen / Vision Press, [1958]. 1st English edition. Dustwrapper (light edge wear, few tiny tears). *(Dermont)* **$50 [≃£26]**
- Goldmund. London: Peter Owen / Vision Press, [1958]. 1st English edition. Some soiling to boards. 2nd impression dustwrapper (lightly used). *(Dermont)* **$50 [≃£26]**
- Pater Camenzind. London: Peter Owen / Vision Press, [1961]. 1st English edition. Dustwrapper (lightly used). *(Dermont)* **$50 [≃£26]**
- The Prodigy. London: Peter Owen / Vision Press, [1961]. 1st English edition. Dustwrapper (lightly used). *(Dermont)* **$50 [≃£26]**

Heyer, Georgette

- Detection Unlimited. London: Heinemann, 1953. Edges lightly foxed. Dustwrapper (spine slightly darkened). *(Mordida)* **$65 [≃£33]**
- No Wind of Blame. Garden City: Doubleday Crime Club, 1939. 1st American edition. Bookplate. Dustwrapper (spine slightly faded and worn at foot). *(Mordida)* **$55 [≃£28]**

Higgins, Adrian

- Langrishe, Go Down. London: Calder & Boyars, 1966. Edges slightly marked. Dustwrapper (rubbed). *(Hazeldene)* **£35 [≃$67]**

Higgins, George V.

- The Digger's Game. New York: Knopf, 1973. 1st US edition. Dustwrapper. *(Moorhouse)* **£25 [≃$47]**
- The Friends of Eddie Coyle. New York: Knopf, 1972. 1st US edition. Price-clipped dustwrapper. His 1st book. *(Moorhouse)* **£35 [≃$67]**
- The Friends of Eddie Coyle. New York: Knopf, 1972. 1st US edition. Price-clipped dustwrapper (slightly nicked). His 1st book. *(Moorhouse)* **£20 [≃$38]**

Highsmith, Patricia

- Deep Water. New York: Harper, 1957. 1st edition. Dustwrapper (couple of tiny tears, spine slightly darkened). *(Mordida)* **$75 [≃£39]**
- A Dog's Ransom. London: Heinemann, 1972. 1st English edition. Review slip. Dustwrapper (faintly offset onto spine). *(Limestone Hills)* **$45 [≃£23]**
- Edith's Diary. London: Heinemann, 1977. 1st English edition. Review slip. Dustwrapper. *(Limestone Hills)* **$50 [≃£26]**
- A Game for the Living. London: 1954. Slightly bumped. Dustwrapper (slightly chipped). *(McCann)* **£32 [≃$61]**
- The Glass Cell. London: Heinemann, 1965. 1st English edition. Review slip. Dustwrapper. *(Limestone Hills)* **$75 [≃£39]**
- Ripley Underground. London: 1971. Dustwrapper. *(First Issues)* **£20 [≃$38]**

- Strangers on a Train. London: 1950. 1st English edition. Dustwrapper (spine faintly faded). *(Words Etcetera)* **£330 [≃$633]**
- A Suspension of Mercy. London: 1965. Uncorrected proof copy. Spine creased. *(McCann)* **£40 [≃$76]**
- The Talented Mr Ripley. London: 1957. Dustwrapper. *(Words Etcetera)* **£100 [≃$191]**
- Tales of Natural and Unnatural Catastrophes. London: 1987. Dustwrapper. Signed by the author. *(First Issues)* **£20 [≃$38]**

Hijuelos, Oscar

- Our House in the Last World. New York: Persea, (1983). Dustwrapper. *(Between the Covers)* **$65 [≃£33]**

Hill, Geoffrey

- King Log. London: 1968. Dustwrapper (tiny nick). *(Egret)* **£60 [≃$115]**
- King Log. London: 1968. The casebound issue. Dustwrapper (spine slightly faded). *(Blakeney)* **£65 [≃$124]**
- The Lords of Limit. London: 1984. Dustwrapper. *(Buckley)* **£25 [≃$47]**
- The Mystery of the Charity of Charles Peguy. London: 1983. Wrappers. *(Egret)* **£12 [≃$23]**
- The Mystery of the Charity of Charles Peguy. Agenda Editions & Deutsch: 1983. Trade edition. Wrappers. Signed by the author and dated on title. *(Moorhouse)* **£30 [≃$57]**
- Preghiere. Northern House Pamphlets, University of Leeds: 1964. Wrappers. *(Egret)* **£45 [≃$86]**
- Preghiere. Northern House: 1964. Wrappers (slightly marked). *(Halsey)* **£25 [≃$47]**
- Tenebrae. London: 1978. Dustwrapper. *(Egret)* **£15 [≃$28]**
- Tenebrae. London: Deutsch, 1978. Dustwrapper. *(Ash)* **£25 [≃$47]**

Hill, Reginald

- Another Death in Venice. London: Collins, 1976. Dustwrapper. *(Janus)* **$45 [≃£23]**

Hill, Susan

- The Bird of Night. London: Hamilton, 1972. Dustwrapper. *(Lewton)* **£17.50 [≃$34]**
- The Bird of Night. London: Hamilton, 1972. Dustwrapper. *(Ash)* **£25 [≃$47]**
- A Bit of Singing and Dancing. London: 1973. Small stain on foredge. Dustwrapper (very slightly rubbed). *(Ellis)* **£20 [≃$38]**
- The Custodian. Covent Garden Press, 1972. One of 600. Wrappers. *(Any Amount)* **£20 [≃$38]**
- The Custodian. London: 1972. One of 100 signed by the author. Wrappers. *(Ellis)* **£35 [≃$67]**
- I'm the King of the Castle. London: Hamilton, 1970. Dustwrapper (one very tiny tear). *(Virgo)* **£35 [≃$67]**
- In the Springtime of the Year. London: Hamilton, 1974. Dustwrapper. Wraparound band. *(Ash)* **£25 [≃$47]**
- In the Springtime of the Year. London: 1974. Dustwrapper. *(Ellis)* **£20 [≃$38]**
- The Woman in Black. London: Hamilton, 1983. Dustwrapper. Signed by the author. *(Lewton)* **£17.50 [≃$34]**

Hillerman, Tony

- Dance Hall of the Dead. London: Pluto, 1985. 1st English edition. Dustwrapper. Signed by the author. *(Limestone Hills)* **$135 [≃£70]**
- Dance Hall of the Dead. London: Pluto Press, 1985. 1st English edition. Dustwrapper. Signed by the author. *(Mordida)* **$125 [≃£65]**
- The Dark Wind. New York: 1982. Dustwrapper. *(Pettler & Liebermann)* **$75 [≃£39]**
- The Dark Wind. New York: Harper & Row, 1982. Dustwrapper. Signed by the author. *(Mordida)* **$65 [≃£33]**
- The Dark Wind. New York: Harper & Row, 1982. Dustwrapper. *(Mordida)* **$50 [≃£26]**
- The Dark Wind. New York: Harper, 1982. Minor bump. Dustwrapper. Signed by the author. *(Janus)* **$50 [≃£26]**
- The Ghostway. New York: Harper & Row, 1985. 1st trade edition. Dustwrapper. *(Mordida)* **$60 [≃£31]**
- The Great Taos Bank Robbery. Albuquerque: University of New Mexico, 1973. The state with grayish yellow cloth-covered boards and white endpapers. Orangish yellow dustwrapper with blue lettering and two illustrations on back panel. Price-clipped dustwrapper (internal tape mend). *(Mordida)* **$250 [≃£130]**
- Indian Country. Flagstaff: Northland, 1987. 1st hardbound printing. Faint rippling first few pages. Dustwrapper. *(Janus)* **$150 [≃£78]**
- Listening Woman. New York: Harper & Row, 1978. Dustwrapper (couple of crease tears, several short closed tears, couple of tiny nicks base of spine). *(Mordida)* **$100 [≃£52]**

- People of Darkness. New York: Harper & Row, 1980. Uncorrected proof copy. Wrappers. *(Mordida)* **$375 [≃£195]**
- Rio Grande. Photography by Robert Reynolds. Portland: Charles H. Belding, 1975. Dustwrapper (crease on inner front panel). *(Mordida)* **$150 [≃£78]**
- Skinwalkers. New York: Harper & Row, 1986. Dustwrapper. Signed by the author. *(Mordida)* **$35 [≃£18]**
- Skinwalkers. New York: Harper, 1986. Dustwrapper. Signed by the author. *(Janus)* **$45 [≃£23]**
- Talking God. New York: Harper & Row, 1989. One of 300 signed. Slipcase. No dustwrapper issued. *(Mordida)* **$75 [≃£39]**
- A Thief of Time. New York: Harper & Row, 1988. Advance reading copy. Wrappers. *(Mordida)* **$40 [≃£20]**
- A Thief of Time. New York: Harper & Row, 1988. Uncorrected proof copy. Printed wrappers (small label removed from front cover). Signed by the author. *(Mordida)* **$100 [≃£52]**
- A Thief of Time. New York: Harper & Row, 1988. One of 250 signed. Slipcase. No dustwrapper issued. *(Mordida)* **$100 [≃£52]**

Himes, Chester

- The Heat's On. New York: Putnam, (1966). Dustwrapper (nicks). *(Houle)* **$45 [≃£23]**
- The Heat's On. New York: Putnam, 1966. Dustwrapper. *(Janus)* **$45 [≃£23]**
- The Heat's On. New York: Putnam, 1966. Dustwrapper (tiny wear at spine ends). *(Mordida)* **$45 [≃£23]**
- Lonely Crusade. New York: 1947. Price-clipped dustwrapper. *(Pettler & Liebermann)* **$110 [≃£57]**
- Run Man Run. New York: Putnam, 1966. Dustwrapper. *(Mordida)* **$45 [≃£23]**

Hoban, Russell

- The Lion of Boaz-Jachin and Jachin-Boaz. London: Cape, 1973. Uncorrected proof copy. Wrappers. *(David Rees)* **£30 [≃$57]**
- Turtle Diary. London: 1975. Price-clipped dustwrapper. *(Ellis)* **£35 [≃$67]**

Hochhuth, Rolf

- Soldiers. London: 1968. Dustwrapper. Author's inscription. *(Words Etcetera)* **£35 [≃$67]**

Hodgson, William Hope

- Deep Waters. Sauk City: Arkham House, 1967. Dustwrapper. *(Georges)* **£25 [≃$47]**
- The House on the Borderland and Other Novels. Sauk City: Arkham House, 1946. Dustwrapper (extremities slightly rubbed). *(Dyke)* **£150 [≃$287]**

Hoffman, Abbie

- More Than You Ever Wanted to Know About Nuclear Waste Transports. New York: 1982. Wrappers. Signed by the author as Barry Freed. *(Polyanthos)* **$35 [≃£18]**
- Square Dancing in the Ice Age. New York: (1982). Remainder stamp. Dustwrapper. Signed by the author. *(Polyanthos)* **$35 [≃£18]**

Holdstock, Robert

- Eye Among the Blind. London: Faber, 1976. Dustwrapper. Signed by the author. *(Michael Johnson)* **£20 [≃$38]**
- Eye Among the Blind. London: Faber, 1976. Dustwrapper. *(David Rees)* **£5 [≃$9]**
- Eye among the Blind. London: 1976. Dustwrapper. Signed by the author. *(Ellis)* **£25 [≃$47]**
- Mythago Wood. London: Gollancz, 1984. Dustwrapper. *(Michael Johnson)* **£36 [≃$69]**

Hollinghurst, Alan

- Confidential Chats with Boys. Sycamore: 1982. Wrappers. *(Halsey)* **£5 [≃$9]**
- Isherwood is at Santa Barbara. Sycamore Broadsheet 22, 1975. *(Halsey)* **£5.50 [≃$11]**
- The Swimming-Pool Library. London: Chatto & Windus, 1988. Uncorrected proof copy. Wrappers. *(David Rees)* **£15 [≃$28]**

Holmes, H.H.

- Pseudonym used by Anthony Boucher, q.v.

Holmes, John Clellon

- The Horn. New York: 1958. Dustwrapper. *(Pettler & Liebermann)* **$65 [≃£33]**
- The Horn. London: Deutsch, 1959. *(Glyn's)* **£17.50 [≃$34]**

Hopley, George

- See Woolrich, Cornell.

Horovitz, Michael

- The Wolverhampton Wanderer. Latimer: 1971. One of 100 signed by the author & artists. Dustwrapper. *(Any Amount)* **£125 [≃$239]**

Household, Geoffrey

- A Time to Kill. Boston: Little, Brown, [1951]. 1st American edition (precedes the

English edition). Corner of a few pages bumped and paper clip mark. Dustwrapper (small nick). *(Antic Hay)* **$27.50 [≃£14]**

Housman, A.E.

- Last Poems. London: Grant Richards, 1922. Dustwrapper (slightly nicked and dusty). *(Words Etcetera)* **£35 [≃$67]**
- The Name and Nature of Poetry. Cambridge: UP, 1933. Slight internal marking. No dustwrapper issued. *(Hazeldene)* **£15 [≃$28]**

Howard, Brian

- God Save the King and Other Poems. Paris: Hours Press, [1931]. One of 150 signed (this copy unnumbered). Leather spine extremities slightly rubbed, tips of corners slightly chafed, some edges of boards faintly darkened. *(Clearwater)* **£200 [≃$383]**

Howard, Richard

- The Damages. Wesleyan UP: (1967). Dustwrapper. *(Woolmer)* **$45 [≃£23]**
- Quantities. Wesleyan UP: (1962). Early copy with the $1.45 price on rear cover. Wrappers (edges a bit darkened). His 1st book (preceded by a translation). *(Woolmer)* **$85 [≃£44]**

Howard, Robert

- Echoes from an Iron Harp. Grant: [1972]. Dustwrapper. *(Dermont)* **$60 [≃£31]**
- The Marchers of Valhalla. Grant: 1972. Dustwrapper. *(Dermont)* **$50 [≃£26]**
- Singers in the Shadows. Grant: 1970. Dustwrapper. *(Dermont)* **$100 [≃£52]**

Hubbard, L. Ron

- Death's Deputy. Los Angeles: Fantasy Publishing Co, 1948. 1st issue binding. Covers lacquered or shellaced. Dustwrapper. *(Alphabet)* **$110 [≃£57]**
- Dianetics. New York: 1950. Spine lightly sunned, extremities slightly rubbed. Dustwrapper (internally edge strengthened, few small closed tears, spine little sunned, top little chipped, lower spine half-inch missing). *(Polyanthos)* **$150 [≃£78]**

Hudson, Stephen

- The Other Side. London: 1937. 1st English edition. Dustwrapper. *(Words Etcetera)* **£28 [≃$53]**
- Tony. London: 1924. 1st English edition. Dustwrapper. *(Words Etcetera)* **£28 [≃$53]**

Hughes, Dorothy B.

- The Bamboo Blonde. New York: Duell, 1941. Dustwrapper (minor chipping spine ends). *(Janus)* **$250 [≃£130]**
- The Blackbirder. New York: Duell, 1943. Dustwrapper (spine lightly sunned). *(Janus)* **$100 [≃£52]**
- The Candy Kid. New York: Duell, 1950. Dustwrapper. *(Janus)* **$35 [≃£18]**
- The Cross-Eyed Bear. New York: Duell, 1940. Dustwrapper (internally reinforced). Signed by the author. *(Janus)* **$250 [≃£130]**
- The Davidian Report. New York: Duell; Boston: Little, 1952. Dustwrapper. Signed by the author. *(Janus)* **$50 [≃£26]**
- The Delicate Ape. New York: Duell, 1944. Leaned. Dustwrapper (internally reinforced). Author's inscription. *(Janus)* **$50 [≃£26]**
- Dread Journey. New York: Duell, 1945. Dustwrapper. *(Janus)* **$35 [≃£18]**
- The Expendable Man. New York: Random, 1963. Dustwrapper. *(Janus)* **$25 [≃£13]**
- The Fallen Sparrow. New York: Duell, 1942. Dustwrapper (chipped, internally repaired). Author's inscription. *(Janus)* **$100 [≃£52]**
- In a Lonely Place. New York: Duell, 1947. Dustwrapper (chipped). Author's inscription. *(Janus)* **$20 [≃£10]**
- Johnnie. New York: Duell, 1944. Price-clipped dustwrapper (chipped). *(Janus)* **$20 [≃£10]**
- Ride the Pink Horse. New York: Duell, 1946. Pages browned. Dustwrapper. *(Janus)* **$65 [≃£33]**
- The So Blue Marble. New York: Duell, 1940. Dustwrapper (very slight wear). Signed by the author. Her 1st book. *(Janus)* **$750 [≃£390]**

Hughes, Langston

- The Langston Hughes Reader. New York: Braziller, 1958. Dustwrapper (minor rubbing). *(Antic Hay)* **$75 [≃£39]**

Hughes, Richard

- The Fox in the Attic. London: Chatto & Windus, 1961. Dustwrapper (internally strengthened). *(Sklaroff)* **£16 [≃$30]**
- A High Wind in Jamaica. London: Chatto & Windus, 1929. Dustwrapper (slightly foxed and creased). *(Ash)* **£40 [≃$76]**
- The Wooden Shepherdess. London: Chatto & Windus, 1973. Dustwrapper. Wraparound band. *(Sklaroff)* **£25 [≃$47]**

Hughes, Ted

- Adam & the Sacred Nine. Rainbow Press: 1979. One of 200. Signed by the author. Calf. Slipcase. *(Buckley)* **£100 [≃$191]**

- Adam and the Sacred Nine. London: Rainbow Press, (1978). One of 200 signed. Calf. Slipcase. *(Houle)* **$250 [≃£130]**
- The Burning of the Brothel. Turret: 1966. One of 300. Dustwrapper. *(Lewton)* **£47.50 [≃$92]**
- Chiasmadon. Janus Press for Charles Seluzicki, 1977. One of 120 signed by the author and artist, Claire Van Vliet. Wrappers (small stain on upper wrapper). *(Words Etcetera)* **£45 [≃$86]**
- The Coming of the Kings. London: Faber, 1970. Endpapers slightly tanned. Dustwrapper. Signed by the author. *(Hazeldene)* **£50 [≃$95]**
- Crow. London: 1970. Dustwrapper. *(Buckley)* **£25 [≃$47]**
- Crow. London: 1970. Dustwrapper. Author's inscription. *(Buckley)* **£40 [≃$76]**
- Crow: From the Life and Songs of the Crow. London: 1973. One of 400 signed. Slipcase. *(Buckley)* **£110 [≃$211]**
- Crow: From the Life and Songs of the Crow. London: Faber, (1973). 1st edition thus. One of 400 signed by Hughes and Baskin, the illustrator. Calf. Slipcase. *(Houle)* **$195 [≃£101]**
- The Earth Owl and other Moon-People. London: Faber, 1963. Edges and endpapers spotted. Dustwrapper. *(Hazeldene)* **£50 [≃$95]**
- Earth-Moon. London: Rainbow Press, (1976). One of 226 signed. Slipcase. *(Houle)* **$175 [≃£91]**
- Eat Crow. London: Rainbow Press, 1971. One of 150 signed. Leather. Slipcase. *(Houle)* **$250 [≃£130]**
- Ffangs the Vampire Bat and the Kiss of Truth. London: 1986. Dustwrapper. *(Words Etcetera)* **£10 [≃$19]**
- Five Autumn Songs for Children's Voices. Devon: Gilbertson, 1968. One of 150 (of 500) signed and numbered. Pink wrappers. *(Moorhouse)* **£45 [≃$86]**
- Five Autumn Songs for Children's Voices. Gilbertson: 1968. One of 150 signed. Wrappers. *(Lewton)* **£55 [≃$105]**
- Five Autumn Songs. London: 1968. One of 500. Wrappers. *(Buckley)* **£25 [≃$47]**
- Flowers and Insects. London: 1986. Dustwrapper. Signed by the author. *(Egret)* **£25 [≃$47]**
- Fly Inspects. Morrigu Press, 1983. One of 75 signed. Wrappers. *(Words Etcetera)* **£65 [≃$124]**
- Fly Inspects. Morrigu Press, 1983. One of 75 signed. Wrappers. *(Georges)* **£40 [≃$76]**
- Gaudete. London: 1977. Dustwrapper. Signed by the author. *(Buckley)* **£30 [≃$57]**
- Gaudete. London: Faber, 1977. Dustwrapper. *(Lewton)* **£17.50 [≃$34]**
- The Hawk in the Rain. London: Faber, 1957. Dustwrapper (soiled and faded, torn and internally repaired, lacking small chips from spine ends). His 1st book. *(Virgo)* **£95 [≃$182]**
- The Hawk in the Rain. London: 1957. Spine faded, one corner slightly bruised. Dustwrapper (slightly rubbed, one small nick, spine slightly faded). His 1st book. *(Ellis)* **£120 [≃$230]**
- The Hawk in the Rain. London: 1957. Dustwrapper. *(Buckley)* **£100 [≃$191]**
- The Hawk in the Rain. London: 1957. Slightly faded and foxed. *(Buckley)* **£30 [≃$57]**
- The Hawk in the Rain. London: Faber, 1957. One corner slightly bumped. Dustwrapper (small piece 1 x 1/2 inches missing from back panel). His 1st book. *(Virgo)* **£100 [≃$191]**
- Henry Williamson. Rainbow Press: 1979. One of 125. Signed by the author. Handmade paper covers. *(Buckley)* **£75 [≃$143]**
- Henry Williamson. Rainbow Press: 1979. One of 200 signed. Wrappers. *(Words Etcetera)* **£50 [≃$95]**
- How the Whale Became. London: 1963. Signature crossed out on endpaper. Price-clipped dustwrapper. Signed by the author. *(Egret)* **£40 [≃$76]**
- How the Whale Became. US: 1964. Dustwrapper. *(Buckley)* **£20 [≃$38]**
- The Iron Giant. New York: Harper, 1986. Dustwrapper. *(Words Etcetera)* **£15 [≃$28]**
- The Iron Man. London: Faber, 1971. Illustrated by George Adamson. Wrappers. Signed by the author. *(Hazeldene)* **£25 [≃$47]**
- The Iron Man. Penguin, 1973. Illustrated by Colin Smithson. Text differs from 1971. Wrappers. *(Hazeldene)* **£15 [≃$28]**
- Mice are Funny Little Creatures. Morrigu Press: 1983. One of 75 signed. Wrappers. *(Words Etcetera)* **£50 [≃$95]**
- Mice are Funny Little Creatures. Morrigu Press: 1983. One of 75 signed. Wrappers. *(Georges)* **£40 [≃$76]**
- Moon-Bells and Other Poems. London: Chatto & Windus, 1978. Coloured pictorial boards. *(Limestone Hills)* **$35 [≃£18]**
- Moortown Elegies. London: Rainbow Press, (1978). One of 143 (of 175) vellum bound

signed by Hughes. Vellum. Slipcase. *(Houle)* **$275 [≃£143]**

- Moortown. London: Faber, 1979. Dustwrapper. *(Lewton)* **£12.50 [≃$23]**
- Moortown. London: 1979. Dustwrapper. *(Buckley)* **£20 [≃$38]**
- New Selected Poems. New York: 1982. Uncorrected proof. Printed wrappers. *(Blakeney)* **£10 [≃$19]**
- (Adapts) Oedipus by Sophocles. London: Faber, 1969. Dustwrapper. *(Virgo)* **£35 [≃$67]**
- Orpheus; a Play. Chicago: Dramatic Publishing Co, 1973. Wrappers. *(Words Etcetera)* **£25 [≃$47]**
- Orts. London: Rainbow Press, 1978. One of 200 signed. Calf. Slipcase. *(Houle)* **$225 [≃£117]**
- Orts. Rainbow Press: 1978. One of 200 signed. Calf. Slipcase. *(Buckley)* **£100 [≃$191]**
- Poems by Ted Hughes, Ruth Fainlight & Alan Sillitoe. Rainbow Press: 1971. One of 300. Signed by the authors. Leather. Leather slipcase. *(Buckley)* **£70 [≃$134]**
- (Contributes to) Poetry from Cambridge, 1952-54. Edited by Karl Miller. Oxford: Fantasy Press, 1955. Wrappers. Dustwrapper (slightly sunned). Signed by Hughes. His 1st appearance in book form. *(Egret)* **£95 [≃$182]**
- Poetry in the Making. London: Faber, 1967. No dustwrapper issued. *(Hazeldene)* **£30 [≃$57]**
- Prometheus on his Crag. London: Rainbow Press, (1973). One of 160 signed by Hughes, and by Baskin, the illustrator, on the frontispiece in pencil. Morocco. Slipcase. *(Houle)* **$275 [≃£143]**
- Remains of Elmet. London: Rainbow Press, 1979. One of 70 (of 180) bound in calf signed by Hughes and Fay Godwin. Calf. Slipcase. *(Houle)* **$350 [≃£182]**
- River. London: 1983. Dustwrapper. *(Buckley)* **£15 [≃$28]**
- River: Poems. London: 1983. dustwrapper. Signed by the author. *(Words Etcetera)* **£35 [≃$67]**
- River. New Poems. New York: Harper & Row, [1984]. 1st American edition. Review slip, card, and photo laid in. Dustwrapper. *(Dermont)* **$25 [≃£13]**
- Scapegoats & Rabies. Poet & Printer: 1967. Wrappers. *(Lewton)* **£25 [≃$47]**
- Scapegoats and Rabies. London: 1967. Wrappers. *(Blakeney)* **£10 [≃$19]**
- Season Songs. New York: 1975. Dustwrapper. Signed by the author. *(Buckley)* **£30 [≃$57]**
- Season Songs. London: 1976. Dustwrapper. *(Buckley)* **£12 [≃$23]**
- Season Songs. London: Faber, 1976. Dustwrapper. *(Limestone Hills)* **$30 [≃£15]**
- A Solstice. Sceptre Press: 1978. One of 350. Yellow wrappers. *(First Issues)* **£25 [≃$47]**
- A Solstice. Sceptre Press: 1978. One of 350. Wrappers. Signed by the author and dated. *(Buckley)* **£40 [≃$76]**
- Spring Summer Autumn Winter. London: Rainbow Press, (1973). One of 140 signed. Acetate dustwrapper. Slipcase. *(Houle)* **$325 [≃£169]**
- Spring Summer Autumn Winter. Rainbow Press: 1973. One of 140 signed. Cork slipcase. *(Hazeldene)* **£250 [≃$479]**
- Sunstruck. Sceptre Press: 1977. One of 100 signed. Wrappers. *(Egret)* **£70 [≃$134]**
- Under the North Star. Illustrated by Leonard Baskin. 1981. Dustwrapper. Author's presentation copy. *(Words Etcetera)* **£40 [≃$76]**
- Weasels at Work. Morrigu Press: 1983. One of 75 signed. Wrappers. *(Words Etcetera)* **£50 [≃$95]**
- Weasels at Work. Morrigu Press: 1983. One of 75 signed. Wrappers. *(Georges)* **£40 [≃$76]**
- What is the Truth? London: 1984. Dustwrapper. *(Buckley)* **£10 [≃$19]**
- Wodwo. London: 1967. Dustwrapper (slightly worn and stained). *(Buckley)* **£25 [≃$47]**
- Wolfwatching. London: 1989. Uncorrected proof copy. Wrappers. *(Ellis)* **£45 [≃$86]**
- Wolf-Watching. Morrigu Press, 1982. One of 75 signed. Wrappers. *(Georges)* **£40 [≃$76]**

Hulme, Keri

- The Bone People. London: Hodder & Stoughton, 1985. 1st issue, printed in Singapore. Dustwrapper. *(Lewton)* **£17.50 [≃$34]**

Humphries, Barry

- Bizarre. London: Elek, 1965. Dustwrapper. *(Any Amount)* **£25 [≃$47]**

Hutson, Shaun

- Breeding Ground. London: Allen, 1985. Dustwrapper. Signed by the author. *(Paul Brown)* **£17.50 [≃$34]**
- Relics. London: Allen, 1986. Dustwrapper.

Signed by the author.
(*Paul Brown*) **£15 [≃$28]**

- Victims. London: Allen, 1987. Dustwrapper. Signed by the author. (*Paul Brown*) **£15 [≃$28]**

Huxley, Aldous

- After Many a Summer Dies the Swan. New York & London: Harper, 1939. Occasional foxing. Edges rubbed, slight soiling. Author's presentation. (*Heritage*) **$300 [≃£156]**
- After Many a Summer. London: 1939. Dustwrapper (repaired). (*Roberts*) **£12.50 [≃$24]**
- Antic Hay. London: 1923. Spine label discoloured. (*Roberts*) **£18 [≃$34]**
- Apennine. Gaylordsville: The Slide Mountain Press, 1930. One of 91 signed by the author. Several small nicks and scuff marks, edges and corners rubbed. (*Heritage*) **$400 [≃£208]**
- Arabia Infelix and Other Poems. New York: Fountain Press, 1929. One of 692. Glassine dustwrapper (little torn, piece missing from top of spine). Signed by the author. (*Polyanthos*) **$100 [≃£52]**
- The Art of Seeing. New York: 1942. (*Polyanthos*) **$25 [≃£13]**
- Beyond the Mexique Bay. London: Chatto & Windus, 1934. One of 210 signed. Acetate dustwrapper. (*Black Sun*) **$375 [≃£195]**
- Brave New World. London: 1932. Slight crease in spine. (*Roberts*) **£40 [≃$76]**
- Brave New World. New York: Doubleday, 1932. 1st US trade edition. Spine faded. (*Sklaroff*) **£40 [≃$76]**
- Brave New World Revisited. London: Chatto & Windus, 1959. 1st English edition. Dustwrapper. (*Limestone Hills*) **$50 [≃£26]**
- Brief Candles. New York: 1930. One of 842 signed. Two corners bumped, rubbed. (*King*) **$85 [≃£44]**
- Brief Candles. New York: The Fountain Press; London: Chatto & Windus, 1930. Extremities slightly rubbed. Signed by the author. (*Heritage*) **$125 [≃£65]**
- The Burning Wheel. Oxford: 1916. Wrappers, printed label, fine. Quarter morocco box. His 1st book. (*Black Sun*) **$850 [≃£442]**
- The Cicadas & Other Poems. London: 1931. Signed limited edition. Buckram backed boards, t.e.g., edges very slightly dull. (*Whiteson*) **£60 [≃$115]**
- The Cicadas and Other Poems. London: Chatto & Windus, 1931. Dustwrapper (chipped & faded). (*Bromer*) **$50 [≃£26]**
- The Cicadas. London: 1931. Dustwrapper (top edge very chipped, spine sunned). (*Buckley*) **£20 [≃$38]**
- The Devils of Loudon. London: 1952. Dustwrapper (repaired). (*Roberts*) **£12.50 [≃$24]**
- The Doors of Perception. London: 1954. Dustwrapper (very slightly nicked). (*Buckley*) **£15 [≃$28]**
- The Doors of Perception. London: Chatto, 1954. Dustwrapper (edge chipped). (*Paul Brown*) **£20 [≃$38]**
- (Edits) An Encyclopaedia of Pacificism. London: Chatto & Windus, Peace Pledge Union, 1937. Printed wrappers. (*Limestone Hills*) **$40 [≃£20]**
- Essays New and Old. London: Chatto & Windus at the Florence Press, 1926. One of 650 signed by the author. Dustwrapper (faded, edges torn and chipped, two large chips at spine and back panel). (*Heritage*) **$250 [≃£130]**
- Eyeless in Gaza. London: 1936. One of 200 signed by the author. Corners slightly rubbed. (*Ellis*) **£150 [≃$287]**
- Eyeless in Gaza. London: Chatto & Windus, 1936. (*Sklaroff*) **£16 [≃$30]**
- The Genius & The Goddess. London: 1955. Dustwrapper (slightly rubbed, two small closed tears). (*Buckley*) **£15 [≃$28]**
- The Genius and the Goddess. London: Chatto, 1955. Dustwrapper. (*Paul Brown*) **£15 [≃$28]**
- Leda. London: Chatto & Windus, 1920. One of 160 signed. Cloth backed boards (slightly soiled). Prospectus for "The Young Visiters" laid-in. (*Bromer*) **$300 [≃£156]**
- Leda. London: 1922. One of 160 signed. Cloth backed boards (slightly rubbed and marked). Spare label. (*First Issues*) **£225 [≃$431]**
- Limbo. London: Chatto & Windus, 1920. A little external wear. (*Glyn's*) **£30 [≃$57]**
- Literature and Science. London: Chatto, 1963. Dustwrapper. (*Paul Brown*) **£12.50 [≃$24]**
- Little Mexican & Other Stories. London: Chatto & Windus, 1924. Covers lightly spotted. Dustwrapper. (*Limestone Hills*) **$85 [≃£44]**
- Music at Night. London: 1931. Dustwrapper (spine sunned). (*Buckley*) **£25 [≃$47]**
- The Olive Tree. London: 1936. (*Roberts*) **£25 [≃$47]**
- The Perennial Philosophy. London: 1946. Dustwrapper (chipped). (*Roberts*) **£15 [≃$28]**

- Point Counter Point. London: 1928. Black cloth. *(First Issues)* **£20 [≈$38]**
- Rotunda. London: Chatto & Windus, 1932. *(Sklaroff)* **£18 [≈$34]**
- Selected Poems. Oxford: Blackwell, 1925. Uncut. Tiny chip top of spine. No dustwrapper issued. *(Polyanthos)* **$50 [≈£26]**
- Those Barren Leaves. London: 1925. Dustwrapper. *(Black Sun)* **$75 [≈£39]**
- Vulgarity in Literature. London: Chatto & Windus, 1930. One of 260 signed by the author. Largely unopened. *(Heritage)* **$275 [≈£143]**
- Vulgarity in Literature. London: 1930. Paper covered decorated boards (extremities slightly rubbed). *(Roberts)* **£20 [≈$38]**
- Vulgarity in Literature. London: Chatto & Windus, Dolphin Books, 1930. Dustwrapper. *(Limestone Hills)* **$45 [≈£23]**
- What Are You Going to Do About It? London: 1936. Wrappers. *(Roberts)* **£10 [≈$19]**
- Words and their Meanings. Los Angeles: Zeitlin, (1940). One of 100 signed. Dustwrapper (lightly chipped). *(Bromer)* **$350 [≈£182]**

Iles, Francis

- Malice Aforethought ... see Berkeley, Anthony.

Innes, Michael

- Appleby's End. London: Gollancz, 1945. Dustwrapper. *(Limestone Hills)* **$40 [≈£20]**
- Operation Pax. London: Gollancz, 1951. Endpapers and edges spotted. Dustwrapper (marked, spine faded). *(Hazeldene)* **£30 [≈$57]**
- Silence Observed. London: Gollancz, 1961. Dustwrapper. *(Limestone Hills)* **$35 [≈£18]**
- Silence Observed. London: Gollancz, 1961. Corner bump. Dustwrapper (slightly soiled). *(Janus)* **$35 [≈£18]**
- What Happened at Hazelwood. London: 1946. Dustwrapper (slightly nicked and faded at spine). *(Buckley)* **£50 [≈$95]**

Ionesco, Eugene

- Present Past Past Present. New York: Grove, (1971). Price-clipped dustwrapper. Author's inscription. *(Between the Covers)* **$75 [≈£39]**

Irving, John

- The Cider House Rules. New York: (1985). One of 795 signed. Acetate dustwrapper. Box. *(Polyanthos)* **$75 [≈£39]**
- The Cider House Rules. PA: Franklin Library, 1985. Limited edition signed. Leather gilt, a.e.g. *(Polyanthos)* **$45 [≈£23]**
- The Cider House Rules. Franklin Center: The Franklin Library, 1985. Signed limited edition (limitation unknown). Leather, a.e.g. Supposedly precedes other editions. *(Antic Hay)* **$60 [≈£31]**
- The Cider House Rules. New York: Morrow, 1985. One of 750 (of 795) signed. Buckram. Slipcase. *(Alphabet)* **$125 [≈£65]**
- The Hotel New Hampshire. New York: 1981. Proof copy. Wrappers (slightly soiled). *(Polyanthos)* **$65 [≈£33]**
- The Hotel New Hampshire. New York: 1981. One of 550 signed. Leather. Box. *(Polyanthos)* **$95 [≈£49]**
- The Hotel New Hampshire. New York: 1981. Dustwrapper. Author's signed presentation copy. *(Polyanthos)* **$60 [≈£31]**
- The Hotel New Hampshire. New York: 1981. Dustwrapper. Signed by the author. *(Polyanthos)* **$45 [≈£23]**
- The Hotel New Hampshire. 1981. 1st American edition. Dustwrapper. *(First Issues)* **£20 [≈$38]**
- How to Spell. New York: International Paper, (1983). Offprint. Single sheet. *(Lopez)* **$65 [≈£33]**
- A Prayer for Owen Meany. New York: (1989). Boxed tape. *(Polyanthos)* **$35 [≈£18]**
- A Prayer for Owen Meany. New York: (1989). Proof copy. Wrappers. *(Polyanthos)* **$45 [≈£23]**
- Setting Free the Bears. New York: Random House, (1968). Dustwrapper. His 1st book. *(Woolmer)* **$275 [≈£143]**
- The Water-Method Man. New York: 1972. Proof copy. Wrappers (spine sunned). *(Polyanthos)* **$150 [≈£78]**
- The Water-Method Man. New York: Random House, 1972. Dustwrapper. *(Nouveau)* **$100 [≈£52]**
- The Water-Method Man. New York: Random House, 1972. Name. Yellow boards a bit stained. Price-clipped dustwrapper. *(Alphabet)* **$85 [≈£44]**
- The World according to Garp. New York: Dutton, (1978). Advance reading copy. printed wrappers, very lightly creased on spine. *(Lopez)* **$100 [≈£52]**
- The World according to Garp. New York: Dutton, (1978). Dustwrapper. Signed by the author. *(Lopez)* **$150 [≈£78]**
- The World According to Garp. New York: Dutton, (1978). Small bump top of rear

board. Price-clipped dustwrapper (tiny slice from same spot as the bump).
(Between the Covers) **$50 [≃£26]**

Isherwood, Christopher

- The Berlin Stories. New Introduction by the Author. New Directions: 1945. Review slip. Dustwrapper (slightly torn). *(Words Etcetera)* **£65 [≃$124]**
- The Berlin Stories. New York: New Directions, 1945. 1st collected edition. Grey cloth. Signed by the author. *(First Issues)* **£125 [≃$239]**
- Christopher and his Kind 1929-1939. London: Eyre Methuen, (1977). 1st English edition. Dustwrapper. *(Lopez)* **$30 [≃£15]**
- The Condor and the Cows. New York: Random House, (1949). Dustwrapper (few nicks). Signed by the author. *(Houle)* **$125 [≃£65]**
- The Condor and the Cows. London: 1949. Inscription. Dustwrapper (chipped, sunned). *(Buckley)* **£25 [≃$47]**
- Down There on a Visit. London: 1962. Dustwrapper (faintly sunned). *(Buckley)* **£25 [≃$47]**
- Down there on a Visit. London: Methuen, 1962. Dustwrapper. *(Dyke)* **£20 [≃$38]**
- Goodbye to Berlin. London: 1939. Slightly dull. *(Whiteson)* **£30 [≃$57]**
- The Last of Mr Norris; a Novel. New York: 1935. 1st American edition of Mr Norris Changes Trains. Dustwrapper (spine ends minutely nicked). *(Words Etcetera)* **£300 [≃$575]**
- Lions & Shadows. London: 1938. Dustwrapper (little dull). *(Whiteson)* **£85 [≃$163]**
- Lions & Shadows. London: 1938. Binding slightly marked. *(Whiteson)* **£30 [≃$57]**
- My Guru and his Disciple. New York: 1980. Dustwrapper. Author's signed presentation copy. *(Polyanthos)* **$75 [≃£39]**
- My Guru and His Disciple. New York: Farrar, Straus & Giroux, [1980]. Dustwrapper. Signed by the author. *(Antic Hay)* **$85 [≃£44]**
- Prater Violet. London: 1946. Dustwrapper (internally strengthened). *(Egret)* **£40 [≃$76]**
- Prater Violet. London: 1946. Dustwrapper (slightly torn). *(Sklaroff)* **£28 [≃$53]**
- (Preface to) Prison Etiquette by the Inmates. Bearville, New York: Retort Press, 1950. Flexible boards. Dustwrapper (some foxing and soiling). *(Between the Covers)* **$175 [≃£91]**
- The World in the Evening. London: 1954. Dustwrapper. *(Georges)* **£35 [≃$67]**
- The World in the Evening. London: 1954. Dustwrapper (chipped). *(Buckley)* **£20 [≃$38]**

Ishiguro, Kazuo

- An Artist of the Floating World. London: Faber, 1986. Uncorrected proof copy. Wrappers. *(Moorhouse)* **£55 [≃$105]**
- An Artist of the Floating World. London: Faber, 1986. Dustwrapper. *(Dyke)* **£18.50 [≃$36]**
- The Remains of the Day. London: Faber, 1989. Dustwrapper. Signed by the author. *(Moorhouse)* **£30 [≃$57]**
- The Remains of the Day. London: Faber, (1989). Dustwrapper. Signed by the author. *(Lopez)* **$125 [≃£65]**
- The Remains of the Day. London: 1989. Dustwrapper. Signed by the author. *(First Issues)* **£30 [≃$57]**
- The Remains of the Day. London: Faber, 1989. Dustwrapper. *(Dyke)* **£15 [≃$28]**
- The Remains of the Day. New York: Knopf, 1989. Uncorrected proof copy. Wrappers. *(Lopez)* **$75 [≃£39]**

Jackson, Shirley

- The Bird's Nest. New York: Farrar, Straus & Giroux, [1954]. Dustwrapper (light soil, tiny tear rear panel). *(Antic Hay)* **$75 [≃£39]**
- Hangsman. New York: (1951). Dustwrapper (lightly edgeworn). *(Between the Covers)* **$85 [≃£44]**
- Raising Demons. New York: FSG, (1957). Couple small spots bottom edge of pages. Dustwrapper (tiny nick foot of spine). *(Between the Covers)* **$60 [≃£31]**
- The Sundial. New York: Farrar, Straus & Giroux, [1958]. Dustwrapper (small tear). *(Antic Hay)* **$60 [≃£31]**

James, Clive

- Brilliant Creatures. London: Cape, 1983. Dustwrapper. *(Moorhouse)* **£5 [≃$9]**
- Visions Before Midnight. London: Cape, 1977. Name on endpaper. Dustwrapper. *(Moorhouse)* **£5 [≃$9]**

James, Edward

- The Bones of my Hand. London: 1938. Dustwrapper (slightly frayed). *(Clearwater)* **£70 [≃$134]**
- The Gardener Who Saw God. London: 1937. *(Words Etcetera)* **£25 [≃$47]**

James, Norah C.

- Sleeveless Errand. Paris: Henry Babou and Jack Kahane, 1929. Spine little sunned, corners little rubbed. Her 1st book. *(Polyanthos)* **$55 [≃£28]**

James, P.D.

- The Black Tower. London: Faber, 1975. Some spots on top edge. Dustwrapper (spine edge and corners rubbed, two short closed tears, scratch and crease back panel). *(Mordida)* **$80 [≃£41]**
- Cover Her Face. New York: Scribner, 1966. 1st American edition. Dustwrapper (short closed tear, couple of tiny nicks, short crease back flap). *(Mordida)* **$100 [≃£52]**
- Death of an Expert Witness. London: Faber, 1977. Dustwrapper. Signed by the author. *(Limestone Hills)* **$85 [≃£44]**
- Death of an Expert Witness. London: Faber, 1977. Dustwrapper. Signed by the author. *(Dyke)* **£35 [≃$67]**
- Death of an Expert Witness. London: Faber, 1977. Dustwrapper. Signed by the author (1987). *(Marlborough B'shop)* **£28 [≃$53]**
- Death of an Expert Witness. London: Faber, 1977. Dustwrapper. *(Mordida)* **$50 [≃£26]**
- Devices and Desires. London: Faber, 1989. Dustwrapper. Signed by the author. *(Dyke)* **£20 [≃$38]**
- Devices and Desires. London: Faber, 1989. Dustwrapper. Signed by the author. *(Limestone Hills)* **$45 [≃£23]**
- Devices and Desires. London: Faber, 1989. Dustwrapper. *(Mordida)* **$45 [≃£23]**
- Innocent Blood. New York: Scribner's, [1980]. Uncorrected proof copy. Wrappers. *(Antic Hay)* **$50 [≃£26]**
- Innocent Blood. London: 1980. Dustwrapper (slight crinkling). *(Egret)* **£25 [≃$47]**
- (With T.A. Critchley) The Maul and the Pear Tree. London: Constable, 1971. Price-clipped dustwrapper (light edge wear). *(Janus)* **$125 [≃£65]**
- The Skull beneath the Skin. London: Faber, 1982. Dustwrapper. *(Limestone Hills)* **$35 [≃£18]**
- A Taste for Death. London: Faber, 1986. Dustwrapper. *(Lewton)* **£15 [≃$28]**
- A Taste for Death. London: Faber, 1986. Dustwrapper. *(Virgo)* **£35 [≃$67]**
- A Taste of Death. London: Faber, 1986. Review slip. Dustwrapper. *(Limestone Hills)* **$55 [≃£28]**
- Unnatural Causes. New York: Scribner's, 1967. 1st American edition. Dustwrapper. *(Mordida)* **$85 [≃£44]**
- Unnatural Causes. New York: Scribner, 1967. 1st American edition. Dustwrapper. *(Mordida)* **$85 [≃£44]**
- An Unsuitable Job for a Woman. London: Faber, 1972. Dustwrapper. *(David Rees)* **£70 [≃$134]**

Jarrell, Randall

- Little Friend, Little Friend. Dial: 1945. Bookplate. Dustwrapper (minor chipping). *(Nouveau)* **$100 [≃£52]**
- Pictures from an Institution. London: 1954. Dustwrapper. *(Clearwater)* **£28 [≃$53]**
- Pictures from an Institution. New York: Knopf, 1954. Price-clipped dustwrapper (edge tears, light rubbing). *(Nouveau)* **$50 [≃£26]**

Jeffers, Robinson

- Be Angry at the Sun. New York: 1941. Small mark front cover. Dustwrapper (spine sunned, top of spine slightly chipped, two edge chips and two tears). *(Polyanthos)* **$50 [≃£26]**
- Dear Judas and Other Poems. New York: Liveright, 1929. One of 375 signed. Vellum and boards. Slipcase (minor wear). *(Antic Hay)* **$285 [≃£148]**
- Give Your Heart to the Hawks. New York: 1933. Name address and date. Dustwrapper. *(Pettler & Liebermann)* **$100 [≃£52]**
- Solstice and Other Poems. New York: Random House, 1935. One of 320 signed. Some discolouration endpapers. Dustwrapper (some browning, chip head of spine). *(Antic Hay)* **$300 [≃£156]**
- Solstice and Other Poems. New York: Random House, 1935. Spine slightly faded, paper clip impression on title margin. *(Wreden)* **$110 [≃£57]**

Jennings, Elizabeth

- The Animals' Arrival. London: 1969. Uncorrected proof copy. *(Buckley)* **£15 [≃$28]**
- Every Changing Shape. London: 1961. Dustwrapper (frayed). *(Egret)* **£6 [≃$11]**
- Let's Have Some Poetry. London: 1960. Dustwrapper. *(Egret)* **£12 [≃$23]**
- The Mind Has Mountains. London: 1966. Dustwrapper. *(Egret)* **£20 [≃$38]**
- Poems. Fantasy Press: 1953. Wrappers. *(Egret)* **£45 [≃$86]**
- (Contributes to) Poetry from Oxford. 1950. Dustwrapper. *(Egret)* **£20 [≃$38]**

- Song for a Birth or a Death. London: 1961. Dustwrapper. *(Egret)* **£20 [≃$38]**
- A Way of Looking. New York: Rinehart, [1955]. 1st American edition. Dustwrapper. *(Dermont)* **$35 [≃£18]**

Jhabvala, Ruth Prawer

- Heat and Dust. London: Murray, 1975. Dustwrapper. *(Ash)* **£50 [≃$95]**

Johns, W.E.

- Adventure Bound. London: Nelson, 1955. Dustwrapper. *(Green Meadow)* **£15 [≃$28]**
- Adventures of the Junior Detection Club. London: Parrish, 1960. Dustwrapper. *(Green Meadow)* **£85 [≃$163]**
- Another Job for Biggles. London: Hodder & Stoughton, 1951. Dustwrapper. *(Green Meadow)* **£25 [≃$47]**
- Biggles and the Black Mask. London: Hodder & Stoughton, 1964. Dustwrapper. *(Green Meadow)* **£65 [≃$124]**
- Biggles and the Black Mask. London: Hodder & Stoughton, 1964. Dustwrapper (very slightly rubbed). *(Ash)* **£50 [≃$95]**
- Biggles and the Black Raider. London: Hodder & Stoughton, 1953. Dustwrapper. *(Green Meadow)* **£45 [≃$86]**
- Biggles and the Black Raider. London: Hodder & Stoughton, 1953. Dustwrapper (worn and sellotaped). *(Green Meadow)* **£35 [≃$67]**
- Biggles and the Dark Intruder. London: Brockhampton Knight Books, 1967. Card wrappers. *(Green Meadow)* **£15 [≃$28]**
- Biggles and the Lost Sovereigns. London: Brockhampton, 1964. Dustwrapper. *(Green Meadow)* **£55 [≃$105]**
- Biggles and the Missing Millionaire. London: Brockhampton, 1961. Dustwrapper. *(Green Meadow)* **£55 [≃$105]**
- Biggles at World's End. London: Brockhampton, 1959. Dustwrapper. *(Green Meadow)* **£40 [≃$76]**
- The Biggles Book of Treasure Hunting. London: Max Parrish, 1962. *(Green Meadow)* **£45 [≃$86]**
- Biggles Charter Pilot. OUP: 1943. Pictorial cloth. *(Green Meadow)* **£75 [≃$143]**
- Biggles Defies the Swastika. OUP: 1945. reprint. Pictorial cloth. Dustwrapper (slightly chipped). *(Green Meadow)* **£40 [≃$76]**
- Biggles Foreign Legionnaire. London: Hodder & Stoughton, 1954. Dustwrapper (slightly torn). *(Green Meadow)* **£47.50 [≃$92]**
- Biggles Goes Alone. London: Hodder & Stoughton, 1962. Dustwrapper. *(Green Meadow)* **£47.50 [≃$92]**
- Biggles Goes Home. London: Hodder & Stoughton, 1960. Dustwrapper. *(Green Meadow)* **£45 [≃$86]**
- Biggles Goes to School. London: Hodder & Stoughton, 1951. Dustwrapper (slightly worn). *(Green Meadow)* **£25 [≃$47]**
- Biggles in Australia. London: Hodder & Stoughton, 1955. Dustwrapper. *(Green Meadow)* **£35 [≃$67]**
- Biggles in Mexico. London: Brockhampton, 1959. Dustwrapper. *(Green Meadow)* **£35 [≃$67]**
- Biggles in the Gobi. London: Hodder & Stoughton, 1953. Dustwrapper. *(Green Meadow)* **£45 [≃$86]**
- Biggles Investigates. London: Brockhampton, 1964. Dustwrapper (slightly rubbed). *(Green Meadow)* **£40 [≃$76]**
- Biggles Investigates. London: Brockhampton, 1964. Dustwrapper. *(Green Meadow)* **£55 [≃$105]**
- Biggles Learns to Fly. London: Brockhampton, 1955. Dustwrapper (slightly chipped). *(Green Meadow)* **£85 [≃$163]**
- Biggles Looks Back. London: Hodder & Stoughton, 1965. Dustwrapper. *(Green Meadow)* **£55 [≃$105]**
- Biggles Makes Ends Meet. London: Hodder & Stoughton, 1957. Dustwrapper. *(Green Meadow)* **£35 [≃$67]**
- Biggles of the Interpol. London: Brockhampton, 1957. Dustwrapper (edgeworn). *(Bookmark)* **£17.50 [≃$34]**
- Biggles of the Interpol. London: Brockhampton, 1957. Dustwrapper. *(Green Meadow)* **£35 [≃$67]**
- Biggles on Mystery Island. London: Hodder & Stoughton, 1958. Dustwrapper. *(Green Meadow)* **£45 [≃$86]**
- Biggles Presses On. London: Brockhampton, 1958. Dustwrapper. *(Green Meadow)* **£30 [≃$57]**
- Biggles Scores a Bull. London: Brockhampton, 1966. 2nd impression. Dustwrapper. *(Green Meadow)* **£45 [≃$86]**
- Biggles Sees it Through. OUP: 1941. Pictorial cloth. *(Green Meadow)* **£45 [≃$86]**
- Biggles Sees It Through. OUP: 1941. Lightly marked. *(Bookmark)* **£27.50 [≃$53]**
- Biggles Sees Too Much. London: Brockhampton, 1970. Ex lib. Dustwrapper. *(Green Meadow)* **£55 [≃$105]**
- Biggles Sets a Trap. London: Hodder &

Stoughton, 1962. Dustwrapper. *(Green Meadow)* **£75 [≃$143]**

- Biggles Sweeps the Desert. London: Hodder & Stoughton, 1942. *(Green Meadow)* **£10 [≃$19]**
- Biggles Takes a Hand. London: Hodder & Stoughton, 1963. Dustwrapper. *(Green Meadow)* **£55 [≃$105]**
- Biggles Takes Charge. London: Hodder & Stoughton, 1956. Dustwrapper. *(Green Meadow)* **£25 [≃$47]**
- Biggles Takes it Rough. London: Brockhampton, 1963. Dustwrapper. *(Green Meadow)* **£55 [≃$105]**
- Biggles Takes the Case. London: Hodder & Stoughton, 1952. Dustwrapper (slightly worn). *(Green Meadow)* **£25 [≃$47]**
- Biggles' Chinese Puzzle. London: Brockhampton, 1955. Dustwrapper (slightly chipped). *(Green Meadow)* **£45 [≃$86]**
- Biggles' Combined Operation. London: Hodder & Stoughton, 1959. Dustwrapper. *(Green Meadow)* **£45 [≃$86]**
- Biggles Second Case. London: Hodder & Stoughton, 1948. Dustwrapper. *(Green Meadow)* **£27.50 [≃$53]**
- Biggles' Special Case. London: Brockhampton, 1963. Dustwrapper. *(Green Meadow)* **£65 [≃$124]**
- Champion of the Main. OUP: 1938. Frontispiece taped in. Pictorial cloth. *(Green Meadow)* **£25 [≃$47]**
- The Death Rays of Ardilla. London: Hodder & Stoughton, 1959. Dustwrapper (glazed to boards). *(Green Meadow)* **£17.50 [≃$34]**
- Fighting Planes and Aces. London: John Hamilton, [n.d.]. Pictorial cloth. Dustwrapper. *(Green Meadow)* **£175 [≃$335]**
- Flying Stories. London: John Hamilton. Pictorial boards. *(Green Meadow)* **£75 [≃$143]**
- Flying Stories. London: John Hamilton. Spine worn. *(Green Meadow)* **£85 [≃$163]**
- Gimlet Bores In. London: Brockhampton, 1950. Dustwrapper (repaired). *(Green Meadow)* **£15 [≃$28]**
- Gimlet Lends a Hand. London: Brockhampton, 1949. Dustwrapper. *(Green Meadow)* **£12.50 [≃$24]**
- Gimlet Mops Up. London: Brockhampton, 1947. Dustwrapper. *(Green Meadow)* **£10 [≃$19]**
- Gimlet's Oriental Quest. London: Brockhampton, 1948. Dustwrapper. *(Green Meadow)* **£10 [≃$19]**
- Kings of Space. London: Hodder & Stoughton, 1954. Top edge a bit faded. Dustwrapper (worn). *(Bookmark)* **£12.50 [≃$24]**
- Kings of Space. London: Hodder & Stoughton, 1954. Dustwrapper. *(Green Meadow)* **£17.50 [≃$34]**
- Modern Boy's Annual. London: Fleetway House, 1932. Cloth backed pictorial boards (slightly rubbed). *(Green Meadow)* **£45 [≃$86]**
- Modern Boy's Annual. London: Fleetway House, 1933. Cloth backed pictorial boards. *(Green Meadow)* **£45 [≃$86]**
- Modern Boy's Annual. London: Fleetway House, 1934. Cloth backed pictorial boards (spine slightly worn). *(Green Meadow)* **£45 [≃$86]**
- Modern Boy's Annual. London: Fleetway House, 1935. Cloth backed pictorial boards (slightly marked). *(Green Meadow)* **£40 [≃$76]**
- Modern Boy's Annual. London: Fleetway House, 1936. Cloth backed pictorial boards. *(Green Meadow)* **£45 [≃$86]**
- Modern Boy's Annual. London: Fleetway House, 1937. Cloth backed pictorial boards. *(Green Meadow)* **£75 [≃$143]**
- Modern Boy's Annual. London: Fleetway House, 1938. Cloth backed pictorial boards. *(Green Meadow)* **£75 [≃$143]**
- Modern Boy's Book of Aircraft. London: Fleetway House. Cloth backed pictorial boards (slightly spotted). *(Green Meadow)* **£65 [≃$124]**
- Modern Boy's Book of Pirates. London: [n.d.]. Frontispiece stuck to front board. Cloth backed pictorial boards. *(Green Meadow)* **£55 [≃$105]**
- Modern Boy's Book of True Adventure. London: Fleetway House. Cloth backed pictorial boards. *(Green Meadow)* **£45 [≃$86]**
- Modern Boy's New Book of Aircraft. London: Fleetway House. Cloth backed pictorial boards. *(Green Meadow)* **£75 [≃$143]**
- No Motive for Murder. London: Hodder & Stoughton, 1958. Dustwrapper (slightly chipped). *(Green Meadow)* **£125 [≃$239]**
- No Rest for Biggles. London: Hodder & Stoughton, 1956. Dustwrapper (slightly worn). *(Green Meadow)* **£27.50 [≃$53]**
- Quest for the Perfect Planet. London: Hodder & Stoughton, 1961. Dustwrapper. *(Green Meadow)* **£17.50 [≃$34]**
- The Raid. London: John Hamilton, [n.d.]. Front endpaper removed. *(Green Meadow)* **£85 [≃$163]**

- The Raid. London: John Hamilton. Dustwrapper (some wear). *(Green Meadow)* **£175 [≃$335]**
- Return to Mars. London: Hodder & Stoughton, 1959. Dustwrapper glazed to boards. *(Green Meadow)* **£17.50 [≃$34]**
- The Rustlers of Rattlesnake Valley. London: Nelson, 1948. Dustwrapper. *(Green Meadow)* **£40 [≃$76]**
- Sinister Service. OUP: 1942. Dustwrapper. *(Green Meadow)* **£125 [≃$239]**
- Some Milestones of Aviation. London: John Hamilton, [n.d.]. *(Green Meadow)* **£49.50 [≃$95]**
- Some Milestones of Aviation. London: John Hamilton. Picture from dustwrapper on front endpaper. *(Green Meadow)* **£75 [≃$143]**
- Where the Golden Eagle Soars. London: Hodder & Stoughton, 1960. Dustwrapper. *(Green Meadow)* **£40 [≃$76]**
- Wings - Flying Adventures. London: John Hamilton. Fine. *(Green Meadow)* **£95 [≃$182]**

Johnson, B.S.

- Aren't You Rather Young to be Writing Your Memoirs? London: 1973. Stiff wrappers issue. Dustwrapper. *(Clearwater)* **£12 [≃$23]**
- Christie Malry's Own Double-Entry. London: Collins, 1973. Dustwrapper. *(Any Amount)* **£18 [≃$34]**
- A Dublin Unicorn. Byron Press: (1975). One of 250. Wrappers. *(Hazeldene)* **£40 [≃$76]**
- Everyone Knows Somebody Who's Dead. London: 1973. One of 100 signed by the author. Wrappers (very slightly soiled). *(Ellis)* **£90 [≃$172]**
- House Mother Normal. London: 1971. One of 100 signed by the author. Cellophane dustwrapper. *(Ellis)* **£140 [≃$268]**
- House Mother Normal. London: 1971. Dustwrapper (slightly rubbed, spine slightly faded). Author's inscription. *(Ellis)* **£70 [≃$134]**
- Poems. London: Constable, 1964. Dustwrapper. Author's signed presentation inscription. *(Any Amount)* **£55 [≃$105]**
- Poems. London: 1964. Spine ends slightly bruised. Dustwrapper (very slightly frayed, one nick). Signed by the author. *(Ellis)* **£80 [≃$153]**
- Poems. London: Constable, (1964). Dustwrapper. *(Woolmer)* **$50 [≃£26]**
- Poems Two. Trigram Press: 1972. Dustwrapper. Author's signed presentation inscription. *(Any Amount)* **£48 [≃$92]**
- Poems Two. London: 1972. One of 100 signed by the author. Cellophane dustwrapper. *(Ellis)* **£50 [≃$95]**
- Poems Two. Trigram Press: 1972. Dustwrapper (rubbed). One of ca 400 clothbound copies. *(Moorhouse)* **£20 [≃$38]**
- Statement Against Corpses. With Zulfikar Ghose. London: 1964. Dustwrapper (very slightly rubbed). Presentation copy inscribed and signed by Johnson. *(Ellis)* **£85 [≃$163]**
- Travelling People. London: 1963. Advance copy. Wrappers (crease to corner of lower flap). Dustwrapper (slightly rubbed, nicked, lacks piece at top of supper panel). His 1st book. *(Ellis)* **£125 [≃$239]**
- Trawl. London: 1966. Dustwrapper (very slightly frayed, two nicks). *(Ellis)* **£50 [≃$95]**
- The Unfortunates. London: 1969. 27 sections. Removable wrapper. Laminated box (some wear along the hinge). *(Ellis)* **£120 [≃$230]**

Johnson, Pamela Hansford

- Blessed Above Women. London: Chapman & Hall, 1936. Little dull. *(Whiteson)* **£30 [≃$57]**
- Here Today. London: Champan & Hall, 1937. Binding dull. *(Whiteson)* **£25 [≃$47]**
- Too Dear for My Possessing. London: Collins, 1940. Little dull. *(Whiteson)* **£20 [≃$38]**
- The Unspeakable Skipton. London: 1959. Spine slightly faded. Dustwrapper (slightly rubbed, few very small nicks). Author's signed inscription (1960). *(Ellis)* **£40 [≃$76]**
- The Unspeakable Skipton. London: Macmillan, 1959. Edges slightly faded. Dustwrapper (slightly rubbed). *(Whiteson)* **£12.50 [≃$24]**

Johnston, Mary

- The Slave Ship. Boston: Little, Brown, 1924. Some mottling of cloth. Ink presentation. Dustwrapper (tear on spine fold and across spine). *(Antic Hay)* **$50 [≃£26]**

Jolas, Eugene

- I Have Seen Monsters and Angels. Paris: Transition Press, 1938. Wrappers (slightly marked). *(Words Etcetera)* **£30 [≃$57]**

Jones, Brian

- Poems. London: Alan Ross, 1966. Wrappers. His 1st book. *(Woolmer)* **$20 [≃£10]**

Jones, David

- Anathemata. London: 1952. Dustwrapper

(slightly frayed, faded in patches). *(Ellis)* **£100 [≃$191]**
- The Fatigue. 1965. One of 285 (this copy unnumbered). Wrappers. With the Proposal Leaf. *(Words Etcetera)* **£100 [≃$191]**
- In Parenthesis. London: 1937. *(Words Etcetera)* **£60 [≃$115]**
- In Parenthesis. London: Faber, (1937). *(Woolmer)* **$35 [≃£18]**
- In Parenthesis. London: 1961. One of 70 copies signed by the author and T.S. Eliot. Fine. *(Words Etcetera)* **£1,500 [≃$2,879]**
- In Parenthesis. London: Faber, (1961). One of 70 (this copy out of series and unsigned). Original plastic jacket. *(Woolmer)* **$350 [≃£182]**
- The Sleeping Lord. London: Faber, 1974. One of 150 signed. Slipcase. *(Dyke)* **£125 [≃$239]**
- The Sleeping Lord. London: Faber, (1974). One of 150 signed by the author. Cloth. Slipcase. *(Black Sun)* **$250 [≃£130]**
- The Sleeping Lord and Other Fragments. London: Faber, 1974. Dustwrapper. *(Glyn's)* **£20 [≃$38]**
- The Tribune's Visitation. Fulcrum: 1969. Dustwrapper (faintly rubbed). *(Halsey)* **£19 [≃$36]**
- The Tribune's Visitation. London: 1969. Wrappers. *(First Issues)* **£5 [≃$9]**
- The Tribune's Visitation. London: 1969. Dustwrapper. *(Georges)* **£20 [≃$38]**

Jones, Glyn
- The Blue Bed and Other Stories. London: Cape, 1937. Spine faded. His 1st book. *(Sklaroff)* **£18 [≃$34]**

Jones, James
- From Here to Eternity. New York: Scribner's, 1951. Dustwrapper (somewhat tired). His 1st book. *(Chapel Hill)* **$100 [≃£52]**
- From Here to Eternity. London: Collins, 1952. 1st English edition. Dustwrapper (two closed tears). *(Nouveau)* **$100 [≃£52]**
- Some Came Running. New York: Scribners, 1957. Name. Dustwrapper. *(Nouveau)* **$75 [≃£39]**
- Whistle: A Work in Progress. Bloomfield Hills: Bruccoli Clark, 1974. One of 50 (of 350) signed. Wrappers. *(Between the Covers)* **$125 [≃£65]**

Jones, LeRoi
- Dutchman & The Slave. New York: Morrow, 1964. Dustwrapper. *(Antic Hay)* **$50 [≃£26]**

Jong, Erica
- Fanny. New York: New American Library, [1980]. Dustwrapper. Author's signed presentation (1990). *(Antic Hay)* **$35 [≃£18]**
- Fear of Flying. New York: Holt, Rinehart & Winston, [1973]. Dustwrapper (minor wear). Signed by the author. *(Antic Hay)* **$50 [≃£26]**
- Fruits & Vegetables. London: 1973. Dustwrapper. Author's presentation copy. *(Egret)* **£25 [≃$47]**
- Half-Lives. London: 1974. Dustwrapper. Author's presentation copy. *(Egret)* **£20 [≃$38]**
- Loveroot. New York: Holt, Rinehart & Winston, [1975]. Dustwrapper. Signed by the author and dated. *(Antic Hay)* **$35 [≃£18]**
- Ordinary Miracles. New York: New American Library, [1983]. Promotional material inserted. Dustwrapper. Signed by the author. *(Antic Hay)* **$45 [≃£23]**
- Parachutes & Kisses. New York: New American Library, [1984]. Uncorrected proof copy. Wrappers. Signed by the author and dated. *(Antic Hay)* **$75 [≃£39]**

Jordan, Neil
- The Past. London: Cape, 1980. One of 50 signed. Slipcase. *(David Rees)* **£45 [≃$86]**
- The Past. London: Cape, 1980. Dustwrapper. *(Lewton)* **£20 [≃$38]**

Joyce, James
- Chamber Music. Boston: The Cornhill Company, [1918]. 1st American (unauthorized) edition. Minute label removed lower edge rear cover. His 1st book. *(Polyanthos)* **$275 [≃£143]**
- Chamber Music. London: Elkin Mathews, 1918. 2nd edition. Wrappers (dull, slight wear). *(Whiteson)* **£175 [≃$335]**
- Collected Poems. New York: Black Sun Press, 1936. One of 800. Patterned boards, unopened (spine tips sunned). Tissue dustwrapper (missing very small piece top edge). *(Polyanthos)* **$400 [≃£208]**
- Collected Poems. New York: Black Sun, 1936. One of 750. Boards. Glassine jacket (chipped). *(Alphabet)* **$450 [≃£234]**
- Collected Poems. New York: The Black Sun Press, 1936. One of 750 (of 800). Ribbon marker. Glassine dustwrapper. Minor browning foot of spine due to small chip to dustwrapper. *(Antic Hay)* **$750 [≃£390]**
- Dedalus. Paris: Editions de la Sirene, 1924. 1st French edition. Wrappers, partly unopened. Glassine dustwrapper. *(Polyanthos)* **$300 [≃£156]**

- Finnegans Wake. London: 1939. Prelims slightly foxed. *(Edrich)* **£80 [≃$153]**
- Finnegans Wake. London: Faber, 1939. Endpapers spotted. Largely unopened. *(Hazeldene)* **£300 [≃$575]**
- Finnegans Wake. New York: 1939. Dustwrapper (some small tears mended internally with some of the tape showing, spine extremities one-eighth inch missing). *(Polyanthos)* **$150 [≃£78]**
- Finnegans Wake. New York: Viking, 1939. 1st American edition. Dustwrapper (couple of tiny tears). *(Alphabet)* **$450 [≃£234]**
- Finnegans Wake. New York: 1939. Neat name. *(Polyanthos)* **$75 [≃£39]**
- Haveth Childers Everywhere. Paris: Henry Babou & Jack Kahane; New York: The Fountain Press, 1930. One of 500 (of 600). Tiny name label. Printed wrappers. Glassine dustwrapper (missing along most of spine). Box (small piece missing). *(Polyanthos)* **$450 [≃£234]**
- Haveth Childers Everywhere. London: Criterion Miscellany, 1931. Hardbound issue. *(Edrich)* **£30 [≃$57]**
- Haveth Childers Everywhere. London: Criterion Miscellany, 1931. Wrappers (very slightly frayed). *(Edrich)* **£15 [≃$28]**
- A James Joyce Yearbook. Edited by Maria Jolas. Paris: Transition Press, 1949. One of 1000. Wrappers (spine a bit cocked, spine edges slightly rubbed). Glassine dustwrapper (soiled). *(Dermont)* **$75 [≃£39]**
- Letters. Edited by Stuart Gilbert. New York: 1957. Dustwrapper (tiny chip top of spine). *(Polyanthos)* **$75 [≃£39]**
- Letters. New York: Viking, 1957. 1st American edition. Dustwrapper (chip upper edge rear panel). *(Lopez)* **$45 [≃£23]**
- Letters. London: Faber, 1957-66. Vol 2 corners slightly bumped. Dustwrappers (vol 1 slightly chipped with several small closed tears head of spine; vol 2 slightly chipped, small closed tear; vol 3 slightly chipped). *(Virgo)* **£150 [≃$287]**
- The Mime of Mick, Nick and the Maggies. Servire Press: London: Faber, 1934. One of 1000. Faber imprint. Stiff paper wrappers (slightly dusty). Lacks slipcase. *(First Issues)* **£150 [≃$287]**
- Pastimes of James Joyce. London: 1941. Limited edition. Wrappers. *(Whiteson)* **£25 [≃$47]**
- Poems Penyeach. Paris: Shakespeare & Co, 1927. Errata slip. Spine and covers little sunned. *(Polyanthos)* **$125 [≃£65]**
- Pomes Penyeach. London: 1933. 1st English edition. Wrappers. Dustwrapper (torn and defective at foot of spine). *(Edrich)* **£35 [≃$67]**
- Pomes Penyeach. London: 1933. Wrappers. *(Ellis)* **£50 [≃$95]**
- A Portrait of the Artist as a Young Man. New York: B.W. Huebsch, 1916. Bookplate. Tiny hole in rear free endpaper. Pencil notes. *(Chapel Hill)* **$750 [≃£390]**
- A Portrait of the Artist as a Young Man. New York: Huebsch, 1916. Precedes the UK edition. Inscription. Spine little sunned, extremities and corners little rubbed. *(Polyanthos)* **$400 [≃£208]**
- A Portrait of the Artist as a Young Man. London: Egoist Press, 1917. 2nd edition. 1st English edition. Covers very slightly marked. *(Edrich)* **£35 [≃$67]**
- A Portrait of the Artist as a Young Man. London: The Egoist, [1917]. 1st British edition (from the American sheets). A few leaves slightly creased. Cloth a touch dull, boards slightly discoloured in places. Some wear to foredge of front cover. *(Ash)* **£400 [≃$767]**
- A Portrait of the Artist as a Young Man. London: Egoist Press, 1917. One of 750 produced from American sheets with the Egoist title page. Slight offsetting & thumb marks to endsheets. Boards a little marked with some damp marking to front edge. *(Blakeney)* **£175 [≃$335]**
- Stephen Hero. London: 1944. Ownership signature on endpaper. Dustwrapper (slightly dusty, tear to upper panel and some resultant creasing, repaired with archival tape, chipping at corners with small loss to top of spine). *(First Issues)* **£75 [≃$143]**
- Stephen Hero. London: Cape, 1944. Dustwrapper (slightly marked and nicked). *(Clearwater)* **£60 [≃$115]**
- Stephen Hero. London: Cape, 1944. *(Whiteson)* **£25 [≃$47]**
- (Contributes) Three Poems, [in] The Dublin Book of Irish verse. Introduction by J. Cooke. 1909. Small rubber stamp on title. *(Edrich)* **£20 [≃$38]**
- Two Tales of Shem and Shaun. London: 1932. Head of spine rubbed. Dustwrapper (torn). *(Edrich)* **£25 [≃$47]**
- Two Tales of Shem and Shaun. London: Faber, 1932. Name and date on endpaper. Dustwrapper (creased). *(Sklaroff)* **£55 [≃$105]**
- Two Tales of Shem and Shaun. London: Faber, 1932. Dustwrapper, mint. *(Whiteson)* **£60 [≃$115]**

- Two Tales of Shem and Shaun. London: 1932. Some staining to spine and lower boards, spine ends bumped. dustwrapper (rubbed, few nicks, 1-inch closed tear). *(Ellis)* **£60 [≃$115]**
- Two Tales of Shem and Shaun. London: 1932. Covers foxed, spine little sunned. Dustwrapper (spine and corners very slightly chipped, spine edges little rubbed). *(Polyanthos)* **$65 [≃£33]**
- Ulysses. Paris: Shakespeare & Co, 1922. 1st printing. One of 1000. Three quarter leather, marbled boards, t.e.g., original wrappers bound in. *(Polyanthos)* **$5,000 [≃£2,604]**
- Ulysses. Paris: Shakespeare & Co, 1922. 1st printing. One of 1000. Lacks the initial blank designed for insertion below the flap of the wrappers. Edge tear endpaper. Some damp staining on many blank lower margs. Lacks wrappers. Recent three quarter calf. *(Polyanthos)* **$1,500 [≃£781]**
- Ulysses. Paris: John Rodker, published for the Egoist Press, London, 1922. The second edition. English issue of the Paris edition. Wrappers detached & much worn, 1st blank torn. Some light damp staining to top edge of last few leaves. *(Blakeney)* **£325 [≃$623]**
- Ulysses. Paris: Shakespeare & Co, 1924. 5th printing. 8vo. 736 pp. Paper somewhat browned as normal. Rebound in red half morocco, original (soiled) wrappers bound in. *(Frew Mackenzie)* **£210 [≃$403]**
- Ulysses. Paris: Shakespeare & Co, 1925. 6th printing. Half calf, spine gilt with raised bands, t.e.g., original wrappers bound in. *(Polyanthos)* **$250 [≃£130]**
- Ulysses. Paris: Shakespeare & Co, 1925. 6th printing. Half calf, spine gilt with raised bands, t.e.g., original wrappers not bound in. *(Polyanthos)* **$150 [≃£78]**
- Ulysses. Paris: Shakespeare & Co, 1928. 10th printing. 8vo. 735 pp. Edges browned. Rebound in half morocco, original upper wrapper bound in. *(Frew Mackenzie)* **£160 [≃$307]**
- Ulysses. Odyssey Press: 1932. Revised by S. Gilbert. 2 vols. Name on half-title. Paper wrappers very slightly marked. Slocum A20. *(Edrich)* **£50 [≃$95]**
- Ulysses. London: John Lane; The Bodley Head, (1936). 1st English edition (printed in England). One of 100 (of 1000) on mould-made paper signed. Vellum, fine. Later slipcase. *(Houle)* **$7,000 [≃£3,645]**
- Ulysses. London: 1936. 1st British edition. One of 1000. Inscription on endpaper. Dustwrapper (mounted on paper, foot of spine defective). *(Edrich)* **£225 [≃$431]**
- Ulysses. London: Bodley Head, 1936. 1st English limited edition. One of 900. Spine and small part of back cover slightly faded, foredge very slightly spotted. *(Virgo)* **£300 [≃$575]**

Joyce, Stanislaus

- My Brother's Keeper. Introduction by T.S. Eliot. Viking Press: 1958. One of 375. No dustwrapper issued. *(Edrich)* **£40 [≃$76]**

Kafka, Franz

- The Great Wall of China and Other Pieces. London: 1946. Dustwrapper. *(Words Etcetera)* **£25 [≃$47]**

Kaminsky, Stuart M.

- Murder on the Yellow Brick Road. New York: St. Martin, 1977. Dustwrapper (short edge tear). *(Janus)* **$50 [≃£26]**

Kavan, Anna

- Goose Cross. By Helen Ferguson. London: Lane, 1936. Spine slightly faded, 'mild differential fading. *(Any Amount)* **£30 [≃$57]**

Kavanagh, Dan

- Pseudonym used by Julian Barnes, q.v.

Kavanagh, Paul

- Pseudonym used by Lawrence Block, q.v.

Kaye, M.M.

- The Far Pavilions. London: 1978. Dustwrapper. Author's signed presentation inscription. *(Words Etcetera)* **£30 [≃$57]**

Keeler, Harry Stephen

- The Mysterious Mr. I. New York: Dutton, 1938. Dustwrapper (minor wear at spine ends). *(Mordida)* **$45 [≃£23]**
- The Peacock Fan. New York: Dutton, 1941. Dustwrapper (some tiny tears). *(Mordida)* **$45 [≃£23]**

Keillor, Garrison

- Happy to Be Here. New York: Atheneum, 1982. Dustwrapper. His 1st book. *(Michael Johnson)* **£100 [≃$191]**
- Lake Wobegon Days. New York: Viking, 1985. Uncorrected proof copy. Blue wrappers. *(Michael Johnson)* **£120 [≃$230]**
- Lake Wobegon Days. New York: Viking, 1985. Dustwrapper. *(Moorhouse)* **£25 [≃$47]**
- Lake Wobegon Days. New York: Viking, 1985. Dustwrapper (edge creased, minor

closed tear). *(Paul Brown)* **£15 [≃$28]**
- Lake Wobegon Days. London: Faber, 1986. Dustwrapper. *(Moorhouse)* **£25 [≃$47]**

Kell, Joseph
- Pseudonym used by Anthony Burgess, q.v.

Kellerman, Jonathan
- Silent Partner. London: Macdonald, 1989. Precedes the American edition. Dustwrapper. *(Mordida)* **$45 [≃£23]**

Kelly, Robert
- The Common Shore Books I-V. Black Sparrow: 1969. One of 250 hardcover signed. Acetate dustwrapper. *(Halsey)* **£30 [≃$57]**

Kelman, James
- The Busconductor Hines. Edinburgh: Polygon, 1984. Dustwrapper. *(Moorhouse)* **£20 [≃$38]**
- The Busconductor Hines. Edinburgh: Polygon, 1984. Dustwrapper (very slightly rubbed). Signed by the author. *(David Rees)* **£25 [≃$47]**
- The Busconductor Hines. Edinburgh: Polygon, 1984. Dustwrapper. *(Lewton)* **£27.50 [≃$53]**
- A Chancer. Edinburgh: Polygon, 1985. Dustwrapper. *(Moorhouse)* **£18 [≃$34]**
- A Disaffection. London: Secker, 1989. Uncorrected proof copy. Wrappers. *(Any Amount)* **£16 [≃$30]**
- A Disaffection. London: Secker, 1989. Dustwrapper. *(David Rees)* **£25 [≃$47]**

Kemelman, Harry
- The Nine Mile Walk. New York: Putnam, 1967. Dustwrapper. *(Janus)* **$45 [≃£23]**
- The Nine Mile Walk. London: Hutchinson, 1968. Dustwrapper. *(Paul Brown)* **£20 [≃$38]**

Kemp, Harry
- Collected Poems. Privately Printed: 1985. Author's presentation inscription. *(Patterson)* **£25 [≃$47]**
- The Thresher's Wife. New York: Boni, 1914. Boards (top of spine chipped). *(Woolmer)* **$85 [≃£44]**

Keneally, Thomas
- The Chant of Jimmy Blacksmith. Sydney: Angus & Robertson, 1972. Dustwrapper (slightly rubbed). *(Moorhouse)* **£30 [≃$57]**
- The Chant of Jimmy Blacksmith. 1972. 1st Australian edition. Dustwrapper (slightly rubbed). *(Ellis)* **£60 [≃$115]**
- The Cut-Rate Kingdom. London: Allen Lane, 1984. 1st English edition. Dustwrapper. *(Limestone Hills)* **$25 [≃£13]**
- Schindlers Ark. London: Hodder & Stoughton, 1982. Dustwrapper. *(Lewton)* **£13.50 [≃$26]**
- The Survivor. London: 1970. Top corner of upper cover slightly scraped. Dustwrapper. *(Ellis)* **£45 [≃$86]**

Kennedy, William
- Billy Phelan's Greatest Game. New York: 1978. Dustwrapper (less than usual rubbing). *(Pettler & Liebermann)* **$75 [≃£39]**
- Billy Phelan's Greatest Game. New York: 1978. Dustwrapper (rubbed, a bit worn). *(Pettler & Liebermann)* **$45 [≃£23]**
- The Ink Truck. London: 1970. 1st English edition. Dustwrapper (very slightly tanned around extreme edges). *(Words Etcetera)* **£100 [≃$191]**
- Ironweed. New York: 1983. Dustwrapper. *(Pettler & Liebermann)* **$125 [≃£65]**
- Ironweed. London: Viking, 1983. 1st British edition. Dustwrapper. *(Michael Johnson)* **£25 [≃$47]**
- Legs. London: Cape, 1976. 1st British edition. Dustwrapper. *(Michael Johnson)* **£50 [≃$95]**
- Legs. London: Cape, 1976. Dustwrapper. *(Glyn's)* **£20 [≃$38]**
- O Albany. New York: 1983. Remainder stamp. Dustwrapper. *(Pettler & Liebermann)* **$65 [≃£33]**
- Quinn's Book. London: Cape, 1988. Dustwrapper. *(Moorhouse)* **£6 [≃$11]**
- Quinn's Book. New York: Viking, 1988. 1st US edition. Dustwrapper. *(Moorhouse)* **£10 [≃$19]**

Kerouac, Jack
- American Haikus. Caliban Press: 1986. One of 125. Wrappers. *(Nouveau)* **$50 [≃£26]**
- Big Sur. New York: Farrar, Straus & Cudahy, 1962. Dustwrapper. *(Glyn's)* **£30 [≃$57]**
- The Dharma Bums. London: (1959). Bookplate and small name. Dustwrapper (rubbed, chipped, tears head of spine). *(Ellis)* **£60 [≃$115]**
- Doctor Sax. Faust Part Three. New York: Grove Press, 1959. Wrappers. *(Limestone Hills)* **$30 [≃£15]**
- Doctor Sax. New York: Grove Press, Evergreen Original, (1959). Review slip laid in. Printed wrappers (tiny hole front

wrapper). *(Polyanthos)* **$25 [≃£13]**

- Doctor Sax. London: Deutsch, 1977. Dustwrapper. *(Hazeldene)* **£25 [≃$47]**
- Hymn - God Pray for Me. Montclair: Caliban Press, 1985. One of 150. Printed wrappers. *(Alphabet)* **$65 [≃£33]**
- Jack Kerouac [four Chorus poems]. Verona: Corubolo & Castiglioni, American Authors Series, 1981. One of 60. Signed etching by Enrico Baj. Wrappers. *(Bromer)* **$250 [≃£130]**
- Lonesome Traveller. London: Deutsch, 1962. Upper cover slightly faded, top edges spotted. Dustwrapper (mended, with loss and creasing). *(Hazeldene)* **£20 [≃$38]**
- Lonesome Traveller. London: Deutsch, 1962. 1st British edition. Price-clipped dustwrapper (spine extremities lightly chipped). *(Alphabet)* **$50 [≃£26]**
- Lonesome Traveller. London: Pan, 1964. 1st British paper edition. Issue without a price on cover (no priority known). *(Alphabet)* **$35 [≃£18]**
- Maggie Cassidy. London: Deutsch, 1974. Edges slightly spotted. Dustwrapper. *(Hazeldene)* **£25 [≃$47]**
- Mexico City Blues. New York: Grove Press, 1959. 1st trade paper edition. Wrappers. *(Alphabet)* **$35 [≃£18]**
- On the Road. London: Deutsch, 1958. Dustwrapper (rear panel slightly dusty, three short tears). *(Dyke)* **£180 [≃$345]**
- On the Road. London: 1958. 1st English edition. Dustwrapper (two tiny tears). *(Georges)* **£350 [≃$671]**
- Pic. New York: Grove Press, 1971. 1st printing. Wrappers. *(Limestone Hills)* **$45 [≃£23]**
- Pic. New York: Grove Press, 1971. Photo wrappers. *(Alphabet)* **$20 [≃£10]**
- Satori in Paris. London: Deutsch, 1967. Edges slightly spotted. Dustwrapper (damp marked and spotted). *(Hazeldene)* **£35 [≃$67]**
- Satori in Paris. London: Deutsch, 1967. 1st British edition. Dustwrapper. *(Alphabet)* **$85 [≃£44]**
- The Subterraneans. New York: Grove Press, 1958. One of 100 specially bound and numbered. Foredge corner bumped. No dustwrapper issued. *(Alphabet)* **$750 [≃£390]**
- The Subterraneans. London: 1960. 1st British edition. 1st issue, in red boards. Price-clipped dustwrapper. *(Pettler & Liebermann)* **$110 [≃£57]**
- Take Care of My Ghost, Ghost. With Allen Ginsberg. N.p.: The Ghosts, 1977. One of 200 (supposedly suppressed). Stapled wrappers. Mailing envelope (stamp cancelled). *(Alphabet)* **$135 [≃£70]**
- The Town and the City. New York: (1950). Inscription partially erased, four removal marks on endpapers. Dustwrapper (chipped and frayed). His 1st book. *(King)* **$125 [≃£65]**
- Tristessa. New York: (1960). Wrappers (slight wear). *(King)* **$60 [≃£31]**
- Tristessa. London: World Distributors / Consul Edition, 1961. 1st English edition. *(Alphabet)* **$125 [≃£65]**
- Two Early Stories. New York: Aloes / Oliphant Press, 1971. One of 175. Printed wrappers. *(Alphabet)* **$110 [≃£57]**
- Vanity of Duluoz. London: 1969. Tiny label removed. 1st issue dustwrapper, priced in shillings. *(Polyanthos)* **$95 [≃£49]**
- The Vanity of Duluoz. London: 1969. Dustwrapper. *(Blakeney)* **£45 [≃$86]**
- Visions of Cody. New Directions: 1959. One of 750 signed. Covers little darkened at edges. Flyer for the book loosely inserted. Original mylar unprinted dustwrapper. *(Woolmer)* **$650 [≃£338]**

Kesey, Ken

- Caverns. By O.U. Levon [pseud.]. New York: Penguin, (1990). Uncorrected proof copy. Small ink mark on front cover. Wrappers. Written by Kesey and members of his writing class at the University of Oregon. *(Lopez)* **$45 [≃£23]**
- The Day After September Died. Northridge: Lord John Press, 1980. One of 300 signed by the author. *(Heritage)* **$85 [≃£44]**
- Demon Box. New York: Viking, (1986). Dustwrapper. Author's inscription and underlinings. *(Between the Covers)* **$85 [≃£44]**
- Demon Box. New York: Viking, [1986]. Dustwrapper. Signed by the author. *(Heritage)* **$75 [≃£39]**
- Demon Box. New York: Viking, 1986. Remainder strip tail edge. Dustwrapper. *(Paul Brown)* **£7.50 [≃$15]**
- Kesey's Garage Sale. New York: 1973. Pictorial wrappers. Bookplate signed by the author. *(Polyanthos)* **$45 [≃£23]**
- Kesey's Garage Sale. New York: Viking, (1973). The hardcover issue. Price-clipped dustwrapper. *(Lopez)* **$65 [≃£33]**
- One Flew Over the Cuckoo's Nest. New York: Viking, 1962. Owner name and date on front free endpaper. Price-clipped

dustwrapper (moderate wear at spine extremities, very lightly stained at head of spine). *(Lopez)* **$300 [≃£156]**
- One Flew Over the Cuckoo's Nest. London: 1962. Dustwrapper (edges slightly worn, spine little darkened). *(Sclanders)* **£75 [≃$143]**
- One Flew Over the Cuckoo's Nest. London: 1962. Dustwrapper (slightly frayed, spine slightly faded). *(Ellis)* **£80 [≃$153]**

King, Francis
- The Custom House. London: Longmans, 1961. Dustwrapper. *(Sklaroff)* **£18 [≃$34]**

King, Stephen
- Bare Bones. One of 1000. Slipcase. Shrink-wrapped. *(Polyanthos)* **$80 [≃£41]**
- Carrie. New York: 1974. Advance Reading Copy. Promotional letter dated Jan. 1974 laid in. Printed wrappers (tiny tear to spine repaired). Bookplate signed by the author. His 1st book. *(Polyanthos)* **$750 [≃£390]**
- Christine. London: Hodder & Stoughton, 1983. Uncorrected proof copy. Wrappers. Proof dustwrapper (slightly rubbed). *(David Rees)* **£90 [≃$172]**
- Christine. London: Hodder & Stoughton, 1983. Dustwrapper. *(David Rees)* **£10 [≃$19]**
- Creepshow. NAL: 1982. Wrappers. *(David Rees)* **£20 [≃$38]**
- Cujo. London: Macdonald, 1982. Dustwrapper. *(Paul Brown)* **£25 [≃$47]**
- Danse Macabre. New York: 1981. Dustwrapper (a bit rubbed). *(Pettler & Liebermann)* **$40 [≃£20]**
- The Dark Half. New York: Viking, (1989). Uncorrected proof copy. Bumped at crown. *(Lopez)* **$175 [≃£91]**
- The Dark Tower II: The Drawing of the Three. New York: Plume, 1989. 1st edition. Paperback. Special Advance Readers Copy. Pictorial wrappers. *(Michael Johnson)* **£60 [≃$115]**
- The Dead Zone. New York: 1979. Dust-wrapper. *(Pettler & Liebermann)* **$45 [≃£23]**
- Firestarter. New York: Viking, 1980. 1st US edition. Dustwrapper. *(Moorhouse)* **£20 [≃$38]**
- Firestarter. London: Macdonald, 1980. Edges slightly browned. Dustwrapper. *(David Rees)* **£22 [≃$42]**
- "The Night Flier" [in] Prime Evil. New York: 1988. This copy states "Advance Reading Copy, Not for Sale". Wrappers. *(Polyanthos)* **$100 [≃£52]**
- Night Shift. Garden City: Doubleday, 1978. Advance Review Copy with slip laid in. Dustwrapper (slightest of rubbing to extremities). *(Between the Covers)* **$950 [≃£494]**
- Night Shift. New York: 1978. Dustwrapper (few tiny edge nicks). Bookplate signed by the author. *(Polyanthos)* **$600 [≃£312]**
- Night Shift. New York: 1978. Name. Price-clipped dustwrapper. Signed by the author. *(Polyanthos)* **$250 [≃£130]**
- Pet Sematary. New York: 1983. Proof copy taken from the typescript. Pictorial wrappers. *(Polyanthos)* **$250 [≃£130]**
- Pet Sematary. Garden City: 1983. Price-clipped dustwrapper. *(Pettler & Liebermann)* **$22.50 [≃£11]**
- Pet Sematary. Garden City: Doubleday, 1983. Dustwrapper. *(Houle)* **$75 [≃£39]**
- Salem's Lot. NEL: 1975. Publisher's stamp (the letter R) on title. Lower corners very slightly bumped. Price-clipped dustwrapper. *(David Rees)* **£125 [≃$239]**
- The Shining. 1977. 1st US edition. Dustwrapper (slightly rubbed). *(Ellis)* **£180 [≃$345]**
- The Stand. The Complete and Uncut Edition. New York: Doubleday, 1990). Advance reading copy. Wrappers. *(Lopez)* **$225 [≃£117]**

Kinnell, Galway
- Black Light. Boston: H-M, 1966. Dustwrapper. *(Woolmer)* **$65 [≃£33]**
- Flower Herding on Mount Monadnock. 1964. Review copy with slip. Dustwrapper. *(Dermont)* **$100 [≃£52]**
- What a Kingdom It Was. Boston: H-M, 1960. Dustwrapper (some darkening, tiny closed tear back of spine). His 1st book (preceded by a translation). Author's presentation inscription. *(Woolmer)* **$200 [≃£104]**

Kinsella, Thomas
- Another September. Dolmen Press: 1958. Dustwrapper. *(Edrich)* **£25 [≃$47]**
- Butcher's Dozen. Dublin: Peppercanister, 1972. One of 125 signed. Leather backed cloth boards. *(Blakeney)* **£75 [≃$143]**
- Butcher's Dozen. 1972. One of 125 signed and numbered. Tissue dustwrapper. *(Edrich)* **£30 [≃$57]**
- Downstream. Dolmen Press: 1962. Dustwrapper. *(Edrich)* **£16 [≃$30]**
- Downstream. Dublin: Dolmen Press, 1962. Dustwrapper (very slightly rubbed & nicked). *(Blakeney)* **£30 [≃$57]**

- New Poems 1973. Dublin: Dolmen, 1973. Wrappers very slightly rubbed. *(Blakeney)* **£20 [≃$38]**
- Notes from the Land of the Dead. Cuala Press: 1972. One of 500 numbered. Unopened. *(Edrich)* **£35 [≃$67]**
- Tear. Cambridge, Mass.: Pym Randall Press, 1969. One of 200 (of 226) numbered signed. Wrappers. *(Blakeney)* **£45 [≃$86]**
- Wormwood. Dublin: Dolmen Editions, 1966. One of 350 signed. Faint name on pastedown. Original unprinted glassine (slightly torn & creased). *(Blakeney)* **£80 [≃$153]**

Kinsella, W.P.

- The Alligator Report. Minn.: Coffee House Press, 1985. Self-wrappers. Signed by the author. *(Between the Covers)* **$65 [≃£33]**
- The Alligator Report. Minneapolis: Coffee House, 1985. Wrappers. Signed by the author. *(Lopez)* **$45 [≃£23]**
- The Ballad of the Public Trustee. Vancouver: Standard Editions, 1982. One of 26 (of 326) signed. Linen boards. No dustwrapper issued. *(Alphabet)* **$175 [≃£91]**
- The Ballad of the Public Trustee. Vancouver: Standard Editions, 1982. One of 326. Wrappers. *(Alphabet)* **$30 [≃£15]**
- Born Indian. N.p.: Oberon, (1981). The wrappers issue. Signed by the author. *(Lopez)* **$85 [≃£44]**
- Born Indian. N.p.: Oberon, 1981. Simultaneous paperbound issue. Wrappers. Signed by the author. *(Between the Covers)* **$75 [≃£39]**
- Chapter One of a Work in Progress. Vancouver: W. Hoffer, 1988. One of 26 signed. Boards. No dustwrapper issued. *(Alphabet)* **$150 [≃£78]**
- Chapter One of a Work in Progress. (Vancouver): Hoffer, 1988. One of 300 (of 326) signed by the author. *(Between the Covers)* **$85 [≃£44]**
- Chapter One of a Work in Progress. Vancouver: William Hoffer, (1988). One of 300 (of 326) in wrappers signed. *(Lopez)* **$55 [≃£28]**
- Dance Me Outside. [Ottawa]: Oberon Press, 1977. Wrappers issue (one of several undistinguishable printings). His 1st book. *(Alphabet)* **$45 [≃£23]**
- Dance Me Outside. Boston: Godine, (1986). 1st American edition. Dustwrapper. Signed by the author. *(Lopez)* **$55 [≃£28]**
- Dance Me Outside. Boston: Godine, (1986). 1st US edition. Dustwrapper (slightest trace of rubbing). Signed by the author. His 1st book. *(Between the Covers)* **$65 [≃£33]**
- The Fencepost Chronicles. Boston: Houghton Mifflin, 1986. 1st American edition. Trade wrappers issue. *(Alphabet)* **$8 [≃£4]**
- Five Stories. Vancouver: Tanks 1,2, 1986. One of 100 (of 250). Blue linen. Signed by the author. No dustwrapper issued. *(Alphabet)* **$150 [≃£78]**
- Five Stories. (Vancouver): Tanks, (1986). Wrappers. Signed by the author. *(Between the Covers)* **$85 [≃£44]**
- Five Stories. Vancouver: William Hoffer / Tanks, (1986). Wrappers. Dustwrapper. Signed by the author. *(Lopez)* **$55 [≃£28]**
- The Further Adventures of Slugger McBatt. Toronto: Collins, (1988). Dustwrapper. Signed by the author. *(Lopez)* **$65 [≃£33]**
- The Iowa Baseball Confederacy. Toronto: Collins, 1986. The correct 1st edition. Small rubber stamp on title. Dustwrapper. *(Alphabet)* **$25 [≃£13]**
- The Miss Hobbema Pageant. Toronto: Harper & Collins, (1989). Wrappers. Signed by the author. *(Lopez)* **$55 [≃£28]**
- The Moccasin Telegraph & Other Stories. Toronto: Penguin Books, 1983. 1st edition. Wrappers. *(Alphabet)* **$30 [≃£15]**
- The Moccasin Telegraph. Boston: Godine, (1984). Dustwrapper. Signed by the author. *(Between the Covers)* **$85 [≃£44]**
- The Moccasin Telegraph and Other Indian Tales. Boston: Godine, (1984). 1st hardcover edition & 1st US edition. Dustwrapper. Signed by the author. *(Lopez)* **$65 [≃£33]**
- Rainbow Warehouse. With Ann Knight. Nova Scotia: Pottersfield, (1989). Wrappers. Signed by the authors. *(Lopez)* **$60 [≃£31]**
- Red Wolf Red Wolf. Toronto: Collins, (1987). Dustwrapper. Signed by the author. *(Lopez)* **$65 [≃£33]**
- Red Wolf, Red Wolf. Toronto: Collins, 1987. Dustwrapper. *(Alphabet)* **$12.50 [≃£6]**
- Scars. N.p.: Oberon, (1978). Hardcover edition. Dustwrapper. Signed by the author. *(Lopez)* **$250 [≃£130]**
- Scars. N.p.: Oberon, (1978). Wrappers edition. Signed by the author. *(Lopez)* **$85 [≃£44]**
- Scars. (Toronto): Oberon, (1978). Simultaneous softcover edition. Wrappers. Signed by the author. *(Between the Covers)* **$100 [≃£52]**
- Scars. (Toronto): Oberon, (1978). Hardcover edition. Dustwrapper (minimal wear). Signed by the author. *(Between the Covers)* **$300 [≃£156]**

- Scars: Stories. [Ottawa]: Oberon Press, 1978. Cloth. Dustwrapper. Signed by the author. *(Alphabet)* **$250 [≃£130]**
- Shoeless Joe Jackson Comes to Iowa. N.p.: Oberon, (1980). Hardcover edition. Dustwrapper (lightly rubbed). Signed by the author. *(Lopez)* **$375 [≃£195]**
- Shoeless Joe Jackson Comes to Iowa. N.p.: Oberon, (1980). Wrappers edition. Signed by the author. *(Lopez)* **$100 [≃£52]**
- Shoeless Joe. Boston: HM, 1982. Dustwrapper. Signed by the author. *(Lopez)* **$225 [≃£117]**
- The Thrill of the Grass. Three Plays about Baseball. Vancouver, BC: The New Play Centre, (1988). [One of ca 200]. Stapled wrappers. Signed by the author. *(Lopez)* **$75 [≃£39]**
- The Thrill of the Grass. Vancouver: William Hoffer, (1984). One of 300 in wrappers signed. Inscribed by the author. *(Lopez)* **$55 [≃£28]**

Kizer, Carolyn

- The Ungrateful Garden. Bloomington: Indiana UP, [1961]. Dustwrapper (slightly worn). *(Dermont)* **$60 [≃£31]**

Kneale, Nigel

- Tomato Cain and Other Stories. Foreword by Elizabeth Bowen. London: Collins, 1949. His 1st book. *(Sklaroff)* **£16 [≃$30]**

Knight, Clifford

- The Affair of the Fainting Butler. New York: Dodd, 1943. Dustwrapper (lightly chipped). *(Janus)* **$65 [≃£33]**
- Death of a Big Shot. New York: Dutton, 1951. Dustwrapper (light spine wear). *(Janus)* **$35 [≃£18]**

Koestler, Arthur

- Dialogue With Death. New York: Macmillan, 1942. 1st American edition of Spanish Testament. Dustwrapper. *(Alphabet)* **$15 [≃£7]**
- Reflections on Hanging. London: Gollancz, 1946. Errata slip. Dustwrapper. *(Alphabet)* **$45 [≃£23]**
- Spanish Testament. London: Left Book Club & Gollancz, 1937. Pages browned. Limp orange cloth (spine slightly soiled and faded). His 1st book. *(Virgo)* **£50 [≃$95]**
- Spanish Testament. London: Left Book Club, 1937. Linen wrappers. His 1st book. *(Buckley)* **£35 [≃$67]**

Koontz, Dean

- The Bad Place. New York: Putnam, (1990). Uncorrected proof copy. Promotional material laid in. Wrappers. *(Lopez)* **$100 [≃£52]**
- The Bad Place. New York: Putnam, 1990. One of 250 signed. Slipcase. *(Nouveau)* **$110 [≃£57]**
- The Flesh in the Furnace. New York: Bantam Books, 1972. Paperback original. Wrappers (minor wear front cover). *(Mordida)* **$25 [≃£13]**
- Lightning. Ultramarine: 1988. One of 200 signed. Quarter leather. *(Nouveau)* **$175 [≃£91]**
- Shattered. By K.R. Dwyer. New York: Random House, 1973. Top edge spotted. Dustwrapper. *(Mordida)* **$125 [≃£65]**
- Strangers. New York: 1986. Dustwrapper. Author's presentation copy. *(David Rees)* **£25 [≃$47]**
- Strangers. London: Allen, 1986. Dustwrapper. *(Lewton)* **£15 [≃$28]**
- Surrounded. By Brian Coffey. Indianopolis: Bobbs-Merrill, 1974. Dustwrapper (tiny wear at spine ends and corners). *(Mordida)* **$165 [≃£85]**

Kosinski, Jerzy

- Being There. New York: Harcourt Brace Jovanovich, [1970]. Bookseller's label. Dustwrapper (lightly worn). Signed by the author. *(Heritage)* **$125 [≃£65]**
- The Painted Bird. Boston: Houghton Mifflin, 1965. 1st state, with spurious line top of page 270. Dustwrapper (short closed tear in front panel). *(Chapel Hill)* **$175 [≃£91]**

Kotzwinkle, William

- E.T. The Extra-Terrestrial. London: Barker, 1982. Dustwrapper. *(Lewton)* **£8.50 [≃$17]**

Kovacs, Ernie

- Zoomar. Garden City: Doubleday, 1957. Dustwrapper. His 1st book. *(Limestone Hills)* **$65 [≃£33]**

Kovic, Ron

- Born on the Fourth of July. McGraw-Hill: [1976]. Uncorrected proof copy. Printed wrappers. *(Dermont)* **$150 [≃£78]**

Kundera, Milan

- The Joke. New York: 1969. 1st US edition. Inscription. Dustwrapper. His 1st book. *(Pettler & Liebermann)* **$100 [≃£52]**
- Laughable Loves. London: Murray, 1978. Dustwrapper. *(Moorhouse)* **£20 [≃$38]**

Lamantia, Philip

- Erotic Poems. Berkeley: Bern Porter, 1946. Paper boards and tape bound spine (boards a bit rubbed). His 1st book. *(Alphabet)* **$300 [≃£156]**

Langton, Jane

- Dark Nantucket Moon. New York: Harper, 1975. Dustwrapper. *(Janus)* **$75 [≃£39]**
- The Memorial Hall Murder. New York: Harper, 1978. Dustwrapper. *(Janus)* **$40 [≃£20]**

Lansdale, Joe R.

- By Bizarre Hands. Shingleton: Zeising, 1989. One of 500 signed. Also signed by the illustrator. Dustwrapper. Slipcase. *(Michael Johnson)* **£55 [≃$105]**

Lardner, Ring W.

- The Young Immigrants. Indianopolis: Bobbs, (1920). Foxing to page edges, little offsetting from flaps. Dustwrapper (very small stain on top edge of rear panel, slight rubbing). *(Between the Covers)* **$275 [≃£143]**

Lardner, Ring W., Jr.

- The Ecstasy of Owen Muir. London: Jonathan Cape, 1954. Dustwrapper. *(Sklaroff)* **£35 [≃$67]**

Larkin, Philip

- Aubade. Oregon: 1980. One of 250 initialled by the author and the illustrator, Kathleen Gray Schallock. Wrappers. Envelope. *(David Rees)* **£95 [≃$182]**
- Collected Poems. London: Faber, 1988. Dustwrapper. *(David Rees)* **£25 [≃$47]**
- The Explosion. Poem of the Month Club. Signed by the author. *(Whiteson)* **£25 [≃$47]**
- Femmes Damnees: a Poem. Oxford: Sycamore Broadsheet 27, 1978. Single sheet folded twice. *(Words Etcetera)* **£45 [≃$86]**
- High Windows. London: 1974. Dustwrapper. *(Buckley)* **£50 [≃$95]**
- High Windows. London: 1974. Neat name. Dustwrapper. *(Words Etcetera)* **£40 [≃$76]**
- Introduction to Antiquarian Book Fair. London: 1972. Wrappers. *(Words Etcetera)* **£15 [≃$28]**
- The North Ship. London: Fortune Press, 1945. Covers slightly rubbed. His 1st book. *(Moorhouse)* **£90 [≃$172]**
- Required Writing. London: Faber, 1984. 1st hardbound edition. Dustwrapper. *(Virgo)* **£25 [≃$47]**
- What Jazz. London: 1970. Dustwrapper. *(Words Etcetera)* **£35 [≃$67]**
- The Whitsun Weddings. London: 1964. Dustwrapper. *(Egret)* **£90 [≃$172]**
- The Whitsun Weddings. London: 1964. Dustwrapper. *(Egret)* **£85 [≃$163]**

Lathen, Emma

- A Place for Murder. New York: Macmillan, 1963. Dustwrapper (light wear). *(Janus)* **$120 [≃£62]**

Latimer, Jonathan

- Headed for a Hearse. Garden City: Doubleday Crime Club, 1935. *(Mordida)* **$35 [≃£18]**
- Red Gardenias. Garden City: Doubleday Crime Club, 1939. Some spotting on edges and darkening of endpapers. Dustwrapper (couple of short closed tears and minor wear at spine ends). *(Mordida)* **$250 [≃£130]**
- Sinners and Shrouds. New York: Simon and Schuster, 1955. Dustwrapper (couple of tiny tears). *(Mordida)* **$50 [≃£26]**

Latweed, Shakesbeat

- Pseudonym used by Margaret Atwood, q.v.

Lawrence, D.H.

- Aaron's Rod. London: Secker, 1922. Dustwrapper (small piece missing at foot of spine, larger piece from head of rear panel). *(Words Etcetera)* **£75 [≃$143]**
- Amores Poems. London: Duckworth, (1916). Roberts variant 3. Cover spotted. Tiny library stamp blacked out on dedication page. Dustwrapper (darkened, some chipping at edges). *(Woolmer)* **$175 [≃£91]**
- Amores. London: 1916. Roberts' variant 3, without adverts. Spine slightly creased. Dustwrapper (chipped, 1/2 inch tear at foot). *(Buckley)* **£150 [≃$287]**
- Apocalypse. London: Secker, (1932). Edges and spine faded. *(Woolmer)* **$75 [≃£39]**
- Apocalypse. London: Secker, 1932. Covers and spine faded and marked, endpapers tanned. *(Hazeldene)* **£20 [≃$38]**
- Assorted Articles. London: Secker, 1930. Dustwrapper (slightly chipped and dusty). *(Clearwater)* **£60 [≃$115]**
- (Translates) Cavalleria Rusticana and Other Stories. By Giovanni Verga. London: 1928. Edges foxed. Dustwrapper (slightly chipped). *(Buckley)* **£25 [≃$47]**
- The Collected Poems. London: 1928. 1st trade edition. 2 vols. Cloth gilt (minor wear and soil). *(King)* **$35 [≃£18]**
- The Complete Plays. London: 1965.

Dustwrapper (slightly rubbed).
(Ellis) **£25 [≃$47]**

- David. New York: Knopf, 1926. 1st US edition. Dustwrapper (slightly dusty, one small chip). *(Moorhouse)* **£65 [≃$124]**
- David: a Play. New York: Knopf, 1926. Dustwrapper (dusty & worn, one small chip). *(Moorhouse)* **£50 [≃$95]**
- England, My England. London: (1924). 1st English edition. Top edge soil. Dustwrapper (chipped, torn, spine darkened). *(King)* **$65 [≃£33]**
- Fantasia of the Unconscious. New York: 1922. The correct 1st edition. Pages slightly cockled. Spine dull, boards slightly marked. *(Blakeney)* **£35 [≃$67]**
- Glad Ghosts. London: 1926. One of 500. Wrappers (slightly nicked, little torn at foot of spine). *(Buckley)* **£50 [≃$95]**
- Lady Chatterley's Lover. [Paris]: Privately Printed, 1929. "The Author's Unabridged Popular Edition". Uncut, crudely opened with some tears. Recent half calf. *(Glyn's)* **£85 [≃$163]**
- Lady Chatterley's Lover. New York: Knopf, 1932. 1st US (expurgated) edition. *(Sklaroff)* **£50 [≃$95]**
- The Ladybird. London: Secker, 1923. Dustwrapper (torn, partly defective across upper panel). *(Words Etcetera)* **£50 [≃$95]**
- The Ladybird: The Fox: The Captain's Doll. London: Secker, 1923. Neat inscription on endpaper. *(Sklaroff)* **£30 [≃$57]**
- (Translates) Lasca's Story of Dottor Manente. Florence: 1929. One of 1000. Slight browning near edges. Unopened. Dustwrapper (faintly sunned). *(Buckley)* **£75 [≃$143]**
- Last Poems. New York: 1933. Spine sunned. Dustwrapper (tiny piece missing top of spine). *(Polyanthos)* **$60 [≃£31]**
- Letters to Martin Secker 1911-1930. Privately Printed: 1970. One of 500. Dustwrapper (small brown mark on spine). *(Virgo)* **£45 [≃$86]**
- The Lost Girl. London: Secker, 1920. One small mark on lower cover. *(Words Etcetera)* **£30 [≃$57]**
- Love Among the Haystacks & Other Pieces. London: Nonesuch Press, 1930. One of 1600. Page edges soiled. Light cover wear. Dustwrapper (soiled, chipped, worn, torn in two). *(King)* **$60 [≃£31]**
- Love Among the Haystacks and Other Pieces. London: 1930. One of 1600. Buckram boards (faintly sunned). *(Buckley)* **£40 [≃$76]**
- The Lovely Lady. London: Secker, (1932). Dustwrapper (faintly chipped and soiled). *(Bromer)* **$185 [≃£96]**
- The Man Who Died. London: Secker, 1931. 1st English edition. Spine cloth and strip on upper cover faded, endpapers lightly browned. *(Sotheran's)* **£58 [≃$111]**
- The Man Who Died. London: Secker, 1931. One of 2000. Dustwrapper. *(Nouveau)* **$150 [≃£78]**
- The Man Who Died. London: Secker, 1931. 1st edition. Limited edition. Buckram, t.e.g. (very slightly dull). *(Whiteson)* **£30 [≃$57]**
- Movements in European History. London: 1925. 1st illustrated edition. *(Ellis)* **£40 [≃$76]**
- My Skirmish With Jolly Roger. New York: 1929. 1st copyright edition. One of 600. Errata slip. Original glassine (a little worn). *(Blakeney)* **£75 [≃$143]**
- Pansies. London: 1929. One of 500 signed. Tear at back top inner gutter. Stiff paper wrappers. Glassine dustwrapper (soiled, darkened, chipped). *(King)* **$250 [≃£130]**
- Pornography and Obscenity. London: Faber, 1929. Clothbound issue. Tissue dustwrapper. *(Nouveau)* **$210 [≃£109]**
- Psychoanalysis & The Unconscious. London: Secker, 1923. Spine little faded. *(Whiteson)* **£15 [≃$28]**
- The Rainbow. New York: Huebsch, 1921 [1915]. 2nd American edition. Cloth, paper label stating "Limited Edition". Slight foxing to endpapers and edges. Dustwrapper (diamond-shaped cut-out on spine). *(Houle)* **$275 [≃£143]**
- Rawdon's Roof. London: 1928. One of 500 (of 530) signed. Page edges soiled, offsetting to endpapers. Dustwrapper (soiled, chipped, stained). *(King)* **$250 [≃£130]**
- Rawdon's Roof. London: The Woburn Books, 1928. One of 530 signed. Dustwrapper (small tear on spine). *(Black Sun)* **$350 [≃£182]**
- Rawdon's Roof. London: Woburn Books, 1928. One of 530 signed. Dustwrapper (internal repair). *(Black Sun)* **$350 [≃£182]**
- The Ship of Death. London: 1941. Proof copy. Pages faintly browned. *(Buckley)* **£60 [≃$115]**
- (Contributes to) Some Imagist Poets. London: Constable, 1916. English issue (American sheets with cancel title). Presentation blind stamp. Covers faded, some extremities rubbed, extreme head of spine defective. *(Clearwater)* **£85 [≃$163]**
- Sons and Lovers. New York: Mitchell Kennerley, 1913. 1st American edition. Spine fading. *(Houle)* **$250 [≃£130]**

- Sons and Lovers. London: Duckworth, 1913. Variant with dated cancel-title. Foredge slightly spotted. Top corner slightly bumped, gilt on spine slightly dull. *(Virgo)* **£250 [≃$479]**
- The Spirit of Place. London: Heinemann, (1935). Price-clipped dustwrapper (darkened). *(Woolmer)* **$45 [≃£23]**
- St. Mawr. London: (1925). 1st issue. Spine gilt fading. Page edges soiled, slight offsetting to endpapers. Dustwrapper (soiled, chipped, spine darkened). *(King)* **$65 [≃£33]**
- Sun. Privately printed, 1929. 1st unexpurgated edition published in the US. One of 500. Cloth backed painted patterned boards. *(Polyanthos)* **$95 [≃£49]**
- Tortoises. New York: Thomas Secker, 1921. The correct 1st edition, 1st issue. Offsetting to endpaper. Pictorial boards lightly rubbed & a little faded, spine a little chipped. *(Blakeney)* **£95 [≃$182]**
- Touch & Go. London: 1920. Dustwrapper (slightly darkened, crinkled at edges). *(Buckley)* **£60 [≃$115]**
- The Triumph of the Machine. London: Ariel Poem, 1930. One of 400 Large Paper. Covers soiled, spine edge splitting and frayed. *(King)* **$85 [≃£44]**
- The Triumph of the Machine. London: Faber, 1930. 1st edition. Limited edition. Boards slightly dull, small chip top edge of spine. *(Whiteson)* **£25 [≃$47]**
- Women in Love. New York: 1920. 1st edition (precedes the English edition). One of 1250. Spine and top of boards a little faded, slight wear to extremities of spine and boards. New endpapers. *(Larkhill)* **£180 [≃$345]**

Lawrence, T.E.

- A Brief Record of the Advance of the Egyptian Expeditionary Force. Cairo: 1919. Portrait frontispiece laid down on linen. Some thumbing. Cloth backed wrappers (wrappers soiled, upper cover stained along upper edge). *(Sotheran's)* **£78 [≃$149]**
- (Preface to) Catalogue of an Exhibition ... illustrating ... 'Seven Pillars of Wisdom'. Leicester Galleries, 1927. Wrappers. *(Words Etcetera)* **£125 [≃$239]**
- Letters. London: Cape, 1938. Dustwrapper. *(Dyke)* **£30 [≃$57]**
- The Letters. London: Cape, 1938. Name. Dustwrapper (bit frayed and edge worn at spine extremities). *(Alphabet)* **$110 [≃£57]**
- The Mint. London: Cape, (1955). One of 2000. Leatherette and cloth, t.e.g. Slipcase. *(Houle)* **$375 [≃£195]**
- The Mint. London: 1955. One of 2000. Quarter morocco. Slipcase (slightly rubbed). *(Ellis)* **£140 [≃$268]**
- The Mint. London: Cape, (1955). 1st trade edition. Dustwrapper (slight browning to spine and upper edges). *(Houle)* **$125 [≃£65]**
- (Translates) The Odyssey of Homer. London: 1935. 1st English edition. Dustwrapper (couple of nicks at spine ends). *(Words Etcetera)* **£50 [≃$95]**
- Seven Pillars of Wisdom. London: Cape, 1935. 1st trade edition. Dustwrapper (slightly soiled and chipped). *(Sotheran's)* **£85 [≃$163]**
- T.E. Lawrence to his Biographers, Robert Graves & Liddell Hart. New York: Doubleday, Doran, 1938. One of 500 (of 1000) for the US signed by Graves and Hart. 2 vols. Dust- wrappers (some darkening of spines and corners). Publisher's slipcase (lightly worn). *(Chapel Hill)* **$850 [≃£442]**
- See also the companion IRBP volume Travel.

L'Amour, Louis

- Fair Blows the Wind. New York: Dutton, (1978). Dustwrapper. Author's inscription. *(Houle)* **$125 [≃£65]**

Lear, Peter

- Pseudonym used by Peter Lovesey, q.v.

Leary, Timothy

- The Politics of Ecstasy. London: MacGibbon, 1970. 1st UK edition. Dustwrapper. *(Any Amount)* **£14 [≃$26]**
- Start Your Own Religion. Kriya Press (League for Spiritual Discovery): 1967. Pages somewhat wrinkled. Wrappers. *(Any Amount)* **£35 [≃$67]**

Leavis, F.R.

- How To Teach Reading. A Primer for Ezra Pound. Cambridge: The Minority Press, 1932. Card wrappers (spine slightly faded). *(Dalian)* **£25 [≃$47]**
- Revaluation. London: Chatto & Windus, 1936. Cloth a little discoloured as usual. Dustwrapper (lightly rubbed). *(Ash)* **£25 [≃$47]**

Leavitt, David

- Equal Affections. New York: 1989. Advance reading copy. Wrappers. Signed by the author. *(Polyanthos)* **$45 [≃£23]**
- Family Dancing. New York: Knopf, 1984. Dustwrapper. His 1st book. *(Michael Johnson)* **£45 [≃$86]**

- Family Dancing. London: 1985. Dustwrapper. Author's signed presentation copy. *(Polyanthos)* **$40 [≃£20]**
- Lost Language of Cranes. New York: 1986. Dustwrapper. Author's signed presentation copy. *(Polyanthos)* **$35 [≃£18]**
- Lost Language of Cranes. New York: Knopf, 1986. Dustwrapper. *(Michael Johnson)* **£24 [≃$46]**

Le Carre, John

- The Clandestine Muse. Oregon: Seluzicki, 1986. One of 250 signed. Wrappers. *(Moorhouse)* **£60 [≃$115]**
- The Honourable Schoolboy. Pennsylvania: Franklin Library, 1977. Limited First Edition with special printed message by the author. Leather gilt. *(Words Etcetera)* **£75 [≃$143]**
- The Honourable Schoolboy. London: Hodder & Stoughton, 1977. Review slip tipped to half-title verso. Price-clipped dustwrapper. *(Alphabet)* **$65 [≃£33]**
- The Little Drummer Girl. New York: Knopf, 1983. 1st edition (precedes the English edition). One of around 200 with an additional tipped-in sheet signed by the author. Dustwrapper. *(Mordida)* **$200 [≃£104]**
- The Little Drummer Girl. New York: Special Book of the Month Edition, 1983. One of 1048 signed. Buckram backed cloth. Slipcase. *(Words Etcetera)* **£175 [≃$335]**
- The Little Drummer Girl. London: Pan, 1987. 1st edition thus. One of 739 signed. White wrappers. *(Michael Johnson)* **£50 [≃$95]**
- The Looking-Glass War. London: Heinemann, 1965. Dustwrapper (unfaded). *(Lewton)* **£25 [≃$47]**
- The Looking-Glass War. London: Heinemann, 1965. Price-clipped dustwrapper (closed tears, lightly sunned backstrip). *(Nouveau)* **$60 [≃£31]**
- The Looking-Glass War. London: Heinemann, 1965. Dustwrapper. *(Dyke)* **£35 [≃$67]**
- A Perfect Spy. London: London Limited Editions, 1986. One of 250 signed. Cellophane dustwrapper. *(Words Etcetera)* **£150 [≃$287]**
- A Perfect Spy. London: Hodder & Stoughton, 1986. Dustwrapper. *(Mordida)* **$45 [≃£23]**
- A Perfect Spy. New York: Knopf, 1986. 1st American edition. Dustwrapper. Wraparound band. Signed by the author on a special tipped in leaf. *(Michael Johnson)* **£60 [≃$115]**
- A Perfect Spy. New York: Knopf, 1986. 1st American edition. One of around 200 with an additional tipped-in sheet signed by the author. Dustwrapper. *(Mordida)* **$165 [≃£85]**
- The Russia House. New York: Knopf, 1989. 1st American edition (published three weeks before the British edition). Uncorrected proof copy. Info sheet taped to front cover. Wrappers. *(Lopez)* **$125 [≃£65]**
- The Russia House. London: Hodder, 1989. Uncorrected proof copy. Wrappers (slightly rubbed). *(Moorhouse)* **£30 [≃$57]**
- The Russia House. London: Hodder & Stoughton, [1989]. Proof copy. *(Lopez)* **$125 [≃£65]**
- The Russia House. London: London Limited Editions, 1989. One of 250 signed. Glassine dustwrapper. *(Michael Johnson)* **£100 [≃$191]**
- The Russia House. London: Hodder, 1989. Collector's Edition. One of 500 (approximately). Quarter leather. Slipcase. *(Michael Johnson)* **£45 [≃$86]**
- The Russia House. London: Hodder, 1989. Dustwrapper. Signed by the author. *(Moorhouse)* **£30 [≃$57]**
- A Small Town in Germany. London: 1968. Dustwrapper. *(Roberts)* **£21 [≃$40]**
- A Small Town in Germany. London: Heinemann, 1968. Dustwrapper. *(Lewton)* **£12.50 [≃$24]**
- A Small Town in Germany. London: Heinemann, 1968. Dustwrapper. *(Ash)* **£50 [≃$95]**
- Smiley's People. London: Hodder & Stoughton, 1980. Dustwrapper. *(Marlborough B'shop)* **£15 [≃$28]**
- Smiley's People. New York: Knopf, 1980. 1st American edition. Dustwrapper. Signed by the author on a special tipped in leaf. *(Michael Johnson)* **£60 [≃$115]**
- The Spy Who Came in from the Cold. London: Gollancz, 1963. Slight foxing of foredge. Dustwrapper. *(Lewton)* **£120 [≃$230]**
- The Spy Who Came in from the Cold. US: 1963. 1st US edition. Dustwrapper. *(Lewton)* **£25 [≃$47]**

Lee, Dennis

- Kingdom of Absence. Toronto: Anansi, 1967. One of 300. Correct 1st issue. Wrappers. Dustwrapper (somewhat ragged and torn). *(Alphabet)* **$225 [≃£117]**
- Kingdom of Absence. Toronto: Anansi, 1967. One of 300. Correct 1st issue. Wrappers. *(Alphabet)* **$135 [≃£70]**

Lee, Harper

- To Kill a Mocking Bird. London: Heinemann, 1960. 1st English edition. Dustwrapper. *(Alphabet)* **$85 [≃£44]**
- To Kill a Mockingbird. London: Heinemann, 1960. Dustwrapper (rubbed, very slightly frayed). *(Glyn's)* **£30 [≃$57]**
- To Kill a Mockingbird. London: Heinemann, [1960]. 1st English edition. Dustwrapper (tiny edge tear). Author's 1st book. *(Dermont)* **$150 [≃£78]**

Lee, Laurie

- As I Walked Out One Midsummer Morning. London: Deutsch, 1969. Dustwrapper. *(Michael Johnson)* **£22 [≃$42]**
- The Bloom of Candles. London: Lehmann, 1948. Dustwrapper (faded slightly unevenly). *(Marlborough B'shop)* **£20 [≃$38]**
- Cider with Rosie. London: Hogarth Press, 1959. Prelims slightly foxed. Dustwrapper. *(Marlborough B'shop)* **£20 [≃$38]**
- Cider with Rosie. Illustrated by John Ward. London: Hogarth Press, 1959. Small inscription. Dustwrapper. *(Hadley)* **£45 [≃$86]**
- Cider with Rosie. London: Hogarth Press, 1959. Dustwrapper. *(Lewton)* **£30 [≃$57]**
- The Firstborn. London: 1964. Dustwrapper. Inscribed by the author. *(Georges)* **£25 [≃$47]**
- The Firstborn. London: Hogarth Press, 1964. Dustwrapper (slightly rubbed). *(Buckley)* **£15 [≃$28]**
- I Can't Stay Long. London: 1975. Price-clipped dustwrapper. *(Buckley)* **£15 [≃$28]**
- I Can't Stay Long. London: 1975. Dustwrapper. Signed by the author. *(Roberts)* **£15 [≃$28]**
- I Can't Stay Long. US: 1976. 1st US edition. Dustwrapper. *(Buckley)* **£10 [≃$19]**
- Land at War. London: HMSO, 1945. Wrappers. Anonymous. *(Clearwater)* **£20 [≃$38]**

Lee, William

- Pseudonym used by William S. Burroughs, q.v.

Le Guin, Ursula

- Buffalo Gals and Other Animal Presences. Santa Barbara: Capra Press, 1987. Dustwrapper. Author's signed presentation copy. *(Polyanthos)* **$40 [≃£20]**
- City of Illusions. London: 1971. Base of spine very slightly bruised. Dustwrapper (head of spine slightly creased). *(Ellis)* **£60 [≃$115]**
- Wild Angels. Santa Barbara: Capra, 1975. One of 200 signed. *(Lopez)* **$65 [≃£33]**
- The Wind's Twelve Quarters. New York: 1975. Dustwrapper. Signed by the author. *(Polyanthos)* **$30 [≃£15]**

Lehmann, Rosamond

- Dusty Answer. London: 1927. Dustwrapper (slightly chipped, spine browned). Her 1st book. *(Buckley)* **£70 [≃$134]**
- Dusty Answer. London: Chatto, 1927. Spine and foredges slightly foxed. Dustwrapper. *(Clearwater)* **£110 [≃$211]**
- The Echoing Grove. London: Collins, 1953. Dustwrapper. *(Marlborough B'shop)* **£10 [≃$19]**
- The Gipsy's Baby and Other Stories. London: 1946. Covers trifle faded. Dustwrapper (edges little torn). *(Egret)* **£30 [≃$57]**
- The Gipsy's Baby. London: Collins, 1946. Dustwrapper (slightly foxed). *(Ash)* **£20 [≃$38]**
- A Letter to a Sister. London: Hogarth Press, 1931. Scattered foxing. Wrappers. *(Moorhouse)* **£5 [≃$9]**
- A Letter to a Sister. London: Hogarth, 1931. Wrappers. *(Lewton)* **£25 [≃$47]**
- A Note in Music. London: Chatto, 1930. One of 250 signed. Boards, partly unopened, very slightly dull. *(Whiteson)* **£25 [≃$47]**
- A Note in Music. London: Chatto & Windus, 1930. Dustwrapper. *(Lewton)* **£27.50 [≃$53]**
- The Swan in the Evening. London: 1967. Price-clipped dustwrapper (one small closed tear). *(Egret)* **£12 [≃$23]**

Leiber, Fritz

- Night's Black Agents. Sauk City: Arkham House, 1947. One of 3000. Dustwrapper (minimally edge rubbed). Author's signed presentation copy. His 1st book. *(Polyanthos)* **$150 [≃£78]**
- A Spectre is Haunting Texas. London: Gollancz, 1969. Dustwrapper. *(Glyn's)* **£20 [≃$38]**

Lennon, John

- In His Own Write. London: Cape, 1964. Pictorial boards (laminate creased at upper hinge). *(Sklaroff)* **£25 [≃$47]**
- In His Own Write. London: 1964. No dustwrapper issued. His 1st book. *(Clearwater)* **£25 [≃$47]**
- In His Own Write. London: Cape, 1964. Pictorial boards. No dustwrapper issued. *(Limestone Hills)* **$65 [≃£33]**

- The Lennon Play: In His Own Write. By Adrienne Kennedy, John Lennon, and Victor Spinetti. London: 1968. Dustwrapper. *(Sclanders)* **£36 [≃$69]**
- A Spaniard in the Works. London: 1965. No dustwrapper issued. *(Clearwater)* **£15 [≃$28]**
- A Spaniard in the Works. London: Cape, 1965. Pictorial boards. No dustwrapper issued. *(Limestone Hills)* **$50 [≃£26]**

Leonard, Elmore

- The Big Bounce. New York: Armchair Detective, (1989). 1st hardcover edition. One of 26 lettered signed. Slipcase. *(Lopez)* **$200 [≃£104]**
- The Big Bounce. New York: Armchair Detective, (1989). 1st hardcover edition. One of 100 numbered signed. Slipcase. *(Lopez)* **$75 [≃£39]**
- City Primeval. New York: Arbor House, 1980. Dustwrapper. Inscribed by the author. *(Mordida)* **$30 [≃£15]**
- Fifty-Two Pickup. London: 1974. 1st British edition. Dustwrapper. *(Pettler & Liebermann)* **$125 [≃£65]**
- Forty Lashes Less One. New York: Bantam Books, 1972. Paperback original. Wrappers (uncreased, covers rubbed at edges). *(Mordida)* **$25 [≃£13]**
- Freaky Deaky. New York: Arbor House / William Morrow, 1988. Uncorrected proof copy. Wrappers. *(Mordida)* **$75 [≃£39]**
- Freaky Deaky. London: Viking, 1988. 1st English edition. Dustwrapper. Signed by the author. *(Limestone Hills)* **$55 [≃£28]**
- Get Shorty. New York: Delacorte, (1990). Advance Reading copy. Glossy wrappers. Author's brief inscription. *(Between the Covers)* **$85 [≃£44]**
- Last Stand at Saber River. New York: Dell, 1959. Paperback original. Wrappers (crease on back cover). *(Mordida)* **$40 [≃£20]**
- The Moonshine War. Garden City: Doubleday Doran, 1969. Slight scuffing to the boards. Dustwrapper (very small stain front panel). Signed by the author. *(Lopez)* **$400 [≃£208]**
- Swag. New York: Delacorte, 1976. Dustwrapper. *(Michael Johnson)* **£55 [≃$105]**
- Swag. New York: Delacorte, (1976). Dustwrapper. *(Between the Covers)* **$100 [≃£52]**
- Swag. New York: Delacorte, 1976. Dustwrapper. *(Michael Johnson)* **£32 [≃$61]**
- Swag. New York: Delacorte, 1976. Dustwrapper. Inscribed by the author. *(Mordida)* **$85 [≃£44]**
- The Switch. New York: Bantam Books, 1978. Paperback original. Wrappers. *(Mordida)* **$50 [≃£26]**
- Valdez is Coming. Greenwich: Fawcett, 1970. Paperback original. Wrappers. *(Mordida)* **$65 [≃£33]**

Leopold, Aldo

- A Sand Country Almanac. New York: Oxford, 1949. Bump to top of front board. Dustwrapper (couple of very shallow chips and a tear on rear panel). *(Between the Covers)* **$125 [≃£65]**

Le Queux, William

- The Crime Code. New York: Macaulay, 1928. 1st American edition (published in England as "Double Nought'). Dustwrapper (several short closed tears, wear at spine ends and corners, piece torn from inner front flap). *(Mordida)* **$35 [≃£18]**

Leroux, Gaston

- Wolves of the Sea. New York: Macaulay, [1923]. Dustwrapper (light wear, mild soiling). *(Dermont)* **$50 [≃£26]**

The Lesser Known Shag ...

- See Harrison, Tony.

Lessing, Doris

- African Stories. London: 1964. Edges foxed. Dustwrapper. *(Ellis)* **£70 [≃$134]**
- African Stories. London: Michael Joseph, 1964. Name on endpaper. Dustwrapper. *(Virgo)* **£40 [≃$76]**
- Briefing for a Descent into Hell. London: Cape, 1971. Dustwrapper. Signed by the author. *(Lewton)* **£22.50 [≃$44]**
- Briefing for a Descent into Hell. London: 1971. Dustwrapper. Signed by the author. *(Egret)* **£18 [≃$34]**
- Briefing for a Descent into hell. London: 1971. Dustwrapper. *(Roberts)* **£10.50 [≃$21]**
- Collected Stories. London: 1978. 2 vols. Uncorrected proof copy. *(Buckley)* **£25 [≃$47]**
- The Diary of a Good Neighbour. By Jane Somers. London: 1983. Dustwrapper. Signed by the author as 'Jane Somers' and Doris Lessing. *(Egret)* **£20 [≃$38]**
- Each His Own Wilderness. London: New English Dramatists, 1959. Wrappers. Signed by the author. *(Egret)* **£10 [≃$19]**
- The Fifth Child. London: 1988. Advance uncorrected proof copy.

(Buckley) **£10 [≃$19]**

- The Fifth Child. New York: Knopf, 1988. 1st American edition. Dustwrapper. *(Alphabet)* **$12.50 [≃£6]**
- Five. London: 1953. Corners trifle bumped. Dustwrapper (chipped, slightly torn). *(Egret)* **£25 [≃$47]**
- The Four-Gated City. London: 1969. Dustwrapper. Signed by the author. *(Lewton)* **£22.50 [≃$44]**
- Fourteen Poems. London: 1959. One of 500. Wrappers. Dustwrapper (very slightly creased). *(Ellis)* **£50 [≃$95]**
- Fourteen Poems. Scorpion Press: 1959. One of 500 numbered. Wrappers. *(Any Amount)* **£20 [≃$38]**
- The Good Terrorist. London: Cape, 1985. One of 250 signed. *(Whiteson)* **£25 [≃$47]**
- The Good Terrorist. London: 1985. Dustwrapper. Signed by the author. *(Egret)* **£20 [≃$38]**
- The Habit of Loving. London: 1957. Edges spotted. Dustwrapper (slightly spotted, two closed tears). *(McCann)* **£30 [≃$57]**
- The Habit of Loving. London: McGibbon & Kee, 1957. Name on endpaper. *(Sklaroff)* **£15 [≃$28]**
- If the Old Could. By Jane Somers. London: 1984. Dustwrapper. Signed by the author as 'Jane Somers' and Doris Lessing. *(Egret)* **£20 [≃$38]**
- In Pursuit of the English. London: 1960. Dustwrapper (slightly frayed, slightly rubbed). *(Ellis)* **£35 [≃$67]**
- Landlocked. London: 1965. Foredge spotted. One corner bumped. Dustwrapper (little rubbed & soiled, two short tears). *(Blakeney)* **£25 [≃$47]**
- A Man and Two Women. London: MacGibbon & Kee, 1963. Price-clipped dustwrapper. *(Sklaroff)* **£21 [≃$40]**
- The Memoirs of a Survivor. London: 1974. Dustwrapper. *(Buckley)* **£15 [≃$28]**
- Particularly Cats. London: 1967. Dustwrapper (four small closed tears). Signed by the author. *(Egret)* **£18 [≃$34]**
- Play with a Tiger. London: 1962. Dustwrapper (very slightly rubbed). *(Ellis)* **£35 [≃$67]**
- Play With a Tiger. London: 1962. Dustwrapper. Signed by the author. *(Egret)* **£35 [≃$67]**
- Play with a Tiger. London: 1962. Dustwrapper. *(Clearwater)* **£45 [≃$86]**
- A Proper Marriage. London: 1954. Dustwrapper (very slightly chipped). Signed by the author. *(Egret)* **£40 [≃$76]**
- A Ripple from the Storm. London: Michael Joseph, [1958]. 1st English edition. Price-clipped dustwrapper (minor wear and tear). Signed by the author. *(Antic Hay)* **$125 [≃£65]**
- The Story of a Non-Marrying Man. London: Cape, [1972]. Uncorrected proof copy. Printed wrappers (light wear and soiling). *(Dermont)* **$100 [≃£52]**
- The Story of a Non-Marrying Man. London: Cape, 1972. Dustwrapper. Signed by the author. *(Lewton)* **£22.50 [≃$44]**
- The Story of a Non-Marrying Man. London: Cape, (1972). Dustwrapper. *(Lopez)* **$30 [≃£15]**
- The Summer Before the Dark. London: 1973. Dustwrapper. Signed by the author. *(Egret)* **£25 [≃$47]**
- The Summer Before the Dark. London: Cape, 1973. Dustwrapper. *(Glyn's)* **£18 [≃$34]**
- The Temptation of Jack Orkney. Collected Stories Vol. 2. London: 1975. Dustwrapper. Signed by the author. *(Egret)* **£20 [≃$38]**
- This Was the Old Chief's Country. London: Michael Joseph, 1951. Inscription on endpaper. Dustwrapper (faint cup marks rear panel). *(Sklaroff)* **£65 [≃$124]**
- This was the Old Chief's Country. London: Michael London: Michael Joseph, 1951. Dustwrapper (one tiny chip). *(Moorhouse)* **£100 [≃$191]**
- The Wind Blows Away Our Words. London: 1987. Wrappers. Signed by the author, with her textual correction. *(Buckley)* **£25 [≃$47]**
- Brueck, Eric T.: Doris Lessing: A Bibliography of the First Editions. Metropolis, 1984. One of 50 signed. No dustwrapper issued. *(Sklaroff)* **£45 [≃$86]**

Levertov, Denise

- Conversation in Moscow. [San Francisco?]: Hovey Street Press, 1973. One of 200 signed. Wrappers. *(Any Amount)* **£20 [≃$38]**
- Conversation in Moscow. Hovey St. Press: 1973. One of 800 (of 1000). Red wrappers (one small rub spot). *(Nouveau)* **$20 [≃£10]**
- The Double Image. London: Cresset Press, 1946. Dustwrapper. Signed by the author. Her 1st book. *(Bromer)* **$450 [≃£234]**
- The Jacob's Ladder. London: Cape, 1965. Dustwrapper. *(Nouveau)* **$50 [≃£26]**
- With Eyes at the Back of Our Heads. New Directions: 1959. Dustwrapper. *(Nouveau)* **$45 [≃£23]**

Levi, Peter

- The Gravel Ponds. London: 1960. Dustwrapper (rubbed, nicked). Poetry Society bulletin laid in. *(Ellis)* **£20 [≃$38]**

Levi, Primo

- If This is a Man. Orion Press: 1959. Endpapers browned. Two corners bumped. Dustwrapper (somewhat ragged and chipped). His 1st book. *(Moorhouse)* **£20 [≃$38]**

Levin, Ira

- The Boys from Berlin. New York: Random House, 1976. Dustwrapper. *(Mordida)* **$30 [≃£15]**
- A Kiss Before Dying. New York: Simon & Schuster, 1953. Hinges cracked, pages browned as usual. Dustwrapper (chipped & tape repaired). Author's 1st book. *(Alphabet)* **$75 [≃£39]**
- Rosemary's Baby. New York: Random House, 1967. Price-clipped dustwrapper (short internal tape repair). *(Mordida)* **$85 [≃£44]**

Levon, O.U.

- Caverns ... see Kesey, Ken.

Lewis, Alun

- Raider's Dawn. London: 1942. Uncorrected proof. Wrappers, printed label. Sunned at spine with a one inch split at base. *(Blakeney)* **£65 [≃$124]**

Lewis, C.S.

- Beyond Personality. London: 1944. Dustwrapper (slightly chipped). *(Buckley)* **£15 [≃$28]**
- Beyond Personality. London: Bles / Centenary Press, (1944). Dustwrapper (few nicks). *(Houle)* **$125 [≃£65]**
- Broadcast Talks. London: Bles / Centenary Press, (1942). 1st edition ('July 1942'). Price-clipped dustwrapper (slight browning, tape repair). *(Houle)* **$95 [≃£49]**
- Christian Behaviour. London: 1943. Dustwrapper (slightly soiled, spine darkened, 2 inch closed tear). *(Blakeney)* **£7.50 [≃$15]**
- English Literature in the Sixteenth Century excluding Drama. London: 1954. Price-clipped dustwrapper (slightly rubbed, slightly frayed). *(Ellis)* **£45 [≃$86]**
- An Experiment in Criticism. Cambridge: UP, 1961. Review slip. Dustwrapper (very slightly rubbed, small inked number at foot of spine). *(Blakeney)* **£15 [≃$28]**
- The Four Loves. London: 1960. Dustwrapper. *(Buckley)* **£15 [≃$28]**
- The Great Divorce. London: Bles, 1945. Dustwrapper (chipped at edges). Signed by the author. *(Any Amount)* **£60 [≃$115]**
- Miracles. London: 1947. Dustwrapper. *(Buckley)* **£25 [≃$47]**
- Out Of The Silent Planet. London: 1938. 1st issue, with spine lettering gilt, top edge stained brown. Spine a little scuffed, boards very slightly marked. *(Blakeney)* **£75 [≃$143]**
- Perelandra. London: 1943. Ownership inscription. Spine slightly faded. Dustwrapper (frayed and a little torn, some internal repair). *(Blakeney)* **£75 [≃$143]**
- The Silver Chair. London: 1953. Two corners slightly bumped, patch of fading base of spine. Dustwrapper (frayed, chipped, stained, lacks pieces at spine ends). *(Ellis)* **£200 [≃$383]**
- That Hideous Strength. London: 1945. Top edge a little dusty, name. Dustwrapper (several large chips). *(Blakeney)* **£45 [≃$86]**
- Till We Have Faces. London: 1956. Dustwrapper. *(Clearwater)* **£25 [≃$47]**
- The Voyage of the Dawn Treader. London: 1952. Price-clipped dustwrapper (frayed, rubbed, chipped, nicked, some internal reinforcements). *(Ellis)* **£180 [≃$345]**

Lewis, Cecil Day

- See Day-Lewis, Cecil.

Lewis, D.B. Wyndham

- A London Farrago. London: 1922. Newscutting laid down inside front cover. His 1st book. *(Words Etcetera)* **£20 [≃$38]**

Lewis, Sinclair

- Bethel Merriday. New York: Doubleday, 1940. Endpapers slightly yellowed. Dustwrapper. *(Nouveau)* **$50 [≃£26]**
- Bethel Merriday. New York: Doubleday, Doran, 1940. Dustwrapper (slightly used, two closed tears). *(Chapel Hill)* **$75 [≃£39]**
- Cass Timberlane. New York: Random House, [1945]. Dustwrapper. *(Chapel Hill)* **$55 [≃£28]**
- Dodsworth. New York: Harcourt, Brace, [1929]. *(Chapel Hill)* **$40 [≃£20]**
- The God-Seeker. New York: Random House, [1949]. Price-clipped dustwrapper. *(Chapel Hill)* **$45 [≃£23]**
- Kingsblood Royal. New York: Random House, [1947]. Offsetting to front free endpaper. Price-clipped dustwrapper (one

short tear, very slight rubbing). *(Chapel Hill)* **$50 [≃£26]**

- The Man Who Knew Coolidge. New York: (1928). Dustwrapper (spine little sunned, small pieces missing from extremities and edges). *(Polyanthos)* **$100 [≃£52]**
- Work of Art. New York: Doubleday, 1934. Dustwrapper (reinforced, minor edgewear). *(Nouveau)* **$80 [≃£41]**
- World So Wide. New York: Random House, [1951]. Dustwrapper (some chips and tears). *(Chapel Hill)* **$30 [≃£15]**

Lewis, Wyndham

- America and Cosmic Man. London: Nicholson & Watson, 1948. Dustwrapper. *(Sklaroff)* **£22 [≃$42]**
- America and Cosmic Man. London: Nicholson & Watson, 1948. 2nd binding. Dustwrapper (lightly shelfworn, closed tear near base of spine). *(Patterson)* **£45 [≃$86]**
- America, I Presume. New York: Howell, Soskin, [1940]. Endpapers browned. Red cloth. Dustwrapper (some edge wear), $2.00 price. *(Dermont)* **$50 [≃£26]**
- America, I Presume. New York: Howell, Soskin, 1940. Dustwrapper (a bit frayed and chipped along top and bottom edge). *(Patterson)* **£85 [≃$163]**
- The Apes of God. London: The Arthur Press, 1930. One of 750 signed by the author. Spine dulled and lightly stained, foredge water stained just affecting margins of a few leaves. *(Sotheran's)* **£100 [≃$191]**
- The Art of Being Ruled. London: Chatto & Windus, 1926. 1st variant (Morrow & Lafourcade A6a). Foredge slightly spotted. Spine faded and gilt lettering dull. *(Virgo)* **£40 [≃$76]**
- The Art of Being Ruled. London: Chatto & Windus, 1926. 1st state. Spine very slightly faded. *(Virgo)* **£55 [≃$105]**
- The Art of Being Ruled. London: Chatto & Windus, 1926. 2nd binding. Dustwrapper. *(Patterson)* **£135 [≃$259]**
- Blasting and Bombardiering. London: Eyre & Spottiswoode, 1937. 1st issue. *(Sklaroff)* **£55 [≃$105]**
- Blasting and Bombardiering. London: Eyre & Spottiswoode, 1937. 2nd binding. Dustwrapper (lightly worn, spine a bit tanned, very faint ringmark on front panel). *(Patterson)* **£90 [≃$172]**
- Blasting & Bombardiering. London: Eyre & Spottiswoode, 1937. Binding slightly marked. *(Whiteson)* **£35 [≃$67]**
- The Caliph's Design. London: The Egoist Ltd, 1919. Blue paper boards, rebacked. *(Patterson)* **£75 [≃$143]**
- Count Your Dead They Are Alive. London: 1937. Dustwrapper (minutely nicked at top of spine, spine little sunned). *(Blakeney)* **£350 [≃$671]**
- The Diabolical Principle and the Dithyrambic Spectator. London: Chatto & Windus, 1931. 2nd binding. Dustwrapper (lightly worn, fractionally chipped, minute ink stain base of spine). *(Patterson)* **£100 [≃$191]**
- Doom of Youth. London: Chatto & Windus, 1932. Cloth worn, especially on spine. *(Patterson)* **£80 [≃$153]**
- The Doom of Youth. New York: McBride, 1932. Small tear to one leaf. Spine worn. Dustwrapper (top of spine lightly frayed). *(Patterson)* **£100 [≃$191]**
- Filibusters in Barbary. London: Grayson, 1932. Review slip laid in. Dustwrapper (slightly rubbed, single small closed tear). *(Patterson)* **£275 [≃$527]**
- Filibusters in Barbary. New York: National Travel Club, 1932. 1st American edition. Dustwrapper. *(Dermont)* **$125 [≃£65]**
- The Hitler Cult. London: Dent, 1939. Light spotting to endpapers. Dustwrapper (slightly rubbed and dusty, small snag corner front panel). *(Patterson)* **£225 [≃$431]**
- The Hitler Cult. London: 1939. *(Words Etcetera)* **£40 [≃$76]**
- Hitler. London: Chatto & Windus, 1931. 1st binding. Dustwrapper (incomplete, corners chipped, lacks ends of spine panel). *(Patterson)* **£175 [≃$335]**
- The Jews Are They Human? London: Allen & Unwin, 1939. One corner slightly bumped. Dustwrapper (slightly rubbed, spine and foredges sunned). *(Patterson)* **£200 [≃$383]**
- The Jews Are They Human? London: 1939. *(Words Etcetera)* **£40 [≃$76]**
- Left Wings Over Europe. London: Cape, 1936. Dustwrapper (chipped, tear lower front, scuffed tear top back). *(Halsey)* **£50 [≃$95]**
- Left Wings Over Europe. London: 1936. *(Words Etcetera)* **£40 [≃$76]**
- The Lion and the Fox. London: Grant Richards, 1927. 1st binding. *(Patterson)* **£50 [≃$95]**
- The Lion and the Fox. London: Grant Richards, 1927. 2nd variant (Morrow & Lafourcade A7a). Foredge spotted. Spine faded and lettering dull. *(Virgo)* **£55 [≃$105]**
- The Lion and the Fox. London: Harper, [1927]. 1st American edition.

(Patterson) **£50 [≃$95]**

- The Mysterious Mr Bull. London: Robert Hale, 1938. 2nd binding. Dustwrapper (small closed tear and chip at base of spine). *(Patterson)* **£100 [≃$191]**
- The Old Gang and the New Gang. London: Desmond Harmsworth, 1933. 2nd binding. Bookseller's stamp on f.e.p. Dustwrapper, fine. *(Patterson)* **£125 [≃$239]**
- One-Way Song. London: Faber, 1933. Dustwrapper (single small closed tear), fine. *(Patterson)* **£125 [≃$239]**
- The Red Priest. London: 1956. Dustwrapper. *(First Issues)* **£30 [≃$57]**
- The Red Priest. London: 1956. Neat name. Dustwrapper. *(Polyanthos)* **$35 [≃£18]**
- The Red Priest. London: Methuen, 1956. Dustwrapper. *(Patterson)* **£40 [≃$76]**
- The Revenge for Love. London: 1937. Slight offsetting to endpapers, slight spotting to foredge and prelims. Small stain on front free endpaper. 1st state dustwrapper (somewhat torn, usual spine fading, small piece missing at foot). *(Blakeney)* **£165 [≃$316]**
- The Revenge for Love. London: Cassell, 1937. Dustwrapper (spine and top of front panel sunned), fine. *(Patterson)* **£250 [≃$479]**
- Rude Assignment. London: Hutchinson, 1950. Dustwrapper (top edge a little frayed, couple of minute chips). *(Patterson)* **£100 [≃$191]**
- Satire & Fiction. London: The Arthur Press, Enemy Pamphlets 1, 1930. Wrappers (nicked beside staples). *(Patterson)* **£125 [≃$239]**
- Self Condemned. London: Methuen, 1954. Dustwrapper (two minute nicks top edge), fine. *(Patterson)* **£50 [≃$95]**
- Snooty Baronet. London: Cassell, 1932. 2nd binding. Dustwrapper (spine sunned, slightly frayed and chipped along the top), 'Reduced to 1/-' sticker on spine. *(Patterson)* **£175 [≃$335]**
- Snooty Baronet. London: 1932. *(Words Etcetera)* **£40 [≃$76]**
- Snooty Baronet. London: 1932. Small indentation to rear board. *(Blakeney)* **£35 [≃$67]**
- Tarr. New York: Knopf, 1918. 1st priority binding, red cloth lettered in gold. *(Patterson)* **£175 [≃$335]**
- Tarr. London: The Egoist Ltd, 1918. 1st English edition (the American edition precedes). Cloth (soiled, spine a little cockled). *(Sotheran's)* **£135 [≃$259]**
- Tarr. London: 1918. Two small tears on cover. *(Buckley)* **£65 [≃$124]**
- Time and Western Man. London: 1927. Variant 1 on heavy paper. Tissue guard before title. Very slight offsetting to endsheets. Slight soiling to spine. Dustwrapper (torn, chipped, internally repaired). *(Blakeney)* **£45 [≃$86]**
- The Tyro, No. 2. London: The Egoist Press, 1922. Corners of wrappers fractionally nibbled, spine creased. *(Patterson)* **£75 [≃$143]**
- The Wild Body. London: Chatto & Windus, 1927. One of 85 signed. Endpapers spotted and discoloured near bottom edge. Decorative marbled boards (rubbed, spine sunned). *(Patterson)* **£225 [≃$431]**
- The Wild Body. London: Chatto & Windus, 1927. 2nd binding. Dustwrapper (slightly rubbed and chipped at spine extremities). *(Patterson)* **£95 [≃$182]**
- The Writer and the Absolute. London: Methuen, 1952. Dustwrapper (a little tanned on spine and top of back panel), fine. *(Patterson)* **£60 [≃$115]**
- Wyndham Lewis the Artist. London: Laidlaw & Laidlaw, 1939. 1st issue. Dustwrapper (minimally nicked at head of spine). *(Patterson)* **£160 [≃$307]**

Lindsay, Joan

- Picnic at Hanging Rock. Melbourne: 1967. The correct 1st edition. Boards slightly bumped. Price-clipped dustwrapper (creased at top of spine). *(Blakeney)* **£40 [≃$76]**
- Picnic at Hanging Rock. Melbourne: Cheshire, 1967. Dustwrapper. *(Any Amount)* **£20 [≃$38]**

Lindsay, Vachel

- Going to the Sun. New York: Appleton, 1923. Dustwrapper (some edge wear, light chipping). *(Dermont)* **$65 [≃£33]**

Lindsey, John

- Molten Ember. London: 1930. Dustwrapper (nicked at top of spine). His 1st book. *(Blakeney)* **£30 [≃$57]**

Linington, Elizabeth

- The Borrowed Alibi. By Lesley Egan. New York: Harper, 1962. Advance review copy. Dustwrapper (short edge tear). *(Janus)* **$25 [≃£13]**
- Case Pending. By Dell Shannon. New York: Harper, 1960. Dustwrapper (short edge tear). Publisher's bookmark. *(Janus)* **$65 [≃£33]**
- Crime on Their Hands. By Dell Shannon.

New York: Morrow, 1969. Dustwrapper. *(Janus)* **$30 [≃£15]**

- Nightmare. By Anne Blaisdell. New York: Harper, 1961. Dustwrapper. *(Janus)* **$65 [≃£33]**

Linklater, Eric

- The Crusader's Key. White Owl Press, 1933. Pictorial boards. *(Sklaroff)* **£28 [≃$53]**
- Private Angelo. Privately printed for Allen Lane, 1957. 1st edition thus. One of 2000. *(Virgo)* **£20 [≃$38]**
- Private Angelo. Privately printed for Sir Allen & Richard Lane, Christmas, 1957. *(Sklaroff)* **£35 [≃$67]**
- Sealskin Trousers and Other Stories. London: Hart Davis, 1947. Dustwrapper (slightly rubbed). Author's signed presentation. *(Sklaroff)* **£35 [≃$67]**

Lively, Penelope

- Astercote. New York: Dutton, 1971. 1st US edition. Dustwrapper (pinhole and nick in front panel). Her 1st book. *(Moorhouse)* **£25 [≃$47]**
- The Ghost of Thomas Kempe. London: Heinemann, 1973. Dustwrapper (slightly rubbed). *(Moorhouse)* **£35 [≃$67]**
- Going Back. London: Heinemann, 1975. Dustwrapper. Author's inscription. *(Moorhouse)* **£35 [≃$67]**
- The House in Norham Gardens. London: Heinemann, 1974. Bookplate. Dustwrapper. *(Limestone Hills)* **$25 [≃£13]**
- Moon Tiger. Deutsch, 1986. Uncorrected proof copy. Wrappers. *(Moorhouse)* **£25 [≃$47]**
- Moon Tiger. London: Deutsch, 1987. Dustwrapper. *(Lewton)* **£20 [≃$38]**
- Perfect Happiness. London: Heinemann, 1983. Dustwrapper. *(Limestone Hills)* **$40 [≃£20]**
- The Revenge of Samuel Stokes. London: Heinemann, 1981. Dustwrapper (front flap slightly creased). *(Moorhouse)* **£15 [≃$28]**
- The Road to Lichfield. London: Heinemann, 1977. Dustwrapper. *(Lewton)* **£35 [≃$67]**
- A Stitch in Time. London: Heinemann, 1976. Dustwrapper. Signed by the author. *(Limestone Hills)* **$65 [≃£33]**
- A Stitch in Time. London: Heinemann, 1976. Price-clipped dustwrapper. *(Paul Brown)* **£15 [≃$28]**
- The Whispering Knights. London: Heinemann, 1971. Dustwrapper (slightly rubbed and nicked, rear panel slightly damp stained). *(Moorhouse)* **£30 [≃$57]**

Llewellyn, Richard

- How Green Was My Valley. London: Joseph, (1939). Dustwrapper (few nicks). Signed by the author and portrait photograph laid in. *(Houle)* **$250 [≃£130]**

Llosa, Mario Vargas

- The Time of the Hero. London: Cape, 1967. Dustwrapper (slightly marked). *(David Rees)* **£40 [≃$76]**

Lodge, David

- How Far Can You Go? London: 1980. Corners bumped. Dustwrapper. *(Egret)* **£25 [≃$47]**
- Small World. London: Secker, 1984. Dustwrapper. *(Michael Johnson)* **£25 [≃$47]**

Lofting, Hugh

- Doctor Dolittle and the Secret Lake. London: Cape, 1949. Dustwrapper. *(Green Meadow)* **£25 [≃$67]**

Logue, Christopher

- New Numbers. London: 1969. Wrappers. Author's signed presentation copy. *(Polyanthos)* **$20 [≃£10]**
- Wand and Quadrant. Paris: 1953. One of 300 numbered. Card wrappers. Dustwrapper (slightly sunned). *(Ellis)* **£50 [≃$95]**
- Wand and Quadrant. Paris: Collection Merlin, 1953. One of 300 (of 600) numbered. Wrappers. Signed by the author. *(Words Etcetera)* **£30 [≃$57]**
- Wand and Quadrant. Paris: Collection Merlin, 1953. One of 600. The numbered issue on papier d'arches. Wrappers sunned at extremities. *(Blakeney)* **£45 [≃$86]**

The London Aphrodite

- The London Aphrodite. Edited by Jack Lindsay and P.R. Stephenson. London: Fanfrolico Press, August 1928 to July 1929. Numbers 1-6, all published. Original wrappers. *(Blakeney)* **£125 [≃$239]**

The London Magazine

- The London Magazine. 1954-1989. 350 issues. Complete run. Edited by John Lehmann & (latterly) Alan Ross. *(Any Amount)* **£325 [≃$623]**

Longley, Michael

- An Exploded View. London: 1973. Dustwrapper (minute tear, spine and top edge very slightly faded). *(First Issues)* **£50 [≃$95]**

- Fishing in the Sky. Sutton Coldfield: Poet & Printer, 1975. Wrappers. *(Blakeney)* **£30 [≃$57]**
- Secret Marriages. Phoenix Pamphlets Poets Press: 1968. One of 1000. Wrappers. *(First Issues)* **£25 [≃$47]**
- Ten Poems. Belfast: Festival Publications, [1966]. 1st state, with the "Frowning Face" in light purple. Wrappers. His 1st book. *(Blakeney)* **£75 [≃$143]**

Lovecraft, H.P.

- At the Mountains of Madness and Other Novels. London: Gollancz, 1966. 1st UK edition. Edges slightly foxed. Dustwrapper (faint soiling spine, front panel slightly marked). *(Sclanders)* **£50 [≃$95]**
- The Case of Charles Dexter Ward. London: Gollancz, 1951. 1st separate edition. Dustwrapper (internally repaired, slightly nicked at head of spine). *(Sclanders)* **£100 [≃$191]**
- Dagon and Other Macabre Tales. London: Gollancz, 1967. Price-clipped dustwrapper (slightly torn, spine very slightly browned). *(Sclanders)* **£35 [≃$67]**
- The Dark Brotherhood and Other Pieces. Arkham House: 1966. Dustwrapper. *(Sclanders)* **£60 [≃$115]**
- Dreams and Fancies. Arkham House: 1962. Lower corners slightly bumped. Dustwrapper (very slight wear at corners, minor soiling rear panel). *(Sclanders)* **£60 [≃$115]**
- The Dunwich Horror and Other Weird Tales. New York: Bartholomew House, Bart House Mystery 12, 1945. Wrappers. *(Sclanders)* **£45 [≃$86]**
- The Fantasy Fan, Vol 2, No 2. Edited by Charles D. Hornig. Lovecraft Issue. 1934. Edges slightly browned, tiny chip lower edge front panel. *(Sclanders)* **£200 [≃$383]**
- The Haunter of the Dark and Other Tales of Horror. London: Gollancz, 1951. Slight foxing. Dustwrapper (slightly rubbed). *(Sclanders)* **£75 [≃$143]**
- The Shadow Out of Time and Other Tales of Horror. London: Gollancz, 1968. Dustwrapper (slightly rubbed). *(Sclanders)* **£50 [≃$95]**
- The Shuttered Room and Other Pieces. Arkham House: 1959. Dustwrapper (very slightly rubbed). *(Sclanders)* **£110 [≃$211]**
- Supernatural Horror in Literature. New York: Abramson, 1945. 1st separate edition. 1st printing, with 'elft' page 66 line one. Slightly bumped. No dustwrapper issued. *(Sclanders)* **£45 [≃$86]**
- 3 Tales of Terror. Arkham House: 1967. Dustwrapper. *(Sclanders)* **£85 [≃$163]**
- The Weird Shadow Over Innsmouth, and Other Stories of the Supernatural. New York: Bartholomew House, Bart House Mystery 4, 1944. Wrappers, fine. *(Sclanders)* **£50 [≃$95]**
- A Winter Wish. Whispers Press: 1977. One of 200 signed by the three participants. Dustwrapper. Cloth slipcase. *(Sclanders)* **£80 [≃$153]**

Lovecraft, H.P. & Derleth, August

- The Survivor and Others. Arkham House: 1957. Tiny bump base of spine. Dustwrapper. *(Sclanders)* **£60 [≃$115]**

Lovesey, Peter

- A Case of Spirits. London: Macmillan, 1975. Paper browned as usual. Dustwrapper. Signed by the author. *(Dyke)* **£20 [≃$38]**
- A Case of Spirits. London: Macmillan, 1975. Head of spine slightly bumped. Dustwrapper. Signed by the author. *(Limestone Hills)* **$55 [≃£28]**
- Goldengirl. By Peter Lear. Garden City: Doubleday, 1978. 1st American edition. Dustwrapper. *(Mordida)* **$35 [≃£18]**
- The Secret of Spandau. By Peter Lear. London: Michael Joseph, 1986. Dustwrapper. Signed by the author. *(Mordida)* **$35 [≃£18]**
- Spider Girl. By Peter Lear. London: Cassell, 1980. Dustwrapper. *(Mordida)* **$35 [≃£18]**
- Waxworks. London: Macmillan, 1978. Dustwrapper. Signed by the author. *(Limestone Hills)* **$50 [≃£26]**
- Waxworks. London: Macmillan, 1978. Dustwrapper. Signed by the author. *(Dyke)* **£20 [≃$38]**
- Wobble to Death. London: Macmillan, 1970. Paper a little browned as usual. Dustwrapper. His 1st book. *(Dyke)* **£40 [≃$76]**

Lowry, Malcolm

- Hear O Us O Lord from Heaven Thy Dwelling Place. Philadelphia & New York: Lippincott, 1961. Dustwrapper (corners slightly rubbed). *(Alphabet)* **$75 [≃£39]**
- Selected Letters. London: 1967. Dustwrapper. *(Clearwater)* **£35 [≃$67]**
- Selected Poems. San Francisco: City Lights, 1962. 1st issue, with two photos. *(Alphabet)* **$45 [≃£23]**
- Selected Poems. San Francisco: City Lights, Pocket Poets Series 17, [1962]. Wrappers. *(Limestone Hills)* **$45 [≃£23]**
- Ultramarine. Phila: Lippincott, 1962. 1st US

edition. Dustwrapper. *(Nouveau)* **$95 [≃£49]**
- Under the Volcano. London: Cape, 1947. Cloth partially browned. *(Moorhouse)* **£12 [≃$23]**

Lowther, Alice
- When It Was June. London: Hogarth Press, 1923. *(Clearwater)* **£45 [≃$86]**

Lowther, Pat
- The Difficult Flowering. Vancouver: Very Stone House, 1968. Wrappers. Her 1st book. *(Alphabet)* **$55 [≃£28]**

Lucas, Victoria
- Pseudonym used by Sylvia Plath, q.v.

Lucie-Smith, Edward
- A Tropical Childhood and Other Poems. London: OUP, 1961. Dustwrapper. *(Woolmer)* **$45 [≃£23]**

Ludlum, Robert
- The Chancellor Manuscript. New York: Dial Press, 1977. Dustwrapper. *(Mordida)* **$40 [≃£20]**
- The Cry of the Halidon. By Ryder. New York: Delacorte, 1974. Dustwrapper. *(Janus)* **$20 [≃£10]**
- The Parsifal Mosaic. New York: Random, (1982). Dustwrapper (very slight rubbing). Signed by the author on a tipped in leaf. *(Between the Covers)* **$65 [≃£33]**
- The Rhinemann Exchange. New York: Dial Press, 1974. Dustwrapper (short crease-tear on front panel, minor wear at spine ends, short crease on inner back flap). *(Mordida)* **$35 [≃£18]**
- The Road to Gandolfo. By Michael Shepherd. New York: 1975. With 3 variant dustwrappers as usually seen. *(Polyanthos)* **$50 [≃£26]**
- The Road to Gandolfo. By Michael Shepherd. New York: Dial, 1975. In 3 variant dustwrappers. *(Janus)* **$45 [≃£23]**
- The Scarlatti Inheritance. New York: World Publishing, 1971. Dustwrapper (couple of closed tears and 3/4 inch pieces missing from top of spine and back panel not affecting lettering or illustrations). *(Mordida)* **$90 [≃£46]**
- The Scarlatti Inheritance. London: 1971. Slight bump head of spine. Dustwrapper (a few nicks). His 1st book. *(Ellis)* **£30 [≃$57]**

Lurie, Alison
- Imaginary Friends. London: 1967. Dustwrapper. *(Roberts)* **£22.50 [≃$44]**
- Imaginary Friends. London: 1967. Price-clipped dustwrapper. Signed by the author. *(Ellis)* **£50 [≃$95]**
- Love and Friendship. London: Heinemann, 1962. Dustwrapper. *(Moorhouse)* **£40 [≃$76]**
- The Nowhere City. London: Heinemann, [1965]. Dustwrapper. *(Dermont)* **$40 [≃£20]**

Lyall, Gavin
- The Most Dangerous Game. New York: Scribner's, [1963]. Precedes the English edition. Light stains. Dustwrapper (minor edgewear). *(Antic Hay)* **$25 [≃£13]**

Lye, Len
- No Trouble. Majorca: Seizin Press, 1930. One of 200 signed. Buckram backed patterned boards gilt. *(Words Etcetera)* **£150 [≃$287]**

Lyons, Arthur
- All God's Children. New York: Mason / Charter, 1975. Dustwrapper (couple of tiny closed tears, minor wear spine ends and corners, minor rubbing). *(Mordida)* **$175 [≃£91]**
- Dead Ringer. New York: 1977. Dustwrapper. Signed by the author. *(Pettler & Liebermann)* **$60 [≃£31]**
- Hard Trade. New York: 1981. Dustwrapper. Author's inscription. *(Pettler & Liebermann)* **$35 [≃£18]**
- The Killing Floor. New York: Mason / Charter, 1976. Dustwrapper (several short closed tears, wear at spine ends and corners, rubbing along folds). *(Mordida)* **$150 [≃£78]**

McAlmon, Robert
- The Portrait of a Generation. Paris: Contact Press, 1926. One of 200. Wrappers (browning to upper foredge along 1 1/2 inches, spine slightly rubbed). *(Words Etcetera)* **£225 [≃$431]**
- The Portrait of a Generation: including the Revolving Mirror. Paris: Contact, Three Mountains, 1926. One of 190 (of 200). Paper wrappers, chipped at edges and spine top. *(Alphabet)* **$125 [≃£65]**

McAlmon, Robert (ed.)
- Contact Collection of Contemporary Writers. Paris: Contact Press, 1925. Wrappers. *(Any Amount)* **£350 [≃$671]**

Macaulay, Rose
- Fabled Shore. London: Hamish Hamilton, 1949. Dustwrapper (very slightly rubbed and

nicked). *(Dalian)* **£25 [≃$47]**

- Going Abroad. London: Collins, 1934. Endpapers slightly browned. Spine dull. Dustwrapper (slightly nicked). *(Dalian)* **£35 [≃$67]**
- I Would be Private. London: Collins, 1937. Cloth slightly faded and marked. *(Dalian)* **£20 [≃$38]**
- The Lee Shore. London: Hodder & Stoughton, (1912). Foredge and prelims slightly foxed. Covers slightly rubbed. *(Dalian)* **£35 [≃$67]**
- Orphan Island. London: Collins, 1924. Foredge and prelims slightly foxed. Cloth slightly marked. *(Dalian)* **£25 [≃$47]**
- The Secret River. London: Murray, 1909. Prelims foxed. Inscriptions on endpapers. Cloth slightly rubbed. *(Dalian)* **£45 [≃$86]**
- Staying with Relations. London: Collins, 1930. Dustwrapper (slightly nicked). *(Dalian)* **£35 [≃$67]**
- Three Days. London: Constable, 1919. Wrappers (spine very slightly nicked, covers very slightly dusty). *(Dalian)* **£30 [≃$57]**
- Told by an Idiot. New York: Boni and Liveright, (1923). 1st American edition. Dustwrapper (few nicks). *(Houle)* **$65 [≃£33]**
- The Two Blind Countries. London: Sidgwick & Jackson, 1914. Name on endpaper. Cloth slightly dusty. *(Dalian)* **£35 [≃$67]**

McBain, Ed

- Squad Room. New York: S&S, 1961. Pages browned. Dustwrapper. *(Between the Covers)* **$50 [≃£26]**

McCammon, Robert R.

- Baal. New York: Avon, 1978. Wrappers. Signed by the author and inscribed. *(Michael Johnson)* **£55 [≃$105]**
- Bethany's Sin. New York: Avon, 1980. Wrappers. Signed by the author and inscribed. *(Michael Johnson)* **£35 [≃$67]**
- Blue World. London: Grafton, 1989. 1st hardcover. Dustwrapper. *(Michael Johnson)* **£30 [≃$57]**
- Mystery Walk. New York: Holt, 1983. Dustwrapper. Signed by the author. *(Michael Johnson)* **£75 [≃$143]**
- Stinger. New York: Pocket, 1988. Advance Reading Copy. Wrappers. Signed by the author. *(Michael Johnson)* **£48 [≃$92]**
- Stinger. New York: Pocket, 1988. 1st trade edition. Wrappers. Signed by the author. *(Michael Johnson)* **£20 [≃$38]**
- Swan Song. New York: Pocket, 1987. Advance Reading Copy. Wrappers. Signed by the author. *(Michael Johnson)* **£75 [≃$143]**
- Swan Song. New York: Pocket, 1987. 1st trade edition. Wrappers. Signed by the author. *(Michael Johnson)* **£30 [≃$57]**
- They Thirst. New York: Avon, 1981. Wrappers. Signed by the author. *(Michael Johnson)* **£28 [≃$53]**
- Wolf's Hour. New York: Pocket, 1989. Advance Reader's Copy. Wrappers. Signed by the author. *(Michael Johnson)* **£45 [≃$86]**

McCarthy, Cormac

- Blood Meridian. New York: Random, (1985). Uncorrected proof copy. Wrappers (small stain top of front wrapper). *(Between the Covers)* **$125 [≃£65]**
- Child of God. New York: Random House, 1973. Price-clipped dustwrapper. *(Nouveau)* **$90 [≃£46]**
- Child of God. London: Chatto, 1975. 1st English edition. Dustwrapper. *(Nouveau)* **$65 [≃£33]**

McCarthy, Mary

- Birds of America. New York: Harcourt, Brace, Jovanovich, [1971]. 1st printing. Dustwrapper (lightly used). Signed by the author. *(Antic Hay)* **$75 [≃£39]**
- Cannibals and Missionaries. New York: 1979. Dustwrapper. Signed by the author. *(Polyanthos)* **$40 [≃£20]**
- A Charmed Life. New York: Harcourt, Brace, [1955]. Price-clipped dustwrapper (some wear). Signed by the author. *(Antic Hay)* **$100 [≃£52]**
- The Group. New York: Harcourt, Brace & World, [1963]. Dustwrapper (moderate wear). Signed by the author. *(Antic Hay)* **$75 [≃£39]**
- Hanoi. London: Weidenfeld, 1968. Signed presentation copy. *(Any Amount)* **£25 [≃$47]**
- Memories of a Catholic Girlhood. New York: Harcourt, Brace, [1957]. Dustwrapper. Signed by the author. *(Antic Hay)* **$75 [≃£39]**
- On the Contrary. New York: Farrar, Straus & Cudahy, [1961]. 1st printing. Dustwrapper (some soil, small internally repaired tears). Signed by the author. *(Antic Hay)* **$75 [≃£39]**
- Winter Visitors. New York: 1970. Limited edition. Pictorial boards. No dustwrapper issued. Signed by the author. *(Polyanthos)* **$35 [≃£18]**

McClure, James

- The Caterpillar Cop. London: Gollancz, 1972. Dustwrapper. *(Mordida)* **$65 [≃£33]**
- The Gooseberry Fool. London: Gollancz, 1974. Couple of small scrapes on bottom edge of front cover. Dustwrapper. *(Mordida)* **$50 [≃£26]**
- The Steam Pig. London: Gollancz, 1971. Top edge slightly darkened. Dustwrapper (couple of tiny scrapes). *(Mordida)* **$80 [≃£41]**
- The Steam Pig. New York: Harper & Row, 1972. 1st American edition. Dustwrapper. *(Mordida)* **$25 [≃£13]**

McClure, Michael

- Hail Thee Who Play. Los Angeles: Black Sparrow Press, 1968. One of 250 signed. Wrappers. *(Polyanthos)* **$30 [≃£15]**
- Hymns to St Geryon. London: Cape Goliard, 1969. Dustwrapper. Wraparound band. *(Any Amount)* **£20 [≃$38]**
- Poisoned Wheat. San Francisco: 1965. Wrappers. Author's signed presentation copy. *(Polyanthos)* **$35 [≃£18]**

McCrum, Robert

- In the Secret State. London: Hamish Hamilton, 1980. Dustwrapper. His 1st book. *(Dalian)* **£30 [≃$57]**

McCullers, Carson

- The Heart is a Lonely Hunter. London: Cresset, 1943. Covers worn and partly faded. *(Glyn's)* **£20 [≃$38]**
- The Member of the Wedding. Boston: Houghton: 1946. Dustwrapper (chipped and worn). *(Nouveau)* **$75 [≃£39]**
- Reflections in a Golden Eye. Boston: HM, 1941. Offsetting on rear endpapers from clippings laid in. 1st issue dustwrapper, with glassine "window", (some internal tape repairs. Author's inscription. *(Lopez)* **$875 [≃£455]**
- Reflections in a Golden Eye. Boston: 1941. Price clipped 2nd issue dustwrapper (worn). *(Pettler & Liebermann)* **$45 [≃£23]**
- Sweet as a Pickle and Clean as a Pig. Boston: Houghton: 1964. Dustwrapper. *(Nouveau)* **$90 [≃£46]**

McCullough, Colleen

- Tim. New York: (1974). Dustwrapper. Signed by the author "with best wishes". Her 1st book. *(Polyanthos)* **$35 [≃£18]**

McDermott, Alice

- A Bigamist's Daughter. New York: 1982. Dustwrapper. Author's signed presentation copy. Her 1st book. *(Polyanthos)* **$45 [≃£23]**
- A Bigamist's Daughter. New York: 1982. Dustwrapper. *(Pettler & Liebermann)* **$60 [≃£31]**

MacDiarmid, Hugh

- The Company I've Kept. London: Hutchinson, 1966. Dustwrapper. Author's presentation copy. *(Whiteson)* **£25 [≃$47]**
- Contemporary Scottish Studies. First Series. London: Leonard Parsons, 1926. Cloth (lightly worn, spine a little dull). *(Patterson)* **£40 [≃$76]**
- The Fire of the Spirit. Glasgow: Duncan Glen, 1965. One of 350. Sewn printed wrappers. *(Antic Hay)* **$45 [≃£23]**
- In Memoriam James Joyce. London: 1955. Edges slightly rubbed. Not known if dustwrapper issued. *(Ellis)* **£140 [≃$268]**
- Lucky Poet. London: Methuen, 1943. Light wear to spine. *(Patterson)* **£30 [≃$57]**
- Penny Wheep. London: 1926. Page edges foxed. Dustwrapper (slightly sunned). *(Buckley)* **£35 [≃$67]**
- Sangshaw. Edinburgh: Blackwood, 1925. Dustwrapper (slightly rubbed). *(Ash)* **£125 [≃$239]**
- Sangshaw. 1925. Two pages torn without loss. Dustwrapper (faded). *(Buckley)* **£50 [≃$95]**
- Scottish Eccentrics. London: Routledge, 1936. Spine sunned, light wear. *(Patterson)* **£50 [≃$95]**
- Selected Poems. London: 1934. Wrappers (spine a little browned). *(Words Etcetera)* **£16 [≃$30]**
- Song of the Seraphim. London: Covent Garden Press & Inca Books, (1972). One of 600. Dustwrapper (slightly dusty). *(Dalian)* **£25 [≃$47]**
- To Circumjack Cencrastus. Blackwood: 1930. *(Whiteson)* **£30 [≃$57]**
- To Circumjack Cencrastus. London: 1930. Secondary binding. Dustwrapper (slightly frayed, slightly tanned, a few small nicks). *(Ellis)* **£60 [≃$115]**

MacDonald, John D.

- Ballroom of the Skies. New York: Greenberg, [1952]. Dustwrapper (lightly used, several small edge tears). *(Dermont)* **$125 [≃£65]**
- The Barbarous Coast. New York: Knopf, 1956. Dustwrapper (tiny nick at corner, short

closed tear back panel). *(Mordida)* **$300 [≃£156]**

- The Brass Cupcake. New York: Fawcett, 1950. Paperback original. Hinge cracked. *(Janus)* **$50 [≃£26]**
- Bright Orange for the Shroud. Greenwich: Fawcett, 1965. Paperback original. Very small scuff. *(Janus)* **$30 [≃£15]**
- Condominium. Phila: Lippincott, 1977. One of 995 signed. Dustwrapper. *(Mordida)* **$150 [≃£78]**
- Country Pleasure. New York: Appleton Century Crofts, 1954. Name stamp. Dustwrapper. *(Alphabet)* **$65 [≃£33]**
- The Crossroads. New York: S&S, 1959. Edges of paper yellowed. Dustwrapper (few nicks and short tears). *(Between the Covers)* **$85 [≃£44]**
- The Deep Blue Good-by. Greenwich: Fawcett, 1964. Paperback original. Some browning to margins. No spine crease. *(Janus)* **$65 [≃£33]**
- The Deep Blue Good-by. Phila: Lippincott, 1975. 1st hardbound. Dustwrapper. *(Janus)* **$185 [≃£96]**
- The Dreadful Lemon Sky. Phila: Lippincott, 1974. Dustwrapper. *(Janus)* **$65 [≃£33]**
- The End of the Night. New York: Simon and Schuster, 1960. Dustwrapper (some tiny tears and wear at spine ends and corners). *(Mordida)* **$90 [≃£46]**
- The Girl in the Plain Brown Wrapper. Phila: Lippincott, 1973. 1st hardbound. Dustwrapper (slightly rubbed, spine very slightly sunned). *(Janus)* **$165 [≃£85]**
- Murder for the Bride. New York: Fawcett, 1951. Light wear, no spine crease. *(Janus)* **$45 [≃£23]**
- Nightmare in Pink. Greenwich: Fawcett Publications, 1964. Paperback original Gold Medal no. k1406. Wrappers. *(Mordida)* **$50 [≃£26]**
- Nightmare in Pink. Greenwich: Fawcett, 1964. Paperback original. Small scuff at top edge. No spine crease. *(Janus)* **$30 [≃£15]**
- A Purple Place for Dying. Greenwich: Fawcett, 1964. Paperback original. No spine crease. *(Janus)* **$35 [≃£18]**
- The Quick Red Fox. Greenwich: Fawcett, 1964. Paperback original. Very small scuff. No spine crease. *(Janus)* **$30 [≃£15]**
- The Scarlet Ruse. Greenwich: Fawcett, 1973. Paperback original. Very small scuff. No spine crease. *(Janus)* **$30 [≃£15]**
- The Scarlet Ruse. New York: Lippincott & Crowell, 1980. 1st US hardbound. Dustwrapper. *(Janus)* **$165 [≃£85]**
- The Scarlet Ruse. New York: Lippincott and Crowell, 1980. 1st American hardcover edition. Price-clipped dustwrapper. *(Mordida)* **$85 [≃£44]**
- The Scarlet Ruse. New York: Lippincott & Crowell, 1980. 1st American hardcover edition. Dustwrapper. *(Mordida)* **$90 [≃£46]**
- A Tan and Sandy Silence. Greenwich: Fawcett, 1972. Paperback original. No spine crease. *(Janus)* **$35 [≃£18]**
- A Tan and Sandy Silence. Phila: Lippincott, 1979. 1st hardbound. Dustwrapper. *(Janus)* **$165 [≃£85]**
- A Tan and Sandy Silence. Phila: Lippincott, 1979. 1st American hardcover edition. Dustwrapper. Signed by the author. *(Mordida)* **$200 [≃£104]**
- A Tan and Sandy Silence. Phila: Lippincott, 1979. 1st American hardcover edition. Tiny wear at base of spine. Dustwrapper. *(Mordida)* **$100 [≃£52]**
- The Turquoise Lament. Phila: Lippincott, 1973. Dustwrapper (edgewear). *(Janus)* **$50 [≃£26]**
- The Turquoise Lament. Phila: Lippincott, (1973). Price-clipped dustwrapper (tiny nick). *(Between the Covers)* **$60 [≃£31]**

Macdonald, John Ross

- See Macdonald, Ross.

MacDonald, Philip

- The Link. Garden City: Doubleday, 1930. 1st US edition. Price-clipped dustwrapper (internally reinforced). *(Janus)* **$125 [≃£65]**

Macdonald, Ross (Kenneth Millar)

- Blue City. By Kenneth Millar. New York: Knopf, 1947. Dustwrapper (lightly worn and soiled, few tiny edge tears). *(Dermont)* **$150 [≃£78]**
- The Doomsters. New York: Knopf, 1958. Dustwrapper (couple of short closed tears and tiny wear at corners). Inscribed by the author. *(Mordida)* **$750 [≃£390]**
- The Far Side of the Dollar. New York: Knopf, 1965. Dustwrapper (rubbing at spine ends). *(Mordida)* **$140 [≃£72]**
- Find a Victim. New York: Knopf, 1954. Dustwrapper (chipped at rear, several pinholes in flap creases). *(Janus)* **$175 [≃£91]**
- The Goodbye Look. New York: Knopf, 1969. Dustwrapper. *(Janus)* **$45 [≃£23]**
- The Instant Enemy. New York: Knopf, 1968. Dustwrapper. *(Janus)* **$125 [≃£65]**

- The Instant Enemy. New York: Knopf, 1968. Dustwrapper. *(Lopez)* **$55 [≃£28]**
- The Instant Enemy. New York: Knopf, 1968. Price-clipped dustwrapper. *(Janus)* **$80 [≃£41]**
- The Name is Archer. By John Ross Macdonald. New York: Bantam Books, 1955. Paperback original Bantam no. 1295. Wrappers. *(Mordida)* **$75 [≃£39]**
- The Name is Archer. New York: Bantam, 1955. Paperback original. Small snag on spine. No spine crease. *(Janus)* **$50 [≃£26]**
- The Wycherly Woman. New York: Knopf, 1961. Dustwrapper (internally reinforced). *(Janus)* **$125 [≃£65]**
- The Wycherly Woman. London: Collins Crime Club, 1962. 1st English edition. Dustwrapper (internal tape repair, wear at spine ends and along edges). *(Mordida)* **$45 [≃£23]**

McElroy, Joseph

- Ship Rock. Concord: Ewert, 1980. One of 226 signed. No dustwrapper issued. Author's signed presentation copy. *(Polyanthos)* **$45 [≃£23]**
- A Smuggler's Bible. New York: Harcourt, Brace & World, (1968). Dustwrapper. His 1st book. *(Houle)* **$200 [≃£104]**
- Women and Men. New York: 1987. Dustwrapper. Author's signed presentation copy. *(Polyanthos)* **$45 [≃£23]**

McEwan, Ian

- Between the Sheets. London: 1978. Dustwrapper. *(Words Etcetera)* **£37.50 [≃$72]**
- The Cement Garden. London: Cape, 1978. Dustwrapper. *(Lewton)* **£25 [≃$47]**
- The Cement Garden. London: 1978. Price-clipped dustwrapper. Signed by the author. *(Egret)* **£25 [≃$47]**
- The Cement Garden. New York: Simon & Schuster, 1978. 1st American edition. Dustwrapper. *(Dalian)* **£15 [≃$28]**
- The Child in Time. London: Cape & London Limited Editions, 1987. One of 150 signed. Cloth backed marbled boards. Glassine wrapper. *(Dyke)* **£30 [≃$57]**
- The Child in Time. London: Cape, 1987. Dustwrapper. Signed by the author. *(Lewton)* **£12.50 [≃$24]**
- The Child in Time. London: 1987. Dustwrapper. Signed by the author. *(Egret)* **£20 [≃$38]**
- The Comfort of Strangers. London: 1981. Dustwrapper. Signed by the author. *(Egret)* **£35 [≃$67]**
- The Comfort of Strangers. London: Cape, 1981. Dustwrapper. *(Dalian)* **£16 [≃$30]**
- First Love, Last Rites. London: Cape, 1975. Dustwrapper. His 1st book. *(Moorhouse)* **£100 [≃$191]**
- In Between the Sheets. London: 1978. Dustwrapper. Signed by the author. *(Egret)* **£70 [≃$134]**
- The Innocent. London: 1990. Uncorrected proof copy. Wrappers. Signed by the author. *(David Rees)* **£22 [≃$42]**
- The Innocent. London: 1990. Uncorrected proof copy. Wrappers. *(Dyke)* **£55 [≃$105]**
- The Innocent. London: 1990. Dustwrapper. Signed by the author. *(David Rees)* **£18 [≃$34]**
- The Innocent. London: 1990. Dustwrapper. Signed by the author. *(Egret)* **£25 [≃$47]**
- Or Shall We Die? London: Cape, 1983. Dustwrapper. Signed by the author. *(Lewton)* **£12.50 [≃$24]**
- Or Shall We Die? London: Cape, 1983. Pictorial dustwrapper. *(Paul Brown)* **£10 [≃$19]**
- Or Shall We Die? London: Cape, 1983. Plain dustwrapper. *(Paul Brown)* **£10 [≃$19]**
- The Ploughman's Lunch. Methuen, 1985. Wrappers. Signed by the author. *(Moorhouse)* **£10 [≃$19]**
- Soursweet. London: Faber, 1988. The screenplay of Timothy Mo's novel. Wrappers. Signed by the author. *(Moorhouse)* **£8 [≃$15]**

MacEwen, Gwendolyn

- King of Egypt, King of Dreams. Toronto: Macmillan, 1971. Review slip. Dustwrapper. *(Alphabet)* **$65 [≃£33]**

McGahern, John

- Amongst Women. London: Faber, 1990. Dustwrapper. Signed by the author. *(David Rees)* **£20 [≃$38]**

McGinley, Patrick

- Bogmail. Martin Brian & O'Keefe: 1978. Dustwrapper. *(Moorhouse)* **£45 [≃$86]**

McGuane, Thomas

- Ninety-Two in the Shade. London: Collins, 1974. 1st English edition. Dustwrapper (one tiny closed tear). *(Nouveau)* **$50 [≃£26]**
- An Outside Chance. New York: Farrar, 1980. Uncorrected proof copy. Wrappers. Signed by the author. *(Nouveau)* **$120 [≃£62]**

- The Sporting Club. New York: Simon & Schuster, [1968]. Black ink line on bottom edge. Dustwrapper (slightly used). His 1st book. *(Dermont)* **$50 [≃£26]**

McInerney, Jay

- Bright Lights, Big City. New York: Vintage, (1984). Uncorrected proof copy. *(Lopez)* **$125 [≃£65]**
- Bright Lights, Big City. London: Cape, 1985. Dustwrapper. *(Paul Brown)* **£20 [≃$38]**
- Bright Lights, Big City. London: Cape, 1985. 1st British edition. 1st hardbound edition. Dustwrapper. *(Michael Johnson)* **£20 [≃$38]**
- Ransom. New York: Vintage, 1985. Remainder mark. Dustwrapper. *(Michael Johnson)* **£20 [≃$38]**
- Story of My Life. London: Bloomsbury, 1988. Precedes US edition. Dustwrapper. Signed by the author. *(Michael Johnson)* **£25 [≃$47]**
- Story of My Life. New York: Atlantic, 1988. 1st American edition. Dustwrapper. Signed by the author. *(Michael Johnson)* **£25 [≃$47]**

Mackenzie, Compton

- Fairy Gold. London: 1926. Corners slightly faded, spine slightly faded. Signed by the author. *(Ellis)* **£20 [≃$38]**
- Guy and Pauline. London: Secker, 1915. Endpapers browned. Inscription. Spine and covers slightly darkened. *(Dalian)* **£35 [≃$67]**
- Our Street. London: Cassell, 1931. Foredge slightly foxed. Cloth slightly faded. Dustwrapper (slightly soiled and chipped). *(Dalian)* **£30 [≃$57]**
- Poems. London: 1907. Wrappers (edges creased and frayed, spine slightly rubbed and tanned). His 1st book. *(Ellis)* **£85 [≃$163]**
- Poems. Oxford & London: 1907. Printed wrappers (top of spine slightly nicked). Half morocco slipcase. 6-line presentation inscription by the author. *(Black Sun)* **$200 [≃£104]**
- Sylvia and Michael. London: Secker, 1919. Dustwrapper (slightly soiled, tanned, chipped). *(Dalian)* **£45 [≃$86]**

Maclaren-Ross, Julian

- Bitten by the Tarantula. London: 1945. Two light scratches to front board. Dustwrapper (scratched on front panel, small chip at top of spine, a little internal repair). *(Blakeney)* **£25 [≃$47]**
- Bitten by the Tarantula. London: 1945. Edges foxed. Dustwrapper (slightly rubbed, slightly frayed, a few small nicks). *(Ellis)* **£60 [≃$115]**
- The Funny Bone. London: 1956. Review copy. Dustwrapper (slightly chipped). Suppressed. *(Buckley)* **£40 [≃$76]**
- The Nine Men of Soho. London: 1946. Edges and endpapers foxed. Dustwrapper (chipped, torn, frayed). *(Ellis)* **£40 [≃$76]**
- The Weeping and the Laughter. London: 1953. Offsetting to endpapers. Dustwrapper (one short tear). *(Blakeney)* **£35 [≃$67]**

MacLaverty, Bernard

- Lamb. London: 1980. Dustwrapper. Inscribed by the author. *(Words Etcetera)* **£25 [≃$47]**
- Lamb. London: 1980. Dustwrapper. Signed by the author. *(Ellis)* **£50 [≃$95]**
- Secrets and Other Stories. Belfast: Blackstaff Press, 1977. Dustwrapper. Signed by the author. His 1st book. *(Moorhouse)* **£45 [≃$86]**

Maclean, Alistair

- The Guns of Navarone. London: Collins, 1957. Dustwrapper (very slightly rubbed). *(Ash)* **£25 [≃$47]**
- H.M.S. Ulysses. London: 1955. Dustwrapper (one small chip, one nick). His 1st book. *(Ellis)* **£30 [≃$57]**

Macleish, Archibald

- America Was Promises. New York: 1939. Dustwrapper. *(Polyanthos)* **$20 [≃£10]**
- Before March. New York: Knopf, Borzoi Chap Book, 1932. Wrappers. *(Woolmer)* **$20 [≃£10]**
- The Conquistador. Boston: Houghton, Mifflin, 1932. Some browning of endpaper gutters. Dustwrapper (moderate browning). *(Antic Hay)* **$125 [≃£65]**
- Einstein. Paris: Black Sun Press, 1929. One of 100 (of 150). Wrappers. Original tissue jacket (lacking large piece at bottom). *(Woolmer)* **$125 [≃£65]**
- Frescoes for Mr. Rockefeller's City. New York: (1933). Wrappers. *(Polyanthos)* **$20 [≃£10]**
- Frescoes for Mr. Rockefeller's City. New York: John Day Pamphlet, (1933). Wrappers. *(Woolmer)* **$35 [≃£18]**
- The Hamlet of Archibald MacLeish. Boston: (1928). Spine darkened. *(Woolmer)* **$45 [≃£23]**
- The Happy Marriage and Other Poems. Boston: 1924. Spine faded. *(Woolmer)* **$45 [≃£23]**

- Herakles. Boston: Houghton, Mifflin, 1967. Dustwrapper. *(Antic Hay)* **$25 [≃£13]**
- New and Collected Poems, 1917-1976. Boston: 1976. One of 500 signed. Box. *(Polyanthos)* **$50 [≃£26]**
- New Found Land. Boston (Paris printed by the Black Sun Press for): Houghton Mifflin, 1930. One of 500. Bookplate. *(Woolmer)* **$65 [≃£33]**
- New Found Land. Boston (Paris printed by the Black Sun Press for): Houghton Mifflin, 1930. One of 500. Slight wear to spine ends. Slipcase. *(Woolmer)* **$85 [≃£44]**
- Nobodaddy. Cambridge: Dunster House, 1926. One of 750. *(Woolmer)* **$45 [≃£23]**
- Panic. A Play in Verse. Boston: 1935. Dustwrapper. *(Woolmer)* **$35 [≃£18]**
- Poems, 1924-1933. Boston: 1933. Dustwrapper (dusty, some wear top edge). *(Woolmer)* **$35 [≃£18]**
- The Pot of Earth. Boston: 1925. Price-clipped dustwrapper. *(Woolmer)* **$35 [≃£18]**
- Public Speech. Poems. New York: Farrar, (1936). One of 275 signed. Leather (spine ends slightly rubbed). Slipcase (some wear at edges). *(Woolmer)* **$75 [≃£39]**
- Songs for Eve. Boston: 1954. Box (slightly soiled). No dustwrapper issued. Signed by the author. *(Polyanthos)* **$50 [≃£26]**
- Tower of Ivory. Yale: UP, 1917. Boards (spine edges worn). *(Woolmer)* **$100 [≃£52]**

MacLennan, Hugh

- Barometer Rising. Toronto: Collins, 1941. 1st Canadian edition. Dustwrapper. *(Alphabet)* **$110 [≃£57]**

McMahon, Thomas

- A Random State. London: Macmillan, 1970. Dustwrapper. *(Dalian)* **£20 [≃$38]**

McMurtry, Larry

- All My Friends Are Going to be Strangers. New York: 1972. Dustwrapper, fine. *(Pettler & Liebermann)* **$125 [≃£65]**
- All My Friends Are Going to be Strangers. New York: 1972. Dustwrapper, near fine. *(Pettler & Liebermann)* **$100 [≃£52]**
- All My Friends Are Going to be Strangers. London: Secker & Warburg, 1973. 1st English edition. Slightly rubbed. Dustwrapper (browned and chipped). *(Limestone Hills)* **$65 [≃£33]**
- Anything for Billy. New York: 1988. Dustwrapper. Author's signed presentation copy. *(Antic Hay)* **$50 [≃£26]**
- Anything for Billy. New York: (1988). Wrappers. *(Lopez)* **$125 [≃£65]**
- Cadillac Jack. New York: 1982. Name. Dustwrapper. Not a remainder. *(Pettler & Liebermann)* **$40 [≃£20]**
- Cadillac Jack. New York: Simon & Schuster, 1982. Dustwrapper. *(Alphabet)* **$40 [≃£20]**
- The Desert Rose. New York: (1983). Uncorrected proof copy. Wrappers. *(Lopez)* **$125 [≃£65]**
- The Desert Rose. New York: Simon and Schuster, (1983). One of 250 signed. Slipcase. *(Houle)* **$175 [≃£91]**
- Horseman, Pass By. New York: Harper, (1961). Light offsetting to endpapers from dustwrapper flaps. Dustwrapper. His 1st book. *(Lopez)* **$650 [≃£338]**
- Horseman, Pass By. New York: Harper, [1961]. Two date stamps on front pastedown. Dustwrapper flaps neatly attached to endpapers. His 1st book. *(Limestone Hills)* **$145 [≃£75]**
- In a Narrow Grave. Austin: Encino: 1968. Dustwrapper. Signed by the author. *(Lopez)* **$400 [≃£208]**
- In a Narrow Grave. Austin: Encino: 1968. Tiny scrape bottom edge rear cover. Dustwrapper. Signed by the author. *(Lopez)* **$300 [≃£156]**
- In a Narrow Grave. Austin: Encino, 1968. 2nd issue. Dustwrapper (tiny gutter tear). Inscribed by the author to Michael Korda. *(Lopez)* **$475 [≃£247]**
- Lonesome Dove. New York: (1985). Uncorrected proof copy. Wrappers. *(Lopez)* **$400 [≃£208]**
- Lonesome Dove. New York: 1985. Dustwrapper. *(Pettler & Liebermann)* **$200 [≃£104]**
- Moving On. New York: (1970). Dustwrapper. *(Lopez)* **$50 [≃£26]**
- Moving On. New York: 1970. Dustwrapper. *(Antic Hay)* **$85 [≃£44]**
- Moving On. London: Weidenfeld & Nicolson, 1971. Dustwrapper (two inner repairs). *(Dalian)* **£35 [≃$67]**
- Some Can Whistle. New York: (1989). Uncorrected proof copy. Wrappers. *(Lopez)* **$135 [≃£70]**
- Some Can Whistle. New York: (1989). Dustwrapper. Signed by the author. *(Lopez)* **$65 [≃£33]**
- Somebody's Darling. New York: (1978). Remainder mark bottom edge of pages, very slight shelfwear. Dustwrapper. Signed by the author. *(Lopez)* **$85 [≃£44]**

- Somebody's Darling. New York: (1978). No remainder mark. Dustwrapper (few edge tears). *(Lopez)* **$35 [≃£18]**
- Somebody's Darling. New York: (1978). Remainder mark. Dustwrapper. *(Lopez)* **$35 [≃£18]**
- Someone Can Whistle. New York: Simon & Schuster, [1989]. Dustwrapper. Signed by the author. *(Antic Hay)* **$75 [≃£39]**
- Terms of Endearment. New York: Simon & Schuster, 1975. Remainder mark on bottom edge. Dustwrapper. *(Alphabet)* **$110 [≃£57]**
- Texasville. New York: S&S, (1987). Uncorrected proof copy. *(Lopez)* **$125 [≃£65]**
- See also Ray, Ophelia.

MacNeice, Louis

- Autumn Journal. London: 1939. Dustwrapper (couple of small chips head of upper panel). *(Words Etcetera)* **£110 [≃$211]**
- The Burning Perch. London: 1963. Dustwrapper. Poetry Book Society Bulletin laid in. *(Edrich)* **£16 [≃$30]**
- Christopher Columbus. London: 1944. Dustwrapper (slightly rubbed). *(Clearwater)* **£30 [≃$57]**
- Collected Poems 1925-1948. London: 1949. Dustwrapper. *(Edrich)* **£16 [≃$30]**
- The Dark Tower and Other Radio Scripts. London: 1947. Proof copy. Wrappers. *(Edrich)* **£35 [≃$67]**
- The Earth Compels. London: 1938. Inscription on endpaper. Dustwrapper. *(Edrich)* **£20 [≃$38]**
- Eighty-Five Poems. London: 1959. Dustwrapper. *(Edrich)* **£12 [≃$23]**
- Holes in the Sky. London: Faber, 1948. Endpapers tanned. Spine slightly faded. Dustwrapper (tanned). *(Hazeldene)* **£40 [≃$76]**
- The Last Ditch. Dublin: Cuala Press, 1940. One of 450. Canvas backed boards. *(Words Etcetera)* **£95 [≃$182]**
- The Mad Islands and the Administrator. London: Faber, 1964. Price-clipped dustwrapper (slightly tanned). *(Dalian)* **£40 [≃$76]**
- The Mad Islands and the Administrator. London: 1964. Dustwrapper. *(Edrich)* **£12.50 [≃$24]**
- Meet the U.S. Army. London: HMSO, 1943. Printed wrappers (very slightly dusty). *(Dalian)* **£140 [≃$268]**
- Meet the US Army. London: HMSO, 1943. Wrappers (spine rubbed). *(Ellis)* **£120 [≃$230]**
- One for the Grave. London: 1968. Dustwrapper (torn at foot of spine). *(Edrich)* **£10 [≃$19]**
- The Other Wing. London: Faber, Ariel Poems, 1954. Wrappers, envelope. *(Edrich)* **£8 [≃$15]**
- Out of the Picture. London: 1937. Dustwrapper. *(Edrich)* **£30 [≃$57]**
- Out of the Picture. London: Faber, 1937. Dustwrapper (repair to upper cover). *(Dalian)* **£65 [≃$124]**
- Persons from Porlock and Other Plays for Radio. London: 1969. Dustwrapper. *(Buckley)* **£15 [≃$28]**
- Persons from Porlock. London: 1969. Dustwrapper. *(Green Meadow)* **£20 [≃$38]**
- Persons from Porlock. London: BBC, 1969. Dustwrapper. *(Ash)* **£20 [≃$38]**
- Poems, 1925-1940. New York: (1940). Dustwrapper (couple of tiny spots on book and wrapper). *(Lopez)* **$40 [≃£20]**
- Selected Poems. Edited by W.H. Auden. London: Faber, 1964. Wrappers. *(Hazeldene)* **£20 [≃$38]**
- Solstices. London: 1961. Dustwrapper (trifle browned on spine). Signed by the author (1961). *(Words Etcetera)* **£55 [≃$105]**
- The Strings Are False. London: 1965. Uncorrected proof copy. Wrappers. *(Edrich)* **£30 [≃$57]**
- The Strings are False. London: 1965. Edges very lightly foxed. Price-clipped dustwrapper (slightly rubbed, slightly creased). *(Ellis)* **£15 [≃$28]**
- Varieties of Parable. Cambridge: UP, 1965. Advance uncorrected proof. Printed wrappers. *(Dalian)* **£35 [≃$67]**
- Varieties of Parable. Cambridge: UP, 1965. Dustwrapper. *(Any Amount)* **£14 [≃$26]**
- Varieties of Parable. London: 1965. One corner bumped. Price-clipped dustwrapper (slightly rubbed). *(Ellis)* **£20 [≃$38]**
- Visitations. London: 1957. Dustwrapper (a little creased). Poetry Book Society Bulletin laid in. *(Edrich)* **£16.50 [≃$32]**
- Zoo. London: 1938. 1st issue binding. *(Edrich)* **£30 [≃$57]**

McPhee, John

- The Control of Nature. New York: Farrar Straus Giroux, 1989. Dustwrapper. Signed by the author. *(Limestone Hills)* **$65 [≃£33]**
- The Curve of Binding Energy. New York: FSG, (1974). Top edge of front cover slightly rubbed. Dustwrapper. *(Lopez)* **$55 [≃£28]**

- Encounters with the Archdruid. New York: FSG, (1971). Owner name and date. Dustwrapper (1 1/2 inch tear front panel). *(Lopez)* **$45 [≃£23]**
- The Pine Barrens. New York: FSG, (1968). Light crease on half-title. Name and date. Dustwrapper (small creases on front flap). *(Lopez)* **$85 [≃£44]**
- La Place de la Concorde Suisse. New York: FSG, (1984). Uncorrected proof copy. Wrappers. *(Lopez)* **$60 [≃£31]**

Madge, Charles

- The Father Found. London: Faber, (1937). Uncorrected proof copy. Printed wrappers (slightly rubbed and nicked). *(Dalian)* **£35 [≃$67]**

Mahon, Derek

- Beyond Howth Head. Dublin: Dolmen Press, Poetry Ireland Editions, 1970. Wrappers very slightly dusty with one or two small marks. Author's signed presentation inscription. *(Blakeney)* **£95 [≃$182]**
- Ecclesiastes. Manchester: Phoenix Pamphlet Poets, 1970. One of 60 (of 700) in cloth, signed. Dustwrapper (little dusty). *(Blakeney)* **£75 [≃$143]**
- The Hunt By Night. London: OUP, 1982. Wrappers. *(Blakeney)* **£25 [≃$47]**
- Light Music. Belfast: Ulsterman, 1977. Wrappers. *(Blakeney)* **£20 [≃$38]**
- Light Music. Belfast: Ulsterman, 1977. Wrappers. *(Halsey)* **£15 [≃$28]**
- Lives. London: OUP, 1972. Wrappers, price sticker on back wrapper. *(Blakeney)* **£25 [≃$47]**
- Night Crossing. London: OUP, 1968. Wrappers (some marks). *(Blakeney)* **£45 [≃$86]**
- Night-Crossing. OUP: 1968. Very slight bruise lower corner. Wrappers (slightly rubbed at rear). *(Halsey)* **£20 [≃$38]**
- The Snow Party. London: OUP, 1975. Wrappers very slightly rubbed, small puncture at inner margin of front free endpaper. Elizabeth Jennings's signature. *(Blakeney)* **£55 [≃$105]**

Mailer, Norman

- Advertisements for Myself. New York: (1959). 1st binding. Dustwrapper. Author's signed presentation copy. *(Polyanthos)* **$65 [≃£33]**
- Ancient Evenings. London: Macmillan, 1983. Advance uncorrected proof copy. Printed wrappers. Proof dustwrapper. *(Dalian)* **£30 [≃$57]**
- The Armies of the Night. NAL: 1968. Price-clipped dustwrapper. *(Nouveau)* **$35 [≃£18]**
- Barbary Shore. 1951. 1st edition. In the red variant dustwrapper (no priority). Signed by the author. *(Antic Hay)* **$225 [≃£117]**
- Barbary Shore. 1951. 1st American edition. Dustwrapper (slightly rubbed and nicked). *(First Issues)* **£30 [≃$57]**
- Barbary Shore. New York: Rinehart, 1951. Price-clipped dustwrapper. *(Nouveau)* **$110 [≃£57]**
- Barbary Shore. London: Cape, 1952. Endpapers very slightly foxed. Dustwrapper (slightly rubbed). *(Dalian)* **£30 [≃$57]**
- Deaths for the Ladies. New York: Putnam, [1962]. Dustwrapper (lightly rubbed, single small tear). *(Dermont)* **$125 [≃£65]**
- Deaths for the Ladies and other Disasters. London: Deutsch, 1962. Wrappers. No dustwrapper issued. *(Dalian)* **£22 [≃$42]**
- The Deer Park. New York: Putnam's, [1955]. Moderate wear. Dustwrapper (minor edgewear). Author's name in orange on front panel of dustwrapper. *(Antic Hay)* **$75 [≃£39]**
- The Executioner's Song. Boston: Little, Brown, 1979. Dustwrapper. *(Nouveau)* **$35 [≃£18]**
- The Last Night. Targ Editions: 1984. One of 250 signed. Tissue dustwrapper. *(Nouveau)* **$100 [≃£52]**
- The Naked & The Dead. New York: Rinehart, 1948. Name. Dustwrapper. His 1st book. *(Alphabet)* **$350 [≃£182]**
- The Naked and the Dead. London: Wingate, 1949. Dustwrapper. *(Dyke)* **£150 [≃$287]**
- The Naked and the Dead. London: Wingate, 1949. Dustwrapper (small closed tears to one corner and spine). *(Paul Brown)* **£60 [≃$115]**
- The Naked and the Dead. London: Wingate, 1949. Dustwrapper. *(Lewton)* **£55 [≃$105]**
- Of a Fire on the Moon. Boston: Little, Brown, 1970. Dustwrapper. *(Nouveau)* **$45 [≃£23]**
- Of Women and their Elegance. London: Hodder & Stoughton, 1980. Dustwrapper. *(Dalian)* **£25 [≃$47]**
- The Presidential Papers. New York: Putnam, 1963. Dustwrapper. *(Nouveau)* **$45 [≃£23]**
- A Transit to Narcissus. New York: 1978. Inscription. Two small frayed spots at spine top. Price-clipped dustwrapper (spine chipped). *(Pettler & Liebermann)* **$50 [≃£26]**
- Why Are We in Vietnam? A Novel. London: Weidenfeld & Nicolson, 1969. Dustwrapper. *(Dalian)* **£25 [≃$47]**

Malamud, Bernard

- The Assistant. New York: 1957. Tiny sticker on pastedown. Dustwrapper (lightly chipped). *(Pettler & Liebermann)* **$100 [≃£52]**
- Dubin's Lives. New York: 1979. One of 750 specially bound. Glassine dustwrapper. *(David Rees)* **£30 [≃$57]**
- Dubin's Lives. New York: Farrar, 1979. One of 750. Red boards. *(Nouveau)* **$60 [≃£31]**
- God' Grace. New York: 1983. Signed limited edition. Slipcase. *(Pettler & Liebermann)* **$75 [≃£39]**
- Rembrandt's Hat. New York: Farrar, Straus & Giroux, [1973]. Dustwrapper. Signed by the author. *(Antic Hay)* **$85 [≃£44]**

Malouf, David

- Bicycle and Other Poems. Australia: 1970. Small inscription. Wrappers (slightly marked and nicked). Signed by the author. His 1st book. *(David Rees)* **£22 [≃$42]**
- Bicycle and Other Poems. Queensland: UP, 1970. Name. Wrappers (rubbed, three small holes). Signed by the author. His 1st book. *(Moorhouse)* **£15 [≃$28]**

Mandela, Nelson

- No Easy Walk to Freedom. US: Basic Books, 1965. Dustwrapper (spine rucked). *(Paul Brown)* **£30 [≃$57]**

Mann, Thomas

- Death in Venice. London: 1928. 1st English edition. Dustwrapper (upper panel slightly spotted). *(Words Etcetera)* **£385 [≃$739]**
- Early Sorrow. London: 1929. 1st UK edition. *(Roberts)* **£35 [≃$67]**
- Joseph the Provider. New York: Knopf, 1944. 1st American edition. Dustwrapper (spine faintly sunned). Signed by the author. *(Chapel Hill)* **$250 [≃£130]**

Manning, Hugo

- The It and the Odyssey of Henry Miller. Enitharmon Press: 1972. One of 75 signed. Morocco backed boards (extreme foot of spine minutely rubbed). *(Words Etcetera)* **£30 [≃$57]**
- Modigliani: a Poem. Enitharmon Press: 1976. One of 45 signed. Morocco backed boards. *(Words Etcetera)* **£36 [≃$69]**

Manning, Olivia

- Growing Up. London: Heinemann, 1948. Endpapers browned, page edges very spotted. Cover edges and spine slightly darkened. Dustwrapper (soiled and worn). *(Virgo)* **£30 [≃$57]**
- My Husband Cartwright. Melbourne, London, Toronto: Heinemann, 1956. Dustwrapper (tear and wrinkle on lower back panel). *(Limestone Hills)* **$75 [≃£39]**
- The Rain Forest. London: Heinemann, 1974. Dustwrapper. *(Limestone Hills)* **$55 [≃£28]**
- The Spoilt City. London: 1962. Dustwrapper (light edge wear). *(First Issues)* **£30 [≃$57]**

Mansfield, Katherine

- The Aloe. London: Constable, 1930. One of 750. T.e.g. Cloth a little sunned but gilt lettering bright. *(Egret)* **£40 [≃$76]**
- The Aloe. New York: 1930. One of 975. Minimal corner rubbing. Box (sunned, edge rubbed). *(Polyanthos)* **$45 [≃£23]**
- The Garden Party and Other Stories. London: Constable, [1922]. Spine very lightly rubbed, endpapers browned. *(Dalian)* **£60 [≃$115]**
- Je Ne Parle Pas Francais. Hampstead: Heron Press, 1919. Printed wrappers. Specially made slipcase. *(Black Sun)* **$2,000 [≃£1,041]**
- Katherine Mansfield's Letters to John Middleton Murry, 1913-1922. London: Constable, 1951. Name on endpaper. Dustwrapper (chipped and repaired). *(Dalian)* **£35 [≃$67]**
- Novels & Novelists. London: 1930. Dustwrapper (slightly chipped, spine darkened). *(Buckley)* **£35 [≃$67]**

Mara, Bernard

- Pseudonym used by Brian Moore, q.v.

Markham, Robert

- Pseudonym used by Kingsley Amis, q.v.

Marquand, J.P.

- No Hero. Boston: Little, Brown, 1935. Foxing to endpapers and page edges. Dustwrapper (two small nicks at crown, modest chip rear panel). *(Between the Covers)* **$125 [≃£65]**

Marquez, Gabriel Garcia

- The Autumn of the Patriarch. London: Cape, 1977. Dustwrapper. *(Dalian)* **£35 [≃$67]**
- The Autumn of the Patriarch. London: 1977. 1st British edition. Price-clipped dustwrapper. *(Pettler & Liebermann)* **$75 [≃£39]**
- Chronicle of a Death Foretold. London: Cape, 1982. Advance uncorrected proof copy. Printed wrappers. *(Dalian)* **£35 [≃$67]**

- Chronicle of a Death Foretold. New York: Knopf, 1983. Dustwrapper. *(Between the Covers)* **$45 [≃£23]**
- Love in the Time of Cholera. New York: 1988. 1st US edition. Dustwrapper. *(Pettler & Liebermann)* **$30 [≃£15]**
- One Hundred Years of Solitude. New York: Harper, (1970). Dustwrapper (slightest trace of wear). *(Between the Covers)* **$750 [≃£390]**
- The Story of a Shipwrecked Sailor. New York: Knopf, 1986. Uncorrected proof copy. Wrappers. *(Nouveau)* **$80 [≃£41]**

Mars-Jones, Adam

- Lantern Lecture and Other Stories. London: Faber, 1981. Dustwrapper. His 1st book. *(Dalian)* **£30 [≃$57]**

Marsh, Ngaio

- Clutch of Constables. London: Collins, 1968. Top front corner bumped. Dustwrapper. *(Limestone Hills)* **$30 [≃£15]**
- False Scent. London: 1960. Dustwrapper (slightly torn). Dustwrapper. *(Buckley)* **£10 [≃$19]**
- Final Curtain. London: 1947. Dustwrapper (head of spine slightly torn). *(Words Etcetera)* **£15 [≃$28]**
- Off With His Head. London: 1957. Dustwrapper (very slightly rubbed). *(Ellis)* **£20 [≃$38]**
- Off With His Head. London: Collins, 1957. Dustwrapper (small tears to back panel). *(Limestone Hills)* **$40 [≃£20]**
- Opening Night. London: 1951. Bookseller's sticker, slight offsetting to endpapers. Dustwrapper (slightly creased and rubbed), one small internal repair). *(Blakeney)* **£25 [≃$47]**
- Opening Night. London: 1951. Dustwrapper (slightly creased and chipped). *(Words Etcetera)* **£22 [≃$42]**
- Scales of Justice. London: 1955. Dustwrapper. *(Buckley)* **£10 [≃$19]**
- Singing in the Shrouds. London: 1958. Dustwrapper. *(Words Etcetera)* **£12.50 [≃$24]**
- Singing in the Shrouds. London: Collins, 1959. Dustwrapper. *(Limestone Hills)* **$35 [≃£18]**
- Swing, Brother, Swing. London: Collins, 1949. Bookplate. Dustwrapper (somewhat worn). *(Limestone Hills)* **$70 [≃£36]**
- Tied Up In Tinsel. London: Collins Crime Club, (1972). Uncorrected proof copy. Wrappers. Dustwrapper. *(Between the Covers)* **$50 [≃£26]**

Mason, Bobbie Ann

- In Country. New York: 1985. Dustwrapper. Signed by the author. *(Pettler & Liebermann)* **$40 [≃£20]**
- In Country. London: Chatto & Windus, 1986. Dustwrapper. Signed by the author. *(David Rees)* **£22 [≃$42]**
- Shiloh and Other Stories. New York: Harper & Row, [1982]. Dustwrapper. *(Dermont)* **$125 [≃£65]**

Masters, Edgar Lee

- The Great Valley. New York: Macmillan, 1916. *(Antic Hay)* **$65 [≃£33]**
- The Serpent in the Wilderness. New York: Sheldon Dick, [1933]. One of 400 signed and numbered. Acetate dustwrapper supplied, lacks slipcase. *(Antic Hay)* **$100 [≃£52]**
- Spoon River Anthology. New York: Macmillan, 1915. 1st state, measuring 7/8 inch across the top. Small ink numeral on dedication page. *(Antic Hay)* **$200 [≃£104]**
- Spoon River Anthology. New York: Macmillan, 1915. Dustwrapper (faintly chipped). Morocco backed slipcase. Signed by the author (1933). *(Bromer)* **$2,000 [≃£1,041]**
- Starved Rock. New York: Macmillan, 1919. Gift inscription. *(Antic Hay)* **$50 [≃£26]**

Masters, John

- Bhowani Junction. London: 1954. One corner slightly bumped. Dustwrapper. *(Clearwater)* **£20 [≃$38]**
- Bhowani Junction. London: Michael Joseph, 1954. Price-clipped dustwrapper. *(Dyke)* **£30 [≃$57]**
- Coromandel! London: 1955. Dustwrapper (slightly chipped). *(Buckley)* **£10 [≃$19]**
- Nightrunners of Bengal. London: 1951. Dustwrapper (chipped, slightly torn). *(Buckley)* **£30 [≃$57]**
- To the Coral Strand. London: 1952. Uncorrected proof copy. Wrappers (slightly marked). *(Buckley)* **£25 [≃$47]**

Matheson, Richard

- A Stir of Echoes. Phila: Lippincott, 1958. Dustwrapper. *(Alphabet)* **$75 [≃£39]**

Matthiessen, Peter

- At Play in the Fields of the Lord. New York: 1965. Advance reading copy. Wrappers. *(Pettler & Liebermann)* **$60 [≃£31]**
- At Play in the Fields of the Lord. New York: RH, (1965). Advance reading copy. Printed wrappers. *(Lopez)* **$85 [≃£44]**

- At Play in the Fields of the Lord. New York: 1965. Small bookplate. Dustwrapper (tiny chip lower spine). Signed by the author. *(Polyanthos)* **$45 [≃£23]**
- The Cloud Forest. New York: 1961. Dustwrapper. Signed by the author. *(Polyanthos)* **$60 [≃£31]**
- In the Spirit of Crazy Horse. New York: Viking, [1983]. 1st edition (withdrawn). Price-clipped dustwrapper. *(Chapel Hill)* **$195 [≃£101]**
- In the Spirit of Crazy Horse. New York: Viking, [1983]. 1st edition (suppressed). Dustwrapper. *(Antic Hay)* **$125 [≃£65]**
- Men's Lives. New York: 1986. Dustwrapper. Signed by the author. *(Polyanthos)* **$45 [≃£23]**
- Nine-Headed Dragon River. Boston: 1986. Proof copy. Wrappers. Signed by the author. *(Polyanthos)* **$50 [≃£26]**
- Oomingmak. New York: Hastings House, (1967). Dustwrapper. *(Lopez)* **$45 [≃£23]**
- Partisans. New York: 1955. Spine extremities minimally bumped. Dustwrapper (spine extremities minimally rubbed). Signed by the author. *(Polyanthos)* **$95 [≃£49]**
- Partisans. London: Secker & Warburg, 1956. Name on endpaper. Dustwrapper (slightly chipped). *(Dalian)* **£55 [≃$105]**
- Partisans. London: 1956. 1st English edition. Dustwrapper (one minute closed tear). *(Words Etcetera)* **£75 [≃$143]**
- Race Rock. New York: 1954. Spine extremities minimally rubbed. Dustwrapper (spine little rubbed, few tiny edge tears at top, very slightly soiled). Signed by the author. His 1st book. *(Polyanthos)* **$100 [≃£52]**
- Raditzer. New York: Viking, 1961. Dustwrapper (chipped at crown). *(Lopez)* **$45 [≃£23]**
- Sal Si Puedes. New York: RH, (1969). Price-clipped dustwrapper. Signed by the author. *(Lopez)* **$55 [≃£28]**
- The Tree Where Man Was Born. Photographs by Peter Porter. New York: 1972. Dustwrapper. Signed by the author. *(Polyanthos)* **$50 [≃£26]**
- Under the Mountain Wall. New York: 1962. Tiny crease top corner front cover. Dustwrapper (spine extremities minimally rubbed). Signed by the author. *(Polyanthos)* **$50 [≃£26]**
- Wildlife in America. New York: Viking, 1959. Small ink stamp. Dustwrapper (minor wear and rubbing). *(Antic Hay)* **$125 [≃£65]**
- Wildlife in America. New York: Viking, 1959. Price-clipped dustwrapper (a bit rubbed). *(Pettler & Liebermann)* **$85 [≃£44]**
- Wildlife in America. New York: Viking, 1959. Dustwrapper. *(Lopez)* **$100 [≃£52]**

Maugham, Robin

- Behind the Mirror. London: Longmans, 1955. Price-clipped dustwrapper. *(Dalian)* **£18 [≃$34]**
- Line on Ginger. London: Chapman & Hall, 1949. Dustwrapper (slightly nicked, slightly dusty). *(Dalian)* **£16 [≃$30]**
- The Man With Two Shadows. London: Longmans, 1958. Dustwrapper. Inscribed presentation copy, signed and dated (1958). *(Dalian)* **£20 [≃$38]**

Maugham, W. Somerset

- Ah King. London: 1933. Dustwrapper (slightly chipped). *(Words Etcetera)* **£75 [≃$143]**
- Ashenden. London: 1928. Dustwrapper (minimal rubbing to extreme foot of spine). *(Words Etcetera)* **£1,250 [≃$2,399]**
- Ashenden. London: Heinemann, 1928. Spine and covers marked. *(Dalian)* **£55 [≃$105]**
- The Book-Bag. Florence: Orioli, 1932. One of 725 with portrait frontispiece signed by Maugham. Cloth and boards (some fading of boards). Dustwrapper (some browning and soil). *(Antic Hay)* **$225 [≃£117]**
- Books and You. London: 1940. Dustwrapper (somewhat marked, two very small tears). *(Words Etcetera)* **£35 [≃$67]**
- Books and You. London: Heinemann, 1940. Foredge slightly browned. Bookplate. Dustwrapper (slightly rubbed and nicked). *(Dalian)* **£30 [≃$57]**
- Cakes and Ale. London: (1953). One of 100 signed by the author and the artist, Graham Sutherland. Head of spine slightly snagged. Slipcase. *(Ellis)* **£250 [≃$479]**
- Cakes and Ale. London: 1930. Dustwrapper (spine trifle browned, few small chips). *(Words Etcetera)* **£45 [≃$86]**
- Cakes and Ale. London: Heinemann, 1930. Dustwrapper (repaired but complete). *(Ash)* **£100 [≃$191]**
- Catalina. London: 1948. Dustwrapper. *(Words Etcetera)* **£20 [≃$38]**
- Christmas Holiday. London: [1939]. Dustwrapper (head of spine nicked). *(Words Etcetera)* **£50 [≃$95]**
- The Circle. London: Heinemann, 1921. Boards issue. Paper boards (slightly marked and tanned). *(Dalian)* **£200 [≃$383]**
- The Constant Wife. London: Heinemann,

1927. Issued from the American sheets with a new title-page. Cloth (slightly marked and faded). Photo of author pasted to rear endpaper. *(Dalian)* **£45 [≃$86]**

- The Constant Wife. London: 1927. *(Ellis)* **£85 [≃$163]**
- Cosmopolitans. London: 1936. Dustwrapper (slightly dusty). *(Words Etcetera)* **£45 [≃$86]**
- Creatures of Circumstance. London: 1947. Dustwrapper (spine faded). *(Words Etcetera)* **£22 [≃$42]**
- Don Fernando. London: 1935. One of 175 signed. Buckram (spine trifle browned). Slipcase. *(Words Etcetera)* **£165 [≃$316]**
- Don Fernando. London: 1935. Covers considerably damp marked. Dustwrapper (a few chips). *(Words Etcetera)* **£45 [≃$86]**
- Don Fernando or Variations on Some Spanish Themes. London: Heinemann, 1935. Covers slightly marked. Bookplate. *(Dalian)* **£35 [≃$67]**
- Don Fernando. London: 1935. One of 175 signed. Spine slightly discoloured. Slipcase. *(Words Etcetera)* **£225 [≃$431]**
- East of Suez. London: Heinemann, 1922. Buckram (very slightly rubbed, spine slightly faded). No dustwrapper issued. *(Dalian)* **£45 [≃$86]**
- East of Suez. New York: Doran, 1922. 1st American edition. Covers slightly marked, spine chipped at head. Author's signed presentation inscription (1923). *(Dalian)* **£150 [≃$287]**
- First Person Singular. London: 1931. Dustwrapper (slightly browned and chipped). *(Words Etcetera)* **£45 [≃$86]**
- First Person Singular. London: Heinemann, [1931]. 1st English edition. Dustwrapper (moderate soil and browning). *(Antic Hay)* **$85 [≃£44]**
- The Gentleman in the Parlour. London: Heinemann, 1930. Foredge and endpapers slightly foxed. Dustwrapper (slightly dusty and tanned). *(Dalian)* **£85 [≃$163]**
- The Judgement Seat. London: Centaur Press, 1934. One of 150 signed, and frontispiece signed by Ulrica Hyde. Cloth, t.e.g. *(Houle)* **$325 [≃£169]**
- Liza of Lambeth. The Jubilee Edition. London: Heinemann, 1947. One of 1000 signed. Vellum and decorative boards, t.e.g. Minor browning and foxing endpapers. Dustwrapper (spine lightly faded). *(Antic Hay)* **$150 [≃£78]**
- The Merry-Go-Round. London: Heinemann, 1905. 1st issue, with gilt lettering on front cover. Foredge and endpapers slightly foxed. Inscription on endpaper. Small crinkle tip of spine. *(Dalian)* **£85 [≃$163]**
- The Moon and Sixpence. London: Heinemann, 1919. 1st issue, with 2 advert leaves at end, and listing 6 novels by Eden Phillpotts, 3 by Zangwill, &c. Paper browned. Inscription. *(Dalian)* **£110 [≃$211]**
- The Narrow Corner. Garden City: Doubleday, Doran, 1932. 1st American edition. Dustwrapper (slight crease on spine). *(Houle)* **$175 [≃£91]**
- Our Betters. London: Heinemann, 1923. No dustwrapper issued. *(Dalian)* **£45 [≃$86]**
- The Painted Veil. New York: Doran, [1925]. One of 250 signed. Precedes the English edition. Vellum and boards, t.e.g., (small stain lower portion spine). Acetate dustwrapper. *(Antic Hay)* **$350 [≃£182]**
- The Painted Veil. London: 1925. Upper cover trifle bowed. *(Words Etcetera)* **£65 [≃$124]**
- Points of View. London: Heinemann, [1958]. 1st English edition. Dustwrapper (minor browning). *(Antic Hay)* **$40 [≃£20]**
- Princess September. London: Collins, 1970. Dustwrapper. *(Dalian)* **£35 [≃$67]**
- The Razor's Edge. London: 1944. Dustwrapper (head of spine slightly torn). *(Words Etcetera)* **£30 [≃$57]**
- The Sacred Flame. Garden City: Doubleday, Doran, 1928. 1st American edition (precedes the English edition). Dustwrapper (minor browning of spine). *(Antic Hay)* **$175 [≃£91]**
- Sheppey. London: Heinemann, 1933. Dustwrapper (very slightly dusty). *(Dalian)* **£45 [≃$86]**
- Strictly Personal. Garden City: Doubleday, Doran, 1941. One of 515 signed (precedes both the English and American trade editions). Buckram, t.e.g. Slipcase (minor fade). *(Antic Hay)* **$225 [≃£117]**
- Strictly Personal. London: 1942. Covers a little marked. Dustwrapper (foot of spine chipped). *(Words Etcetera)* **£35 [≃$67]**
- The Summing Up. Garden City: Doubleday, 1954. One of 391 signed. Slipcase (some fade and small stains). *(Antic Hay)* **$275 [≃£143]**
- Theatre. London: 1937. Dustwrapper (minutely chipped). *(Words Etcetera)* **£35 [≃$67]**
- Then and Now. London: 1946. Dustwrapper. *(Words Etcetera)* **£20 [≃$38]**
- The Trembling of a Leaf. London: 1921. Flyleaves cut short. Endpapers browned. *(Words Etcetera)* **£45 [≃$86]**

- Up at the Villa. London: 1941. Covers a little shaken. Dustwrapper (worn). *(Words Etcetera)* **£20 [≃$38]**
- A Writer's Notebook. London: 1949. Dustwrapper (slightly dusty), wraparound band. *(Words Etcetera)* **£25 [≃$47]**
- A Writer's Notebook. New York: 1949. One of 1000 signed. Buckram, t.e.g. Slipcase. *(Words Etcetera)* **£135 [≃$259]**
- A Writer's Notebook. New York: Doubleday, 1949. One of 1000 signed. Spine a little faded. Slipcase. *(Words Etcetera)* **£125 [≃$239]**
- Bason, Frederick T.: A Bibliography of the Writings of William Somerset Maugham. London: Unicorn Press, 1931. One of 950. Cloth very slightly darkened. Author's presentation inscription. *(Dalian)* **£65 [≃$124]**
- Stott, Raymond Toole: Maughamiana. London: Heinemann, 1950. Covers slightly marked. Dustwrapper (tanned, torn with loss). *(Hazeldene)* **£18 [≃$34]**
- See also the companion IRBP volume Literature.

Maurois, Andre

- Ariel. Penguin Books (Penguin Number One), 1935. 1st edition thus. Name inside upper wrapper. Wrappers (slightly rubbed). Dustwrapper (rubbed, chipped, spine tanned). *(Ellis)* **£90 [≃$172]**

Maxwell, Gavin

- Ring of Bright Water. London: Longmans, 1960. Dustwrapper. *(Paul Brown)* **£15 [≃$28]**

Maxwell, William

- Time Will Darken It. New York: Harper, 1948. Dustwrapper (spine darkened). *(Lopez)* **$75 [≃£39]**

Mayne, William

- The Glass Ball. London: Hamish Hamilton, 1961. Dustwrapper (slightly rubbed). *(Green Meadow)* **£25 [≃$47]**
- While the Bells Ring. OUP: 1979. Dustwrapper. *(Green Meadow)* **£25 [≃$47]**

McLuhan, Herbert Marshall

- The Mechanical Bride. New York: (1951). Ink name. Minor wear to spine ends. Dustwrapper (chipped, slightly torn). His 1st book. *(King)* **$75 [≃£39]**

Melville, James

- The Chrysanthemum Chain. London: Secker, 1980. Price-clipped dustwrapper. *(Janus)* **$45 [≃£23]**
- The Wages of Zen. London: Secker, 1979. Dustwrapper. His 1st book. *(Janus)* **$65 [≃£33]**

Mencken, H.L.

- Menckeniana: A Schimpflexikon. New York: Knopf, 1928. One of 230 signed. Some browning of spine, many pages unopened. Slipcase. *(Antic Hay)* **$225 [≃£117]**
- Prejudices: Fifth Series. New York: Knopf, [1926]. One of 192 (of 200) numbered and signed. Slipcase (somewhat soiled, few small cracks). *(Antic Hay)* **$250 [≃£130]**
- Treatise on the Gods. New York: Knopf, 1930. One of 375 signed. Dustwrapper (somewhat chipped and darkened). *(Bromer)* **$450 [≃£234]**

Menen, Aubrey

- The Prevalence of Witches. London: Chatto & Windus, 1947. Dustwrapper (slightly rubbed, slightly chipped). Author's 1st book. *(Dalian)* **£35 [≃$67]**

Mercer, David

- Three TV Comedies. London: Calder, 1966. Dustwrapper. Signed by the author (1966). *(Any Amount)* **£22 [≃$42]**

Meredith, William

- Love Letters from an Impossible Land. Yale: UP, 1944. Name. Dustwrapper (spine a little sunned with tiny chip at top, slightly edge sunned). Author's signed presentation copy. His 1st book. *(Polyanthos)* **$75 [≃£39]**

Merrill, James

- The Black Swan and Other Poems. Athens: Icaros, 1946. One of 100. Several glue marks on page (2). Wrappers (unevenly faded). *(Woolmer)* **$1,500 [≃£781]**
- Braving the Elements. London: 1973. Dustwrapper. *(Words Etcetera)* **£9 [≃$17]**
- Bronze. Nadja: 1984. One of 150 signed. *(Nouveau)* **$140 [≃£72]**
- Peter. Deerfield Press: 1982. One of 300 signed. dustwrapper. *(David Rees)* **£25 [≃$47]**
- The Seraglio. London: 1958. 1st English edition. Dustwrapper (minimal wear to extremities). *(Words Etcetera)* **£45 [≃$86]**

Merton, Thomas

- The Ascent to the Truth. London: Hollis & Carter, 1951. Dustwrapper (very slightly dusty). *(Dalian)* **£25 [≃$47]**

- The Black Revolution. Atlanta: Southern Christian Leadership Conference, [1963?]. Printed wrappers. *(Alphabet)* **$75 [≃£39]**
- Boris Pasternak / Thomas Merton. Six Letters. Lexington: King Library Press, 1973. One of 150. *(Bromer)* **$350 [≃£182]**
- Bread in the Wilderness. London: Hollis & Carter, 1954. Dustwrapper. *(Dalian)* **£22 [≃$42]**
- The Diaries. London: Weidenfeld & Nicolson, 1976. Dustwrapper. *(Dalian)* **£25 [≃$47]**
- Hagia Sophia. Lexington: Stamperia del Santuccio, 1962. One of 69 signed. Dustwrapper. *(Bromer)* **$650 [≃£338]**
- A Man in the Divided Sea. Norfolk: New Directions, (1946). Dustwrapper (narrow strip upper edge front panel missing). *(Lopez)* **$45 [≃£23]**
- No Man is an Island. New York: HB, (1955). Price-clipped dustwrapper. *(Lopez)* **$25 [≃£13]**
- The Secular Journal. New York: (1959). Dustwrapper (spine sunned). *(Polyanthos)* **$30 [≃£15]**
- Seeds of Destruction. New York: Farrar, Straus & Giroux, [1964]. Dustwrapper (few short tears). *(Antic Hay)* **$35 [≃£18]**
- Selected Poems. London: Hollis & Carter, 1950. Price-clipped dustwrapper (very slightly rubbed). *(Dalian)* **£35 [≃$67]**
- The Seven Storey Mountain. London: Sheldon Press, 1975. Dustwrapper. *(Dalian)* **£25 [≃$47]**
- The Sign of Jonas. London: Hollis & Carter, 1953. Dustwrapper. Evelyn Waugh wraparound band. *(Dalian)* **£30 [≃$57]**
- The Silent Life. London: Burns Oates, 1957. Dustwrapper (repaired). *(Dalian)* **£20 [≃$38]**
- The Silent Life. London: Thames & Hudson, 1957. Dustwrapper. *(Dalian)* **£35 [≃$67]**
- The Silent Life. New York: Farrar, Straus & Cudahy, [1957]. Dustwrapper (few small stains, minor darkening). *(Antic Hay)* **$40 [≃£20]**
- The Strange Islands. London: Hollis & Carter, 1957. Book label. Dustwrapper. *(Dalian)* **£25 [≃$47]**
- The Tears of the Blind Lions. New York: New Directions, (1949). Top of spine lightly bumped. Dustwrapper. *(Bromer)* **$75 [≃£39]**
- Thirty Poems. Norfolk: New Directions, (1944). Hardcover issue. Dustwrapper. His 1st book. *(Lopez)* **$300 [≃£156]**
- Thirty Poems. Norfolk: New Directions, (1944). Marginal pencil annotations. Dustwrapper. His 1st book. *(Bromer)* **$150 [≃£78]**
- The Waters of Silence. With a Foreword by Evelyn Waugh. London: Hollis & Carter, 1950. Cloth slightly spotted. Dustwrapper (slightly nicked). *(Dalian)* **£20 [≃$38]**

Merwin, W.S.

- Green With Beasts. London: Hart Davis, 1956. Precedes the American edition. Dustwrapper, Poetry Book Society wraparound. *(Dalian)* **£85 [≃$163]**
- The Poem of the Cid. London: Dent, 1959. 1st state binding in yellow cloth. Dustwrapper. *(Dalian)* **£45 [≃$86]**

Meyerstein, E.H.W.

- Black and White Magic by E.H.W.M. and Wilfrid Blair. Oxford: Blackwell, 1917. Boards a bit rubbed. *(Words Etcetera)* **£30 [≃$57]**

Meynell, Laurence

- Die by the Book. London: Collins, 1966. Dustwrapper. *(Janus)* **$35 [≃£18]**

Michener, James A.

- The Bridges at Toko-Ri. New York: Random House, [1953]. Issue with blue endpapers, possibly the earliest. Fade along top edge. Dustwrapper (moderate wear). *(Antic Hay)* **$85 [≃£44]**
- Centennial. New York: Random House, [1974]. 1st trade edition. Price-clipped dustwrapper. *(Antic Hay)* **$25 [≃£13]**
- Chesapeake. New York: Random House, (1978). One of 500 signed. Slipcase. *(Houle)* **$275 [≃£143]**
- Return to Paradise. New York: Random House, [1951]. Special Presentation Edition to the booksellers of America, numbered (limitation unknown). Acetate dustwrapper (small chip). *(Antic Hay)* **$125 [≃£65]**
- Tales of the South Pacific. New York: Macmillan, 1950. One of 1500 signed. Gilt spine lettering dulled. No dustwrapper issued. His 1st book. *(Antic Hay)* **$175 [≃£91]**

Millar, Kenneth

- Used pseudonym Ross Macdonald, q.v.

Millar, Margaret

- The Cannibal Heart. New York: Random House, [1949]. Dustwrapper (moderately chipped). Author's presentation copy. *(Limestone Hills)* **$75 [≃£39]**

- Fire Will Freeze. New York: Random, 1944. Dustwrapper (chipped). *(Janus)* **$45 [≃£23]**

Millay, Edna St. Vincent

- Invocation to the Muses. New York: January 18, 1941. One of 60 numbered. String-tied printed wrappers, publisher's cloth folding case, paper label, fine. *(Black Sun)* **$800 [≃£416]**
- The King's Henchman. New York: Harper, 1927. One of 500 signed. Slipcase (external tape repairs). *(Antic Hay)* **$150 [≃£78]**
- Renascence and Other Poems. New York: Mitchell Kennerley, 1917. 1st issue. Dustwrapper. Her 1st book. *(Black Sun)* **$1,350 [≃£703]**
- Renascence and Other Poems. New York: Mitchell Kennerley, 1917. One of 15 [actually 17] deluxe signed by the author. Some slight soiling and wear to the cover. *(Black Sun)* **$6,250 [≃£3,255]**

Miller, Arthur

- After the Fall. New York: 1964. One of 500 signed. Box. *(Polyanthos)* **$100 [≃£52]**
- After the Fall. New York: Viking, 1964. One of 995 signed. Slipcase. *(Nouveau)* **$110 [≃£57]**
- After the Fall. New York: 1964. Dustwrapper (spine slightly sunned). Author's signed presentation copy. *(Polyanthos)* **$75 [≃£39]**
- After the Fall. New York: Viking, [1964]. Dustwrapper (minor wear). Signed by the author. *(Antic Hay)* **$85 [≃£44]**
- Death of a Salesman. New York: 1949. Cloth a little soiled. Author's signed presentation copy. *(Polyanthos)* **$100 [≃£52]**
- Death of a Salesman. New York: Viking, 1949. Ink name. Some rubbing edge rear endpapers. Dustwrapper (some rubbing and edgewear, thin chip head of spine). *(Antic Hay)* **$150 [≃£78]**
- Incident at Vichy. New York: Viking, [1965]. Dustwrapper. Signed by the author. *(Antic Hay)* **$75 [≃£39]**
- Timebends. New York: 1987. Dustwrapper. Publicity photo laid in. Author's signed presentation copy. *(Polyanthos)* **$50 [≃£26]**
- Two-Way Mirror. London: Methuen, [1984]. Dustwrapper. Author's signed presentation inscription. *(Dermont)* **$75 [≃£39]**
- A View from the Bridge. New York: Viking, 1955. Price-clipped dustwrapper (slightly used). *(Chapel Hill)* **$50 [≃£26]**

Miller, Henry

- Art & Outrage. London: 1959. 1st British edition (precedes US edition). Dustwrapper. *(Pettler & Liebermann)* **$40 [≃£20]**
- Black Spring. London: Calder & Boyars, 1965. Dustwrapper. *(Dalian)* **£20 [≃$38]**
- The Books in My Life. London: Peter Owen, [1952]. 1st English edition. Dustwrapper (torn, soiled and chipped). *(Dermont)* **$150 [≃£78]**
- The Books in My Life. New York: [1952]. 1st issue, with 4 photos, list of illustrations, and notice of further volumes. Price-clipped dustwrapper (some marks). *(Pettler & Liebermann)* **$50 [≃£26]**
- The Colossus of Maroussi. London: 1942. Dustwrapper (slightly rubbed and nicked at edges). *(Sclanders)* **£35 [≃$67]**
- The Colossus of Maroussi. London: Secker & Warburg, 1942. Cloth slightly spotted. Dustwrapper (slightly rubbed). *(Dalian)* **£85 [≃$163]**
- The Cosmological Eye. London: Poetry London, 1945. Three ownership stamps. Slightly cocked. Dustwrapper (slightly rubbed, several nicks). *(Ellis)* **£35 [≃$67]**
- (Contributes to) Four Visions of America. Santa Barbara: Capra Press, [1977]. One of 225 signed by Miller, Boyle, Jong and Sanchez. Dustwrapper. *(Dermont)* **$60 [≃£31]**
- Gliding into the Everglades. Santa Barbara: Lost Pleiade Press, 1977. One of 250 signed. *(Bromer)* **$75 [≃£39]**
- Hamlet: Volume I. With Michael Fraenkel. Santurce: Carrefour, [1939]. One of 500. Wrappers. *(Dermont)* **$150 [≃£78]**
- Insomnia or the Devil at Large. New York: (1974). Dustwrapper (two small tears, minimally edge rubbed). *(Polyanthos)* **$25 [≃£13]**
- Joey ... Volume III, Book of Friends. Santa Barbara: Capra Press, 1979. One of 250 signed by the author. Price-clipped dustwrapper. *(Heritage)* **$125 [≃£65]**
- Just Wild About Harry. London: MacGibbon & Kee, 1964. Dustwrapper (slightly dusty). *(Dalian)* **£20 [≃$38]**
- (Foreword to) Life without Principle by Henry David Thoreau. Stanford: James Ladd Delkin, 1946. One of 500. Dustwrapper. Original tissue protective wrapper (chipped). *(Dermont)* **$150 [≃£78]**
- Love Between the Sexes. New York: Greenwich Books, 1978. One of 26 lettered and signed by Miller and the cover illustrator Tom Bloom. Sewn wrappers. *(Antic Hay)* **$150 [≃£78]**
- Murder the Murderer. [Berkeley/Big Sur:

Porter/Miller, 1944]. Printed wrappers (minor wear and fade). *(Antic Hay)* **$100 [≃£52]**

- My Bike & Other Friends. Volume II, Book of Friends. Santa Barbara: Capra Press, 1978. Limited edition signed by the author. Price-clipped dustwrapper. *(Heritage)* **$125 [≃£65]**
- Nexus. London: 1964. Price-clipped dustwrapper. *(Polyanthos)* **$30 [≃£15]**
- Nexus. New York: Grove Press, 1965. Dustwrapper (slightly soiled, tiny nick). *(Polyanthos)* **$25 [≃£13]**
- Notes on "Aaron's Rod". Santa Barbara: Black Sparrow, 1980. One of 276 hardbound, signed by the author. *(Heritage)* **$75 [≃£39]**
- Notes on "Aaron's Rod". Santa Barbara: Black Sparrow Press, 1980. One of 276 (of 750) hardbound signed. Glassine wrappers. *(Virgo)* **£70 [≃$134]**
- Order and Chaos chez Hans Reichel. [Tucson]: Loujon Press, [1966]. The Leather Edition. One of 99 signed by the author. Slipcase. *(Heritage)* **$150 [≃£78]**
- Order and Chaos Chez Hans Reichel. London: 1966. One of 1399 Cork Edition. Slipcase (small puncture to spine). *(Ellis)* **£100 [≃$191]**
- Plexus: The Rosy Crucifixion. Book Two. Paris: Olympia Press, [1953]. 1st English language edition. One of 2000. 2 vols. printed wrappers. *(Dermont)* **$175 [≃£91]**
- Plexus. Paris: Olympia Press, 1953. 2 vols. Wrappers (edges rubbed). *(Ellis)* **£100 [≃$191]**
- Plexus. London: Weidenfeld & Nicolson, (1963). 1st UK edition. Dustwrapper (very slight soiling). *(Between the Covers)* **$65 [≃£33]**
- Plexus. New York: 1965. 1st US edition. Dustwrapper. *(Pettler & Liebermann)* **$20 [≃£10]**
- Reflections on the Maurizius Case. Santa Barbara: Capra Press, 1974. Dustwrapper. Signed by the author. *(Polyanthos)* **$40 [≃£20]**
- Scenario (A Film With Sound). Paris: Obelisk Press, 1937. One of 200 signed (this copy numbered 201). With the frontispiece. Unbound signatures laid into printed wrappers (yapped edges of wrappers chipped with a few tears). *(Dermont)* **$450 [≃£234]**
- Sunday After the War. Norfolk: (1944). Cloth (slight soil). Dustwrapper (torn, frayed, soiled). *(King)* **$25 [≃£13]**
- The Theatre & Other Pieces. [New York]: Stroker, [1979]. Wrappers. Inscribed by the author. *(Heritage)* **$100 [≃£52]**
- Tropic of Cancer. Paris: Obelisk Press, [1934]. One page poorly opened, blank piece missing from corner of last page. Rebacked with original covers (some dust soiling, chipping along edges, front inside flap detached). Quarter morocco slipcase. Presentation inscription. (1934) *(Heritage)* **$1,500 [≃£781]**
- Tropic of Cancer. London: Calder, 1963. Dustwrapper. *(Sklaroff)* **£10 [≃$19]**
- Tropic of Capricorn. New York: 1961. 1st US edition. Ink price on endpaper. Dustwrapper. *(Pettler & Liebermann)* **$25 [≃£13]**
- What Are You Going To Do About Alf. With Alfred Perles. Turret Books, 1971. One of 100 specially bound signed by both authors. Sw. *(Sklaroff)* **£75 [≃$143]**
- The World of Sex. (Chicago: 1940). One of 250. Dustwrapper (spine sunned, little rubbed, two very small tears at extremities, rear panel tiny area rubbed, tiny piece missing lower edge). *(Polyanthos)* **$250 [≃£130]**

Milligan, Spike

- A Book of Bits. London: Dobson, 1965. Price-clipped dustwrapper. *(Paul Brown)* **£10 [≃$19]**
- The Little Pot Boiler. London: Dobson, 1963. Dustwrapper. *(Paul Brown)* **£10 [≃$19]**
- Monty, His Part in My Victory. London: Michael Joseph, 1976. Dustwrapper. *(Paul Brown)* **£10 [≃$19]**
- Mussolini, His Part in My Downfall. London: Michael Joseph, 1978. Price-clipped dustwrapper. *(Paul Brown)* **£10 [≃$19]**
- "Rommel?" "Gunner Who?". London: Michael Joseph, 1974. Dustwrapper. *(Sklaroff)* **£8 [≃$15]**

Milne, A.A.

- By Way of Introduction. New York: (1929). One of 166 signed. Paper box (slightly worn). *(Black Sun)* **$150 [≃£78]**
- The Christopher Robin Story Book. London: Methuen, 1929. *(Green Meadow)* **£45 [≃$86]**
- The House at Pooh Corner. London: Methuen, 1928. Cloth very slightly faded. *(Green Meadow)* **£55 [≃$105]**
- The House at Pooh Corner. London: Methuen, 1928. *(Roberts)* **£36 [≃$69]**
- Michael and Mary. London: 1930. One of 260 signed. Buckram (spine trifle faded). *(Words Etcetera)* **£45 [≃$86]**
- Now We Are Six. London: Methuen, (1927).

Dustwrapper, fine. *(Houle)* **$350 [≃£182]**
- Now We Are Six. London: Methuen, (1927). Dustwrapper (a few small chips). *(Houle)* **$275 [≃£143]**
- Now We Are Six. London: Methuen, 1927. A few faint marks. Dustwrapper (slightly darkened, head of spine a little chipped). *(Ash)* **£200 [≃$383]**
- Now We Are Six. New York: Dutton, [1927]. One of 200, signed by Milne and the illustrator, E.H. Shepard. Minor fade front pastedown. Dustwrapper (light soil, some browning). *(Antic Hay)* **$750 [≃£390]**
- Once Upon a Time. London: Hodder & Stoughton, 1917. Front free endpaper removed. *(Green Meadow)* **£35 [≃$67]**
- Prince Rabbit and the Princess who could not Laugh. London: Ward, 1966. Dustwrapper (slightly worn). *(Green Meadow)* **£25 [≃$47]**
- The Secret and Other Stories. New York: The Fountain Press, 1929. One of 400 (of 742 signed) for America. Acetate dustwrapper. *(Antic Hay)* **$175 [≃£91]**
- When We Were Very Young. London: 1974. 1st edition thus. Limited edition signed by Christopher Milne. Leather gilt, a.e.g. (spine very slightly faded). *(Whiteson)* **£100 [≃$191]**
- Winnie the Pooh. London: Methuen, 1971. Reproduction of the original MS. 1st edition thus. Slipcase. *(Green Meadow)* **£75 [≃$143]**
- Year In, Year Out. London: Methuen, 1952. *(Green Meadow)* **£25 [≃$47]**

Milosz, Czeslaw
- The Seizure of Power. New York: Criterion, 1955. Dustwrapper (slightly rubbed). *(Alphabet)* **$45 [≃£23]**

Mishima, Yukio
- Five Modern No Plays. New York: Knopf, 1957. Dustwrapper. Inscribed by the author. ('1952'). *(Lopez)* **$950 [≃£494]**
- Forbidden Colours. London: Secker & Warburg, 1968. Cloth very slightly faded. Dustwrapper (slightly torn). *(Dalian)* **£25 [≃$47]**
- The Sound of Waves. New York: Knopf, 1956. Dustwrapper. Inscribed by the author (1957). *(Lopez)* **$950 [≃£494]**
- The Sound of Waves. London: Secker & Warburg, 1957. Dustwrapper (slightly soiled and chipped). *(Dalian)* **£45 [≃$86]**
- Thirst for Love. London: Secker & Warburg, 1970. Dustwrapper. *(Dalian)* **£20 [≃$38]**

Mitchell, Margaret
- Gone With the Wind. New York: Macmillan, 1936. 1st issue book and dustwrapper. Dustwrapper (1/4 inch tear). *(Alphabet)* **$2,250 [≃£1,171]**

Mitchison, Naomi
- Behold Your King. London: Muller, 1957. Dustwrapper (slightly rubbed). *(Dalian)* **£20 [≃$38]**
- The Blood of the Martyrs. London: Constable, 1939. Tips of covers marked, endpapers slightly browned. Dustwrapper (slightly tanned, nicked, dusty). *(Dalian)* **£30 [≃$57]**
- The Delicate Fire. London: Cape, 1933. Dustwrapper (very slightly dusty). *(Dalian)* **£45 [≃$86]**
- An End and a Beginning and Other Plays. London: Constable, 1937. Foredge foxed. *(Dalian)* **£25 [≃$47]**
- The Home and a Changing Civilisation. London: John Lane; The Bodley Head, 1934. Spine and covers faded. Dustwrapper (marked). *(Dalian)* **£25 [≃$47]**
- Lobsters on the Agenda. London: Gollancz, 1952. Foredge and endpapers slightly foxed. Dustwrapper (slightly foxed). *(Dalian)* **£22 [≃$42]**
- We Have Been Warned. London: Constable, 1935. Dustwrapper (repair to top of spine). *(Dalian)* **£45 [≃$86]**

Mitford, Nancy
- Highland Fling. London: Thornton Butterworth, 1931. Covers dull and rather soiled, binding cracked at one signature, label removed from rear endpaper. Her 1st book. *(Clearwater)* **£40 [≃$76]**
- Noblesse Oblige. London: Hamish Hamilton, 1956. Dustwrapper. *(Dalian)* **£25 [≃$47]**
- The Sun King. London: Hamish Hamilton, 1966. Dustwrapper. *(Dalian)* **£30 [≃$57]**
- Voltaire in Love. London: 1957. Dustwrapper (slightly rubbed). *(Buckley)* **£20 [≃$38]**
- The Water Beetle. London: Hamish Hamilton, 1962. Uncorrected proof copy. Printed wrappers. *(Dalian)* **£20 [≃$38]**

Mo, Timothy
- An Insular Possession. London: Chatto & Windus, 1986. Uncorrected proof copy. Pictorial wrappers. *(Limestone Hills)* **$45 [≃£23]**
- An Insular Possession. London: Chatto & Windus, 1986. Dustwrapper. Signed by the

author. *(Virgo)* **£17.50 [≃$32]**

- The Monkey King. London: 1978. Bookplate. Dustwrapper. His 1st book. *(First Issues)* **£75 [≃$143]**
- The Monkey King. London: 1978. Dustwrapper. Author's inscription (1982). His 1st book. *(Blakeney)* **£135 [≃$259]**
- The Monkey King. Garden City: Doubleday, 1980. 1st American edition. Remainder spray bottom edge of pages. Dustwrapper. *(Lopez)* **$65 [≃£33]**
- Sour Sweet. London: Deutsch, 1982. 1st issue 'Chinese' dustwrapper. *(Lewton)* **£55 [≃$105]**
- Sour Sweet. London: Deutsch, 1982. 2nd issue Booker Prize dustwrapper. *(Dalian)* **£55 [≃$105]**
- Sour Sweet. London: Deutsch, 1982. 2nd state (Booker prize list) price-clipped dustwrapper. *(Moorhouse)* **£20 [≃$38]**
- Sour Sweet. London: Deutsch, 1982. Dustwrapper. *(Limestone Hills)* **$75 [≃£39]**

Momaday, N. Scott

- House Made of Dawn. New York: 1968. Dustwrapper. *(Pettler & Liebermann)* **$80 [≃£41]**

Monsarrat, Nicholas

- The Cruel Sea. London: Cassell, 1951. Edge foxing, head of covers slightly sunned. Dustwrapper (edge damaged). *(Paul Brown)* **£15 [≃$28]**
- The Cruel Sea. London: Cassell, 1951. Foredge slightly marked. Dustwrapper (an inner repair). *(Dalian)* **£35 [≃$67]**
- Depends What You Mean By Love. London: Cassell, 1947. Dustwrapper. *(Limestone Hills)* **$65 [≃£33]**
- The Kappillan of Malta. London: Cassell, 1973. Dustwrapper. Signed by the author. *(Limestone Hills)* **$50 [≃£26]**
- The Master Mariner. Book I. Running Proud. London: Cassell, 1978. Dustwrapper. Signed by the author. *(Limestone Hills)* **$50 [≃£26]**
- The Story of Esther Costello. London: Cassell, 1953. Dustwrapper. *(Dalian)* **£22 [≃$42]**
- The Story of Esther Costello. London: Cassell, 1953. Price-clipped dustwrapper (slightly frayed). The film edition in variant dustwrapper. *(Dalian)* **£20 [≃$38]**

Moorcock, Michael

- Behold the Man. London: 1969. Dustwrapper. *(Buckley)* **£20 [≃$38]**

Moore, Brian

- An Answer from Limbo. Boston: 1962. Dustwrapper (spine slightly sunned, small chip, edge rubbed). Author's signed presentation copy. *(Polyanthos)* **$45 [≃£23]**
- Black Robe. London: 1985. Uncorrected proof copy. Wrappers. *(Ellis)* **£20 [≃$38]**
- Black Robe. London: Cape, 1985. Dustwrapper. *(Lewton)* **£7.50 [≃$15]**
- Cold Heaven. London: 1983. Dustwrapper. *(Words Etcetera)* **£12.50 [≃$24]**
- The Colour of Blood. London: Cape, 1987. Uncorrected proof copy. Wrappers. Signed by the author. *(David Rees)* **£20 [≃$38]**
- The Colour of Blood. London: 1987. Dustwrapper. Author's presentation copy. *(Egret)* **£18 [≃$34]**
- The Colour of Blood. London: Cape, 1987. Dustwrapper. Signed by the author. *(David Rees)* **£20 [≃$38]**
- The Colour of Blood. London: Cape, 1987. Dustwrapper. *(Lewton)* **£7.50 [≃$15]**
- The Doctor's Wife. New York: 1976. Dustwrapper. Author's signed presentation copy. *(Polyanthos)* **$45 [≃£23]**
- The Emperor of Ice-Cream. London: Deutsch, 1966. Dustwrapper (slightly rubbed). Signed by the author. *(Moorhouse)* **£40 [≃$76]**
- Fergus. New York: 1970. Price-clipped dustwrapper (tiny tear). Author's signed presentation copy. *(Polyanthos)* **$40 [≃£20]**
- Fergus. London: Cape, 1971. Price-clipped dustwrapper. *(Virgo)* **£25 [≃$47]**
- The Great Victorian Collection. New York: 1975. Dustwrapper. Author's signed presentation copy. *(Polyanthos)* **$45 [≃£23]**
- I Am Mary Dunne. London: 1968. Dustwrapper. Author's presentation copy. *(Egret)* **£45 [≃$86]**
- I Am Mary Dunne. London: 1968. Dustwrapper. Signed by the author. *(First Issues)* **£50 [≃$95]**
- I am Mary Dunne. London: Cape, 1968. Review slip. Dustwrapper (slightly marked). *(First Issues)* **£30 [≃$57]**
- I am Mary Dunne. London: 1968. Dustwrapper. *(First Issues)* **£55 [≃$105]**
- I Am Mary Dunne. London: 1968. Dustwrapper. *(Clearwater)* **£26 [≃$49]**
- Intent to Kill. By Michael Bryan. New York: Dell, 1956. Correct 1st issue. Wrappers. *(Alphabet)* **$45 [≃£23]**
- Lies of Silence. Bloomsbury: 1990. Uncorrected proof copy. Wrappers. Signed by the author. *(David Rees)* **£20 [≃$38]**

- Lies of Silence. Bloomsbury: 1990. One of 150 signed. Glassine dustwrapper. *(David Rees)* **£45 [≃$86]**
- Lies of Silence. Bloomsbury: 1990. Dustwrapper. Signed by the author. *(David Rees)* **£20 [≃$38]**
- Lies of Silence. London: Bloomsbury, 1990. Dustwrapper. Signed by the author. *(First Issues)* **£15 [≃$28]**
- The Luck of Ginger Coffey. London: Deutsch, 1960. Dustwrapper (slightly soiled). *(Dalian)* **£30 [≃$57]**
- The Luck of Ginger Coffey. Boston: Little Brown, 1960. 1st American edition. Dustwrapper. Inscribed by the author. *(First Issues)* **£90 [≃$172]**
- The Mangan Inheritance. London: 1979. Dustwrapper. Author's presentation copy. *(Words Etcetera)* **£100 [≃$191]**
- The Mangan Inheritance. New York: 1979. Dustwrapper. Author's signed presentation copy. *(Polyanthos)* **$45 [≃£23]**
- The Mangan Inheritance. London: Cape, 1979. Dustwrapper. *(Dalian)* **£20 [≃$38]**
- The Mangan Inheritance. London: Cape, 1979. Dustwrapper. *(David Rees)* **£12 [≃$23]**
- Murder in Majorca. By Michael Bryan. London: Eyre & Spottiswoode, 1958. Cream boards. Dustwrapper. *(David Rees)* **£60 [≃$115]**
- Murder in Majorca. By Michael Bryan. London: Eyre & Spottiswoode, 1958. Cream boards. Dustwrapper (slightly chipped). *(David Rees)* **£40 [≃$76]**
- The Revolution Script. New York: 1971. Dustwrapper (slightly chipped). *(David Rees)* **£10 [≃$19]**
- The Temptation of Eileen Hughes. London: Cape, 1981. Uncorrected proof copy. Printed wrappers. *(Dalian)* **£25 [≃$47]**
- The Temptation of Eileen Hughes. London: 1981. Dustwrapper. Author's presentation copy. *(Egret)* **£25 [≃$47]**
- This Gun for Gloria. By Bernard Mara. New York: 1956. Wrappers (some wear). *(David Rees)* **£45 [≃$86]**
- Two Stories. Santa Susana Press, California: 1978. One of 326 signed. *(Words Etcetera)* **£75 [≃$143]**

Moore, C.L.

- Shambleau and Others. New York: Gnome Press, 1953. Rear cover little spotted. Dustwrapper (few tiny edge tears). *(Polyanthos)* **$100 [≃£52]**

Moore, Fergus

- Catholics. London: Cape, 1972. Price-clipped dustwrapper (very slightly chipped). *(David Rees)* **£15 [≃$28]**
- Cold Heaven. London: Cape, 1983. Dustwrapper. *(David Rees)* **£10 [≃$19]**
- Fergus. London: Cape, 1971. Uncorrected proof copy. Wrappers, with publisher's label and title inked on spine (edges slightly marked). *(David Rees)* **£12 [≃$23]**
- Two Stories. California: 1978. One of 300 (of 326) signed. *(David Rees)* **£65 [≃$124]**

Moore, Marianne

- The Arctic Ox. London: 1964. Dustwrapper. *(Buckley)* **£25 [≃$47]**
- Collected Poems. New York: Macmillan, 1951. 1st American edition. 1st (suppressed) issue. Errata slip. Minor browning and ink name stamp front endpaper. Dustwrapper. Signed by the author (Dec 1951). *(Antic Hay)* **$850 [≃£442]**
- Eight Poems. New York: Museum of Modern Art, (1962). One of 195 signed by the author and by the artist, Robert Andrew Parker. Errata slip. Original publication announcement. Cloth backed boards. Matching box, fine. *(Black Sun)* **$750 [≃£390]**
- Like a Bulwark. London: 1957. Dustwrapper. *(Polyanthos)* **$20 [≃£10]**
- A Marianne Moore Reader. New York: 1961. Dustwrapper (slightly faded, slightly torn at head of spine). *(Words Etcetera)* **£20 [≃$38]**
- O to be a Dragon. New York: 1959. Dustwrapper (three tiny nicks, slightly edge rubbed). *(Polyanthos)* **$30 [≃£15]**
- The Pangolin & Other Verse. Brendin: 1936. No dustwrapper issued. *(Any Amount)* **£450 [≃$863]**
- Poems. London: Egoist Press, 1921. Wrappers (lower edge of cover very slightly nicked). *(Virgo)* **£275 [≃$527]**
- Poems. London: Egoist Press, 1921. Wrappers (trifling wear to edges of lower cover). Her 1st book. *(Any Amount)* **£200 [≃$383]**
- Poems. London: The Egoist Press, 1921. Very light spotting throughout. Wrapper a touch rubbed at extremities. Her 1st book. *(Blakeney)* **£175 [≃$335]**
- Predilections. New York: 1955. Dustwrapper (very small piece missing, few tiny chips). *(Polyanthos)* **$30 [≃£15]**
- Tell Me, Tell Me. New York: Viking, [1966]. Dustwrapper. Signed by the author. *(Antic Hay)* **$225 [≃£117]**

- Tell Me, Tell Me Granite, Steel, and Other Topics. New York: Viking, (1966). Dustwrapper. *(Woolmer)* **$45 [≃£23]**

Moore, Nicholas

- Buzzing Around with a Bee. London: Poetry London, [n.d.]. Wrappers. *(Any Amount)* **£28 [≃$53]**
- The Glass Tower. London: Editions Poetry London, [1944]. Dustwrapper. *(Dermont)* **$75 [≃£39]**

Moore, Susanna

- The Whiteness of Bones. New York: Doubleday, [1989]. Dustwrapper. Signed by the author. *(Antic Hay)* **$35 [≃£18]**

Morante, Elsa

- House of Liars. New York: 1951. 1st US edition. Dustwrapper (very slightly chipped). Her 1st book. *(Pettler & Liebermann)* **$60 [≃£31]**

Morgenstern, S.

- See Goldman, William.

Morris, Jan

- Places. By James Morris. London: Faber, 1972. Dustwrapper. *(Lewton)* **£12.50 [≃$24]**

Morris, Willie

- North Toward Home. Boston: 1967. Price-clipped dustwrapper. His 1st book. *(Pettler & Liebermann)* **$25 [≃£13]**

Morrison, Toni

- Beloved. London: Chatto, 1987. 1st British edition. Uncorrected proof copy. Wrappers. *(Michael Johnson)* **£48 [≃$92]**
- Beloved. London: Chatto, 1987. 1st English edition. Uncorrected proof copy. Wrappers. *(Nouveau)* **$60 [≃£31]**
- Beloved. London: 1987. Dustwrapper. Author's signed presentation copy. *(Polyanthos)* **$55 [≃£28]**
- Beloved. London: Chatto, 1987. 1st British edition. Dustwrapper. Signed by the author. *(Michael Johnson)* **£25 [≃$47]**
- Beloved. London: Chatto, 1987. 1st British edition. Dustwrapper. *(Michael Johnson)* **£15 [≃$28]**
- Beloved. New York: Knopf, 1987. Dustwrapper. *(Michael Johnson)* **£28 [≃$53]**
- The Bluest Eye. London: 1979. Price-clipped dustwrapper. Author's signed presentation copy. *(Polyanthos)* **$75 [≃£39]**
- The Bluest Eye. London: Chatto, 1979. 1st British edition. Dustwrapper. *(Michael Johnson)* **£25 [≃$47]**
- Song of Solomon. London: Chatto, 1978. 1st British edition. Dustwrapper. *(Michael Johnson)* **£18 [≃$34]**
- Sula. New York: Knopf, 1974. Dustwrapper. *(Michael Johnson)* **£70 [≃$134]**
- Tar Baby. New York: 1981. Dustwrapper. Author's signed presentation copy. *(Polyanthos)* **$45 [≃£23]**
- Tar Baby. London: Chatto, 1981. 1st British edition. Uncorrected proof copy. Wrappers. *(Michael Johnson)* **£35 [≃$67]**

Mortimer, John

- Answer Yes or No. London: 1950. Dustwrapper. *(Words Etcetera)* **£45 [≃$86]**
- Charade. London: Bodley Head, 1947. Spine cocked, upper board soiled. Dustwrapper (torn and chipped). His 1st book. *(Moorhouse)* **£5 [≃$9]**
- Paradise Postponed. London: Viking, 1985. Dustwrapper. Signed by the author. *(Ash)* **£25 [≃$47]**
- Summer's Lease. London: Viking, 1988. Dustwrapper. Signed by the author. *(Ash)* **£25 [≃$47]**
- Will Shakespeare. London: 1977. Dustwrapper. *(Words Etcetera)* **£20 [≃$38]**
- The Wrong Side of the Park. London: Heinemann, 1960. Dustwrapper. *(Limestone Hills)* **$75 [≃£39]**
- The Wrong Side of the Park. London: Heinemann, 1960. Dustwrapper (slightly rubbed and soiled). *(Moorhouse)* **£40 [≃$76]**

Mosley, Nicholas

- African Switchback. London: Weidenfeld & Nicolson, 1958. Dustwrapper (frayed). *(Dalian)* **£25 [≃$47]**

Motion, Andrew

- Dangerous Play. Salamander: 1984. Dustwrapper. Signed by the author. *(Lewton)* **£12 [≃$23]**
- Independence. Edinburgh: The Salamander Press, 1981. One of 600 cloth. Dustwrapper. *(Egret)* **£20 [≃$38]**
- The Pleasure Steamers. Manchester: Carcanet, 1978. Wrappers. *(Moorhouse)* **£25 [≃$47]**
- The Poetry of Edward Thomas. London: Routledge, 1980. Dustwrapper. *(Lewton)* **£7.50 [≃$15]**

Muir, Edwin

- First Poems. London: 1925. Boards (rubbed and dull). *(Whiteson)* **£45 [≃$86]**
- First Poems. New York: Huebsch, 1925. *(Polyanthos)* **$45 [≃£23]**
- John Knox. London: Cape, 1929. Bookplate. *(Dalian)* **£35 [≃$67]**
- The Narrow Place. London: 1943. Dustwrapper (faintly sunned). *(Buckley)* **£20 [≃$38]**
- Scottish Journey. London: 1935. Proof copy. Wrappers. *(Words Etcetera)* **£15 [≃$28]**
- Social Credit and the Labour Party. London: 1935. Wrappers. *(Words Etcetera)* **£45 [≃$86]**
- We Moderns. New York: 1920. 1st US edition. Cloth backed boards (edges a little faded). His 1st book. *(Words Etcetera)* **£30 [≃$57]**
- We Moderns. New York: 1920. Covers slightly soiled. dustwrapper. His 1st book. *(Buckley)* **£35 [≃$67]**

Muir, Emily

- Small Potatoes. New York: 1940. Dustwrapper (short tear front panel, little edge chipped and rubbed). Author's signed presentation copy. Her 1st book. *(Polyanthos)* **$45 [≃£23]**

Muldoon, Paul

- New Weather. London: 1973. Wrappers. Signed by the author. *(First Issues)* **£50 [≃$95]**
- The O-O's Party New Years Eve. Dublin: Gallery Press, 1980. One of 100 signed. Linocuts by Tim Engelland. Wrappers. *(Any Amount)* **£28 [≃$53]**

Mullen, Stanley

- Kinsmen of the Dragon. Chicago: Shasta, [1951]. Dustwrapper (closed tear in front panel). Author's inscription. *(Dermont)* **$100 [≃£52]**

Muller, Marcia

- Edwin of the Iron Shoes. New York: McKay / Washburn, 1977. Dustwrapper. Signed by the author. Her 1st book. *(Janus)* **$45 [≃£23]**

Munro, Alice

- Dance of the Happy Shades. Toronto: Ryerson Press, 1968. 1st issue dustwrapper. Her 1st book. *(Alphabet)* **$300 [≃£156]**
- The Progress of Love. Toronto: M&S, 1986. Advance copy. Printed wrappers. *(Alphabet)* **$100 [≃£52]**

Murdoch, Iris

- Acastos. London: Chatto & Windus, 1985. Uncorrected proof copy. Printed wrappers. Proof dustwrapper. *(Dalian)* **£45 [≃$86]**
- An Accidental Man. London: 1971. Proof copy. Wrappers. *(Edrich)* **£20 [≃$38]**
- An Accidental Man. London: 1971. Dustwrapper. *(Edrich)* **£12 [≃$23]**
- An Accidental Man. London: 1971. Dustwrapper. *(Roberts)* **£15 [≃$28]**
- The Bell. London: 1958. Dustwrapper (chipped, slightly marked). Signed by the author on bookplate. *(Buckley)* **£45 [≃$86]**
- The Bell. London: 1958. Dustwrapper (chipped, browned). *(Buckley)* **£35 [≃$67]**
- The Bell. London: 1958. Dustwrapper. *(Lewton)* **£45 [≃$86]**
- The Book and the Brotherhood. London: 1987. Advance uncorrected proof copy. *(Buckley)* **£20 [≃$38]**
- The Book and the Brotherhood. London: 1987. Uncorrected proof copy. Wrappers. *(Edrich)* **£20 [≃$38]**
- The Book and the Brotherhood. New York: Viking Press, 1988. 1st American edition. Dustwrapper. Author's signed presentation inscription. *(Dalian)* **£55 [≃$105]**
- Bruno's Dream. London: 1968. Proof copy. Wrappers. Publication date stamped on upper wrapper. *(Edrich)* **£25 [≃$47]**
- Bruno's Dream. London: Chatto & Windus, 1961. Price-clipped dustwrapper. *(Sklaroff)* **£18 [≃$34]**
- The Existentialist Political Myth. The Delos Press: 1989. One of 45 (of 225) signed. Wrappers. Slipcase. *(Moorhouse)* **£65 [≃$124]**
- The Existentialist Political Myth. The Delos Press: 1989. One of 225. Wrappers. *(Moorhouse)* **£30 [≃$57]**
- The Existentialist Political Myth. Mosley, Birmingham: The Delos Press, 1989. One of 225. Printed wrappers. *(Dalian)* **£25 [≃$47]**
- The Existentialist Political Myth. London: 1989. One of 225. Signed. *(Buckley)* **£35 [≃$67]**
- The Good Apprentice. London: Hogarth Press, 1985. Uncorrected proof copy. Wrappers. *(Edrich)* **£20 [≃$38]**
- The Good Apprentice. London: Hogarth Press, 1985. One of 250 signed. Marbled paper and cloth over boards. *(Nouveau)* **$90 [≃£46]**
- The Good Apprentice. London: London First Editions, 1985. One of 250 signed. Tissue dustwrapper. *(Edrich)* **£35 [≃$67]**

- The Good Apprentice. London: Chatto & Hogarth, 1985. Dustwrapper. Signed by the author. *(Dyke)* **£30 [≃$57]**
- The Good Apprentice. London: Chatto & Windus, 1985. Dustwrapper. *(Dalian)* **£22 [≃$42]**
- (Introduces) Harry Weinberger. Paintings and Drawings. Exhibition catalogue. Coventry: Herbert Art Gallery, 1983. Tips of pages very slightly creased. Stiff glossy wrappers. *(Dalian)* **£30 [≃$57]**
- Henry and Cato. London: 1976. Dustwrapper. *(Edrich)* **£12 [≃$23]**
- Introduction to a Catalogue of Paintings by Henry Weinberger. Herbert Art Gallery: 1983. Wrappers. *(Buckley)* **£30 [≃$57]**
- The Italian Girl. London: Chatto & Windus, 1964. Dustwrapper. *(Antic Hay)* **$35 [≃£18]**
- The Italian Girl. London: Chatto & Windus, 1964. Inscription on endpaper. Dustwrapper. *(Sklaroff)* **£18 [≃$34]**
- The Message to the Planet. London: London Limited, 1989. One of 150 signed. Marbled paper and cloth over boards. Dustwrapper. *(Nouveau)* **$110 [≃£57]**
- The Message to the Planet. London: Chatto & Windus, 1989. Dustwrapper. Signed by the author. *(Dalian)* **£35 [≃$67]**
- The Message to the Planet. New York: Viking, (1990). Advance review copy. Dustwrapper. *(Lopez)* **$25 [≃£13]**
- The Message to the Planet. New York: Viking, (1990). Uncorrected proof copy. Wrappers. *(Lopez)* **$45 [≃£23]**
- The Nice and the Good. London: 1968. Proof copy. Wrappers. Rubber stamped publication date on upper wrapper. *(Edrich)* **£25 [≃$47]**
- The Nice and the Good. London: Chatto, 1968. Dustwrapper. *(Paul Brown)* **£15 [≃$28]**
- Nuns and Soldiers. London: Chatto, 1980. Dustwrapper. *(Hadley)* **£15 [≃$28]**
- Nuns and Soldiers. New York: 1981. Proof copy. Wrappers. Bookplates signed by the author. *(Polyanthos)* **$35 [≃£18]**
- The Philosopher's Pupil. London: Hogarth Press, 1983. Advance proof copy. Wrappers. dustwrapper. *(Edrich)* **£20 [≃$38]**
- The Philosopher's Pupil. London: Hogarth Press, 1983. Proof copy. Wrappers. *(Edrich)* **£18.50 [≃$34]**
- The Philosopher's Pupil. London: Hogarth Press, 1983. Dustwrapper. *(Edrich)* **£12 [≃$23]**
- Philosopher's Pupil. London: Chatto, 1983. Dustwrapper. *(Hadley)* **£15 [≃$28]**
- The Red and the Green. London: 1965. Proof copy. Wrappers. *(Edrich)* **£20 [≃$38]**
- The Red and the Green. London: Chatto & Windus, 1965. Dustwrapper. *(Antic Hay)* **$40 [≃£20]**
- Reynolds Stone. Warren Editions: 1981. One of 750 signed. Wrappers. *(Lewton)* **£48 [≃$92]**
- The Sandcastle. New York: Viking, 1957. 1st American edition. Dustwrapper (spine sunned). *(Dalian)* **£45 [≃$86]**
- Sartre. Cambridge: Bowes & Bowes, 1953. Endpapers very slightly browned. Price-clipped dustwrapper. Her 1st book. *(Dalian)* **£95 [≃$182]**
- Sartre. Cambridge: Bowes, 1953. Very slightly dull. Her 1st book. *(Whiteson)* **£50 [≃$95]**
- The Sea, the Sea. London: Chatto & Windus, 1978. Uncorrected proof copy. Faint water stain near foot of spine. *(Sklaroff)* **£50 [≃$95]**
- A Severed Head. London: 1961. Dustwrapper (chipped, one closed tear). *(Buckley)* **£20 [≃$38]**
- A Severed Head: A Play in Three Acts. With J.B. Priestley. London: 1964. Price-clipped dustwrapper. *(Buckley)* **£30 [≃$57]**
- The Sovereignty of Good Over Other Concepts. Cambridge: UP, 1967. Wrappers (spine slightly faded). *(Virgo)* **£50 [≃$95]**
- Sovereignty of Good over Other Concepts. London: 1967. Wrappers. *(Edrich)* **£36 [≃$69]**
- The Three Arrows and the Servants and the Snow. London: Chatto & Windus, 1973. Uncorrected proof copy. Wrappers (spine slightly faded, initials on upper cover). *(Moorhouse)* **£30 [≃$57]**
- Under the Net. London: Chatto & Windus, 1954. Top edge dusty. Dustwrapper (chipped and faded at spine, short tears front and rear panels). *(Moorhouse)* **£165 [≃$316]**
- Under the Net. New York: Viking, 1954. 1st US edition. Dustwrapper (wear at extremities). *(Marlborough B'shop)* **£28 [≃$53]**
- The Unicorn. London: Chatto & Windus, 1963. Dustwrapper. *(Lewton)* **£22 [≃$42]**
- An Unofficial Rose. London: Chatto & Windus, 1962. Dustwrapper (spine very slightly faded). *(Dalian)* **£45 [≃$86]**
- An Unofficial Rose. London: C&W, 1962. Dustwrapper. *(Lewton)* **£22 [≃$42]**

Murphy, Dervla

- Full Tilt. London: Murray, 1965. Small name on endpaper. Dustwrapper. Her 1st book. *(Dalian)* **£35 [≃$67]**
- Tibetan Foothold. London: Murray, 1966. Dustwrapper. *(Dalian)* **£25 [≃$47]**

Murphy, Richard

- Sailing to an Island. 1963. Dustwrapper. Poetry Society Bulletin laid in. *(Edrich)* **£20 [≃$38]**
- Selected Poems. 1979. Uncorrected proof copy. Wrappers. *(Edrich)* **£10 [≃$19]**
- The Woman of the House. Dolmen Press: 1959. One of 250. Wrappers. Author's presentation to Edith Starkie. *(Edrich)* **£65 [≃$124]**
- The Woman of the House. Dolmen Press: 1959. One of 250. Wrappers. *(Edrich)* **£45 [≃$86]**

Murry, John Middleton

- The Evolution of an Intellectual. London: Cobden-Sanderson, 1920. Spine and covers slightly marked. *(Dalian)* **£45 [≃$86]**
- Fyodor Dostoevsky. London: Secker, 1916. Name on endpaper. Tissue guard slightly browned. Covers slightly rubbed. His 1st book. *(Dalian)* **£65 [≃$124]**
- The Things We Are. London: Constable, 1922. Cloth marked. Name on endpaper. *(Dalian)* **£30 [≃$57]**

Nabokov, Vladimir

- Ada. New York: McGraw Hill, (1969). Slightly musty. Dustwrapper. *(Lopez)* **$50 [≃£26]**
- Ada. London: 1969. Dustwrapper. *(Polyanthos)* **$30 [≃£15]**
- Bend Sinister. New York: 1947. Spine bumped at top edge. Dustwrapper (slightly rubbed and frayed, touch of damp to rear panel, traces of a sticker removed from front panel). *(Blakeney)* **£30 [≃$57]**
- Bend Sinister. New York: 1947. Tape residue marks to pastedowns and inside of dustwrapper. *(Pettler & Liebermann)* **$85 [≃£44]**
- The Defence. London: 1964. Dustwrapper (slightly rubbed, several small nicks). *(Ellis)* **£40 [≃$76]**
- Despair. London: Weidenfeld & Nicolson, 1966. Revised version. Dustwrapper. *(Dalian)* **£35 [≃$67]**
- (Translates) Eugene Onegin. A Novel in Verse by Alexandr Pushkin. New York: 1964. 4 vols. Foredges very slightly spotted, spines very slightly faded. Dustwrappers. *(Blakeney)* **£125 [≃$239]**
- The Eye. Phaedra: 1965. 1st US edition. Dustwrapper. *(Nouveau)* **$85 [≃£44]**
- The Eye. New York: 1965. Dustwrapper (spine and folds sunned, little soiled). *(Polyanthos)* **$30 [≃£15]**
- The Eye. London: Weidenfeld & Nicolson, 1966. Uncorrected proof copy. Printed wrappers. *(Dalian)* **£75 [≃$143]**
- Invitation to a Beheading. New York: 1959. 1st US edition. Price-clipped dustwrapper (one tiny chip). *(Pettler & Liebermann)* **$40 [≃£20]**
- Invitation to a Beheading. New York: Putnam, 1959. 1st US edition. Dustwrapper. *(Nouveau)* **$75 [≃£39]**
- Laughter in the Dark. By Vladimir Nabokoff. Indianopolis: Bobbs-Merrill, (1938). 1st (American) edition. 1st issue, in green cloth. Dustwrapper (few nicks). *(Houle)* **$650 [≃£338]**
- Laughter in the Dark. New Directions: 1960. 1st edition thus. Dustwrapper (light edgewear). *(Nouveau)* **$50 [≃£26]**
- Lolita. New York: 1958. 1st US edition. Name. Price-clipped dustwrapper (lightly chipped). *(Pettler & Liebermann)* **$75 [≃£39]**
- Lolita. London: Weidenfeld, 1959. 1st UK edition. Dustwrapper. *(Any Amount)* **£25 [≃$47]**
- Look at the Harlequins! New York: McGraw Hill, 1974. 1st US edition. Dustwrapper. *(Moorhouse)* **£6 [≃$11]**
- Mary. New York: 1970. Dustwrapper. *(Polyanthos)* **$20 [≃£10]**
- Nabokov's Quartet. Phaedra, 1966. 1st US edition. Dustwrapper (one chip on front panel). *(Nouveau)* **$40 [≃£20]**
- Nikolai Gogol. Norfolk: New Directions, 1944. 1st issue. Dustwrapper. *(Alphabet)* **$175 [≃£91]**
- Nikolai Gogol. Norfolk: New Directions, [1944]. Dustwrapper (lightly used). *(Dermont)* **$75 [≃£39]**
- Nikolai Gogol. Poetry London: 1947. Page edges browned. Dustwrapper (slightly torn without loss). *(Moorhouse)* **£40 [≃$76]**
- Nikolai Gogol. London: Poetry London, 1947. Page edges slightly browned. Dustwrapper (rubbed and chipped). *(Buckley)* **£70 [≃$134]**
- Nine Stories. New Directions: [1947]. Wrappers (dust soiling and scratch mark on front cover). *(Dermont)* **$35 [≃£18]**
- Pnin. Garden City: Doubleday, 1957.

Inscription. Dustwrapper. *(Lopez)* **$85 [≃£44]**

- Pnin. New York: Doubleday, 1957. 1st US edition. Bookplate. Dustwrapper. *(Nouveau)* **$75 [≃£39]**
- Poems. London: 1962. Top edge faded, spine very slightly lightened. Dustwrapper (little sunned and soiled, top of spine just a little frayed). *(Blakeney)* **£45 [≃$86]**
- (Translates) Pushkin, Lemontov, Tyutchev. Poems. London: Lindsay Drummond, 1947. Dustwrapper (spine ends very slightly rubbed). *(Dalian)* **£65 [≃$124]**
- The Real Life of Sebastian Knight. Norfolk: New Directions, (1941). Rough cloth binding with paper labels, the 1st issue. Tiny marginal tears to upper edge of 1st three pages. Dustwrapper (roughly worn, several chips and tears). *(Lopez)* **$300 [≃£156]**
- The Real Life of Sebastian Knight. London: Editions Poetry, [1945]. 1st English edition. Dustwrapper (few edge tears). *(Dermont)* **$35 [≃£18]**
- The Real Life of Sebastian Knight. London: Editions Poetry, 1945. Spine lettering dull. Dustwrapper (slightly faded, slightly marked). *(Dalian)* **£75 [≃$143]**
- The Waltz Invention. New York: 1966. 1st (pink) dustwrapper. *(Polyanthos)* **$30 [≃£15]**
- The Waltz Invention. Phaedra: 1966. 1st issue pink dustwrapper. *(Nouveau)* **$95 [≃£49]**

Naipaul, Shiva

- The Chip-Chip Gatherers. Deutsch, 1973. Dustwrapper (slightly worn). *(Glyn's)* **£42.50 [≃$82]**
- Fireflies. London: Deutsch, 1970. Dustwrapper. Author's 1st book. *(David Rees)* **£100 [≃$191]**
- Fireflies. New York: Deutsch, 1970. Signature. Dustwrapper. *(Lewton)* **£110 [≃$211]**
- Fireflies. 1971. 1st American edition. Dustwrapper. *(First Issues)* **£35 [≃$67]**
- Fireflies. New York: Knopf, 1971. 1st US edition. Dustwrapper. *(Nouveau)* **$40 [≃£20]**
- An Unfinished Journey. London: Hamish Hamilton, 1986. Dustwrapper. *(Dalian)* **£16 [≃$30]**

Naipaul, V.S.

- Among the Believers. London: Deutsch, 1981. Dustwrapper. *(Dalian)* **£25 [≃$47]**
- Among the Believers. London: Deutsch, 1981. Dustwrapper. *(Lewton)* **£15 [≃$28]**
- An Area of Darkness. Deutsch, 1964. Price-clipped dustwrapper (slightly worn). *(Glyn's)* **£25 [≃$47]**
- An Area of Darkness. London: 1964. Dustwrapper (slightly frayed). *(Roberts)* **£30 [≃$57]**
- A Bend in the River. London: Deutsch, 1979. Price-clipped dustwrapper. *(Sklaroff)* **£20 [≃$38]**
- A Bend in the River. New York: Knopf, 1979. 1st American edition. Advance review copy. Dustwrapper. Review slip and promotional sheet laid in. *(Lopez)* **$50 [≃£26]**
- A Congo Diary. California: Sylvester & Orphanos, 1980. One of 330 signed. No dustwrapper issued. *(Virgo)* **£90 [≃$172]**
- A Congo Diary. Los Angeles: Sylvester & Orphanos, 1980. One of 330 signed. No dustwrapper issued. *(Alphabet)* **$100 [≃£52]**
- A Congo Diary. Sylvester & Orphanos: 1980. One of 330 signed. No dustwrapper issued. *(Words Etcetera)* **£90 [≃$172]**
- A Congo Diary. Sylvester & Orphanos, 1980. One of 300 (of 330) signed. *(David Rees)* **£90 [≃$172]**
- The Enigma of Arrival. London: 1987. Dustwrapper. *(Words Etcetera)* **£16 [≃$30]**
- The Enigma of Arrival. Viking, 1987. Dustwrapper. *(Dalian)* **£20 [≃$38]**
- The Enigma of Arrival. Viking: 1987. Dustwrapper. *(Moorhouse)* **£6 [≃$11]**
- Finding the Centre. Deutsch, 1984. Uncorrected proof copy. Wrappers. Proof dustwrapper (slightly creased). *(David Rees)* **£60 [≃$115]**
- Guerillas. London: Deutsch, 1975. Dustwrapper. *(Lewton)* **£25 [≃$47]**
- Guerillas. London: Deutsch, 1975. Dustwrapper. *(Sklaroff)* **£25 [≃$47]**
- Guerillas. New York: Knopf, 1975. 1st American edition. Advance review copy. Review slip. Dustwrapper. *(Lopez)* **$75 [≃£39]**
- Guerillas. New York: Knopf, 1975. 1st American edition. Remainder mark. Dustwrapper. *(Lopez)* **$35 [≃£18]**
- A House for Mr. Biswas. London: 1961. Dustwrapper (slightly chipped). *(Egret)* **£75 [≃$143]**
- A House for Mr. Biswas. London: Deutsch, 1961. Dustwrapper (unfaded, a bit frayed and edge worn at spine extremities). *(Alphabet)* **$250 [≃£130]**
- In a Free State. London: 1971. Dustwrapper. *(Egret)* **£30 [≃$57]**

- In a Free State. London: Deutsch, 1971. Dustwrapper. *(Lewton)* **£27.50 [≃$53]**
- India. London: London Limited Editions, 1990. One of 150 signed. Cellophane dustwrapper. *(Words Etcetera)* **£35 [≃$67]**
- The Loss of El Dorado. London: Deutsch, 1969. Dustwrapper (with a nick). *(David Rees)* **£20 [≃$38]**
- The Middle Passage. New York: Macmillan, 1963. Dustwrapper. *(Lopez)* **$135 [≃£70]**
- The Mimic Men. London: Deutsch, 1967. Dustwrapper. *(Lewton)* **£48 [≃$92]**
- Mr Stone and the Knights Companion. London: Deutsch, (1963). Price-clipped dustwrapper. *(Lopez)* **$200 [≃£104]**
- Mr. Stone and the Knights Companion. London: Deutsch, 1963. Tape marks on covers. Dustwrapper. *(Dalian)* **£85 [≃$163]**
- Mr. Stone and the Knight's Companion. New York: 1964. 1st US edition. Dustwrapper (bit chipped at head of spine). *(Pettler & Liebermann)* **$45 [≃£23]**
- The Return of Eva Peron. London: 1980. Dustwrapper. *(Egret)* **£12 [≃$23]**
- A Turn in the South. London: Viking, 1989. Dustwrapper. Signed by the author. *(David Rees)* **£25 [≃$47]**
- A Turn in the South. Viking: 1989. Dustwrapper. Signed by the author. *(Moorhouse)* **£25 [≃$47]**

Narayan, R.K.

- An Astrologer's Day and Other Stories. London: 1947. Dustwrapper (lightly rubbed, very slightly frayed). *(Blakeney)* **£35 [≃$67]**

Nash, Ogden

- Hard Lines. New York: 1931. Cloth (slightly soiled). Dustwrapper (slightly worn). His 1st book. *(King)* **$100 [≃£52]**
- Hard Lines and Others. London: 1932. Cloth backed boards (one corner a trifle bumped). Dustwrapper (browned). His 1st book. *(Words Etcetera)* **£35 [≃$67]**
- The Private Dining Room and Other Verses. London: Dent, 1953. Prelims slightly foxed. Dustwrapper (very slightly marked). *(Dalian)* **£22 [≃$42]**

Naughton, Bill

- Alfie. London: Samuel French, [1963]. The acting edition of the play. Wrappers (a few faint marks). *(Ash)* **£20 [≃$38]**
- Alfie. London: 1966. Dustwrapper (small stain rear panel). *(Lewton)* **£27.50 [≃$53]**

Naylor, Gloria

- The Women of Brewster Place. London: 1983. 1st British edition. Dustwrapper. Her 1st book. *(Pettler & Liebermann)* **$80 [≃£41]**

Nemerov, Howard

- The Blue Swallows. Chicago: 1967. Dustwrapper (two tiny pieces missing, very slightly edge rubbed). Author's signed presentation copy. *(Polyanthos)* **$35 [≃£18]**
- A Commodity of Dreams and Other Stories. London: Secker & Warburg, 1960. Price-clipped dustwrapper. *(Dalian)* **£25 [≃$47]**
- The Image and the Law. New York: 1947. Editorial stamp on rear endpaper. Dustwrapper (tiny tear). Author's signed presentation copy. 45-word TLS (1958). His 1st book. *(Polyanthos)* **$100 [≃£52]**
- The Salt Garden. Boston: 1955. Review slip laid in. Spine extremities rubbed. Dustwrapper (top of spine little torn, internally mended, slightly edge rubbed). Signed by the author. *(Polyanthos)* **$35 [≃£18]**
- The Winter Lighting. London: Rapp & Whiting, 1968. Dustwrapper (tanned). *(Hazeldene)* **£15 [≃$28]**

Neruda, Pablo

- Extravagaria. London: Cape, 1972. Edges slightly marked. Dustwrapper. *(Hazeldene)* **£30 [≃$57]**
- Selected Poems. London: Cape, 1970. Edges slightly marked. Dustwrapper. *(Hazeldene)* **£30 [≃$57]**

New Measure

- New Measure. Edited by Peter Jay and John Aczel. Oxford: 1965-69. Nos 1-10. Complete run. Wrappers. *(Any Amount)* **£50 [≃$95]**

Newby, Eric

- A Short Walk in the Hindu Kush. London: Secker & Warburg, 1958. Endpapers slightly marked. Dustwrapper (torn and frayed). *(Dalian)* **£30 [≃$57]**
- Something Wholesale. London: Secker & Warburg, 1962. Dustwrapper. *(Dalian)* **£35 [≃$67]**

Newby, P.H.

- A Lot to Ask. London: Faber, 1972. Price-clipped dustwrapper. *(Dalian)* **£15 [≃$28]**
- Something to Answer For. London: 1968. Dustwrapper. Author's presentation copy. *(Egret)* **£35 [≃$67]**
- Something to Answer For. London: 1968.

Dustwrapper. Author's presentation copy. *(Egret)* **£35 [≃$67]**

Nichol, B.P.. sic

- Two Novels. Toronto: Coach Press, 1969. One of 250 (of 300). Dustwrapper (bit chipped at spine, faded). *(Alphabet)* **$175 [≃£91]**

Nichols, Beverley

- Garden Open Tomorrow. London: Heinemann, 1968. Dustwrapper. *(Dalian)* **£25 [≃$47]**
- Prelude. London: Chatto & Windus, 1929. Pages slightly browned. Covers marked, spine rubbed. His 1st book. *(Dalian)* **£45 [≃$86]**
- Puck at Brighton. Brighton: (1934). Metallic covers (oxidised). *(Dalian)* **£35 [≃$67]**
- The Rich Die Hard. London: Hutchinson, 1957. Dustwrapper. *(Dalian)* **£22 [≃$42]**
- Sunlight on the Lawn. London: Cape, 1956. Name on endpaper. Dustwrapper (slightly dusty). *(Dalian)* **£30 [≃$57]**
- Uncle Samson. London: Evans Bros, (1950). Dustwrapper (slightly nicked). *(Dalian)* **£18 [≃$34]**
- Verdict on India. London: Cape, 1944. Dustwrapper (slightly rubbed). *(Dalian)* **£22 [≃$42]**

Nichols, John

- The Magic Journey. New York: HRW, (1978). Hardcover issue. Abrasion to front pastedown from bookplate removal. Dustwrapper. Signed by the author. *(Lopez)* **$275 [≃£143]**
- The Milagro Beanfield War. New York: HRW, (1974). Dustwrapper (small hole near bottom edge of rear panel). *(Lopez)* **$135 [≃£70]**
- The Milagro Beanfield War. New York: 1974. Name and date. Dustwrapper (some chipping to spine). *(Pettler & Liebermann)* **$125 [≃£65]**
- The Nirvana Blues. New York: HRW, (1981). Advance review copy with promotional material laid in. Dustwrapper. *(Lopez)* **$35 [≃£18]**

Nicholson, Norman

- The Fire of the Lord. London: 1944. *(Moon)* **£30 [≃$57]**
- Wednesday Early Closing. London: Faber, 1975. Dustwrapper. *(Moon)* **£35 [≃$67]**

Nicolson, Harold

- The Meaning of Prestige. Cambridge: UP, 1937. Endpapers slightly foxed. Boards. No dustwrapper issued. *(Dalian)* **£25 [≃$47]**

Nin, Anais

- Collages. Chicago: 1964. Softbound original. Wrappers. *(Pettler & Liebermann)* **$15 [≃£7]**
- D.H. Lawrence. Paris: 1932. One of 550. Copy number ticket present. Front inner hinge cracked, minor cover soil, darkened, chipped. Her 1st book. *(King)* **$150 [≃£78]**
- D.H. Lawrence. London: 1961. 1st British edition. Dustwrapper. *(Pettler & Liebermann)* **$45 [≃£23]**
- The Diary. New York: Harcourt Brace, 1966-80. 7 vols. Dustwrappers (vols 1 & 3 small piece missing from back panel). Vol 4 signed by the author. *(Virgo)* **£110 [≃$211]**
- The Four-Chambered Heart. London: Peter Owen, 1959. Dustwrapper. *(Dalian)* **£22 [≃$42]**
- The Novel of the Future. New York: 1968. Dustwrapper. *(Pettler & Liebermann)* **$25 [≃£13]**
- Seduction of the Minotaur. London: Owen, 1961. Dustwrapper. *(Dalian)* **£20 [≃$38]**
- A Spy in the House of Love. Paris & New York: British Book Centre, [1954]. 1st American edition. Dustwrapper. *(Antic Hay)* **$50 [≃£26]**
- Under a Glass Bell and Other Stories. New York: Dutton, 1948. Dustwrapper. *(Chapel Hill)* **$85 [≃£44]**
- Winter of Artifice. With Engravings by Ian Hugo. N.p.: 1944. One of 500. *(Woolmer)* **$50 [≃£26]**

Nine

- Nine. A Magazine of Poetry and Criticism. Edited and Published by Peter Russell. London: 1949-56. Numbers 1-11, all published. Spines almost entirely undamaged. *(Blakeney)* **£150 [≃$287]**

Niven, Larry

- Inconstant Moon. London: Gollancz, 1973. Dustwrapper. *(Lewton)* **£85 [≃$163]**
- Inconstant Moon. London: 1973. Name and date on endpaper. Spine slightly leaned. Price-clipped dustwrapper (lightly creased). Signed by the author. *(Sclanders)* **£140 [≃$268]**
- Neutron Star. London: Macdonald, 1969. Dustwrapper. *(Sklaroff)* **£200 [≃$383]**
- World of Ptaavs. London: Macdonald, 1968. Dustwrapper. *(Lewton)* **£90 [≃$172]**

Norton, Mary

- The Magic Bedknob. London: Dent, 1945. Dustwrapper (slightly worn). *(Green Meadow)* **£45 [≃$86]**

Nothing Doing in London

- Nothing Doing in London. London: 1966-68. One of 500. Vols 1-2. All published. Wrappers. *(Any Amount)* **£30 [≃$57]**

Nott, Kathleen

- Landscapes and Departures. London: Editions Poetry, (1947). Slight tanning to top of front cover. *(Dalian)* **£25 [≃$47]**

Nuttall, Jeff

- Snipe's Spinster. London: Calder & Boyars, 1975. Dustwrapper. *(Dalian)* **£12 [≃$23]**

Nye, Robert

- Falstaff. London: Hamish Hamilton, 1976. Dustwrapper. *(Dalian)* **£25 [≃$47]**
- Taliesin. London: Faber, 1966. Dustwrapper. *(Green Meadow)* **£30 [≃$57]**

O'Brian, Patrick

- The Last Pool and Other Stories. London: Secker & Warburg, 1950. Dustwrapper (spine extremities lightly chipped). *(Limestone Hills)* **$80 [≃£41]**
- Master & Commander. London: Collins, 1970. Dustwrapper. *(Limestone Hills)* **$55 [≃£28]**

O'Brien, Edna

- August is a Wicked Month. London: Cape, 1965. Dustwrapper (spine sunned). *(Paul Brown)* **£15 [≃$28]**
- Casualties of Peace. London: 1966. Uncorrected proof copy. Wrappers. *(Edrich)* **£18 [≃$34]**
- The Country Girls. London: 1960. Minimal foxing of endpapers. *(Roberts)* **£20 [≃$38]**
- The Country Girls Trilogy. London: Cape, 1987. Dustwrapper. Signed by the author. *(Michael Johnson)* **£15 [≃$28]**
- Girls in their Married Bliss. London: Cape, 1964. Dustwrapper (slightly soiled). *(Lewton)* **£17.50 [≃$34]**
- The High Road. London: Weidenfeld, 1988. Dustwrapper. Signed by the author. *(Michael Johnson)* **£17.50 [≃$34]**
- James and Nora. Lord John Press: 1981. One of 250 signed. No dustwrapper issued. *(Dermont)* **$35 [≃£18]**
- The Lonely Girl. London: 1962. Uncorrected proof copy. Wrappers. *(Edrich)* **£25 [≃$47]**
- The Lonely Girl. London: Cape, 1962. Dustwrapper. *(Lewton)* **£27.50 [≃$53]**
- The Love Object. New York: Knopf, 1969. 1st American edition. Dustwrapper. Signed by the author and inscribed. *(Michael Johnson)* **£16 [≃$30]**
- A Pagan Place. London: Weidenfeld, 1970. Dustwrapper. Signed by the author. *(Michael Johnson)* **£15 [≃$28]**
- A Pagan Place [play]. London: Faber, 1973. Price-clipped dustwrapper. *(Dalian)* **£20 [≃$38]**
- A Scandalous Woman. London: 1974. Uncorrected proof copy. Wrappers. *(Edrich)* **£18 [≃$34]**
- A Scandalous Woman. London: Weidenfeld, 1974. Dustwrapper. Signed by the author. *(Michael Johnson)* **£15 [≃$28]**
- Virginia: A Play. New York: Harcourt Brace Jovanovich, (1981). 1st American edition. Dustwrapper (small chip top of spine). *(Houle)* **$30 [≃£15]**

O'Brien, Flann

- At Swim-Two-Birds. New York: Pantheon, [1951]. Dustwrapper (a few faint scratches). *(Polyanthos)* **$95 [≃£49]**
- At Swim-Two-Birds. New York: Pantheon, 1951. 1st American edition, 1939 stated on copyright page. Dustwrapper. *(First Issues)* **£85 [≃$163]**
- The Best of Myles. London: 1968. Dustwrapper. *(Edrich)* **£36 [≃$69]**
- The Dalkey Archive. London: MacGibbon & Kee, 1968. Dustwrapper. *(Dalian)* **£65 [≃$124]**
- The Dalkey Archive. US: 1965. 1st US edition. Dustwrapper. *(Words Etcetera)* **£45 [≃$86]**
- The Hard Life. London: 1961. Dustwrapper. *(Words Etcetera)* **£48 [≃$92]**
- The Hard Life. London: MacGibbon & Kee, 1961. Dustwrapper (very slightly rubbed). *(Dalian)* **£125 [≃$239]**
- The Hard Life. London: 1961. Dustwrapper (slightly rubbed and marked, repaired). *(Clearwater)* **£90 [≃$172]**
- The Poor Mouth (An Beal Bacht) ... Edited by Myles na Gopaleen. London: Hart-Davis, MacGibbon, 1973. 1st edition in English. Dustwrapper. *(Limestone Hills)* **$55 [≃£28]**

O'Brien, Kate

- The Anteroom. Garden City: Doubleday, Doran, 1934. 1st American edition. Dustwrapper. Her 1st book. *(Alphabet)* **$75 [≃£39]**

O'Brien, Tim

- Going After Cacciato. London: 1978. 1st British edition. Dustwrapper. *(Pettler & Liebermann)* **$35 [≃£18]**
- If I Die in a Combat Zone. London: 1973. Price-clipped dustwrapper. His 1st book. *(Sclanders)* **£40 [≃$76]**
- Northern Lights. New York: 1975. Dustwrapper. Signed by the author. *(Pettler & Liebermann)* **$125 [≃£65]**
- The Nuclear Age. New York: Knopf, 1985. Uncorrected proof copy. Wrappers. Signed by the author. *(Antic Hay)* **$85 [≃£44]**
- The Nuclear Age. New York: Knopf, 1985. Uncorrected proof copy. Wrappers. *(Dermont)* **$60 [≃£31]**
- The Nuclear Age. New York: Knopf, 1985. Dustwrapper. Signed by the author. *(Antic Hay)* **$45 [≃£23]**
- The Nuclear Age. London: Collins, 1986. 1st English edition. Advance review copy. Dustwrapper. *(Lopez)* **$50 [≃£26]**

O'Casey, Sean

- The Silver Tassie. London: 1928. *(Edrich)* **£20 [≃$38]**
- The Story of the Irish Citizen Army. By P.O. Cathasaigh. Dublin: Maunsel, 1919. 1st issue in grey wrappers. His 1st book (preceded by a few broadsides and pamphlets). *(Woolmer)* **$125 [≃£65]**
- The Story of the Irish Citizen Army. 1919. Wrappers. *(Edrich)* **£70 [≃$134]**
- Windfalls. London: Macmillan, 1934. Dustwrapper (some holes on back cover). *(Dalian)* **£35 [≃$67]**
- Windfalls. London: Macmillan, 1934. Dustwrapper. *(Lewton)* **£25 [≃$47]**

O'Connor, Flannery

- The Complete Stories. New York: 1971. Dustwrapper. *(Pettler & Liebermann)* **$75 [≃£39]**
- Everything that Rises must Converge. London: Faber, 1966. 1st English edition. Dustwrapper (one small closed tear). *(Limestone Hills)* **$95 [≃£49]**
- A Good Man is Hard to Find and Other Stories. New York: Harcourt, (1955). Publisher's compliments slip inserted. Slight wear at spine ends. 1st issue (without reviews on back panel) dustwrapper (spine faded, minor wear at edges). *(Woolmer)* **$225 [≃£117]**
- A Good Man is Hard to Find and Other Stories. London: 1968. Dustwrapper. *(Words Etcetera)* **£75 [≃$143]**
- Home of the Brave. New York: 1981. One of 200. Wrappers. *(Words Etcetera)* **£45 [≃$86]**
- Mystery and Manners and Occasional Pieces. London: Faber, 1972. Price-clipped dustwrapper. *(Dalian)* **£35 [≃$67]**
- The Violent Bear It Away. New York: Farrar, 1960. Dustwrapper (minor edgewear). *(Nouveau)* **$190 [≃£98]**
- The Violent Bear It Away. London: Longmans, 1960. 1st English edition. Stamp on endpaper. Dustwrapper. *(Alphabet)* **$85 [≃£44]**
- The Violent Bear It Away. London: 1960. Light stain on tail edges. Dustwrapper (very slightly chipped and torn). *(Egret)* **£20 [≃$38]**
- The Violent Bear It Away. London: 1960. 1st British edition. Dustwrapper. *(Pettler & Liebermann)* **$110 [≃£57]**
- Wise Blood. New York: Harcourt, (1952). Dustwrapper (several repairs). *(Lopez)* **$650 [≃£338]**
- Wise Blood. London: Neville Spearman, 1955. Dustwrapper. Author's 1st book. *(Dalian)* **£150 [≃$287]**
- Wise Blood. London: 1955. Dustwrapper (slightly marked and nicked). Her 1st book. *(Clearwater)* **£75 [≃$143]**
- Wise Blood. London: 1955. Some foxing to endpapers. Dustwrapper (slightly faded, foxed in places). *(Egret)* **£60 [≃$115]**
- Wise Blood. London: 1955. Top corners very slightly bumped. *(Edrich)* **£18 [≃$34]**

O'Connor, Frank

- Guests of the Nation. London: 1931. Spine sunned. His 1st book. *(Edrich)* **£35 [≃$67]**
- A Picture Book. Cuala Press: 1943. One of 480, numbered. *(Edrich)* **£50 [≃$95]**
- Three Old Brothers and Other Poems. London: 1936. Dustwrapper. *(Edrich)* **£45 [≃$86]**

O'Connor, Philip

- The Lower View. London: Faber, 1960. Dustwrapper (very slightly nicked and rubbed). *(Dalian)* **£18 [≃$34]**
- Memoirs of a Public Baby. London: 1958. Dustwrapper (some staining to spine). His 1st book. *(Ellis)* **£20 [≃$38]**
- Steiner's Tour. Paris: Olympia Press, 1960. The correct 1st edition. Printed wrappers. dustwrapper. *(Dalian)* **£25 [≃$47]**

O'Faolain, Sean

- Midsummer Night Madness. London: 1932.

Dustwrapper (slightly rubbed, spine slightly faded). His 1st book. *(Ellis)* **£65 [≃$124]**

O'Flaherty, Liam

- The Assassin. London: 1928. One of 150 numbered and signed. *(Edrich)* **£65 [≃$124]**
- The Assassin. London: 1928. Dustwrapper. *(Edrich)* **£50 [≃$95]**
- The Assassin. London: 1928. Inscription on endpaper. Covers a little marked. *(Edrich)* **£12.50 [≃$24]**
- The Black Soul. London: Cape, 1924. Dustwrapper (slightly tanned). *(Dalian)* **£95 [≃$182]**
- The Black Soul. London: 1924. Covers badly faded and slightly marked. *(Edrich)* **£16 [≃$30]**
- The Child of God. Privately Printed: 1926. One of 100 numbered and signed. Wrappers. *(Edrich)* **£150 [≃$287]**
- Civil War. Privately Printed: 1925. One of 100 numbered and signed. Wrappers. *(Edrich)* **£150 [≃$287]**
- The Ecstasy of Angus. London: Chiswick Press, 1931. One of 350 signed. Spine little sunned, extremities slightly rubbed. *(Polyanthos)* **$100 [≃£52]**
- The Fairy Goose and Two Other Stories. New York: Crosby Gaige, 1927. One of 1190 signed. Dustwrapper (torn). *(Dermont)* **$45 [≃£23]**
- Famine. London: Gollancz, 1937. Dustwrapper (spine slightly faded). *(Edrich)* **£60 [≃$115]**
- The House of Gold. London: 1929. Dustwrapper. Signed by the author. *(Edrich)* **£60 [≃$115]**
- Land. London: 1946. Dustwrapper (spine and edges sunned). *(Polyanthos)* **$45 [≃£23]**
- The Puritan. London: Cape, 1932. Dustwrapper (slightly nicked and dusty). *(Dalian)* **£65 [≃$124]**
- The Puritan. London: 1932. Orange cloth. Dustwrapper. *(Polyanthos)* **$75 [≃£39]**
- Return of the Brute. London: 1929. Dustwrapper. *(Edrich)* **£65 [≃$124]**
- Spring Sowing. London: 1924. Dustwrapper (defective at spine ends). *(Edrich)* **£35 [≃$67]**
- The Tent. London: 1926. Signed by the author. *(Edrich)* **£30 [≃$57]**
- The Terrorist. Privately Printed: 1926. One of 100 numbered and signed. Wrappers. *(Edrich)* **£150 [≃$287]**
- A Tourist's Guide to Ireland. London: Mandrake Press, 1929. Inscription on endpaper. *(Edrich)* **£12.50 [≃$24]**
- Two Years. London: 1930. Dustwrapper (slightly soiled and frayed). *(Edrich)* **£20 [≃$38]**

O'Hara, Frank

- Frank O'Hara. Verona: Corubolo & Castiglioni, American Authors Series, 1983. One of 65. Signed etching by Roger Seldon. Wrappers. *(Bromer)* **$250 [≃£130]**
- Oranges. New York: Angel Hair Books, [1968]. One of 200. Stapled mimeo wrappers (white paper covers browning slightly). *(Alphabet)* **$65 [≃£33]**
- Second Avenue. New York: Totem / Corinth, 1960. 1st issue. Wrappers. *(Alphabet)* **$45 [≃£23]**

O'Hara, John

- Butterfield 8. New York: (1935). Dustwrapper (frayed, slightly chipped). *(King)* **$75 [≃£39]**
- Hope of Heaven. New York: 1938. Price-clipped dustwrapper (a bit worn). *(Pettler & Liebermann)* **$100 [≃£52]**
- Hope of Heaven. New York: Harcourt Brace, 1938. Dustwrapper (small rub on spine). *(Alphabet)* **$350 [≃£182]**
- Ourselves to Know. London: Cresset Press, 1960. Dustwrapper. *(Sklaroff)* **£18 [≃$34]**
- Sermons and Soda Water. London: Cresset, 1961. 1st English edition. Dustwrapper. *(Limestone Hills)* **$40 [≃£20]**

O'Neill, Eugene

- All God's Chillun Got Wings: And Welded. New York: Boni & Liveright, (1924). *(Houle)* **$75 [≃£39]**
- "Anna Christie". New York: 1930. One of 775 signed. Uncut. Corners little rubbed, top edges and covers little sunned. *(Polyanthos)* **$100 [≃£52]**
- Days Without End. New York: Random House, [1934]. One of 325 signed. Leather (some rubbing). *(Antic Hay)* **$275 [≃£143]**
- Dynamo. New York: 1929. One of 775 signed. Spine sunned. Box (extremities rubbed). *(Polyanthos)* **$120 [≃£62]**
- Dynamo. New York: Liveright, 1929. Hinges starting. Dustwrapper (slight browning). Author's inscription (1942). *(Houle)* **$600 [≃£312]**
- Dynamo. New York: Liveright, 1929. Dustwrapper (slight rubbing, small chips, short tears). *(Houle)* **$85 [≃£44]**
- Dynamo. New York: Liveright, 1929. Dustwrapper, fine. *(Houle)* **$150 [≃£78]**
- The Emperor Jones. Cincinnati: Stewart

Kidd, (1921). 1st separate edition. Printed wrappers. Chemise and slipcase. Signed by the author. *(Bromer)* **$750 [≃£390]**

- The Iceman Cometh. New York: Random House, (1946). 1st book edition. Dustwrapper (few nicks). *(Houle)* **$95 [≃£49]**
- The Iceman Cometh. New York: Random House, [1946]. Dustwrapper. *(Chapel Hill)* **$70 [≃£36]**
- Lazarus Laughed. New York: Boni & Liveright, 1927. 1st trade edition. Dustwrapper (small nicks). *(Houle)* **$150 [≃£78]**
- Long Day's Journey into Night. London: 1956. 1st English edition. Dustwrapper (spine slightly browned). *(Words Etcetera)* **£35 [≃$67]**
- Marco Millions. New York: Boni & Liveright, 1927. One of 450 signed. Boards. Slipcase (some rubbing). *(Antic Hay)* **$275 [≃£143]**
- Marco Millions. New York: 1927. Price-clipped dustwrapper. *(Polyanthos)* **$60 [≃£31]**
- Marco Millions. New York: Boni & Liveright, 1927. 1st trade edition. *(Houle)* **$75 [≃£39]**
- A Moon for the Misbegotten. New York: Random House, [1952]. Price-clipped dustwrapper. *(Chapel Hill)* **$70 [≃£36]**
- More Stately Mansions. Yale: UP, 1964. Dustwrapper. *(Polyanthos)* **$15 [≃£7]**
- Mourning Becomes Electra. A Trilogy. NY (1931). One of 500 signed. Vellum gilt, uncut (spine little sunned). *(Polyanthos)* **$200 [≃£104]**
- Mourning Becomes Electra. New York: 1931. Cloth slightly spotted. Dustwrapper (two tiny pieces missing side of spine). *(Polyanthos)* **$40 [≃£20]**
- Mourning Becomes Electra: A Trilogy. New York: Horace Liveright, 1931. Dustwrapper (slight browning, few nicks). *(Houle)* **$175 [≃£91]**
- Strange Interlude. New York: Boni & Liveright, 1928. Dustwrapper, fine. *(Houle)* **$250 [≃£130]**
- Thirst: and Other One Act Plays by Eugene G. O'Neill. Boston: Gorham Press, (1914). Slight rubbing to spine. Acetate dustwrapper. His 1st book. *(Houle)* **$450 [≃£234]**
- A Touch of the Poet. New Haven: 1957. Dustwrapper (one tiny tear, very slightly rubbed). *(Polyanthos)* **$25 [≃£13]**

O'Sullivan, Maurice

- Twenty Years a'Growing. Introductory Note by E.M. Forster. London: Chatto & Windus, 1933. Covers faded at edges. Dustwrapper (some wear at edges). *(Woolmer)* **$75 [≃£39]**

Oates, Joyce Carol

- Do With Me What You Will. New York: Vanguard, (1973). Price-clipped dustwrapper. Signed by the author. *(Between the Covers)* **$50 [≃£26]**
- Dreaming America & Other Poems. Aloe: 1973. One of 150 signed. Wrappers. *(Nouveau)* **$75 [≃£39]**
- Expensive People. London: 1969. Dustwrapper. Signed by the author. *(Egret)* **£30 [≃$57]**
- Queen of the Night. Northridge: Lord John, 1979. One of 300 signed. No dustwrapper issued. *(Lopez)* **$65 [≃£33]**
- Upon the Sweeping Flood and Other Stories. London: Gollancz, 1973. Dustwrapper. *(Dalian)* **£18 [≃$34]**
- The Wheel of Love. London: 1971. Dustwrapper. Signed by the author. *(Egret)* **£25 [≃$47]**
- Wonderland. London: 1972. Dustwrapper. Signed by the author. *(Egret)* **£22 [≃$42]**

Oliver, Mary

- American Primitive. Boston: Little, Brown, [1983]. Uncorrected proof copy. Printed wrappers. Signed by the author. *(Dermont)* **$75 [≃£39]**
- No Voyage and Other Poems. London: Dent, [1963]. Dustwrapper (spine darkened). Signed by the author. Her 1st book. *(Dermont)* **$200 [≃£104]**
- No Voyage and Other Poems. Boston: HMCO, 1965. 1st American edition. Printed wrappers. Signed by the author. Her 1st book. *(Dermont)* **$150 [≃£78]**

Olivia

- Olivia. London: Hogarth Press, 1949. Dustwrapper (minor closed tear to front panel edge). *(Paul Brown)* **£7.50 [≃$15]**

Olsen, Tillie

- Yonnondio from the Thirties. New York: 1974. Dustwrapper (very small tear side of spine). Author's signed presentation copy. *(Polyanthos)* **$45 [≃£23]**

Olson, Charles

- The Maximus Poems 1-10. Stuttgart, Jonathan Williams, Jargon 7, 1953. One of 300. Promotional by Creeley inserted. Name. Printed self wrappers (few minute edge nicks). *(Polyanthos)* **$350 [≃£182]**

- The Maximus Poems 11-22. Stuttgart, Williams, 1956. One of 350. Name. Printed self wrappers (three tiny pieces missing from extremities, three tiny tears lower edge front wrapper). *(Polyanthos)* **$350 [≃£182]**
- Some Early Poems. Iowa City: Windhover, 1978. One of 300. Cloth and boards. No dustwrapper issued. *(Alphabet)* **$200 [≃£104]**
- The Special View of History. Berkeley: Oyez, 1960. Price-clipped dustwrapper. *(Alphabet)* **$50 [≃£26]**
- This. Black Mountain College Press: 1952. Large sheet, folded. Lacks the mailing envelope. *(Black Sun)* **$350 [≃£182]**

Olympia

- Olympia. A Monthly Review from Paris. Edited and Published by Maurice Girodias. Paris: January 1962 to April 1963. Numbers 1-4, all published. Light wear to one wrapper. *(Blakeney)* **£80 [≃$153]**

Once, Twice, Thrice ...

- Once, Twice, Thrice, Thrice 1/2, Frice, Vice, Spice, Slice, Slice 2, Ice, Nice. Edited by Tom Clark. Essex: [ca 1965-68]. Eleven issues, all published. Roneoed sheets stapled. *(Blakeney)* **£875 [≃$1,679]**

Ondaatje, Michael

- The Collected Works of Billy the Kid. New York: Norton, (1974). 1st American edition. Advance review copy. Erratum slip. Review slip. Dustwrapper. *(Lopez)* **$50 [≃£26]**
- The Collected Works of Billy the Kid. London: Boyars, 1981. 1st English edition. Price-clipped dustwrapper. *(Alphabet)* **$35 [≃£18]**
- Coming through Slaughter. London: Boyars, 1979. Price-clipped dustwrapper. *(David Rees)* **£25 [≃$47]**
- Rat Jelly & Other Poems. London: Boyars, 1980. One of 400 cloth. Dustwrapper. *(Alphabet)* **$75 [≃£39]**
- Running in the Family. London: Gollancz, 1983. 1st English edition. Dustwrapper. *(Alphabet)* **$27.50 [≃£14]**

Opus International

- Opus International. 1967-76. Numbers 1-60, all published. *(Blakeney)* **£350 [≃$671]**

Orton, Joe

- Crimes of Passion. London: 1967. Wrappers. *(Words Etcetera)* **£15 [≃$28]**
- Entertaining Mr Sloane. London: Hamilton, 1964. Dustwrapper. *(Lewton)* **£35 [≃$67]**
- Head to Toe. London: Blond, 1971. Name on endpaper. Dustwrapper (slightly nicked). *(Dalian)* **£18 [≃$34]**
- Head to Toe. London: Blond, 1971. Price-clipped dustwrapper. *(Alphabet)* **$65 [≃£33]**
- Loot. London: 1970. Mimeographed Release script of the film, Loot from Orton's play. Binding pins a little rusty, wrappers nicked here and there. *(Blakeney)* **£150 [≃$287]**
- What the Butler Saw. London: 1969. Dustwrapper. *(Words Etcetera)* **£30 [≃$57]**
- Lahr, John: Prick Up Your Ears. London: Allen Lane, 1978. Dustwrapper. *(Dalian)* **£15 [≃$28]**

Orwell, George

- Animal Farm. London: Secker & Warburg, 1945. Spine ends faded. Dustwrapper (soiled and rubbed, chips from corners and spine ends). *(Virgo)* **£300 [≃$575]**
- Animal Farm. London: 1945. Endsheets very slightly spotted. Quarter inch strip of fading along bottom edge of boards and spine. Dustwrapper (chipped, torn, little rubbed) with Searchlight Books blurb printed in red on inside (probable 2nd state). *(Blakeney)* **£150 [≃$287]**
- Animal Farm. London: Secker & Warburg, 1945. *(Buckley)* **£15 [≃$28]**
- Animal Farm. London: Secker & Warburg, 1945. Tail corners very slightly bruised. *(Sklaroff)* **£85 [≃$163]**
- Animal Farm. Harcourt: 1946. 1st US edition. Dustwrapper. *(Nouveau)* **$125 [≃£65]**
- Animal Farm. New York: 1946. Price-clipped dustwrapper (few edge chips). *(Polyanthos)* **$65 [≃£33]**
- Animal Farm. New York: Harcourt, Brace, 1946. 2nd issue dustwrapper with 'printed in USA' on inner of rear flap (slightly torn, slightly rubbed). *(Dalian)* **£20 [≃$38]**
- Burmese Days. New York: Harper, 1934. 1st edition (precedes English edition). Library bookplate. Part of dustwrapper flap tipped in. Rear hinge cracked. *(Alphabet)* **$85 [≃£44]**
- Burmese Days. London: Gollancz, 1935. Edges and prelims slightly foxed. Covers slightly marked. *(Virgo)* **£150 [≃$287]**
- The Clergyman's Daughter. New York: Harper, 1936. 1st American edition. One of about 500 on a laid type paper, "printed in Great Britain". Dustwrapper (three tiny chips). *(Alphabet)* **$1,500 [≃£781]**
- The Clergyman's Daughter. New York: Harper, 1936. 1st American edition. 1st issue,

on laid paper. Price-clipped dustwrapper (several small chips). *(Alphabet)* **$650 [≃£338]**

- The Collected Essays, Journalism and Letters. London: 1968. 4 vols. Price-clipped dustwrappers (one with two 1-inch closed tears). *(Ellis)* **£120 [≃$230]**
- The Collected Essays, Journalism and Letters. New York: (1968). 4 vols. Dustwrappers (one short tear). *(Polyanthos)* **$95 [≃£49]**
- Coming Up For Air. London: 1939. Ex-library copy, hinges crudely repaired, externally rubbed, a little soiled. Front panel of dustwrapper mounted as a frontispiece. *(Blakeney)* **£75 [≃$143]**
- Critical Essays. London: 1946. Endpapers slightly foxed. Cover slightly faded. *(Roberts)* **£20 [≃$38]**
- Dickens, Dali & Others. New York: 1946. 1st US edition. Dustwrapper (a bit chipped, faint glass ring). *(Pettler & Liebermann)* **$45 [≃£23]**
- Down and Out in Paris and London. London: Gollancz, 1933. Name and date (July 20th 1933). His 1st book. *(Sklaroff)* **£250 [≃$479]**
- Down and Out in Paris & London. London: Gollancz, 1933. Spine lettering slightly dulled. His 1st book. *(Virgo)* **£200 [≃$383]**
- (Introduces) The End of the 'Old School Tie'. By T.C. Worsley. London: Secker & Warburg, 1941. Name on endpaper. Printed wrappers. Dustwrapper (slightly dusty). *(Dalian)* **£35 [≃$67]**
- England Your England and Other Essays. London: Secker & Warburg, 1953. Dustwrapper. *(Sklaroff)* **£36 [≃$69]**
- England, Your England & Other Essays. London: Secker & Warburg, 1953. 1st English edition of "Such, Such Were the Joys". Slight fading to boards. Dustwrapper. *(Alphabet)* **$125 [≃£65]**
- The English People. London: Collins, 1947. Dustwrapper. *(Limestone Hills)* **$65 [≃£33]**
- The English People. London: Collins, 1947. Dustwrapper (rear panel slightly marked). *(Lewton)* **£12.50 [≃$24]**
- The Lion & the Unicorn. London: 1941. Top edge slightly faded. *(Buckley)* **£30 [≃$57]**
- The Lion & the Unicorn. London: 1941. Dustwrapper. *(Lewton)* **£50 [≃$95]**
- The Lion and the Unicorn. London: 1941. Dustwrapper (slightly chipped and torn). *(Blakeney)* **£30 [≃$57]**
- The Lion and the Unicorn. London: Secker & Warburg, 1941. Name and date. Dustwrapper. *(Sklaroff)* **£38 [≃$72]**
- The Lion and the Unicorn. Searchlight Books: 1941. Dustwrapper. *(First Issues)* **£35 [≃$67]**
- The Road to Wigan Pier [abbreviated: Part One only]. London: Gollancz, The Left Book Club, 1937. Orange limp cloth. *(Patterson)* **£300 [≃$575]**
- The Road to Wigan Pier. London: Gollancz, Left Book Club, 1937. Orange wrappers (slightly worn). *(Glyn's)* **£35 [≃$67]**
- The Road to Wigan Pier. London: Gollancz, Left Book Club, 1937. Limp cloth. *(Sklaroff)* **£35 [≃$67]**
- The Road to Wigan Pier. London: Gollancz, 1937. Orange limp wrappers (little marked). *(Whiteson)* **£18 [≃$34]**
- The Road to Wigan Pier. London: Left Book Club, 1937. Linen wrappers. *(Buckley)* **£30 [≃$57]**
- The Road to Wigan Pier. New York: 1958. 1st American edition. Dustwrapper (slightly chipped). *(Georges)* **£50 [≃$95]**
- Shooting an Elephant and Other Essays. London: 1950. Foredge foxed. Spine faded. Dustwrapper (rubbed, slightly frayed, spine slightly faded). *(Ellis)* **£40 [≃$76]**

Osborn, John Jay, Jr.

- The Paper Chase. Boston: Houghton Mifflin, 1971. Dustwrapper. *(Houle)* **$125 [≃£65]**

Osborne, John

- A Better Class of Person. London: Faber, 1981. Dustwrapper. *(Tiger Books)* **£13.50 [≃$24]**
- A Bond Honoured. London: Faber, 1966. Dustwrapper. *(Tiger Books)* **£18 [≃$34]**
- A Bond Honoured. London: 1966. Dustwrapper. *(Buckley)* **£15 [≃$28]**
- The End of Me Old Cigar and Jill and Jack. London: Faber, 1975. Dustwrapper. *(Tiger Books)* **£11 [≃$21]**
- The Entertainer. London: Faber, 1957. Bookplate. Dustwrapper. *(Tiger Books)* **£35 [≃$67]**
- The Entertainer. London: Faber, 1957. Dustwrapper. *(Lewton)* **£25 [≃$47]**
- The Entertainer. London: 1957. Dustwrapper. *(Buckley)* **£35 [≃$67]**
- The Entertainer. London: Faber, 1957. Price-clipped dustwrapper (slightly rubbed). *(Virgo)* **£30 [≃$57]**
- Epitaph for George Dillon. With Anthony Creighton. London: Faber, 1958. Dustwrapper (frayed). *(Dalian)* **£25 [≃$47]**
- Epitaph for George Dillon. With Anthony

Creighton. London: Faber, 1958. Dustwrapper. *(Tiger Books)* **£35 [≃$67]**
- Hedda Gabler. London: Faber, 1972. Dustwrapper. *(Tiger Books)* **£11 [≃$21]**
- Inadmissible Evidence. London: Faber, 1965. Dustwrapper (slightly rubbed). *(Tiger Books)* **£22.50 [≃$44]**
- Look Back in Anger. London: Faber, 1957. Inscription on endpaper. Dustwrapper (several closed tears, small pieces missing). *(Tiger Books)* **£40 [≃$76]**
- Look Back in Anger. London: Faber, 1957. Dustwrapper. *(Lewton)* **£35 [≃$67]**
- Luther, London: Faber, 1961. Dustwrapper. *(Tiger Books)* **£25 [≃$47]**
- A Patriot for Me. London: Faber, 1966. Dustwrapper (slightly rubbed). *(Tiger Books)* **£22.50 [≃$44]**
- The Picture of Dorian Gray. London: Faber, 1973. Dustwrapper. *(Tiger Books)* **£11 [≃$21]**
- A Place Calling Itself Rome. London: Faber, 1973. Dustwrapper. *(Tiger Books)* **£11 [≃$21]**
- Plays for England. London: Faber, 1963. Dustwrapper. *(Tiger Books)* **£27 [≃$51]**
- The Present and Hotel in Amsterdam. London: Faber, 1968. Wrappers. *(Tiger Books)* **£18 [≃$34]**
- The Right Prospectus. London: Faber, 1970. Price-clipped dustwrapper. *(Tiger Books)* **£13.50 [≃$24]**
- A Sense of Detachment. London: Faber, 1973. Dustwrapper. *(Tiger Books)* **£11 [≃$21]**
- A Subject of Scandal and Concern. London: Faber, 1961. Wrappers as first issued. *(Tiger Books)* **£27 [≃$51]**
- Tom Jones. London: Faber, 1964. Dustwrapper. *(Tiger Books)* **£22.50 [≃$44]**
- Very Like a Whale. London: Faber, 1971. Dustwrapper. *(Tiger Books)* **£13.50 [≃$24]**
- Watch It Come Down. London: Faber, 1975. Dustwrapper. *(Tiger Books)* **£11 [≃$21]**
- West of Suez. London: Faber, 1971. Dustwrapper. *(Tiger Books)* **£13.50 [≃$24]**
- The World of Paul Slickey. London: Faber, 1959. Dustwrapper (closed tears). *(Tiger Books)* **£32.50 [≃$63]**
- You're Not Watching Me Mummy and Try a Little Tenderness. London: Faber, 1978. Wraps. *(Tiger Books)* **£11 [≃$21]**

Ostenso, Martha
- A Far Land. New York: Thomas Seltzer, 1924. One of 25 (of 150) signed and lettered. Her 1st book. *(Alphabet)* **$225 [≃£117]**
- The Mad Carews. New York: Dodd Mead, 1927. Top edge a bit foxed. Dustwrapper. *(Alphabet)* **$55 [≃£28]**

Ostrander, Isabel
- How Many Cards? New York: McBride, 1920. Dustwrapper (spine slightly darkened, two internal tape repairs, wear at corners). *(Mordida)* **$45 [≃£23]**

Owens, Agnes
- Gentlemen of the West. Polygon, 1984. Cover illustration by Alasdair Gray. Dustwrapper. Her 1st book. *(David Rees)* **£20 [≃$38]**
- Like Birds in the Wilderness. Fourth Estate, 1987. Dustwrapper. *(David Rees)* **£20 [≃$38]**

Oxenham, Elsie Jeanette
- The Abbey Girls Go Back to School. London: Collins, [1922]. New front endpaper. Two small nicks head of spine, tips rubbed. *(Bookmark)* **£45 [≃$86]**
- A Fiddler for the Abbey. London: Muller, 1948. Dustwrapper (torn). *(Green Meadow)* **£65 [≃$124]**
- The Girls of Gwynfa. London: Warne, 1924. Lacks free endpaper. Spine faded. *(Bookmark)* **£45 [≃$86]**
- Pernel Wins. London: Muller, 1942. Dustwrapper. *(Green Meadow)* **£65 [≃$124]**
- Tomboys at the Abbey. London: Collins, 1957. Dustwrapper. *(Green Meadow)* **£25 [≃$47]**

Ozick, Cynthia
- Art and Ardor. New York: 1983. Dustwrapper. Signed by the author. *(Polyanthos)* **$30 [≃£15]**
- Bloodshed and Three Novellas. New York: Knopf, 1976. Dustwrapper. Author's signed presentation. *(Antic Hay)* **$50 [≃£26]**
- Bloodshed and Three Novellas. New York: 1976. Spine extremities minimally rubbed. Dustwrapper. Signed by the author. *(Polyanthos)* **$30 [≃£15]**
- Bloodshed and Three Novellas. London: Secker & Warburg, 1976. Dustwrapper. *(Dalian)* **£20 [≃$38]**
- The Cannibal Galaxy. New York: 1983. Dustwrapper. Author's signed presentation copy. *(Polyanthos)* **$35 [≃£18]**
- The Messiah of Stockholm. New York: 1987. Dustwrapper. Author's signed presentation copy. *(Polyanthos)* **$35 [≃£18]**

- Metaphor and Memory. New York: 1989. Dustwrapper. Signed by the author. *(Polyanthos)* **$30 [≃£15]**
- The Pagan Rabbi. London: 1972. Price-clipped dustwrapper. Author's signed presentation copy. *(Polyanthos)* **$40 [≃£20]**
- Trust. London: MacGibbon & Kee, 1966. Dustwrapper (slightly marked). Her 1st book. *(Dalian)* **£35 [≃$67]**

Paley, Grace

- The Little Disturbances of Man. Doubleday: 1959. Slight bubbling of rear board. Dustwrapper. Her 1st book. *(Nouveau)* **$60 [≃£31]**

Palinurus

- Pseudonym used by Cyril Connolly, q.v.

Pangborn, Edgar

- A Mirror for Observers. New York: Doubleday, 1954. Dustwrapper (lightly rubbed). *(Dermont)* **$125 [≃£65]**
- West of the Sun. New York: Doubleday, 1953. Dustwrapper. *(Dermont)* **$125 [≃£65]**

Paretsky, Sara

- Toxic Shock. London: Gollancz, 1988. Precedes US edition. Dustwrapper. *(Michael Johnson)* **£20 [≃$38]**

Pargeter, Edith

- See under her pen-name, Ellis Peters.

Parker, Dorothy

- Not So Deep as a Well: The Collected Poems. New York: Viking, 1936. One of 485 signed. Slipcase (rubbed). *(Houle)* **$225 [≃£117]**
- Not So Deep as a Well. New York: Viking Press, 1936. Endpapers and edges slightly browned. Dustwrapper (browned, rubbed, worn around edges). *(Virgo)* **£30 [≃$57]**

Parker, Robert B.

- A Catskill Eagle. New York: Delacorte, 1985. One of 500 numbered uncorrected proof copies signed on slip pasted to inside front cover. Wrappers. *(Mordida)* **$75 [≃£39]**
- A Catskill Eagle. London: Viking, 1986. 1st English edition. Dustwrapper. *(Limestone Hills)* **$25 [≃£13]**
- Ceremony. New York: Delacorte, 1982. 1st printing. Dustwrapper. Signed by the author. *(Limestone Hills)* **$55 [≃£28]**
- God Save the Child. Boston: 1974. Dustwrapper. Author's inscription. *(Pettler & Liebermann)* **$300 [≃£156]**
- God Save the Child. Boston: Houghton Mifflin, 1974. Dustwrapper. Inscribed by the author. *(Mordida)* **$300 [≃£156]**
- God Save the Child. London: Deutsch, 1975. 1st English edition. Dustwrapper. *(Limestone Hills)* **$75 [≃£39]**
- The Godwulf Manuscript. Boston: Houghton Mifflin, 1974. Dustwrapper (slightly soiled, several tiny tears). *(Mordida)* **$175 [≃£91]**
- The Judas Goat. New York: Delacorte, 1978. Dustwrapper. Signed by the author. *(Michael Johnson)* **£26 [≃$49]**
- Mortal Stakes. Boston: Houghton Mifflin, 1975. Staining on edges. Dustwrapper (tiny wear at spine ends and corners). *(Mordida)* **$165 [≃£85]**
- Mortal Stakes. London: 1976. No free endpaper as issued. Dustwrapper. Signed by the author. *(First Issues)* **£25 [≃$47]**
- Mortal Stakes. London: Deutsch, 1976. 1st English edition. Dustwrapper. *(Limestone Hills)* **$55 [≃£28]**
- Mortal Stakes. London: Deutsch, 1976. 1st British edition. Covers very slightly soiled. Dustwrapper. Signed by the author. *(Michael Johnson)* **£30 [≃$57]**
- Pale Kings and Princes. New York: Delacorte, 1987. One of 225 signed. Slipcase. No dustwrapper issued. *(Mordida)* **$125 [≃£65]**
- Playmates. New York: Putnam's, 1989. One of 250 signed. Slipcase. No dustwrapper issued. *(Mordida)* **$75 [≃£39]**
- The Private Eye in Hammett and Chandler. Northridge: Lord John Press, 1984. One of 300 signed. No dustwrapper issued. *(Mordida)* **$75 [≃£39]**
- Promised Land. New York: Boston: Houghton, 1976. Price-clipped dustwrapper. Signed by the author. *(Michael Johnson)* **£50 [≃$95]**
- Promised Land. Boston: Houghton Mifflin, 1976. Dustwrapper (spine slightly darkened, several short closed tears). *(Mordida)* **$65 [≃£33]**
- Promised Land. Boston: Houghton Mifflin, 1976. Dustwrapper. Signed by the author. *(Mordida)* **$125 [≃£65]**
- Promised Land. London: Deutsch, 1977. 1st British edition. Dustwrapper. Signed by the author. *(Michael Johnson)* **£28 [≃$53]**
- Promised Land. London: Deutsch, 1977. 1st British edition. Dustwrapper. *(Michael Johnson)* **£16 [≃$30]**
- Promised Land. London: Deutsch, 1977. 1st English edition. Dustwrapper. *(Limestone Hills)* **$45 [≃£23]**

- Valediction. New York: Delacorte, 1984. Uncorrected proof copy. Small smudge on bottom edge. Wrappers (tiny speck on front cover). *(Mordida)* **$100 [≃£52]**
- Wilderness. New York: Delacorte / Seymour Lawrence, 1979. Dustwrapper. *(Mordida)* **$45 [≃£23]**
- Wilderness. London: Deutsch, 1980. 1st English edition. Dustwrapper. *(Limestone Hills)* **$35 [≃£18]**

Parkinson, C. Northcote

- Parkinson's Law. London: 1958. Dustwrapper. *(Roberts)* **£6.25 [≃$11]**

Patchen, Kenneth

- Cloth of the Tempest. New York: Harper, 1943. One of 2000. Dustwrapper (lightly browned along spine). Signed by the author. *(Alphabet)* **$200 [≃£104]**
- The Memoirs of a Shy Pornographer. London: Grey Walls Press, 1948. Dustwrapper. *(Clearwater)* **£50 [≃$95]**
- Outlaw of the Lowest Planet. London: Grey Walls Press, 1946. Dustwrapper. *(Polyanthos)* **$60 [≃£31]**
- Red Wine and Yellow Hair. New York: New Directions, [1949]. Dustwrapper (slightly soiled). *(Dermont)* **$50 [≃£26]**
- See You in the Morning. New York: Padell, [1947]. Dustwrapper (lightly used). *(Dermont)* **$50 [≃£26]**
- See You in the Morning. Padell: 1947. Dustwrapper (light edgewear). *(Nouveau)* **$125 [≃£65]**
- See You in the Morning. London: Grey Walls Press, 1949. Tip of spine slightly worn, endpapers slightly browned. Dustwrapper (slightly soiled and rubbed). *(Dalian)* **£30 [≃$57]**
- Sleepers Awake. (New York: Padell, 1946). Black Paper edition. One of 148 signed. *(Black Sun)* **$275 [≃£143]**
- The Teeth of the Lion. CT: Poet of the Month, (1942). Wrappers. Dustwrapper (spine minimally sunned). *(Polyanthos)* **$25 [≃£13]**
- The Teeth of the Lion. CT: Poet of the Month, (1942). Boards. Dustwrapper (spine and edges slightly sunned). *(Polyanthos)* **$45 [≃£23]**
- They Keep Riding Down All the Time. New York: Padell, [1946]. Wrappers. *(Dermont)* **$35 [≃£18]**
- CCCLXXIV Poems. [New York: Padell, 1948]. One of 126 signed. Dustwrapper. *(Black Sun)* **$250 [≃£130]**
- CCCLXXIV Poems. New York: Padell, 1947-48. One of 126 signed. Made up from the sheets of "First Will & Testament" and "Cloth of the Tempest" in a special binding. Gilt stamped linen. *(Alphabet)* **$175 [≃£91]**

Patrick, Q. (Richard Wilson Webb)

- Murder at Cambridge. New York: Farrar, 1933. Slight slant. Dustwrapper. *(Janus)* **$150 [≃£78]**

Patten, Brian

- Little Johnny's Confessions. London: 1967. Advance uncorrected proof copy. Cover slightly marked. His 1st book. *(Buckley)* **£25 [≃$47]**

Pavic, Milorad

- Dictionary of the Khazars. London: 1989. The 'Male Edition'. *(First Issues)* **£15 [≃$28]**

Peake, Mervyn

- All This and Bevin Too ... see Crisp, Quentin.
- A Book of Nonsense. London: Peter Owen, 1972. Dustwrapper. *(Dalian)* **£20 [≃$38]**
- Captain Slaughterboard Drops Anchor. London: Eyre & Spottiswoode, 1945. 2nd edition. Dustwrapper. *(Sklaroff)* **£150 [≃$287]**
- Captain Slaughterboard Drops Anchor. London: Eyre & Spottiswoode, 1945. 2nd edition. Two leaves somewhat creased. Dustwrapper. The true 1st edition (Country Life, 1939) was destroyed by enemy action. *(Dyke)* **£80 [≃$153]**
- Captain Slaughterboard Drops Anchor. London: Eyre & Spottiswoode, 1945. 2nd edition. *(Sklaroff)* **£80 [≃$153]**
- Figures of Speech. London: Gollancz, 1954. Dustwrapper. *(Sklaroff)* **£48 [≃$92]**
- Figures of Speech. London: Gollancz, 1954. *(Sklaroff)* **£28 [≃$53]**
- Gormenghast. London: Eyre & Spottiswoode, 1950. Foredge stained. Dustwrapper (front slightly worn, lower panel stained). *(Sklaroff)* **£80 [≃$153]**
- Gormenghast. London: Eyre & Spottiswoode, 1950. Dustwrapper (dull, very slightly chipped). *(Whiteson)* **£60 [≃$115]**
- Gormenghast. London: Eyre & Spottiswoode, 1950. Spine slightly sunned. *(Dalian)* **£35 [≃$67]**
- Gormenghast. London: Eyre & Spottiswoode, 1968. 1st illustrated edition. Dustwrapper (a few tears repaired). *(Sklaroff)* **£28 [≃$53]**
- Letters from a Lost Uncle. London: Eyre &

Spottiswoode, 1948. Dustwrapper. *(Sklaroff)* **£150 [≃$287]**

- Mr Pye. London: Heinemann, 1953. Dustwrapper (slightly torn, neatly restored). *(Sklaroff)* **£35 [≃$67]**
- Mr Pye. London: Heinemann, 1953. Spine slightly worn. *(Sklaroff)* **£25 [≃$47]**
- (Illustrates) The Pot of Gold and Other Tales by Aaron Judah. London: Faber, 1959. Price-clipped dustwrapper. *(Dalian)* **£25 [≃$47]**
- Prayers and Graces. London: 1944. Inscription. Dustwrapper (little torn, few pieces missing along spine). *(Polyanthos)* **$35 [≃£18]**
- (Illustrates) The Swiss Family Robinson. By Johann Wyss. London: Heirloom Library, (1950). Covers very slightly rubbed. *(Dalian)* **£20 [≃$38]**
- Titus Alone. London: Eyre & Spottiswoode, 1959. Uncorrected proof copy. Printed wrappers. *(Sklaroff)* **£250 [≃$479]**
- Titus Alone. London: Eyre & Spottiswoode, 1959. Dustwrapper. *(Sklaroff)* **£120 [≃$230]**
- Titus Alone. London: Eyre & Spottiswoode, 1959. Dustwrapper (slightly tanned, slightly nicked). *(Dalian)* **£95 [≃$182]**
- Titus Alone. London: Eyre & Spottiswoode, 1959. *(Sklaroff)* **£50 [≃$95]**
- Titus Groan, 1946; Gormenghast, 1950; Titus Alone, 1959. London: Eyre & Spottiswoode, 1946-59. Covers of 1st volume a trifle faded. Dustwrappers (1st one a trifle dusty). *(Dyke)* **£275 [≃$527]**
- Titus Groan. London: Eyre & Spottiswoode, 1946. Some pages slightly discoloured. Little mark front cover. Dustwrapper (little dull). *(Whiteson)* **£50 [≃$95]**
- Titus Groan. London: Eyre & Spottiswoode, 1946. *(Sklaroff)* **£65 [≃$124]**
- Titus Groan. London: Eyre & Spottiswoode, 1946. With the word 'face' reset p 47. *(Sklaroff)* **£60 [≃$115]**
- Titus Groan. London: Eyre & Spottiswoode, 1946. 2nd impression dustwrapper. *(Sklaroff)* **£85 [≃$163]**
- Titus Groan. New York: Reynal & Hitchcock, 1946. 1st US edition. Dustwrapper. *(Sklaroff)* **£100 [≃$191]**
- Titus Groan. New York: Reynal & Hitchcock, 1946. 1st US edition. Dustwrapper (very slightly chipped). *(Sklaroff)* **£85 [≃$163]**
- Titus Groan. Gormenghast. Titus Alone. New York: Weybright & Talley, 1967. 1st US illustrated edition. 3 vols. *(Sklaroff)* **£100 [≃$191]**
- Titus Groan. London: Eyre & Spottiswoode, 1968. 1st illustrated edition. Dustwrapper. *(Sklaroff)* **£30 [≃$57]**

Pearce, Philippa

- Tom's Midnight Garden. London: OUP, 1958. Edges rubbed, corners a little bumped, a few small marks. *(Bookmark)* **£22.50 [≃$44]**

Penguin New Writing

- Penguin New Writing. 1940-50. Complete set 1-40. Wrappers. *(Any Amount)* **£65 [≃$124]**

Percy, Walker

- Lancelot. Farrar: 1977. Dustwrapper. Signed by the author. *(Nouveau)* **$45 [≃£23]**
- Lancelot. New York: FSG, (1977). Dustwrapper. Author's inscription. *(Between the Covers)* **$100 [≃£52]**
- The Last Gentleman. New York: 1966. Dustwrapper. *(Pettler & Liebermann)* **$100 [≃£52]**
- The Last Gentleman. New York: Farrar, 1966. Dustwrapper. *(Nouveau)* **$125 [≃£65]**
- The Last Gentleman. New York: (1966). Top edge stain slightly faded. Dustwrapper. *(Lopez)* **$100 [≃£52]**
- Lost in the Cosmos. New York: FSG, (1983). Dustwrapper. Signed by the author. *(Lopez)* **$50 [≃£26]**
- Love in the Ruins. London: Eyre & Spottiswoode, 1971. Dustwrapper. *(Dalian)* **£35 [≃$67]**
- Love in the Ruins. London: Eyre & Spottiswoode, 1971. 1st English edition. Dustwrapper (a few closed tears, internally repaired). *(Limestone Hills)* **$45 [≃£23]**
- Love in the Ruins. Farrar: 1971. Dustwrapper. *(Nouveau)* **$65 [≃£33]**
- The Moviegoer. New York: Knopf, 1961. Slight offsetting to front endpapers from flap. Dustwrapper (trace of rubbing to spine extremities). *(Between the Covers)* **$1,850 [≃£963]**
- The Moviegoer. New York: Knopf, 1961. Dustwrapper (spine extremities and front panel tips very slightly rubbed). *(Lopez)* **$1,850 [≃£963]**
- The Second Coming. New York: Farrar Straus Giroux, 1980. 1st printing. Dustwrapper. *(Limestone Hills)* **$85 [≃£44]**
- The Second Coming. London: Secker & Warburg, 1981. Dustwrapper. *(Dalian)* **£20 [≃$38]**
- The Second Coming. New York: 1980.

Dustwrapper. Bookplate signed by the author. *(Polyanthos)* **$35 [≃£18]**
- The Second Coming. New York: 1980. Dustwrapper. Author's signed presentation copy. *(Polyanthos)* **$55 [≃£28]**
- The Second Coming. New York: FSG, (1980). Dustwrapper (couple tiny snags). Signed by the author. *(Between the Covers)* **$75 [≃£39]**
- The Second Coming. Farrar: 1980. 1st trade edition. Dustwrapper. *(Nouveau)* **$30 [≃£15]**
- The Thanatos Syndrome. New York: FSG, (1987). One of 250 signed. Slipcase. Apparently preceded by the Franklin Library signed edition. *(Between the Covers)* **$225 [≃£117]**
- The Thanatos Syndrome. New York: 1987. Dustwrapper. Signed by the author. *(Polyanthos)* **$35 [≃£18]**
- The Thanatos Syndrome. New York: FS&G, 1987. Dustwrapper. Signed by the author. *(Lopez)* **$55 [≃£28]**
- The Thanatos Syndrome. New York: FSG, (1987). 1st trade edition. Dustwrapper. Signed by the author. *(Lopez)* **$45 [≃£23]**
- (Preface to) McNaspy, C.J.: At Face Value. New Orleans: Loyola University, (1978). Wrappers. Signed by McNaspy and Walker. *(Lopez)* **$225 [≃£117]**

Perelman, S.J.
- Acres and Pains. Reynal & Hitchcock: 1947. Small bookplate. Dustwrapper. *(Nouveau)* **$75 [≃£39]**
- The Ill-Tempered Clavichord. New York: Simon & Schuster, 1952. Dustwrapper (few nicks). *(Houle)* **$85 [≃£44]**
- Listen to the Mockingbird. New York: Simon, 1949. Dustwrapper (few tears, one small chip base of spine). *(Nouveau)* **$75 [≃£39]**
- The Rising Gorge. New York: Simon & Schuster, 1961. Dustwrapper. *(Limestone Hills)* **$50 [≃£26]**

Perse, St.-J.
- Anabasis ... see T.S. Eliot.

Pessoa, Fernando
- Antinous. Lisbon: Monteiro, 1918. Wrappers (evenly soiled). *(Any Amount)* **£75 [≃$143]**

Peters, Elizabeth
- The Murders of Richard III. New York: Dodd, Mead, 1974. Dustwrapper (couple of tiny tears). *(Mordida)* **$60 [≃£31]**

Peters, Ellis (Edith Pargeter)
- The Assize of the Dying. By Edith Pargeter. Garden City: Doubleday Crime Club, 1958. 1st American edition. Label removed from front endpaper. Dustwrapper (several short closed tears, rubbing on spine and front panel, staining on inner front flap). *(Mordida)* **$35 [≃£18]**
- The Confession of Brother Haluin. London: Headline, 1988. Dustwrapper. Signed by the author. *(Dyke)* **£20 [≃$38]**
- The Confessions of Brother Haluin. Headline: 1988. Dustwrapper. *(Moorhouse)* **£5 [≃$9]**
- The Heretic's Apprentice. London: Headline, 1989. Dustwrapper. Signed by the author on bookplate laid in. *(Limestone Hills)* **$45 [≃£23]**
- Monk's-hood. London: Macmillan, 1980. Dustwrapper. *(Moorhouse)* **£18 [≃$34]**
- A Nice Derangement of Epitaphs. London: Collins, 1965. Dustwrapper (somewhat chipped). *(Limestone Hills)* **$65 [≃£33]**
- The Potter's Field. London: Headline, 1989. Dustwrapper. Signed by the author. *(Limestone Hills)* **$45 [≃£23]**
- The Rose Rent. London: Macmillan, 1986. Signed by the author. *(Dyke)* **£20 [≃$38]**
- The Will and the Deed. London: Crime Club, (1960). Small name. Slightly foxed. Small stain top edge of first two pages. Dustwrapper. *(Lopez)* **$75 [≃£39]**

Petievich, Gerald
- Money Men & One-Shot Deal. New York: Harcourt Brace Jovanovich, 1981. Dustwrapper. *(Mordida)* **$50 [≃£26]**
- Money Men and One-Shot Deal. New York: Harcourt, 1981. Dustwrapper. Signed by the author. His 1st book. *(Janus)* **$50 [≃£26]**
- To Live and Die in L.A. New York: Arbor House, 1984. Dustwrapper. *(Mordida)* **$50 [≃£26]**

Peyrefitte, Roger
- The Exile of Capri. London: Secker & Warburg, 1961. Back cover slightly marked. Dustwrapper. *(Dalian)* **£25 [≃$47]**
- Special Friendships. London: Secker & Warburg, 1958. Dustwrapper (slightly nicked, slightly dusty). *(Dalian)* **£25 [≃$47]**

Phillips, Jayne Anne
- Black Tickets. New York: Delacorte, 1979. Dustwrapper. *(Michael Johnson)* **£75 [≃$143]**
- Fast Lanes. New York: Vehicle, 1984. One of

2000 in wrappers.
(Michael Johnson) **£20 [≃$38]**

- How Mickey Made It. New York: Bookslinger, 1981. One of 1000 in wrappers. Signed by the author. *(Michael Johnson)* **£25 [≃$47]**
- Machine Dreams. London: Faber, 1984. 1st British edition. Dustwrapper. *(Michael Johnson)* **£13 [≃$24]**
- Sweethearts. Carrboro, NC: Truck, 1976. One of 400 in wrappers. Wrappers slightly darkened. Her 1st book. *(Lopez)* **$125 [≃£65]**

Piercy, Marge

- Braided Lives. New York: 1982. Dustwrapper. Author's signed presentation copy. *(Polyanthos)* **$35 [≃£18]**
- Breaking Camp. Wesleyan UP: (1968). Dustwrapper (edges darkened, half inch tear top of back panel). Her 1st book. *(Woolmer)* **$50 [≃£26]**
- Circles on the Water. New York: 1982. Dustwrapper. Author's signed presentation copy. *(Polyanthos)* **$35 [≃£18]**
- Fly Away Home. London: Chatto & Windus, Hogarth Press, 1984. Uncorrected proof copy. Patterned wrappers. *(Dalian)* **£25 [≃$47]**
- Fly Away Home. London: Chatto & Windus, Hogarth Press, 1984. Dustwrapper. *(Dalian)* **£20 [≃$38]**
- Going Down Fast. New York: 1969. Dustwrapper. *(Pettler & Liebermann)* **$40 [≃£20]**
- Gone to Soldiers. New York: 1987. Dustwrapper. Author's signed presentation copy (1987). *(Polyanthos)* **$35 [≃£18]**
- To Be of Use. New York: 1973. Review slip. Dustwrapper. Author's signed presentation copy. *(Polyanthos)* **$35 [≃£18]**
- The Twelve-Spiked Wheel Flashing. New York: 1978. Review slip. Dustwrapper. Author's signed presentation copy. *(Polyanthos)* **$35 [≃£18]**

Pinter, Harold

- Betrayal. London: 1976. Dustwrapper. *(Buckley)* **£10 [≃$19]**
- The Birthday Party & Other Plays. London: 1960. Dustwrapper (rubbed, two small closed tears). *(Buckley)* **£40 [≃$76]**
- The Caretaker. Encore Pub: 1960. Wrappers. *(Lewton)* **£50 [≃$95]**
- The Dwarfs. London: London Limited Editions, 1990. One of 150 signed. Cellophane dustwrapper. *(Words Etcetera)* **£35 [≃$67]**
- The Homecoming. London: Methuen, 1965. Dustwrapper (slightly rubbed). *(Nouveau)* **$75 [≃£39]**
- I Know the Place. Poems. Drawings by Michael Kenny. Greville: n.d. One of 500 signed. Buckram. No dustwrapper issued. *(Halsey)* **£15 [≃$28]**
- Mac. An Essay. Pendragon Press, 1968. One of 1000. Boards very slightly rubbed. *(Dalian)* **£65 [≃$124]**
- Old Times. Karnac: 1971. One of 150 signed. Glassine dustwrapper. *(Any Amount)* **£35 [≃$67]**
- Poems. Enitharmon Press, 1971. 2nd impression with additional poems. One of 100 signed. *(Glyn's)* **£45 [≃$86]**
- The Tea Party. London: Methuen, 1967. Dustwrapper (slightly rubbed). *(Nouveau)* **$70 [≃£36]**

Pirsig, Robert

- Zen and the Art of Motorcycle Maintenance. London: Bodley Head, (1974). 1st English edition. Dustwrapper. *(Lopez)* **$50 [≃£26]**

Plante, David

- The Catholic. London: Chatto & Windus, 1985. Dustwrapper. *(Dalian)* **£18 [≃$34]**
- The Foreigner. London: Hogarth Press, 1984. Dustwrapper. *(Dalian)* **£18 [≃$34]**
- The Ghost of Henry James. London: 1970. 1st British edition. Errata slip partly glued to title as issued. Dustwrapper. *(Pettler & Liebermann)* **$75 [≃£39]**
- Slides. Boston: Gambit Incorporated, 1971. 1st American edition. Dustwrapper (very slightly nicked). *(Dalian)* **£35 [≃$67]**
- Slides. London: 1971. Dustwrapper (one inch tear to upper panel). *(Blakeney)* **£20 [≃$38]**
- Slides. London: 1971. Tips of two corners slightly bumped. Dustwrapper. *(Clearwater)* **£25 [≃$47]**
- Slides. London: MacDonald, 1971. Dustwrapper. *(Dalian)* **£30 [≃$57]**
- The Woods. London: Gollancz, 1982. Dustwrapper. *(Dalian)* **£16 [≃$30]**

Plath, Sylvia

- (Edits) American Poetry Now. London: 1960. Wrappers. *(Buckley)* **£15 [≃$28]**
- Ariel. London: 1965. Dustwrapper, fine. *(First Issues)* **£135 [≃$259]**
- Ariel. London: 1965. Dustwrapper. *(Egret)* **£85 [≃$163]**
- Ariel. London: 1965. Bookplate. Dustwrapper (slightly frayed, several nicks,

spine slightly faded). Poetry Book Society bulletin laid in. *(Ellis)* **£70 [≃$134]**
- Ariel. London: 1965. Dustwrapper, fine. *(Polyanthos)* **$150 [≃£78]**
- Ariel. London: 1965. Neat name. Dustwrapper (three edge tears, little rubbed). *(Polyanthos)* **$65 [≃£33]**
- The Bell Jar. By Victoria Lucas. London: 1964. Contemporary Fiction edition (issued a year after the 1st edition). Faint crease in rear cover. Dustwrapper (slightly rubbed). *(Buckley)* **£50 [≃$95]**
- The Bell Jar. By Victoria Lucas. London: Heinemann Contemporary Fiction, 1964. Dustwrapper (slightly rubbed). *(Sclanders)* **£35 [≃$67]**
- The Bell Jar. New York: 1971. 1st US edition. Dustwrapper. *(Pettler & Liebermann)* **$55 [≃£28]**
- The Bell Jar. New York: Harper & Row, [1971]. 1st American edition. Dustwrapper. *(Antic Hay)* **$45 [≃£23]**
- The Bell Jar. New York: Harper, 1971. 1st US edition. Dustwrapper. *(Nouveau)* **$45 [≃£23]**
- Child. Exeter: 1971. One of 325. Wrappers. Dustwrapper. *(Blakeney)* **£35 [≃$67]**
- Child. Exeter: Rougemont Press, (1971). One of 325. Wrappers. Dustwrapper. *(Waterfield's)* **£20 [≃$38]**
- Child. Rougemont Press: 1971. One of 325. Cardboard covers. Dustwrapper. *(Buckley)* **£70 [≃$134]**
- Crystal Gazer and Other Poems. London: Rainbow Press, 1971. One of 20 (of 400) in vellum. Solander case. *(Houle)* **$950 [≃£494]**
- Dialogue Over a Ouija Board. Rainbow Press: 1981. One of 140. Slipcase. *(Woolmer)* **$275 [≃£143]**
- (Contributes to) The Golden Year. New York: Fine Editions, 1960. One of 2500. Dustwrapper (single scratch on front panel, showing through on cover of book). *(Lopez)* **$75 [≃£39]**
- The Green Rock. Ely: Embers Handpress, 1982. One of 160. Wrappers. One of 6 in envelope, rather than slipcase. *(Woolmer)* **$135 [≃£70]**
- The Green Rock. Ely: Embers Handpress, 1982. One of 160. Wrappers. Slipcase. *(Woolmer)* **$75 [≃£39]**
- Johnny Panic and the Bible of Dreams. London: 1977. Uncorrected proof copy. Wrappers. *(Ellis)* **£90 [≃$172]**
- Johnny Panic & the Bible of Dreams. London: 1977. Extra flyleaf removed. Dustwrapper. *(Buckley)* **£16 [≃$30]**
- Lyonesse. Rainbow Press: 1971. One of 400. Quarter leather. Slipcase. *(Virgo)* **£110 [≃$211]**
- Lyonesse: Poems. London: Rainbow Press, 1971. One of 90 (of 400) in calf. Acetate dustwrapper. Slipcase. *(Houle)* **$425 [≃£221]**
- The Magic Mirror. Powys: Embers Handpress, 1989. One of 226. Dustwrapper. *(Virgo)* **£55 [≃$105]**
- Million Dollar Month. Sceptre Press: 1971. One of 150. Front wrapper slightly creased. *(Buckley)* **£30 [≃$57]**
- Pursuit. London: Rainbow Press, 1973. One of 100, with an original signed etching by Leonard Baskin laid in. Morocco. Slipcase. *(Houle)* **$650 [≃£38,763]**
- Two Poems. Bedfordshire: The Sceptre Press, 1980. One of 300. Wrappers. *(Moorhouse)* **£25 [≃$47]**
- Two Poems. Sceptre Press: 1980. One of 75 (of 300) numbered. Hand sewn. *(Buckley)* **£30 [≃$57]**
- Two Uncollected Poems. Anvil Press: 1980. One of 450. Wrappers. *(Buckley)* **£30 [≃$57]**
- Winter Trees. London: 1971. Dustwrapper (1-inch closed tear). Poetry Book Society Bulletin laid in. *(Ellis)* **£30 [≃$57]**
- Winter Trees. London: Faber, 1971. Dustwrapper. *(Whiteson)* **£16 [≃$30]**

Plomer, William
- The Case is Altered. London: Hogarth Press, 1932. Slightly cocked. Edges spotted. Dustwrapper (rubbed, chipped, faded). *(Ellis)* **£45 [≃$86]**
- Collected Poems. London: Cape, 1973. Price-clipped dustwrapper. *(Glyn's)* **£8 [≃$15]**
- Curlew River. London: 1964. Wrapper. *(Roberts)* **£5.25 [≃$9]**
- The Family Tree. Hogarth Press: 1929. Red paper covered boards (faded). *(Virgo)* **£40 [≃$76]**
- Turbott Wolfe. London: Hogarth Press, 1925. Dustwrapper (slightly torn). Signature of Leonard Woolf. *(Lamb)* **£200 [≃$383]**

Plunkett, James
- Strumpet City. London: Hutchinson, 1989. Uncorrected proof copy. Wrappers. *(David Rees)* **£25 [≃$47]**

Poetry London
- Poetry London. Edited by Tambimuttu, later by Richard Marsh and Nicholas Moore. London: February 1939 to Winter 1951.

Numbers 1-23, all published.
(Blakeney) **£400 [≃$767]**

Polite, Carlene Hatcher

- The Flagellants. New York: 1967. Dustwrapper. Her 1st book.
(Polyanthos) **$35 [≃£18]**

Porter, Katherine Anne

- A Christmas Story. New York: Delacorte, [1967]. One of 500 signed by Porter (twice, the first by autopen) and by Ben Shahn, the illustrator. Cloth. Slipcase.
(Antic Hay) **$200 [≃£104]**
- The Collected Essays and Occasional Writings. New York: 1970. One of 250 signed. Leather, gilt spine, t.e.g. Box.
(Polyanthos) **$125 [≃£65]**
- Flowering Judas. Harcourt: 1930. Cover lightly soiled, spine faded with a few rubbed spots. One of 600. *(Nouveau)* **$120 [≃£62]**
- French Song Book. Paris: Harrison of Paris, (1933). One of 595 signed. Dustwrapper (slight tear to crown). Prospectus inserted.
(Nouveau) **$275 [≃£143]**
- Hacienda. A Story of Mexico. New York: Harrison of Paris, 1934. One of 895. Slipcase. Prospectus inserted. *(Nouveau)* **$75 [≃£39]**
- The Leaning Tower and Other Stories. London: Cape, 1945. Dustwrapper.
(Dalian) **£30 [≃$57]**
- The Leaning Tower. London: Cape, 1945. 1st English edition. Dustwrapper.
(Nouveau) **$65 [≃£33]**
- Ship of Fools. London: Secker, 1962. 1st UK edition. Uncorrected proof copy. Wrappers.
(Any Amount) **£25 [≃$47]**

Potocki of Montalk, Count Geoffrey

- The Whirling River. Plush: Melissa Press, 1964. Wrappers.
(Limestone Hills) **$40 [≃£20]**

Potter, Dennis

- Son of Man. London: Deutsch, 1970. Dustwrapper. His 1st book.
(Moorhouse) **£20 [≃$38]**

Potter, Stephen

- One-Upmanship. London: Hart Davis, 1952. Dustwrapper (somewhat worn).
(Limestone Hills) **$30 [≃£15]**

Potts, Paul

- A Poet's Testament. The Whitman Press: 1940. Wrappers (slightly soiled and browned). His 1st book.
(Moorhouse) **£25 [≃$47]**

Pound, Ezra

- A Lume Spento and Other Early Poems. New York: New Directions, 1965. Glassine dustwrapper (half inch missing lower spine).
(Polyanthos) **$30 [≃£15]**
- A B C of Economics. London: 1933. Spine sunned, covers slightly soiled and edge rubbed. *(Polyanthos)* **$75 [≃£39]**
- ABC of Economics. London: Faber, 1933. Spine and covers slightly faded. Dustwrapper (dusty). *(Clearwater)* **£45 [≃$86]**
- A B C of Reading. London: Routledge, 1934. 1st issue, in rough red cloth. Foredge slightly foxed. Dustwrapper (slightly marked).
(Dalian) **£120 [≃$230]**
- America, Roosevelt and the Causes of the Present War. London: Peter Russell, 1951. 1st edition in English. Wrappers (little yellowed at edges).
(Between the Covers) **$125 [≃£65]**
- Antheil & the Treatise on Harmony. Chicago: Covici, 1927. 1st US edition.
(Any Amount) **£55 [≃$105]**
- An Autobiographical Outline. New York: Nadja, 1980. One of 200. Wrappers.
(Words Etcetera) **£36 [≃$69]**
- Canti Pisani. (Parma): Guanda, (1953). Wrappers. Dustwrapper (slight wear top of spine). *(Woolmer)* **$125 [≃£65]**
- Canto CX. Paris: 1967. One of 224. Sheets loose in wrappers as issued.
(Blakeney) **£40 [≃$76]**
- The Cantos of Ezra Pound. New York: New Directions, [1951]. 2nd printing. One of 1000. 1st issue of this text - uncorrected without the cancels placed in the 2nd binding of this edition. Dustwrapper.
(Alphabet) **$35 [≃£18]**
- Cantos LII-LXXI. New Directions: 1940. 1st US edition. Booklet in rear pocket. Dustwrapper. *(Lewton)* **£28 [≃$53]**
- Cathay. London: Elkin Mathews, 1915. Wrappers (little discoloured).
(Whiteson) **£95 [≃$182]**
- (Introduces) The Chinese Character as a Medium for Poetry. By Ernest Fenollosa. New York: Arrow Editions, 1936. 1st American edition. Green paper boards, paper labels. Dustwrapper (a bit dusty, unchipped).
(Alphabet) **$175 [≃£91]**
- (Introduces) The Chinese Character as a Medium for Poetry. By Ernest Fenollosa. London: Stanley Nott, 1936. Parchment backed black boards (slightly rubbed).
(Dalian) **£45 [≃$86]**

- Collected Shorter Poems. London: Faber, 1968. 2nd edition, enlarged. Dustwrapper. *(Dalian)* **£30 [≃$57]**
- (Translates) Confucius: The Unwobbling Pivot & The Great Digest. New York: New Directions, Pharos 4, 1947. One of 929. Printed wrappers, yapp edges (unfaded, without the usual edge problems). *(Alphabet)* **$125 [≃£65]**
- Confucius The Unwobbling Pivot and The Great Digest. Pharos 4, Winter 1947. Name on half-title. Pink wrappers a little faded at spine. *(Blakeney)* **£45 [≃$86]**
- Culture: The Intellectual Autobiography of a Poet. Norfolk: New Directions, 1938. 1st American edition of "A Guide to Kulchur". One of 519. Dustwrapper (shallow chipping, tears at spine extremities). *(Alphabet)* **$125 [≃£65]**
- Culture. CT: New Directions, 1938. Published in London as Guide to Kulchur. Dustwrapper (very small piece missing from top of spine, small tear side of spine). *(Polyanthos)* **$45 [≃£23]**
- DK / Some Letters. Edited by Louis Dudek. Montreal: (1974). One of 2000. Wrappers. *(Polyanthos)* **$30 [≃£15]**
- A Draft of XXX Cantos. London: Faber, 1933. 1st English edition. 1st impression, with misprint of Fontanelle on page (2). *(Virgo)* **£30 [≃$57]**
- Drafts and Fragments of Cantos CX-CXVII. New York: New Directions, (1968) [sic]. Price-clipped dustwrapper. *(Polyanthos)* **$30 [≃£15]**
- Drafts and Fragments of Cantos CX-CXVII. London: Faber; Iowa City: The Stone Wall Press, 1969 [sic]. One of 310 signed. Errata slip. Red cloth, paper label. Box. *(Polyanthos)* **$400 [≃£208]**
- Drafts and Fragments of Cantos CX - CXVII. London: 1970. Dustwrapper. *(Blakeney)* **£20 [≃$38]**
- Exultations. London: Elkin Mathews, 1909. Maroon boards, fine. *(Polyanthos)* **$300 [≃£156]**
- Exultations. London: Elkin Mathews, 1909. Corners and spine ends slightly rubbed. *(Lewton)* **£125 [≃$239]**
- The Fifth Decad of Cantos. London: Faber, 1937. Two pages carelessly opened. Name on fly. Dustwrapper (nicks and eucks at edges). *(Halsey)* **£40 [≃$76]**
- Gaudier-Brzeska A Memoir. London: John Lane, 1916. 1st, embossed, binding. Some soiling of covers, wear at spine ends. *(Woolmer)* **$150 [≃£78]**
- Gold and Work. London: Peter Russell, 1951. 1st edition in English, 2nd issue. Wrappers (edges little yellowed). *(Between the Covers)* **$100 [≃£52]**
- (Translates) The Natural Philosophy of Love, by Remy de Gourmont. London: The Casanova Society, 1926. One of 1500. Dustwrapper. *(Dalian)* **£55 [≃$105]**
- Homage to Sextus Propertius 'Quia Pauper Amavi'. London: Faber, 1934. Dustwrapper (very slightly dusty). *(Dalian)* **£150 [≃$287]**
- 'If This Be Treason ..." ... (Siena: for Olga Rudge by Tip. Nuova, 1948). Wrappers faded at spine. *(Woolmer)* **$250 [≃£130]**
- Instigations of Ezra Pound: together with an Essay on the Chinese Written Character. New York: Boni & Liveright, 1920. 2nd binding. Good used copy. *(Alphabet)* **$35 [≃£18]**
- Introductory Text Book. Rapallo: (1939). *(Woolmer)* **$150 [≃£78]**
- Introductory Text Book. Rapallo: (1945). Olga Rudge's reprint. Printed on cheaper paper, paper darkened. *(Woolmer)* **$50 [≃£26]**
- Jefferson and / or Mussolini. London: 1935. The unsigned issue. Top edge dusty, very slight offsetting to endsheets, prelims a little spotted. Dustwrapper (slightly rubbed and dusty, spine faded). *(Blakeney)* **£75 [≃$143]**
- The Letters of Ezra Pound 1907-1941. New York: 1950. Dustwrapper. *(Polyanthos)* **$50 [≃£26]**
- The Letters. London: Faber, 1951. 1st UK edition. Dustwrapper (spine faded, small scuff front panel). *(Virgo)* **£40 [≃$76]**
- The Letters of Ezra Pound to James Joyce. New York: New Directions, 1967. Dustwrapper. *(Polyanthos)* **$50 [≃£26]**
- Literary Essays. CT: New Directions, 1954. Small crease top edge rear cover. Dustwrapper *(Polyanthos)* **$45 [≃£23]**
- Literary Essays. London: Faber, 1954. Dustwrapper (spine very slightly tanned). *(Alphabet)* **$85 [≃£44]**
- Lustra. (London: Elkin Mathews, privately printed, 1916). One of 200 with the Dulac stamp on title. Portrait tissue guard foxed. Bookplate. Just a hint of rubbing at spine ends. Unopened. *(Woolmer)* **$900 [≃£468]**
- Lustra of Ezra Pound with Earlier Poems. New York: Knopf, 1917. 1st American edition. 2nd impression, omitting one poem. Covers very slightly soiled. Supplied folding case, leather label. *(Black Sun)* **$475 [≃£247]**
- Make it New. London: Faber, 1934. Cloth worn, faint trace of 'Boots' shield. *(Sklaroff)* **£45 [≃$86]**

- Money Pamphlets by £. London: 1950-52. 1st editions except for no. 5 2nd edition. Printed wrappers (very slightly dust soiled). *(Polyanthos)* **$200 [≃£104]**
- Money Pamphlets. London: Peter Russell, 1950-51. Complete set of six pamphlets. Wrappers. *(Woolmer)* **$200 [≃£104]**
- Personae. London: Elkin Mathews, 1909. 1st issue. Covers a little worn. *(David Rees)* **£125 [≃$239]**
- Personae ... New Directions: 1926. Cloth (very slightly dull at edges and spine). *(Whiteson)* **£100 [≃$191]**
- Personae; The Collected Poems. New York: New Directions, 1949. 1st edition thus. 1st issue dustwrapper, wheatstraw (a couple of tiny chips and tears about the spine). *(Alphabet)* **$75 [≃£39]**
- Poems 1918-21 including Three Portraits and Four Cantos. New York: (1921). Endpapers foxed and little soiled, occasional slight marginal foxing. Rebacked, covers slightly soiled. *(Polyanthos)* **$95 [≃£49]**
- Polite Essays. CT: New Directions, [n.d.]. *(Polyanthos)* **$30 [≃£15]**
- Polite Essays. London: Faber, 1937. Spine cloth starting to fray. *(Alphabet)* **$30 [≃£15]**
- Quarterly Review of Literature: Ezra Pound Issue. Vol V No 2. 1949. Wrappers. *(Whiteson)* **£25 [≃$47]**
- Quia Pauper Amavi. London: Egoist Press, (1919). One of 500. Misprint uncorrected. Boards, buckram spine. *(Whiteson)* **£175 [≃$335]**
- Quia Pauper Amavi. London: The Egoist Ltd, [1919]. 1st trade edition. Top foredge corner bumped and wrinkled. No dustwrapper issued. *(Alphabet)* **$200 [≃£104]**
- Section: Rock-Drill 85-95 de los Cantares. London: Faber, 1957. 1st English edition. Dustwrapper (spine slightly faded). *(Virgo)* **£35 [≃$67]**
- Section: Rock-Drill 85-95 de Los Cantares. London: Faber, 1957. 1st English edition. Dustwrapper. *(Limestone Hills)* **$55 [≃£28]**
- Section: Rock-Drill, 85-95 de los Cantares. London: Faber, 1957. Endpapers very slightly browned. Dustwrapper (slightly dusty and tanned). *(Dalian)* **£35 [≃$67]**
- Section: Rock-Drill, 85-95 de los cantares. London: Faber, 1957. 1st UK edition. *(Halsey)* **£12 [≃$23]**
- Selected Poems. Edited with an Introduction by T.S. Eliot. London: Faber & Gwyer, (1928). 1st binding. *(Woolmer)* **$150 [≃£78]**
- Selected Poems. Edited by T.S. Eliot. London: 1928. One of 1000. Names. Spine sunned and top very slightly chipped, lower spine slightly rubbed. *(Polyanthos)* **$45 [≃£23]**
- Selected Poems 1908-59. London: 1975. Advance proof copy. Faber review / compliments slip laid in. Plain wrappers, title & author inked on spine. *(Blakeney)* **£75 [≃$143]**
- A Selection of Poems. London: Faber, 1940. Dustwrapper. *(Lewton)* **£11 [≃$21]**
- Seventy Cantos. London: Faber, 1950. Uncorrected proof copy. Wrappers. *(Dalian)* **£150 [≃$287]**
- (Translates) Sonnets and Ballate of Guido Cavalcanti. London: 1912. Adverts at end. Cloth (slightly dull). *(Whiteson)* **£125 [≃$239]**
- Ta Hio. The Great Learning. London: Stanley Nott, 1936. Printed paper boards (very slightly marked). *(Dalian)* **£35 [≃$67]**
- Thrones 96 - 109 de los Cantares. Milan: Pesce d'Oro, 1959. 1st edition (precedes US & UK editions). One of 300. Glassine dustwrapper (chipped). Signed by the author on half-title. *(Any Amount)* **£240 [≃$460]**
- Thrones 96-109 de los Cantares. New York: New Directions, (1959). Erratum slip. Dustwrapper. *(Polyanthos)* **$35 [≃£18]**
- Women of Trachis by Sophokles. London: [1956]. Variant (from Gallup) lacking explanatory label on page iv. Initials & date on front free endpaper. Dustwrapper (slightly rubbed & sunned, one short closed tear). *(Blakeney)* **£65 [≃$124]**
- Gallup, Donald: A Bibliography of Ezra Pound. London: Soho Bibliographies, 1969. 2nd impression, corrected. Dustwrapper. *(Words Etcetera)* **£30 [≃$57]**

Powell, Anthony

- The Acceptance World. London: 1955. Name on fly. Dustwrapper (two minute closed nicks at head of spine). *(Words Etcetera)* **£175 [≃$335]**
- The Acceptance World. London: 1955. Dustwrapper (chip away at head of spine). *(Words Etcetera)* **£100 [≃$191]**
- At Lady Molly's. London: Heinemann, 1957. Dustwrapper. *(Alphabet)* **$100 [≃£52]**
- At Lady Molly's. London: 1957. Dustwrapper (slightly rubbed). *(Ellis)* **£120 [≃$230]**
- At Lady Molly's. London: 1957. Some very light foxing. Dustwrapper. *(Words Etcetera)* **£75 [≃$143]**
- Books Do Furnish a Room. London: 1971.

Dustwrapper. *(Words Etcetera)* **£25 [≃$47]**

- A Buyer's Market. London: 1952. Name on fly. Dustwrapper (unchipped, fine). *(Words Etcetera)* **£350 [≃$671]**
- A Buyer's Market. London: Heinemann, 1952. *(Alphabet)* **$40 [≃£20]**
- Casanova's Chinese Restaurant. London: 1960. Dustwrapper. Author's signed inscription. *(Words Etcetera)* **£150 [≃$287]**
- Casanova's Chinese Restaurant. London: 1960. Dustwrapper (two small closed tears to upper panel). *(Words Etcetera)* **£50 [≃$95]**
- Casanova's Chinese Restaurant. London: 1960. Boards somewhat mottled, top edge little dusty. Dustwrapper (slightly frayed, spine faded). *(Blakeney)* **£35 [≃$67]**
- Casanova's Chinese Restaurant. London: 1960. Dustwrapper (very slightly rubbed). *(Ellis)* **£85 [≃$163]**
- The Fisher King. London: Heinemann, 1986. Dustwrapper. Together with uncorrected proof copy. *(Virgo)* **£35 [≃$67]**
- The Fisher King. London: Heinemann, 1986. Dustwrapper. *(Moorhouse)* **£6 [≃$11]**
- From a View to a Death. London: Lehmann, 1948. 2nd edition, revised. Dustwrapper. *(Sklaroff)* **£35 [≃$67]**
- Hearing Secret Harmonies. London: 1975. Dustwrapper. *(Words Etcetera)* **£20 [≃$38]**
- Hearing Secret Harmonies. London: Heinemann, 1975. Erased inscription on endpaper. Dustwrapper. *(Sklaroff)* **£25 [≃$47]**
- John Aubrey & His Friends. London: Eyre & Spottiswoode, 1948. Dustwrapper (spine very slightly browned). *(Alphabet)* **$110 [≃£57]**
- John Aubrey and his Friends. London: 1948. Dustwrapper. *(Words Etcetera)* **£65 [≃$124]**
- John Aubrey and his Friends. London: 1948. Top edge slightly sunned. Dustwrapper (chipped, sunned, two closed tears). *(Buckley)* **£50 [≃$95]**
- John Aubrey & His Friends. New York: Scribner, 1948. 1st American edition. Dustwrapper (used). *(Alphabet)* **$35 [≃£18]**
- The Kindly Ones. London: Heinemann, 1962. *(Sklaroff)* **£25 [≃$47]**
- The Military Philosophers. London: Heinemann, 1968. 1st issue binding and dustwrapper. *(Sklaroff)* **£35 [≃$67]**
- The Military Philosophers. London: Heinemann, 1968. Dustwrapper. *(Paul Brown)* **£30 [≃$57]**
- The Military Philosophers. London: 1968. Dustwrapper. *(Words Etcetera)* **£28 [≃$53]**
- The Military Philosophers. London: Heinemann, 1968. Dustwrapper. *(Whiteson)* **£20 [≃$38]**
- O, How The Wheel Becomes It! London: 1983. Dustwrapper. *(Words Etcetera)* **£11.50 [≃$23]**
- A Question of Upbringing. London: Heinemann, 1951. Name. Dustwrapper (rubbed at folds, chipped at corners). *(Moorhouse)* **£225 [≃$431]**
- A Question of Upbringing. London: 1951. Spine a trifle rubbed. *(Words Etcetera)* **£85 [≃$163]**
- The Soldier's Art. London: Heinemann, 1966. Dustwrapper. Signed by the author. *(Whiteson)* **£130 [≃$249]**
- The Soldier's Art. London: 1966. Dustwrapper. *(Words Etcetera)* **£30 [≃$57]**
- The Soldier's Art. London: Heinemann, 1966. Dustwrapper. *(Sklaroff)* **£40 [≃$76]**
- The Soldier's Art. London: Heinemann, 1966. Dustwrapper (stain to back panel). *(Marlborough B'shop)* **£30 [≃$57]**
- Temporary Kings. London: 1973. Dustwrapper. *(Words Etcetera)* **£25 [≃$47]**
- The Valley of Bones. London: 1964. Dustwrapper. *(Words Etcetera)* **£75 [≃$143]**

Powers, Tim

- The Stress of Her Regard. New York: Charnel, 1989. One of 500 signed. Denim. Denim slipcase. *(Michael Johnson)* **£100 [≃$191]**

Pownall, David

- The Raining Tree War. London: 1974. Dustwrapper (one half-inch nick). His 1st book. *(First Issues)* **£15 [≃$28]**

Powys, John Cowper

- The Art of Happiness. London: John Lane; The Bodley Head, 1935. Dustwrapper (soiled and frayed). *(Dalian)* **£30 [≃$57]**
- The Brazen Head. London: 1956. Dustwrapper. *(Georges)* **£25 [≃$47]**
- Dostoievsky. London: John Lane; The Bodley Head, 1946. Dustwrapper. *(Dalian)* **£35 [≃$67]**
- Ducdame. London: Grant Richards, 1925. 1st English edition. *(Georges)* **£75 [≃$143]**
- Jobber Skald. London: John Lane; The Bodley Head, 1935. 1st English edition (the unexpurgated version was published in the US in 1934 as "Weymouth Sand'). Covers faded and slightly soiled. *(Lloyd-Roberts)* **£25 [≃$47]**
- The Meaning of Culture. New York: W.W.

Norton, 1929. Precedes the English edition. Cloth slightly faded and marked. Book label on front endpaper. Signed by the author. *(Dalian)* **£75 [≃$143]**

- Owen Glendower. New York: 1940. Precedes the British edition. 2 vols. *(Words Etcetera)* **£30 [≃$57]**
- Visions and Revisions. London: MacDonald, 1955. Endpapers slightly browned. Dustwrapper (very slightly rubbed). *(Dalian)* **£25 [≃$47]**
- The War and Culture: A Reply to Professor Munsterberg. New York: G. Arnold Shaw, 1914. Wrappers. *(Alphabet)* **$100 [≃£52]**
- Wolf Solent. London: Cape, 1929. Denoted 'Advance Copy'. Wrappers (some wear). *(Any Amount)* **£95 [≃$182]**

Powys, Llewellyn

- A Baker's Dozen. Herrin, Il.: Trovillion Private Press, [1939]. One of 493, signed by the author and the artist, Mathias Noheimer. Ink name. Slipcase (minor wear). *(Antic Hay)* **$125 [≃£65]**
- Black Laughter. London: 1925. Dustwrapper. *(Dalian)* **£30 [≃$57]**
- Ebony & Ivory. London: 1923. Dustwrapper (trifle chipped). *(Dalian)* **£30 [≃$57]**
- Impassioned Clay. London: Longmans Green, 1931. Dustwrapper. *(Dalian)* **£45 [≃$86]**
- The Verdict of Bridle Goose. London: Cape, 1927. One of 900. Slightly used. *(Dalian)* **£27 [≃$51]**

Powys, T.F.

- Christ in the Cupboard. London: E. Lahr, Blue Moon Booklets, 1930. One of 500 signed. Printed wrappers (slightly faded). *(Dalian)* **£45 [≃$86]**
- The Dewpond. London: 1928. One of 530 signed. Corners bumped. Dustwrapper (slightly chipped, slightly tanned). *(Ellis)* **£35 [≃$67]**
- The Dewpond. London: Elkin Mathews & Marrot, Woburn Books, 1928. One of 530 signed. Dustwrapper. *(Clearwater)* **£45 [≃$86]**
- Goat Green. Golden Cockerel Press: 1937. Faint foxing endpapers. Dustwrapper (slightly chipped and browned). Signed by the author. *(Buckley)* **£60 [≃$115]**
- The Key of the Field. London: 1930. One of 550 signed by the author. *(Ellis)* **£80 [≃$153]**
- Mark Only. London: 1924. Dustwrapper. *(Clearwater)* **£35 [≃$67]**
- The Only Penitent. London: Chatto & Windus, 1931. Endpapers very slightly browned. Dustwrapper (very slightly dusty). *(Dalian)* **£25 [≃$47]**
- Soliloquies of a Hermit. London: Melrose, 1918. Dustwrapper (minor closed tear). Signed. His 1st book. *(Any Amount)* **£135 [≃$259]**

Pratchett, Terry

- The Carpet People. Gerrards Cross: Colin Smythe, 1971. Small area of crossing out in ink on front endpaper. Dustwrapper (protected by plastic, possibly as issued). His 1st book. *(Moorhouse)* **£20 [≃$38]**
- Strata. London: St. Martin's Press, 1981. Dustwrapper (very slightly rubbed). *(David Rees)* **£20 [≃$38]**

Preedy, George

- Pseudonym used by Marjorie Bowen, q.v.

Price, Anthony

- Colonel Butler's Wolf. London: Gollancz, 1972. Dustwrapper. *(Janus)* **$75 [≃£39]**
- The Labyrinth Makers. London: Gollancz, 1970. Neat inscription. Dustwrapper (faintly soiled). *(Any Amount)* **£45 [≃$86]**
- A New Kind of War. London: Gollancz, 1987. Dustwrapper. Signed by the author. *(Limestone Hills)* **$45 [≃£23]**
- Our Man in Camelot. London: Gollancz, 1975. Price-clipped dustwrapper. *(Janus)* **$65 [≃£33]**
- A Prospect of Vengeance. London: Gollancz, 1988. Dustwrapper. Signed by the author. *(Limestone Hills)* **$45 [≃£23]**
- War Games. London: Gollancz, 1976. Price-clipped dustwrapper. *(Janus)* **$55 [≃£28]**

Price, Jonathan

- Jonathan Price. Fantasy Poets 20: 1954. Wrappers. *(Any Amount)* **£20 [≃$38]**

Price, Reynolds

- A Generous Man. New York: 1966. Spine tips very slightly sunned. Price-clipped dustwrapper. Bookplate signed by the author. *(Polyanthos)* **$45 [≃£23]**
- A Long and Happy Life. Atheneum: 1962. Dustwrapper (spine slightly darkened). His 1st trade book. *(Nouveau)* **$85 [≃£44]**
- A Long and Happy Life. London: Chatto & Windus, 1962. Dustwrapper (very slightly rubbed). His 1st book. *(Dalian)* **£35 [≃$67]**
- A Long and Happy Life. New York: Atheneum, 1962. 1st issue dustwrapper (spine sunned). *(Lopez)* **$75 [≃£39]**

- Love and Work. London: Chatto & Windus, 1968. Name on endpaper. Dustwrapper. *(Dalian)* **£18 [≃$34]**
- Things Themselves. New York: 1972. Dustwrapper. Bookplate signed by the author. *(Polyanthos)* **$35 [≃£18]**

Price, Richard

- Ladies' Man. Boston: 1978. Proof copy. Wrappers. Author's signed presentation copy. *(Polyanthos)* **$45 [≃£23]**

Priest, Christopher

- The Affirmation. London: Faber, 1981. Dustwrapper. *(Dalian)* **£25 [≃$47]**
- A Dream of Wessex. London: Faber, 1977. Dustwrapper. Signed by the author. *(Dyke)* **£30 [≃$57]**
- Fugue for a Darkening Island. London: Faber, 1972. Dustwrapper. Signed by the author. *(Sklaroff)* **£40 [≃$76]**
- Fugue for a Darkening Island. London: Faber, 1972. Signed by the author. *(Lewton)* **£30 [≃$57]**
- Fugue for a Darkening Island. London: Faber, 1972. Dustwrapper. *(Dalian)* **£35 [≃$67]**
- The Glamour. London: 1984. Advance uncorrected proof copy. *(Buckley)* **£15 [≃$28]**
- The Glamour. London: Cape, 1984. Dustwrapper. *(Dalian)* **£20 [≃$38]**
- Indoctrinaire. London: Faber, 1970. Dustwrapper. His 1st book. *(First Issues)* **£115 [≃$220]**
- An Infinite Summer. London: Faber, 1979. Dustwrapper. Signed by the author. *(Sklaroff)* **£32 [≃$61]**
- An Infinite Summer. London: 1979. Dustwrapper. Signed by the author. *(Ellis)* **£28 [≃$53]**
- Inverted World. London: Faber, 1974. Dustwrapper. Signed by the author. *(Dalian)* **£45 [≃$86]**
- Inverted World. London: Faber. 1974. Dustwrapper. Signed by the author. *(Sklaroff)* **£38 [≃$72]**
- The Space Machine. London: Faber, 1976. Dustwrapper. Signed by the author. *(Dyke)* **£30 [≃$57]**
- The Space Machine. London: Faber, 1976. Dustwrapper. Signed by the author. *(Sklaroff)* **£35 [≃$67]**

Priestley, J.B.

- Brief Diversions. Cambridge: Bowes & Bowes, 1922. Quarter leather and orange boards (slightly marked). *(Dalian)* **£35 [≃$67]**
- Dangerous Corner. London: Heinemann, 1932. Author's signed presentation copy. *(Any Amount)* **£16 [≃$30]**
- The Doomsday Men. London: Heinemann, 1938. Name. Dustwrapper (slightly torn). *(Dalian)* **£20 [≃$38]**
- The Doors of Stone. London: Hart-Davis, 1963. Small stamp on endpaper. *(Dalian)* **£25 [≃$47]**
- The Good Companions. London: 1929. Dustwrapper (slightly nicked). *(Egret)* **£25 [≃$47]**
- Home is Tomorrow. London: Heinemann, 1949. Dustwrapper (very slightly nicked). *(Dalian)* **£18 [≃$34]**
- Literature and Western Man. London: Heinemann, 1960. Name. Dustwrapper (rubbed and nicked). *(Dalian)* **£18 [≃$34]**
- The Moments and Other Pieces. London: Heinemann, 1961. Dustwrapper. *(Dalian)* **£15 [≃$28]**
- Saturn Over the Water. London: Heinemann, 1961. Dustwrapper (torn). *(Dalian)* **£10 [≃$19]**
- The Town Major of Miraucourt. London: Heinemann, 1930. One of 525 signed. Vellum, t.e.g. Slipcase. *(Chapel Hill)* **$65 [≃£33]**

Prince, F.T.

- Soldiers Bathing and Other Poems. London: Fortune Press, 1954. Dustwrapper. *(Words Etcetera)* **£25 [≃$47]**

Pritchett, V.S.

- Build the Ships. London: HMSO, 1946. Wrappers. Anonymous. *(Clearwater)* **£20 [≃$38]**
- Dead Man Leading. London: 1937. Spine lettering faded as usual. Dustwrapper (minutely chipped at spine ends). *(Words Etcetera)* **£125 [≃$239]**
- Marching Spain. London: Benn, 1928. Late binding, slightly marked in places. Dustwrapper (rubbed, dusty, slightly frayed). His 1st book. *(Clearwater)* **£45 [≃$86]**
- The Turn of the Years. New York: 1982. One of 500 signed. Box. No dustwrapper issued. *(Polyanthos)* **$50 [≃£26]**

Profumo, David

- Sea Music. Secker & Warburg, 1988. Dustwrapper. *(Moorhouse)* **£12 [≃$23]**

Prokosch, Frederic

- Chosen Poems. London: Chatto & Windus, 1944. Precedes the American edition. Dustwrapper (slightly torn and tanned). *(Dalian)* **£30 [≃$57]**
- Death at Sea. London: Chatto & Windus, 1940. Precedes the American edition. *(Dalian)* **£25 [≃$47]**

Pronzini, Bill

- The Snatch. New York: Random House, [1971]. Dustwrapper (tiny tear). His 1st book. *(Antic Hay)* **$50 [≃£26]**

Pudney, John

- Almanac of Hope. London: 1944. Printed boards. *(Roberts)* **£5.25 [≃$9]**

Puig, Manuel

- Betrayed by Rita Hayworth. New York: 1971. 1st US edition. Light stain rear endpaper. Dustwrapper. His 1st book. *(Pettler & Liebermann)* **$30 [≃£15]**
- Kiss of the Spider Woman. Arena, 1984. Pictorial wrappers. *(Dalian)* **£15 [≃$28]**

Purdy, Alfred

- The Blur in Between. Toronto: Emblem Books, 1962. One of 300. Stapled wrappers. Dustwrapper. *(Alphabet)* **$225 [≃£117]**
- Poems for all the Annettes. Toronto: Anansi, 1968. 1st edition (after the Contact edition) revised. Dustwrapper. *(Alphabet)* **$135 [≃£70]**

Purdy, James

- Colour of Darkness. London: Secker & Warburg, 1961. Dustwrapper. *(Dalian)* **£20 [≃$38]**
- Don't Call Me by My Right Name & Other Stories. New York: William-Frederick Press, 1956. This copy in grey wrappers (spine tanned). His 1st book. *(Alphabet)* **$125 [≃£65]**
- Don't Call Me by My Right Name & Other Stories. New York: The William-Frederick Press, 1956. A bit of fading to spine edges. His 1st book. *(Alphabet)* **$110 [≃£57]**
- Eustace Chisholm & The Works. London: Cape, 1968. Dustwrapper. *(Dalian)* **£15 [≃$28]**
- In a Shallow Grave. London: 1978. Price-clipped dustwrapper. Traces of tiny label. Author's signed presentation copy. *(Polyanthos)* **$35 [≃£18]**
- In the Hollow of his Hand. New York: 1986. Dustwrapper. Author's signed presentation copy. *(Polyanthos)* **$35 [≃£18]**
- In the Hollow of his Hand. New York: 1986. Dustwrapper. Signed by the author. *(Polyanthos)* **$25 [≃£13]**
- Malcolm. London: Secker & Warburg, 1960. Spine slightly faded. Dustwrapper (very slightly rubbed and creased). *(Dalian)* **£25 [≃$47]**
- Narrow Rooms. Surrey, UK: 1980. Dustwrapper. Author's signed presentation copy. *(Polyanthos)* **$35 [≃£18]**
- 63: Dream Palace. New York: The William-Frederick Press, 1956. Printed wrappers. *(Alphabet)* **$85 [≃£44]**
- 63 Dream Palace. A Novella and Nine Stories. London: Gollancz, 1957. Dustwrapper (slightly nicked and slightly dusty). *(Dalian)* **£45 [≃$86]**

Puzo, Mario

- Fools Die. New York: Putnam, [1978]. One of 350 signed by the author. *(Heritage)* **$50 [≃£26]**
- The Godfather. London: Heinemann, 1969. Dustwrapper. *(Dyke)* **£40 [≃$76]**
- The Runaway Summer of Davie Shaw. New York: 1966. Inscription. Dustwrapper. *(Pettler & Liebermann)* **$30 [≃£156]**

Pym, Barbara

- Crampton Hodnet. London: 1985. Dustwrapper. *(Words Etcetera)* **£12.50 [≃$24]**
- Excellent Women. London: 1952. Endpapers foxed. Dustwrapper (frayed, rubbed). *(Ellis)* **£100 [≃$191]**
- Excellent Women. London: 1952. Endsheets spotted. Spine slightly cocked and faded at base. Dustwrapper (extremities frayed). *(Blakeney)* **£125 [≃$239]**
- A Few Green Leaves. London: 1980. Dustwrapper. *(Buckley)* **£25 [≃$47]**
- A Few Green Leaves. London: Macmillan, 1980. Dustwrapper. *(Dalian)* **£20 [≃$38]**
- Less than Angels. London: 1955. Dustwrapper (three closed tears to upper panel). *(Words Etcetera)* **£95 [≃$182]**
- No Fond Return of Love. London: 1961. Front endpaper stained. Dustwrapper. [With] Uncorrected proof copy. Printed wrappers. *(Clearwater)* **£165 [≃$316]**
- Quartet in Autumn. London: 1977. Dustwrapper. *(Buckley)* **£50 [≃$95]**
- Some Tame Gazelle. London: 1950. Trifle shaken. Dustwrapper (torn and chipped at spine ends, some rubbing along hinges). Her 1st book. *(Words Etcetera)* **£185 [≃$355]**

- The Sweet Dove Died. [London: Macmillan, 1978]. Uncorrected proof copy. Printed wrappers. Dustwrapper (minor wear). *(Antic Hay)* **$125 [≃£65]**
- An Unsuitable Attachment. London: 1982. Proof copy. Wrappers. *(Words Etcetera)* **£25 [≃$47]**

Pynchon, Thomas

- The Crying of Lot 49. Phila: Lippincott, (1966). Owner name partly erased on front endpaper. Dustwrapper. *(Lopez)* **$125 [≃£65]**
- The Crying of Lot 49. London: 1967. 1st English edition. Dustwrapper. *(Georges)* **£75 [≃$143]**
- The Crying of Lot 49. London: Cape, 1967. Dustwrapper. *(Dyke)* **£75 [≃$143]**
- The Crying of Lot 49. London: 1967. Dustwrapper. *(Sclanders)* **£165 [≃$316]**
- Entropy. N.p.: (1960). 1st book publication. Printed wrappers. *(Polyanthos)* **$20 [≃£10]**
- Gravity's Rainbow. New York: Viking, (1973). Uncorrected proof copy. Revised publication date on cover. *(Lopez)* **$3,500 [≃£1,822]**
- Gravity's Rainbow. New York: Viking, 1973. Dustwrapper. *(Dyke)* **£75 [≃$143]**
- Gravity's Rainbow. New York: Viking, (1973). Price-clipped 1st issue dustwrapper. *(Lopez)* **$450 [≃£234]**
- Gravity's Rainbow. New York: (1973). Dustwrapper. *(King)* **$125 [≃£65]**
- Low-Lands. (London: Aloes, 1978). One of 1500. Wrappers. *(Lopez)* **$40 [≃£20]**
- Mortality and Mercy in Vienna. London: Aloes Books, n.d. Pictorial wrappers. *(Polyanthos)* **$20 [≃£10]**
- Mortality and Mercy in Vienna. Aloes Press: [1976]. Wrappers. *(Buckley)* **£20 [≃$38]**
- The Secret Integration. (London: Aloes, 1980). One of 2500. Wrappers. *(Lopez)* **$40 [≃£20]**
- Slow Learner. Boston: 1984. Dustwrapper. *(Words Etcetera)* **£20 [≃$38]**
- Slow Learner. Boston: (1984). Hardcover edition. Dustwrapper. *(Lopez)* **$35 [≃£18]**
- Slow Learner. London: Cape, [1985]. 1st English edition. Dustwrapper. *(Lopez)* **$35 [≃£18]**
- The Small Rain. (London: Aloes), [1982]. Wrappers. *(Lopez)* **$40 [≃£20]**
- V. Phila: Lippincott, 1963. Advance reading copy. Printed wrappers. His 1st book. *(Alphabet)* **$500 [≃£260]**
- V. Phila: 1963. Dustwrapper, fine. *(Polyanthos)* **$450 [≃£234]**
- V. London: Cape, 1963. 1st British edition. Dustwrapper. *(Ash)* **£200 [≃$383]**
- V. London: Cape, 1963. Dustwrapper. *(Dyke)* **£125 [≃$239]**
- V. London: Cape, 1963. Tape marks on endpapers. Dustwrapper. *(Sklaroff)* **£85 [≃$163]**
- Vineland. Boston: LB, (1990). Advance review copy with sheet of promotional information laid in. Dustwrapper. *(Lopez)* **$125 [≃£65]**
- Vineland. London: Secker & Warburg, 1990. Dustwrapper. *(Dalian)* **£25 [≃$47]**
- Vineland. London: 1990. dustwrapper. *(Lewton)* **£19.50 [≃$38]**
- Vineland. London: Secker & Warburg, 1990. 1st English edition. Dustwrapper. *(Limestone Hills)* **$75 [≃£39]**

Quayle, Eric

- The Collector's Book of Detective Fiction. London: Studio, 1972. Dustwrapper. *(Limestone Hills)* **$85 [≃£44]**

Queen, Ellery

- The French Powder Mystery. New York: Stokes, 1930. Name, small scuff from price removal, light foredge soiling. *(Janus)* **$250 [≃£130]**

Raban, Jonathan

- Foreign Land. London: Collins, 1985. Dustwrapper. Signed by the author. *(Lewton)* **£17.50 [≃$34]**

Raine, Craig

- The Electrification of the Soviet Union. London: 1986. One of 100 signed by the author. Leather backed cloth. Tissue dustwrapper. *(Ellis)* **£65 [≃$124]**
- The Electrification of the Soviet Union. London: Faber, 1986. Dustwrapper. Signed by the author. *(Lewton)* **£12.50 [≃$24]**
- The Electrification of the Soviet Union. London: Faber, 1986. Dustwrapper. *(Lewton)* **£6.50 [≃$13]**
- The Electrification of the Soviet Union. London: 1986. Wrappers. *(Buckley)* **£7 [≃$13]**
- The Onion, Memory. London: 1978. Wrappers. Signed by the author. *(Egret)* **£35 [≃$67]**

Raine, Kathleen

- Living in Time. London: Editions Poetry, 1946. Cloth backed boards (a little soiled).

Dustwrapper (slightly chipped, torn and spotted). *(Words Etcetera)* **£30 [≃$57]**

- Living in Time. London: Poetry London, 1946. Dustwrapper (lacks small piece at top of spine). *(Moorhouse)* **£25 [≃$47]**
- The Presence. Golgonooza Press: 1987. Dustwrapper. *(Words Etcetera)* **£8.50 [≃$17]**
- The Pythoness and Other Poems. London: 1949. Dustwrapper (slightly used). *(Words Etcetera)* **£20 [≃$38]**
- Selected Poems. Golgonooza Press: 1988. One of 100 signed. Slipcase. *(Words Etcetera)* **£45 [≃$86]**
- Selected Poems. New York: Weekend Press, 1952. One of 250 signed. Wrappers (a trifle browned on spine). *(Words Etcetera)* **£95 [≃$182]**
- Year One. London: 1952. Review slip. Dustwrapper. *(Words Etcetera)* **£25 [≃$47]**

Rampling, Anne

- Pseudonym used by Anne Rice, q.v.

Rand, Ayn

- Atlas Shrugged. New York: Random House, (1957). Dustwrapper (few nicks). *(Houle)* **$175 [≃£91]**
- For the New Intellectual. New York: Random House, [1961]. Dustwrapper (minor wear and soil). *(Antic Hay)* **$75 [≃£39]**
- The Fountainhead. Indianopolis: Bobbs-Merrill, 1943. Correct 1st printing. Dustwrapper (a bit chipped and soiled). *(Alphabet)* **$1,000 [≃£520]**
- We The Living. London: Cassell, 1936. Advance copy. Unstamped blue cloth. Spotting to foredge and slight offsetting to endsheets from dustwrapper. Dustwrapper (slightly mottled at spine, ragged two inch tear to lower panel, closed tear to upper). Her 1st book. Precedes the American edition. *(Blakeney)* **£1,250 [≃$2,399]**
- We the Living. New York: Macmillan, 1936. Price-clipped dustwrapper (lightly rubbed and edgeworn). Her 1st book. *(Alphabet)* **$2,000 [≃£1,041]**

Ransom, John Crowe

- Armageddon. Charleston: The Poetry Society of South Carolina, 1923. Stapled wrappers (spine slightly nicked). *(Black Sun)* **$1,000 [≃£520]**
- Grace After Meat. With an Introduction by Robert Graves. Hogarth Press, 1924. One of 400. Endpapers very slightly browned. Green patterned boards, sine. Custom-made wrappers and slipcase. *(Dalian)* **£450 [≃$863]**
- Poems About God. New York: Holt, 1919. Spine label with very tiny scrape, slight rubbing to rear hinge. His 1st book. *(Black Sun)* **$750 [≃£390]**

Raphael, Frederic

- California Time. London: 1975. Dustwrapper. *(Buckley)* **£15 [≃$28]**
- Lindmann. Cassell, 1963. Dustwrapper (very slightly dusty). *(Dalian)* **£25 [≃$47]**
- Two for the Road. London: Cape, 1967. Dustwrapper. *(Dalian)* **£18 [≃$34]**

Rattigan, Terence

- The Winslow Boy. London: 1964. Ink annotation to cast list. Dustwrapper. *(Words Etcetera)* **£30 [≃$57]**

Raven, Simon

- Bring Forth the Body. London: 1974. Dustwrapper. *(Ellis)* **£15 [≃$28]**
- Bring Forth the Body. London: Blond & Briggs, 1974. Dustwrapper (very slightly marked). *(Ash)* **£25 [≃$47]**
- Bring Forth the Body. London: Blond & Briggs, 1974. Dustwrapper (very slightly scratched). *(Virgo)* **£17.50 [≃$34]**
- Close of Play. London: 1962. Price-clipped dustwrapper (slightly rubbed). *(Ellis)* **£35 [≃$67]**
- Come Like Shadows. London: 1972. Dustwrapper (slightly rubbed, few small nicks). *(Ellis)* **£15 [≃$28]**
- Come Like Shadows. London: Blond & Briggs, 1972. Dustwrapper (slightly rubbed). *(Ash)* **£20 [≃$38]**
- Doctors Wear Scarlet. London: Blond, 1960. Dustwrapper (spine faded). *(David Rees)* **£18 [≃$34]**
- The Feathers of Death. London: 1959. Name. Tail of spine slightly bruised. Dustwrapper (frayed, nicked). Signed by the author. His 1st book. *(Ellis)* **£65 [≃$124]**
- The Feathers of Death. London: Blond, 1959. Dustwrapper. *(Clearwater)* **£50 [≃$95]**
- The Feathers of Death. London: Blond, 1959. Dustwrapper. His 1st book. *(Limestone Hills)* **$65 [≃£33]**
- The Feathers of Death. London: Blond, 1959. Dustwrapper (spine very slightly faded). His 1st book. *(Virgo)* **£38 [≃$72]**
- Fielding Gray. London: Blond, 1967. Lower front corner slightly bumped. 2nd issue price-clipped dustwrapper (slightly rubbed). *(Virgo)* **£10 [≃$19]**

- Fielding Gray. London: Blond, 1967. Dustwrapper. *(Any Amount)* **£17.50 [≃$34]**
- Friends in Low Places. London: 1965. Dustwrapper. *(Buckley)* **£30 [≃$57]**
- Friends in Low Places. London: Blond, 1985. Dustwrapper. *(Michael Johnson)* **£24 [≃$46]**
- The Judas Boy, 1968. London: Blond. Dustwrapper. *(Any Amount)* **£17 [≃$32]**
- Places Where They Sing. London: Blond, 1970. Dustwrapper. *(Any Amount)* **£16 [≃$30]**
- The Rich Pay Late. London: Blond, 1964. Dustwrapper. *(Michael Johnson)* **£24 [≃$46]**
- The Survivors. London: 1976. Dustwrapper. *(Ellis)* **£20 [≃$38]**

Rawlings, Marjorie Kinnan

- Cross Creek. New York: Scribner's, 1942. Silver stamping on spine a little flaked. Price-clipped dustwrapper (light edgewear). Signed by the author. *(Chapel Hill)* **$250 [≃£130]**

Raworth, Tom

- The Big Green Day. Illustrated by Jim Dine. Trigram: 1968. One of 100 signed by both. Dustwrapper. *(Any Amount)* **£50 [≃$95]**

Rawson, Clayton

- Death from Nowhere. By Stuart Towne. New York: Weigers Publishing, 1940. Paperback original. Wrappers (covers somewhat wrinkled along spine). Boxed. *(Mordida)* **$275 [≃£143]**

Ray, Ophelia

- Daughter of the Tejas. Greenwich: NYGS, (1965). White dustwrapper. Reportedly ghostwritten by Larry McMurtry. *(Lopez)* **$75 [≃£39]**

Read, Herbert

- Byron. London: Longmans, 1951. Printed wrappers (very slightly tanned). *(Dalian)* **£15 [≃$28]**
- In Retreat. Hogarth Press, 1925. Printed wrappers (slightly marked). *(Dalian)* **£65 [≃$124]**
- The Knapsack. London: Routledge, 1939. Dustwrapper (slightly torn). *(Dalian)* **£25 [≃$47]**

Read, Piers Paul

- Game in Heaven with Tussy Marx. London: Weidenfeld & Nicolson, 1969. Dustwrapper. His 1st book. *(David Rees)* **£20 [≃$38]**

Reading, Peter

- For the Municipality's Elderly. London: 1974. Dustwrapper. *(Egret)* **£30 [≃$57]**

Rechy, John

- City of Night. New York: 1963. Dustwrapper (spine very slightly sunned, rear panel very slightly soiled). His 1st book. *(Polyanthos)* **$35 [≃£18]**
- The Fourth Angel. New York: 1973. Dustwrapper. Author's signed presentation copy. *(Polyanthos)* **$35 [≃£18]**
- Numbers. New York: 1967. Dustwrapper (short edge tear rear panel). *(Polyanthos)* **$20 [≃£10]**
- This Day's Death. New York: 1969. Dustwrapper. *(Polyanthos)* **$20 [≃£10]**

Redgrove, Peter

- The Nature of Cold Weather & Other Poems. London: 1961. Dustwrapper. *(First Issues)* **£20 [≃$38]**

Reed, Kit

- Mother Isn't Dead She's Only Sleeping. New York: 1961. Hinge tender. Dustwrapper (slightly rubbed, one closed tear). Signed inscription to Edmund Crispin. His 1st book. *(Buckley)* **£40 [≃$76]**

Reid, Forrest

- Apostate. London: Constable, 1926. One of 50 signed. Tape marks on endpapers. Spine ends slightly tanned. *(Dalian)* **£225 [≃$431]**
- Brian Westley. London: Faber, 1934. Foredge very slightly foxed. Dustwrapper (chipped and marked). *(Dalian)* **£35 [≃$67]**
- Walter de la Mare. London: Faber, 1929. 2nd issue, green cloth with spine lettering in gilt. Inscription on endpaper. Dustwrapper (slightly nicked and tanned). *(Dalian)* **£45 [≃$86]**

Reilly, Helen

- The Diamond Feather. Garden City: Doubleday, 1930. Dustwrapper. *(Janus)* **$65 [≃£33]**

Remarque, Erich Maria

- All Quiet on the Western Front. Boston: 1929. Dustwrapper (top edge of front panel very slightly chipped). *(Polyanthos)* **$50 [≃£26]**

Renault, Mary

- The Bull from the Sea. London: Longmans, 1962. Price-clipped dustwrapper.

(Paul Brown) **£10 [≃$19]**

- The Mask of Apollo. London: Longmans, 1966. Dustwrapper (repair to lower spine). *(Dalian)* **£15 [≃$28]**
- North Face. London: Longmans, 1949. Dustwrapper. *(Glyn's)* **£17.50 [≃$34]**

Rendell, Ruth

- A Dark-Adapted Eye. By Barbara Vine. London: 1986. Dustwrapper. Signed by the author. *(Egret)* **£20 [≃$38]**
- A Dark Adapted Eye. By Barbara Vine. Viking, 1986. Dustwrapper. *(Paul Brown)* **£10 [≃$19]**
- A Dark-Adapted Eye. By Barbara Vine. London: Viking, 1986. Price-clipped dustwrapper. *(Dyke)* **£8 [≃$15]**
- A Fatal Inversion. By Barbara Vine. Viking: 1987. Dustwrapper (slightly used). Signed by the author. *(Moorhouse)* **£15 [≃$28]**
- A Fatal Inversion. By Barbara Vine. Viking: 1987. Dustwrapper. *(Moorhouse)* **£5 [≃$9]**
- Gallowglass. By Barbara Vine. Viking: 1990. Uncorrected proof copy. Wrappers. *(Moorhouse)* **£14 [≃$26]**
- Gallowglass. By Barbara Vine. London: Viking, 1990. Dustwrapper. Signed by the author (as Rendell). *(David Rees)* **£20 [≃$38]**
- A Guilty Thing Surprised. London: Hutchinson, 1970. Dustwrapper (slightly rubbed). *(Dyke)* **£35 [≃$67]**
- A Guilty Thing Surprised. London: Hutchinson, 1970. Dustwrapper (slightly rubbed and creased). *(Moorhouse)* **£40 [≃$76]**
- A Guilty Thing Surprised. London: Hutchinson, 1970. Spine ends slightly bumped. Dustwrapper (slightly rubbed). Signed by the author. *(Moorhouse)* **£55 [≃$105]**
- Heartstones. London: Hutchinson, 1987. Dustwrapper. Signed by the author. *(Janus)* **$35 [≃£18]**
- A Judgement in Stone. London: Hutchinson, 1977. Dustwrapper. Signed by the author. *(Moorhouse)* **£25 [≃$47]**
- A Judgement in Stone. London: Hutchinson, 1977. Dustwrapper. Signed by the author. *(Limestone Hills)* **$85 [≃£44]**
- The Killing Doll. London: Hutchinson, 1984. Dustwrapper. *(Limestone Hills)* **$35 [≃£18]**
- The Lake of Darkness. London: 1980. Two slight pin holes at foot of upper cover and upper panel of dustwrapper. Dustwrapper. *(Words Etcetera)* **£30 [≃$57]**
- Live Flesh. London: Hutchinson, 1986. Dustwrapper. Signed by the author. *(Dyke)* **£20 [≃$38]**
- Live Flesh. London: Hutchinson, 1986. Dustwrapper. Signed by the author. *(Virgo)* **£20 [≃$38]**
- Make Death Love Me. London: Hutchinson, 1979. Dustwrapper (one short tear). *(Moorhouse)* **£12 [≃$23]**
- Make Death Love Me. London: Hutchinson, 1979. Dustwrapper. *(Limestone Hills)* **$40 [≃£20]**
- Master of the Moor. London: 1982. Dustwrapper. *(Words Etcetera)* **£25 [≃$47]**
- Murder Being Once Done. London: Hutchinson, 1972. Dustwrapper (slightly chipped, small stain head of spine). Signed by the author. *(Moorhouse)* **£40 [≃$76]**
- The New Girlfriend and Other Stories. London: Hutchinson, 1985. Uncorrected proof copy. Wrappers. *(Limestone Hills)* **$50 [≃£26]**
- The New Girl Friend and Other Stories. London: Hutchinson, 1985. Uncorrected proof copy. Printed wrappers. *(Dalian)* **£20 [≃$38]**
- Put On By Cunning. London: Hutchinson, 1981. Dustwrapper. *(Moorhouse)* **£8 [≃$15]**
- Shake Hands for Ever. London: Hutchinson, 1975. Dustwrapper (short closed tear). Signed by the author. *(Mordida)* **$125 [≃£65]**
- A Sleeping Life. London: 1978. Dustwrapper. *(Words Etcetera)* **£35 [≃$67]**
- Some Lie and Some Die. London: Hutchinson, 1973. Dustwrapper (crease front flap). *(Janus)* **$85 [≃£44]**
- The Tree of Hands. London: Hutchinson, 1984. Uncorrected proof copy. Printed wrappers. Proof dustwrapper. *(Dalian)* **£20 [≃$38]**
- The Tree of Hands. London: 1984. Dustwrapper. Signed by the author. *(Egret)* **£30 [≃$57]**
- The Tree of Hands. London: 1984. Dustwrapper. *(Words Etcetera)* **£12 [≃$23]**
- An Unkindness of Ravens. London: 1985. Dustwrapper. Signed by the author. *(Egret)* **£25 [≃$47]**
- The Veiled One. London: Hutchinson, 1988. Dustwrapper. Signed by the author. *(Dyke)* **£20 [≃$38]**
- Wolf to the Slaughter. London: John Long, 1967. Dustwrapper (spine slightly darkened). Signed by the author. *(Moorhouse)* **£135 [≃$259]**

The Review / The New Review

- The Review / The New Review. Edited by Ian Hamilton. Oxford, later London: 1962-72, numbers 1-29/30; 1974-78, numbers 1-50. All published. *(Blakeney)* **£475 [≃$911]**

Rexroth, Kenneth

- American Poetry in the Twentieth Century. New York: Herder & Herder, (1971). Dustwrapper (short internally repaired tear). Signed by the author. *(Between the Covers)* **$85 [≃£44]**
- Beyond the Mountains. New Directions: 1951. Dustwrapper. *(Nouveau)* **$60 [≃£31]**
- The Elastic Retort. New York: Seabury, (1973). Dustwrapper (lightly rubbed). Signed by the author. *(Between the Covers)* **$85 [≃£44]**

Rhys, Jean

- Good Morning Midnight. London: Constable, 1939. Foredge and endpapers slightly foxed and browned. Small label removed from endpaper. Spine and top edge very slightly faded. *(Virgo)* **£90 [≃$172]**
- Good Morning, Midnight. US: 1970. 1st US edition. Dustwrapper (spine slightly rubbed). *(Buckley)* **£25 [≃$47]**
- The Left Bank and Other Stories. London: 1927. Endpapers browned. Covers soiled, spine darkened, spine label rubbed. *(Ellis)* **£80 [≃$153]**
- The Left Bank. London: Cape, 1927. Pencil inscription. Covers a little marked, edges slightly foxed. *(David Rees)* **£60 [≃$115]**
- May Day. New York: Frank Hallman, 1975. 1st American edition. One of 750. Dustwrapper. *(Dalian)* **£35 [≃$67]**
- Sleep It off Lady. London: Deutsch, 1976. Advance proof copy. Wrappers, publication date and one small stain on upper wrapper. *(Blakeney)* **£35 [≃$67]**
- Sleep It Off Lady. London: Deutsch, 1976. Dustwrapper. *(Dalian)* **£35 [≃$67]**
- Smile Please. London: 1979. Dustwrapper. *(Buckley)* **£20 [≃$38]**
- Smile Please. London: Deutsch, 1979. Dustwrapper. *(Dalian)* **£20 [≃$38]**
- Voyage in the Dark. London: Constable, 1934. Lower tip of spine sunned. Name on endpaper. Dustwrapper (soiled, inner repairs). *(Dalian)* **£85 [≃$163]**
- Wide Sargasso Sea. London: Deutsch, 1966. Dustwrapper. *(Dyke)* **£30 [≃$57]**
- Wide Sargasso Sea. London: Deutsch, 1966. Top edge slightly faded, edges spotted. Dustwrapper (slightly nicked). *(Virgo)* **£37.50 [≃$72]**
- Wide Sargasso Sea. London: Deutsch, 1966. Dustwrapper. *(Ash)* **£50 [≃$95]**

Rice, Anne

- Exit to Eden. By Anne Rampling. New York: 1985. Dustwrapper. Signed by the author as Anne Rice and Anne Rampling. *(Polyanthos)* **$75 [≃£39]**
- Feast of All Saints. New York: 1970. Advance uncorrected proof copy. Printed wrappers. *(Pettler & Liebermann)* **$125 [≃£65]**
- Interview with the Vampire. New York: Knopf, 1976. Dustwrapper (slightly edgeworn). Signed by the author. *(Heritage)* **$450 [≃£234]**
- Interview with the Vampire. New York: 1976. Book Club edition. Dustwrapper. Her 1st book. *(Pettler & Liebermann)* **$40 [≃£20]**
- The Mummy. New York: Ballantine, (1989). Uncorrected proof copy. Promotional material inserted. Proof of the trade dustwrapper. *(Lopez)* **$250 [≃£130]**
- The Queen of the Damned. New York: Knopf, 1988. Uncorrected proof copy. Wrappers. Signed by the author. *(Lopez)* **$175 [≃£91]**
- The Queen of the Damned. New York: 1988. Proof copy. Wrappers. Signed by the author. *(Polyanthos)* **$125 [≃£65]**
- See also Roquelare, A.N.

Rich, Adrienne

- The Dream of a Common Language. New York: Norton, [1978]. Uncorrected proof copy. printed wrappers (light soil). *(Antic Hay)* **$65 [≃£33]**

Richards, Frank

- The Autobiography. London: Skilton, 1962. Dustwrapper. *(Green Meadow)* **£25 [≃$47]**
- Bessie Bunter of Cliff House School. By Hilda Richards [i.e. Frank Richards]. London: Skilton, 1949. Front free endpaper removed. Dustwrapper (slightly chipped). *(Green Meadow)* **£45 [≃$86]**
- Bunter the Stowaway. London: Cassell, 1964. Dustwrapper. *(Green Meadow)* **£25 [≃$47]**
- Bunter the Ventriloquist. London: Cassell, 1961. Dustwrapper. *(Green Meadow)* **£25 [≃$47]**
- Just Like Bunter. London: Cassell, 1963. Dustwrapper (slightly chipped). *(Green Meadow)* **£25 [≃$47]**

Richards, Hilda

- See Richards, Frank.

Richardson, Dorothy M.

- Pilgrimage. London: Dent & The Cresset Press, 1938. 1st collected edition. 4 vols. Dustwrappers. *(Egret)* **£65 [≃$124]**

Richler, Mordecai

- The Acrobats. London: Deutsch, 1954. Dustwrapper, fine. His 1st book. *(Alphabet)* **$325 [≃£169]**
- The Apprenticeship of Duddy Kravitz. London: Deutsch, 1959. Dustwrapper (frayed). *(Dalian)* **£45 [≃$86]**
- The Incomparable Atuk. London: Deutsch, 1963. Dustwrapper. *(Dalian)* **£35 [≃$67]**
- Joshua Then and Now. [Toronto]: M&S, 1980. Uncorrected proof copy. Ringbound printed wrappers. *(Alphabet)* **$115 [≃£59]**
- St. Urbains Horseman. New York: Knopf, 1971. 1st American edition. Price-clipped dustwrapper. *(Alphabet)* **$20 [≃£10]**

Richter, Conrad

- A Simple Honourable Man. New York: Knopf, 1962. Dustwrapper (couple of chips and tears). Signed by the author. *(Chapel Hill)* **$60 [≃£31]**

Riding, Laura

- Anarchism is not Enough. London: Cape, 1928. Name on fly. Cloth faded, especially spine. *(Halsey)* **£40 [≃$76]**
- Anarchism is not Enough. London: Cape, 1928. Covers somewhat faded and stained. Dustwrapper (worn, slightly defective). *(Ash)* **£40 [≃$76]**
- The Close Chaplet. By Laura Gottschalk. London: Hogarth Press, 1926. Lacks backstrip but webbing intact, Her 1st book. *(Halsey)* **£90 [≃$172]**
- Collected Poems. London: Cassell, 1938. Front hinge tender. *(Halsey)* **£30 [≃$57]**
- Epilogue: A Critical Summary. Edited by Laura Riding. Assistant Editor Robert Graves. Seizin & Constable: 1935-37. Vols 1-3, all published. Paper covered boards (slightly frail and chipped, two backstrips split at rear edges but intact). *(Halsey)* **£95 [≃$182]**
- Everybody's Letters Collected & Arranged by Laura Riding. London: Barker, 1933. Prelims and edges slightly spotted. *(Halsey)* **£35 [≃$67]**
- Laura and Francisca. Deya: Seizin Press, 1931. One of 200 signed. Some wear to tips and fading of boards. *(Dermont)* **$275 [≃£143]**
- The Life of the Dead. London: Arthur Barker, [1933]. One of 200 signed by Riding and Aldridge, the illustrator. Stiff wrappers with cover label, fine. *(Dermont)* **$375 [≃£195]**
- Poet: A Lying Word. London: Barker, 1933. Cloth slightly rubbed, slight wear to top of spine. *(Halsey)* **£50 [≃$95]**
- The Telling. Athlone: 1972. Dustwrapper. *(Halsey)* **£14.50 [≃$28]**
- The World and Ourselves. London: Chatto & Windus, 1938. Name on endpaper. Covers very slightly rubbed. *(Dalian)* **£75 [≃$143]**

Riding, Laura & Graves, Robert

- A Pamphlet against Anthologies. London: Cape, 1928. Name and date on fly. Top edge dusty. Top of spine slightly pulled. *(Halsey)* **£34 [≃$65]**

Robbe-Grillet, Alain

- In the Labyrinth. London: Calder, 1967. 1st UK edition. Dustwrapper. *(Any Amount)* **£18 [≃$34]**

Robbins, Harold

- The Adventurers. New York: Trident Press, 1966. Minor spotting. Dustwrapper (few short tears). Signed by the author. *(Antic Hay)* **$45 [≃£23]**
- The Betsy. US: Trident, 1971. Dustwrapper (internally marked). Inscribed, dated and signed by the author. *(Paul Brown)* **£15 [≃$28]**
- The Dream Merchants. London: Weidenfeld & Nicolson, 1950. Covers very slightly marked. Dustwrapper (slightly soiled and chipped). *(Dalian)* **£35 [≃$67]**
- The Inheritors. New York: Trident, [1969]. Dustwrapper. Signed by the author. *(Antic Hay)* **$35 [≃£18]**

Robbins, Tom

- Even Cowgirls Get the Blues. London: Corgi, 1977. Printed wrappers. *(Dalian)* **£20 [≃$38]**
- Even Cowgirls Get the Blues. London: Corgi Original, 1977. Wrappers. *(Hazeldene)* **£10 [≃$19]**
- Even Cowgirls Get the Blues. London: 1977. 1st British edition. Paperback original. Name and date. Wrappers. *(Pettler & Liebermann)* **$20 [≃£10]**
- Jitterbug Perfume. Toronto: Bantam, (1984). Uncorrected proof copy. Name on front cover. Wrappers. *(Lopez)* **$50 [≃£26]**

- Still Life with Woodpecker. Bantam: 1980. Advance review copy with slip laid in. Dustwrapper. *(Nouveau)* **$50 [≃£26]**
- Still Life with Woodpecker. New York: 1980. Hardback issue. Dustwrapper. *(Pettler & Liebermann)* **$45 [≃£23]**
- Still Life with Woodpecker. London: Sidgwick & Jackson, 1980. Pictorial wrappers. *(Dalian)* **£15 [≃$28]**

Roberts, Keith

- The Boat of Fate. London: 1971. Dustwrapper. *(Clearwater)* **£45 [≃$86]**
- The Chalk Giants. London: 1974. One corner slightly bumped, tail of spine slightly bruised. Dustwrapper (slightly rubbed, two nicks). *(Ellis)* **£65 [≃$124]**
- The Grain Kings. London: 1976. Dustwrapper. Author's presentation inscription. *(Clearwater)* **£60 [≃$115]**
- Ladies from Hell. London: 1979. Dustwrapper (head of spine slightly creased). Signed by the author. *(Ellis)* **£45 [≃$86]**

Roberts, Lynette

- Poems. London: Faber, [1944]. Small stain to cloth edge. Dustwrapper (lightly soiled). Her 1st book. *(Dermont)* **$75 [≃£39]**

Robins, Elizabeth

- Portrait of a Lady or The English Spirit Old and New. London: Hogarth Press, 1941. Wrappers. *(Woolmer)* **$125 [≃£65]**

Robinson, Marilynne

- Housekeeping. New York: FS&G, (1980). Dustwrapper. *(Lopez)* **$50 [≃£26]**

Roethke, Theodore

- Open House. New York: Knopf, 1941. One of 1000. Dustwrapper (slight wear at spine tips). His 1st book. *(Alphabet)* **$500 [≃£260]**

Rohmer, Sax

- Emperor Fu Manchu. London: Herbert Jenkins, 1959. Dustwrapper (short closed tear on front panel, minor wear spine ends). *(Mordida)* **$125 [≃£65]**
- The Island of Fu Manchu. New York: Doubleday Doran, 1941. Dustwrapper (internally tape repaired). *(Alphabet)* **$75 [≃£39]**
- The Mask of Fu Manchu. New York: The Crime Club, 1932. Small crease top side front panel. Dustwrapper (few tiny edge tears). *(Polyanthos)* **$45 [≃£23]**
- Sand and Stain. London: Herbert Jenkins, 1955. 1st hardcover edition (published in the US as Return of Sumuru). Dustwrapper (light damp stain back panel). *(Mordida)* **$75 [≃£39]**
- Sinister Madonna. London: Herbert Jenkins, 1956. Upper front corner bumped. Dustwrapper (wear at corner, minor wear spine ends). *(Mordida)* **$75 [≃£39]**
- The Wrath of Fu Manchu. New York: Donald A. Wollheim, 1976. 1st American edition. Paperback original Daw Books no. 186. Wrappers. *(Mordida)* **$50 [≃£26]**

Rolfe, Frederick, Baron Corvo

- See Corvo, Baron (Fr. Rolfe)

Roquelare, A.N. (i.e. Anne Rice)

- Beauty's Punishment. New York: Dutton, (1984). The cloth issue. Dustwrapper. *(Lopez)* **$120 [≃£62]**
- Beauty's Punishment. New York: Dutton, (1984). The simultaneous wrappers issue. *(Lopez)* **$20 [≃£10]**
- The Claiming of Sleeping Beauty. New York: Dutton, (1983). Dustwrapper. *(Lopez)* **$135 [≃£70]**

Rosen, Richard

- Fadeaway. New York: Harper & Row, 1986. Dustwrapper. *(Mordida)* **$15 [≃£7]**
- Strike Three You're Dead. New York: Walker, 1984. Dustwrapper. *(Mordida)* **$85 [≃£44]**

Rosenberg, I.

- Poems. London: 1922. 2 pages dampstained in margins. Binding little dull, spine label little rubbed. *(Whiteson)* **£35 [≃$67]**

Ross, Alan

- A Calcutta Grandmother. Poem of the Month, 1971. Large 4to mounted sheet. Signed by the author. *(Dalian)* **£20 [≃$38]**

Rossner, Judith

- Looking for Mr Goodbar. London: Cape, 1975. Dustwrapper. *(Lewton)* **£37.50 [≃$72]**

Roth, Philip

- The Anatomy Lesson. New York: 1983. One of 300 signed. No dustwrapper issued. Box. *(Polyanthos)* **$60 [≃£31]**
- The Anatomy Lesson. PA: The Franklin Library, 1983. Limited edition signed. Leather gilt, a.e.g. *(Polyanthos)* **$40 [≃£20]**
- The Beast. London: Cape, 1973. Uncorrected proof copy. Wrappers. *(Dalian)* **£25 [≃$47]**

- Deception. New York: Simon & Schuster, [1990]. Uncorrected proof copy. Wrappers. *(Dermont)* **$40 [≃£20]**
- The Facts. New York: 1988. Dustwrapper. Signed by the author. *(Polyanthos)* **$35 [≃£18]**
- Goodbye Columbus. London: Deutsch, 1959. 1st English edition. Price-clipped dustwrapper. *(Nouveau)* **$90 [≃£46]**
- Goodbye, Columbus. London: 1959. Dustwrapper. *(Ellis)* **£60 [≃$115]**
- My Life as a Man. London: Cape, 1974. Dustwrapper. *(Dalian)* **£20 [≃$38]**
- Portnoy's Complaint. New York: 1969. One of 600 signed by the author. Dustwrapper. Slipcase. *(Ellis)* **£100 [≃$191]**
- Portnoy's Complaint. New York: 1969. Dustwrapper. *(Polyanthos)* **$45 [≃£23]**
- Portnoy's Complaint. New York: Random House, 1969. Price-clipped dustwrapper. *(Dyke)* **£45 [≃$86]**
- Portnoy's Complaint. London: Cape, 1969. 1st English edition. Dustwrapper. *(Nouveau)* **$30 [≃£15]**
- Portnoy's Complaint. London: 1970. Dustwrapper. *(First Issues)* **£20 [≃$38]**
- The Professor of Desire. New York: Farrar, Straus & Giroux, [1977]. Price-clipped dustwrapper. Signed by the author. *(Chapel Hill)* **$75 [≃£39]**
- The Professor of Desire. New York: 1977. Review slip and two publicity photos laid in. Dustwrapper. *(Polyanthos)* **$35 [≃£18]**
- When She Was Good. New York: 1967. Review slip. Dustwrapper. *(Polyanthos)* **$35 [≃£18]**
- Zuckerman Unbound. New York: 1981. One of 350 signed. Slipcase. *(Words Etcetera)* **£36 [≃$69]**
- Zuckerman Unbound. London: Cape, 1981. Uncorrected proof copy. Printed wrappers. *(Dalian)* **£25 [≃$47]**

Rothenberg, Jerome

- Conversations. Black Sparrow: 1968. One of 50 signed. Unopened. Dustwrapper. *(Dermont)* **$60 [≃£31]**
- Further Sightings. Black Sparrow: 1968. One of 125 signed. Acetate dustwrapper. *(Dermont)* **$65 [≃£33]**

Ruark, Robert

- Grenadine Etching. Garden City, New York: Doubleday, 1947. Price-clipped dustwrapper. His 1st book. *(Chapel Hill)* **$65 [≃£33]**
- One for the Road. Garden City: Doubleday, 1949. Dustwrapper (edgeworn, several short tears). *(Antic Hay)* **$75 [≃£39]**
- Women. New York: NAL, (1967). Very thin strip of front board sunned. Dustwrapper (little sunning to spine). *(Between the Covers)* **$50 [≃£26]**

Rubens, Bernice

- The Elected Member. London: Eyre & Spottiswoode, 1969. Price-clipped dustwrapper. *(Dalian)* **£45 [≃$86]**
- I Sent a Letter to My Love. London: W.H. Allen, 1975. Dustwrapper. *(Dalian)* **£20 [≃$38]**

Runyon, Damon

- All Horse Players Die Broke. N.p.: Del Mar Turf Club, 1946. Leather (some edge stains). Tissue dustwrapper. *(Dermont)* **$25 [≃£13]**

Rushdie, Salman

- Grimus. London: Gollancz, 1974. Uncorrected proof copy. Wrappers. His 1st book. *(David Rees)* **£175 [≃$335]**
- Grimus. London: Gollancz, 1974. Dustwrapper. *(David Rees)* **£125 [≃$239]**
- Grimus. London: Gollancz, 1975. Dustwrapper. *(Lopez)* **$500 [≃£260]**
- Grimus. New York: 1975. Dustwrapper. *(David Rees)* **£50 [≃$95]**
- In Good Faith. N.p.: 1990. 1st US edition. Printed wrappers, stapled. *(Pettler & Liebermann)* **$20 [≃£10]**
- Is Nothing Sacred? Granta: 1990. Wrappers. *(David Rees)* **£6 [≃$11]**
- Is Nothing Sacred? N.p.: 1990. 1st US edition. Printed wrappers, stapled. *(Pettler & Liebermann)* **$20 [≃£10]**
- The Jaguar Smile. London: Picador, 1987. Wrappers. *(David Rees)* **£25 [≃$47]**
- The Jaguar Smile. New York: Viking, 1987. 1st American edition. 1st hardbound edition. Uncorrected proof copy. Red wrappers. *(Michael Johnson)* **£75 [≃$143]**
- The Jaguar Smile. New York: 1987. 1st hardback edition. Remainder mark on lower edge. Dustwrapper. *(David Rees)* **£20 [≃$38]**
- Midnight's Children. New York: Knopf, 1981. 1st American edition (precedes the English edition). Advance review copy. Review slip. Dustwrapper. *(Lopez)* **$200 [≃£104]**
- (Introduces) The Nehrus and the Gandhis. An Indian Dynasty, by Tariq Ali. London: Picador, 1985. Wrappers. *(Dalian)* **£15 [≃$28]**

- The Satanic Verses. London: 1988. Uncorrected proof copy. Pictorial wrappers. *(First Issues)* **£275 [≃$527]**
- The Satanic Verses. London: Penguin Viking, (1988). Uncorrected proof copy. Spine creased. *(Lopez)* **$650 [≃£338]**
- The Satanic Verses. London: Viking, 1988. Uncorrected proof copy. Wrappers. *(David Rees)* **£225 [≃$431]**
- The Satanic Verses. London: Viking, 1988. One of 100 signed. Goatskin and buckram (buckram on lower board slightly scratched). Issued simultaneously with the trade edition. *(Moorhouse)* **£475 [≃$911]**
- The Satanic Verses. London: Viking, 1988. One of 100 signed. Quarter goatskin. Plain dustwrapper (slightly torn). *(David Rees)* **£375 [≃$719]**
- The Satanic Verses. London: 1988. Dustwrapper. *(Roberts)* **£20 [≃$38]**
- The Satanic Verses. New York: Viking, (1989). 1st American edition. Advance review copy with promotional material laid in. Dustwrapper. *(Lopez)* **$125 [≃£65]**
- The Satanic Verses. New York: 1989. 1st US edition. Dustwrapper. *(Pettler & Liebermann)* **$100 [≃£52]**
- The Satanic Verses. New York: Viking, 1989. 1st American edition. Dustwrapper. *(Lopez)* **$100 [≃£52]**
- The Satanic Verses. New York: Viking, 1989. 1st American edition. Dustwrapper. *(Michael Johnson)* **£50 [≃$95]**
- The Satanic Verses. New York: Viking, (1989). 1st American edition. Dustwrapper. *(Lopez)* **$85 [≃£44]**
- Shame. London: Cape, (1983). Uncorrected proof copy. Signed by the author. *(Lopez)* **$500 [≃£260]**
- Shame. London: Cape, 1983. Dustwrapper. Author's signed presentation copy (6th May 1984). *(David Rees)* **£95 [≃$182]**
- Shame. London: Cape, (1983). Dustwrapper. Signed by the author. *(Lopez)* **$375 [≃£195]**
- Shame. London: Cape, 1983. Dustwrapper. *(Lewton)* **£19 [≃$36]**
- Shame. London: Cape, 1983. Dustwrapper. Booker wraparound band. *(David Rees)* **£20 [≃$38]**
- Shame. London: Cape, 1983. Dustwrapper. *(Dyke)* **£25 [≃$47]**
- Shame. London: 1983. Dustwrapper. *(Egret)* **£18 [≃$34]**
- Shame. London: Cape, 1983. Dustwrapper. *(Ash)* **£25 [≃$47]**

Russell, Eric Frank

- Deep Space. London: Eyre & Spottiswoode, 1956. Dustwrapper (edge damaged with slight loss to spine). *(Paul Brown)* **£30 [≃$57]**

Ryder, Jonathan

- Pseudonym used by Robert Ludlum, q.v.

Sackville-West, Edward

- Simpson. A Life. London: Heinemann, 1931. Bookplate. Dustwrapper (slightly tanned and chipped). *(Dalian)* **£35 [≃$67]**

Sackville-West, Vita

- Aphra Behn. London: 1927. Dustwrapper (frayed, tanned). *(Ellis)* **£50 [≃$95]**
- Collected Poems. Volume One [all published]. Hogarth Press, 1933. Foredge and endpapers slightly foxed. *(Dalian)* **£35 [≃$67]**
- Daughter of France. London: Michael Joseph, 1969. Dustwrapper (very slightly rubbed). *(Dalian)* **£35 [≃$67]**
- The Death of Noble Godavary and Gottfried Kunstler. London: Benn, 1932. Printed wrappers. No dustwrapper issued. *(Dalian)* **£25 [≃$47]**
- The Edwardians. London: Hogarth Press, 1930. One of 125 signed. Vellum backed cloth boards (covers lightly soiled, some stubbing at corners). *(Any Amount)* **£140 [≃$268]**
- The Edwardians. London: Hogarth Press, 1930. Foredge slightly foxed. Endpapers slightly browned. Dustwrapper (chipped). *(Dalian)* **£65 [≃$124]**
- The Heir. Privately Printed: [1922]. One of 100 signed. Some foxing, endpapers browned. A few pages carelessly opened. Corners slightly rubbed, spine slightly soiled. *(Virgo)* **£300 [≃$575]**
- The Land. London: Heinemann, 1926. Dustwrapper. *(Houle)* **$175 [≃£91]**
- The Land. London: Heinemann, 1926. Slight bubble to front cover. Dustwrapper (slightly browned and soiled, one small closed tear at head of spine). *(Virgo)* **£55 [≃$105]**
- Orchard and Vineyard. London: 1921. Cloth backed boards, unopened (top corners slightly bumped, spine label very slightly tanned). *(Ellis)* **£120 [≃$230]**
- Orchard and Vineyard. London: John Lane, 1921. Endpapers browned, traces of bookplate removal. Covers slightly soiled, corners bruised. *(Virgo)* **£80 [≃$153]**
- Poems of East and West. London: John Lane, 1917. Bookplate removed from pastedown. Cracking between pages 16 & 17. Covers

marked and soiled, corners bumped and rubbed. Her 1st book. *(Virgo)* **£70 [≃$134]**

- Saint Joan of Arc. London: Cobden-Sanderson, 1936. Spine and covers slightly dusty. *(Dalian)* **£20 [≃$38]**
- Sissinghurst. Hogarth Press: 1931. One of 500 signed. Boards (spine ends a little rubbed). *(Words Etcetera)* **£185 [≃$355]**
- Sissinghurst. Sissinghurst Castle: The National Trust, 1972. 1st trade edition. Printed wrappers. *(Dalian)* **£16 [≃$30]**
- Solitude. London: Hogarth Press, 1938. Dustwrapper (some soiling, lacks 1-inch piece at foot of spine). *(Woolmer)* **$75 [≃£39]**
- The Women's Land Army. London: Michael Joseph, 1944. Endpapers very slightly foxed. Dustwrapper (slightly nicked). *(Dalian)* **£45 [≃$86]**

Sadleir, Michael

- Forlorn Sunset. London: Constable, 1947. Dustwrapper. *(Paul Brown)* **£15 [≃$28]**

Saki (H.H. Munro)

- Reginald. London: Methuen, 1904. Endpapers slightly browned. Covers marked, spine ends slightly worn, *(Dalian)* **£45 [≃$86]**
- The Square Egg and Other Sketches. London: John Lane; The Bodley Head, 1924. Endpapers slightly browned. Covers marked and rubbed. *(Dalian)* **£45 [≃$86]**
- The Toys of Peace and Other Papers. London: John Lane; The Bodley Head, 1919. Foredge slightly foxed. Covers slightly rubbed. *(Dalian)* **£35 [≃$67]**

Salinger, J.D.

- The Catcher in the Rye. Boston: Little, Brown, 1951. Dustwrapper (one inch closed tear at bottom of front panel). *(Chapel Hill)* **$1,500 [≃£781]**
- The Catcher in the Rye. London: 1951. 1st English edition. Dustwrapper (head of spine panel slightly rubbed, back panel trifle dusty). *(Georges)* **£250 [≃$479]**
- The Catcher in the Rye. London: Hamish Hamilton, 1951. Name on endpaper. Top and foredges spotted. Dustwrapper (slightly chipped). *(Moorhouse)* **£110 [≃$211]**
- For Esme - With Love and Squalor. London: Hamish Hamilton, 1953. Top edge slightly dusty. Dustwrapper (spine slightly browned). Published in the US as Nine Stories. *(Moorhouse)* **£120 [≃$230]**
- For Esme - with Love and Squalor and Other Stories. London: 1953. 1st English edition (published in America as 'Nine Stories'). Some foxing at ends. Dustwrapper (head of spine panel slightly frayed). *(Georges)* **£75 [≃$143]**
- Franny and Zooey. London: Heinemann, 1962. Dustwrapper. *(Paul Brown)* **£7.50 [≃$15]**
- Franny and Zooey. London: Heinemann, 1962. Dustwrapper. *(Dalian)* **£25 [≃$47]**

Salter, James

- The Arm of Flesh. New York: Harper, (1961). Bottom rear corner slightly bumped. Dustwrapper (a few nicks at head, two tears on rear panel). *(Lopez)* **$135 [≃£70]**
- Solo Faces. Boston: LB, (1979). Dustwrapper. Inscribed by the author. *(Lopez)* **$40 [≃£20]**

Samphire

- Samphire. Edited by Michael Butler and Kemble William. Ipswich: 1968-81. Numbers 1-40, all published. *(Blakeney)* **£160 [≃$307]**

Sanchez, Thomas

- Mile Zero. New York: Knopf, 1989. Uncorrected proof copy. Wrappers. Signed by the author. *(Nouveau)* **$100 [≃£52]**
- Rabbit Boss. New York: Knopf, 1973. Dustwrapper. Signed by the author. His 1st book. *(Nouveau)* **$135 [≃£70]**

Sandburg, Carl

- The American Songbag. New York: (1927). Name stamps. Signed by the author. *(Polyanthos)* **$60 [≃£31]**
- Cornhuskers. New York: 1918. 1st state. *(Polyanthos)* **$30 [≃£15]**
- Potato Face. New York: 1930. Price-clipped dustwrapper (spine extremities little chipped, few small edge tears). *(Polyanthos)* **$45 [≃£23]**
- Remembrance Rock. New York: Harcourt Brace, 1948. 1st American edition. One of 1000 signed. 2 vols. Slipcase (slightly knocked). *(First Issues)* **£65 [≃$124]**
- Slabs of the Sunburnt West. New York: Harcourt, Brace, (1922). 1st issue. Spine slightly faded. Dustwrapper (slightly chipped). Handbill announcing a reading by Sandburg (1923) inserted. *(Bromer)* **$275 [≃£143]**

Sansom, William

- Among the Dahlias. London: Hogarth, 1957. Dustwrapper. *(Paul Brown)* **£10 [≃$19]**

- The Birth of a Story. London: Hogarth Press, 1972. Dustwrapper. *(Dalian)* **£25 [≃$47]**
- Fire Over London. The Story of the London Fire Service, 1940-41. London: Hutchinson for the London County Council, (1941). Wrappers (slightly creased and soiled). Published anonymously. *(Dalian)* **£85 [≃$163]**
- Fireman Flower and Other Stories. London: Hogarth Press, 1944. Name on endpaper. Dustwrapper (slightly chipped). His 1st book. *(Words Etcetera)* **£45 [≃$86]**
- Goodbye. London: Hogarth, 1966. Price-clipped dustwrapper. *(Paul Brown)* **£7.50 [≃$15]**
- The Last Hours of Sandra Lee. London: Hogarth, 1961. Dustwrapper. *(Paul Brown)* **£7.50 [≃$15]**
- Lord Love Us. London: Hogarth Press, 1954. Dustwrapper. *(Dalian)* **£16 [≃$30]**
- The Loving Eye. London: Hogarth Press, 1956. Dustwrapper (slightly soiled). *(Dalian)* **£15 [≃$28]**

Sapper (H.C. McNeile)

- The Island of Terror. London: 1931. Lower cover slightly discoloured. Dustwrapper (one tear at foredge at head of rear panel). *(Words Etcetera)* **£75 [≃$143]**
- The Lieutenant & Others. London: Hodder, 1915. *(Any Amount)* **£18 [≃$34]**
- See also Fairlie, Gerald.

Saroyan, William

- The Adventures of Wesley Jackson. London: Faber, 1947. 1st English edition. Dustwrapper very slightly nicked, slightly dusty). *(Dalian)* **£30 [≃$57]**
- The Adventures of Wesley Jackson. London: Faber, 1947. 1st English edition. Dustwrapper. *(Limestone Hills)* **$65 [≃£33]**
- The Assyrian and Other Stories. London: Faber, 1950. Dustwrapper (slightly rubbed, very slightly nicked). *(Dalian)* **£25 [≃$47]**
- The Beautiful People and Other Plays. London: Faber, 1943. Dustwrapper (slightly dusty). *(Dalian)* **£30 [≃$57]**
- Boys and Girls Together. London: Peter Davies, 1963. Dustwrapper (slightly nicked). *(Dalian)* **£25 [≃$47]**
- Days of Life and Death and Escape to the Moon. London: Michael Joseph, 1970. Dustwrapper. *(Dalian)* **£16 [≃$30]**
- Dear Baby. London: Faber, 1945. Dustwrapper (very slightly rubbed). *(Dalian)* **£20 [≃$38]**
- Inhale & Exhale. New York: Random House, 1936. Dustwrapper (missing a 1/2 inch chip at top of spine, a few other tiny chips and tears). *(Alphabet)* **$90 [≃£46]**
- My Name is Aram. New York: 1940. Dustwrapper. *(Pettler & Liebermann)* **$75 [≃£39]**
- The Saroyan Special. Selected Short Stories. New York: 1948. 1st printing, with coloured binding. Coloured pictorial cloth (rear cover slightly edge soiled). Dust- wrapper (spine little sunned, extremities slightly chipped, one short tear, small piece missing from edge). *(Polyanthos)* **$60 [≃£31]**

Sassoon, Siegfried

- The Augustan Books of Modern Poetry. (Selected Poems). London: Benn, (1925). White printed wrappers (very slightly dusty). *(Dalian)* **£20 [≃$38]**
- The Heart's Journey. New York: 1927. One of 590 signed by the author. Dustwrapper (a few nicks). *(Ellis)* **£200 [≃$383]**
- The Heart's Journey. New York: Crosby Gaige, 1927. One of 500 signed. *(Black Sun)* **$200 [≃£104]**
- An Octave. Shenval Press: 1966. One of 350. Slipcase. *(David Rees)* **£50 [≃$95]**
- Poems by Pinchbeck Lyre. London: 1931. One of 1000. *(Buckley)* **£30 [≃$57]**
- Poems by Pinchbeck Lyre. London: Duckworth, 1931. Some foxing throughout. *(David Rees)* **£30 [≃$57]**
- Poems Newly Selected 1916-1935. London: Faber, 1940. Endpapers very slightly browned. Dustwrapper (slightly tanned). *(Dalian)* **£25 [≃$47]**
- The Weald of Youth. London: 1942. Dustwrapper (faintly spotted). *(Buckley)* **£30 [≃$57]**

Saville, Malcolm

- The Ambermere Treasure. London: Lutterworth, 1953. Dustwrapper. *(Green Meadow)* **£30 [≃$57]**
- Come to Devon. London: Benn, 1969. Dustwrapper. *(Green Meadow)* **£30 [≃$57]**
- The Elusive Grasshopper. London: Newnes, 1951. Dustwrapper. *(Green Meadow)* **£35 [≃$67]**
- The Flying Fish Adventure. London: Murray, 1950. Dustwrapper. *(Green Meadow)* **£35 [≃$67]**
- King of Kings. London: Nelson, 1958. Dustwrapper. *(Green Meadow)* **£20 [≃$38]**
- Lone Pine London. London: Newnes, 1957. Dustwrapper. *(Green Meadow)* **£35 [≃$67]**

- The Long Passage. London: Evans, 1954. Dustwrapper. *(Green Meadow)* **£25 [≃$47]**
- The Man with Three Fingers. London: Newnes, 1966. Dustwrapper. *(Green Meadow)* **£35 [≃$67]**
- Mystery Mine. London: Newnes, 1959. Dustwrapper. *(Green Meadow)* **£27.50 [≃$53]**
- The Neglected Mountain. London: Newnes, 1953. Dustwrapper. *(Green Meadow)* **£25 [≃$47]**
- A Palace for the Buckinghams. London: Evans, 1963. Dustwrapper. *(Green Meadow)* **£25 [≃$47]**
- Redshank's Warning. London: Lutterworth, 1948. Dustwrapper. *(Green Meadow)* **£25 [≃$47]**
- The Secret of the Gorge. London: Newnes, 1958. Dustwrapper. *(Green Meadow)* **£35 [≃$67]**
- The Sign of the Alpine Rose. London: Lutterworth, 1950. Dustwrapper (slightly chipped). *(Green Meadow)* **£25 [≃$47]**
- The Thin Grey Man. London: Macmillan, 1966. Pictorial boards. *(Green Meadow)* **£25 [≃$47]**
- Three Towers in Tuscany. London: Heinemann, 1963. Dustwrapper. *(Green Meadow)* **£17.50 [≃$34]**
- Treasure at the Mill. London: Newnes, 1957. Dustwrapper. *(Green Meadow)* **£35 [≃$67]**
- Where's My Girl? London: Collins, 1972. Dustwrapper. *(Green Meadow)* **£35 [≃$67]**
- Wings Over Witchend. London: Newnes, 1956. Dustwrapper. *(Green Meadow)* **£27.50 [≃$53]**

Savoy, Willard

- Alien Land. New York: 1949. Dustwrapper (chipped, frayed, soiled). His 1st book. *(King)* **$45 [≃£23]**

Sayer, Paul

- The Comforts of Madness. London: 1988. Dustwrapper. *(First Issues)* **£20 [≃$38]**
- The Comforts of Madness. London: Constable, 1988. Dustwrapper. His 1st book. *(Moorhouse)* **£35 [≃$67]**

Sayers, Dorothy L.

- An Account of Lord Mortimer Wimsey. The Hermit of the Wash ... Bristol: 1816 (actually OUP 1937). Wrappers (browned around spine). TLS by author inserted. *(Any Amount)* **£225 [≃$431]**
- Catholic Tales and Christian Songs. London: 1918. Edges and endpapers foxed, some internal foxing. Card covers (browned, thin strip detached from foredge of upper cover). Dustwrapper (rubbed, frayed, slightly tanned, lacks piece at base of spine). *(Ellis)* **£150 [≃$287]**
- Catholic Tales. Oxford: Blackwell, 1918. Wrappers over stiff boards (spine slightly wrinkled, a few marks). *(Any Amount)* **£100 [≃$191]**
- The Devil to Pay. Canterbury: 1939. Acting edition (precedes 1st trade edition). Wrappers. Signed by the author. *(Ellis)* **£100 [≃$191]**
- The Five Red Herrings. London: 1931. Spine faded and slightly worn at top. *(Buckley)* **£25 [≃$47]**
- (Introduces) The Floating Admiral [by members of the English Detection Club]. Garden City: Doubleday Crime Club, 1932. 1st American edition. Name. Dustwrapper (slight smudge on spine). *(Mordida)* **$200 [≃£104]**
- Further Papers on Dante. London: Methuen, 1957. Dustwrapper (very slightly dusty and nicked). *(Dalian)* **£35 [≃$67]**
- Gaudy Night. London: Gollancz, 1935. Small bookseller's label on rear pastedown. Dust- wrapper (a few minor tears). *(Georges)* **£250 [≃$479]**
- In the Teeth of the Evidence. London: Gollancz, 1939. Dustwrapper (spine slightly darkened), bright. *(Mordida)* **$800 [≃£416]**
- In the Teeth of the Evidence and Other Stories. New York: Harcourt, 1940. 1st US edition. Edges foxed. Dustwrapper. *(Janus)* **$110 [≃£57]**
- The Just Vengeance. London: Gollancz, 1946. The cloth edition. Black cloth. Dustwrapper (torn and soiled). *(Dalian)* **£25 [≃$47]**
- The Just Vengeance. London: Gollancz, 1946. Orange printed wrappers (slightly soiled and creased). *(Dalian)* **£15 [≃$28]**
- The Just Vengeance. Lichfield Festival Play for 1946. Wrappers. *(Buckley)* **£20 [≃$38]**
- The Man Born to be King. London: Gollancz, 1943. Wartime paper, edges tanned. Dustwrapper (tanned, torn with loss). *(Hazeldene)* **£20 [≃$38]**
- The Poetry of Search and the Poetry of Statement and Other Posthumous Essays on Literature, Religion and Language. London: Gollancz, 1963. Dustwrapper. *(Dalian)* **£35 [≃$67]**
- The Recipe Book of the Mustard Club ... Edited by 'Gourmet'. Norwich: J. & J.

Coleman, (1926). Printed wrappers, as issued, with a letter from Coleman's tipped in. *(Dalian)* **£125 [≃$239]**

- The Story of Easter. London: Hamish Hamilton, [1955]. Coloured pictorial stiff wrappers. *(Limestone Hills)* **$45 [≃£23]**
- The Story of Noah's Ark. The Picture Painted by Fritz Wegner. London: Hamish Hamilton, n.d. Decorative wrappers (a little worn & soiled). Illustrator's presentation copy. *(Holmes)* **$125 [≃£65]**
- Strong Meat. London: Hodder & Stoughton, 1939. 1st edition in book form. Erratum slip. Wrappers. *(Limestone Hills)* **$20 [≃£10]**
- The Unpleasantness at the Bellona Club. London: 1928. Spine ends rubbed. *(Ellis)* **£150 [≃$287]**
- Unpopular Opinions. London: Gollancz, 1946. Dustwrapper (faded and soiled). *(Dalian)* **£18 [≃$34]**
- Unpopular Opinions. London: Gollancz, 1946. Dustwrapper. *(Limestone Hills)* **$50 [≃£26]**
- The Zeal of Thy House. London: Gollancz, 1937. Foredge and pages slightly foxed. Covers slightly marked. Dustwrapper (torn). *(Dalian)* **£25 [≃$47]**

Sayles, John

- The Anarchists' Convention. Boston: 1979. Publisher's release. Signed by the author. *(Polyanthos)* **$35 [≃£18]**
- The Anarchists' Convention. Boston: 1979. Dustwrapper (light rubbing). *(Pettler & Liebermann)* **$45 [≃£23]**

Scannell, Vernon

- The Fight. London: Nevill, 1953. Dustwrapper (few tears on folds, back panel discoloured). *(Glyn's)* **£25 [≃$47]**
- Of Love & Music. Mapletree Private Press: 1980. One of 450 signed by the author. Dustwrapper. *(Buckley)* **£15 [≃$28]**

Scarfe, Francis

- Forty Poems and Ballads. London: Fortune Press, (1941). Spine label dull. Dustwrapper (slightly dusty and tanned). *(Dalian)* **£20 [≃$38]**

Schmidt, Michael

- Black Building. Oxford: Carcanet Press, 1969. Wrappers, one small tear. His 1st book. *(Moorhouse)* **£5 [≃$9]**

Schulberg, Budd

- The Disenchanted. London: Bodley Head, 1951. Spine slightly faded. Dustwrapper (chipped and soiled). *(Dalian)* **£25 [≃$47]**

Schwartz, Delmore

- Genesis. Book One [all published]. New York: New Directions, 1943. Endpapers a touch browned. Dustwrapper (slightly frayed and browned). *(Ash)* **£40 [≃$76]**
- Genesis. US: 1943. 1st US edition. Dustwrapper (patchily tanned, chipped). *(Ellis)* **£70 [≃$134]**
- In Dreams Begin Responsibilities. CT: New Directions, (1938). One of 1000. Dustwrapper (one tear mended internally, three tiny tears, spine extremities very slightly rubbed). His 1st book. *(Polyanthos)* **$100 [≃£52]**
- Shenandoah. CT: New Directions, 1941. Wrappers. Price-clipped dustwrapper (spine slightly sunned). *(Polyanthos)* **$55 [≃£28]**
- Shenandoah. Norfolk: New Directions, 1941. Hardbound issue. Bookplate. Dustwrapper (a bit faded along spine). *(Alphabet)* **$100 [≃£52]**
- Summer Knowledge. New York: 1959. Name. Dustwrapper (tiny tear, slightly edge rubbed, rear panel little soiled). *(Polyanthos)* **$35 [≃£18]**
- Summer Knowledge. New York: Doubleday, 1959. Dustwrapper (slightly worn). *(Ash)* **£20 [≃$38]**
- Vaudeville for a Princess & Other Poems. New York: New Directions, 1950. One of 1600. Price-clipped dustwrapper. *(Alphabet)* **$150 [≃£78]**
- The World is a Wedding and Other Stories. London: John Lehmann, 1949. Dustwrapper. *(Dalian)* **£35 [≃$67]**

Scott, Paul

- The Alien Sky. Eyre & Spottiswoode, 1953. Bookseller's label. Price-clipped dustwrapper (slightly chipped). *(Tiger Books)* **£45 [≃$86]**
- The Alien Sky. London: Eyre & Spottiswoode, 1953. Dustwrapper (slightly chipped, spine rubbed). *(David Rees)* **£35 [≃$67]**
- The Bender. London: Secker & Warburg, 1963. Dustwrapper (two short clean tears foot of upper panel). Signed and inscribed by the author. *(Sklaroff)* **£50 [≃$95]**
- The Bender. New York: Morrow, 1963. 1st American edition. Dustwrapper. *(Lopez)* **$35 [≃£18]**
- The Birds of Paradise. London: 1962. Dustwrapper (faintly sunned). *(Buckley)* **£25 [≃$47]**

- The Birds of Paradise. London: Eyre & Spottiswoode, 1962. Dustwrapper. *(Dalian)* **£20 [≃$38]**
- The Birds of Paradise. London: Eyre & Spottiswoode, 1962. Price-clipped dustwrapper. *(Sklaroff)* **£15 [≃$28]**
- The Corrida at San Feliu. London: 1964. Dustwrapper. *(First Issues)* **£10 [≃$19]**
- The Corrida at San Feliu. London: 1964. Dustwrapper. *(Buckley)* **£20 [≃$38]**
- The Day of the Scorpion. London: 1968. Uncorrected proof copy. Wrappers (rubbed and creased at spine, some ink notes). *(Ellis)* **£75 [≃$143]**
- The Day of the Scorpion. London: Heinemann, 1968. Dustwrapper (lower panel very slightly defective). *(Ash)* **£30 [≃$57]**
- A Division of the Spoils. New York: Morrow, 1975. Uncorrected proof copy. Wrappers. *(Lopez)* **$75 [≃£39]**
- A Division of the Spoils. London: Heinemann, 1975. Dustwrapper. *(Virgo)* **£22.50 [≃$44]**
- A Division of the Spoils. London: 1975. Spine very slightly creased. dustwrapper. *(Clearwater)* **£35 [≃$67]**
- Johnny Sahib. London: Eyre & Spottiswoode, 1952. Dustwrapper (slightly rubbed). His 1st book. *(Whiteson)* **£95 [≃$182]**
- Johnny Sahib. Eyre & Spottiswoode, 1952. Bookseller's label. Price-clipped dustwrapper (very slightly frayed). *(Tiger Books)* **£65 [≃$124]**
- Johnny Sahib. London: 1952. Foredges foxed. Dustwrapper (slightly chipped and rubbed). *(Egret)* **£70 [≃$134]**
- A Male Child. Eyre & Spottiswoode, 1956. Dustwrapper. *(Tiger Books)* **£35 [≃$67]**
- A Male Child. London: 1956. Dustwrapper. *(First Issues)* **£60 [≃$115]**
- Pillars of Salt [in] Four Jewish Plays. Edited by H.F. Rubinstein. London: Gollancz, 1948. Dustwrapper (slightly torn). *(Moorhouse)* **£40 [≃$76]**
- Staying On. London: Heinemann, (1977). Dustwrapper. *(Virgo)* **£60 [≃$115]**
- Staying On. London: Heinemann, (1977). Dustwrapper. *(Lopez)* **$75 [≃£39]**
- Staying On. London: 1977. Dustwrapper. *(Ellis)* **£50 [≃$95]**
- Staying On. London: 1977. Dustwrapper. *(Clearwater)* **£60 [≃$115]**
- Staying On. London: Heinemann, 1977. Dustwrapper. *(Ash)* **£50 [≃$95]**

Scott, Zachary

- John Emery ... see under Steinbeck, John.

Selby, Hubert, Jr.

- The Demon. Playboy Press, 1976. Dustwrapper (lightly rubbed). *(Nouveau)* **$20 [≃£10]**
- Last Exit to Brooklyn. New York: Grove Press, [1964]. Uncorrected proof copy. Printed wrappers, spiral bound. *(Dermont)* **$250 [≃£130]**
- Last Exit to Brooklyn. New York: Grove, 1964. Name. Dustwrapper. *(Nouveau)* **$40 [≃£20]**
- Last Exit to Brooklyn. London: Calder, 1966. Dustwrapper (worn). *(Paul Brown)* **£15 [≃$28]**
- The Room. New York: 1971. Dustwrapper. *(Polyanthos)* **$25 [≃£13]**
- The Room. London: Calder, 1972. Dustwrapper. *(Paul Brown)* **£10 [≃$19]**

Selvon, Samuel

- A Brighter Sun. London: Wingate, 1952. Cloth slightly spotted. Label removed from endpaper. Dustwrapper (frayed and torn). His 1st book. *(Dalian)* **£35 [≃$67]**
- Turn Again Tiger. London: MacGibbon & Kee, 1958. Dustwrapper. *(Dalian)* **£35 [≃$67]**

Seth, Vikram

- From Heaven Lake. London: Chatto & Windus, 1983. Dustwrapper. His 1st book. *(Dalian)* **£45 [≃$86]**
- The Golden Gate. London: Faber, 1986. Dustwrapper. Signed by the author. *(Dalian)* **£35 [≃$67]**

Settle, Mary Lee

- The Killing Ground. New York: 1982. Advance Reading Copy. Printed wrappers. Author's signed presentation copy. *(Polyanthos)* **$40 [≃£20]**

Sexton, Anne

- The Book of Folly. Boston: Houghton, Mifflin, 1972. One of 500 signed. Tissue jacket (lightly edgeworn). Slipcase. *(Chapel Hill)* **$75 [≃£39]**
- The Book of Folly. Boston: Houghton, Mifflin, 1972. One of 500 signed. Cloth and boards. Slipcase. *(Antic Hay)* **$75 [≃£39]**
- The Book of Folly. Boston: 1972. One of 500 signed. Dustwrapper. Slipcase. *(Dermont)* **$50 [≃£26]**
- To Bedlam and Part Way Back. Boston:

Houghton, 1960. Dustwrapper (few short tears). Her 1st book. *(Nouveau)* **$100 [≃£52]**
- Transformations. Boston: Houghton, Mifflin, 1971. One of 500 signed. Buckram, a.e.g. Slipcase (small stain). *(Antic Hay)* **$65 [≃£33]**

Shaara, Michael
- The Killer Angels. New York: David McKay, (1974). Advance reading copy. Printed wrappers. *(Lopez)* **$150 [≃£78]**

Shaffer, Anthony
- Sleuth. New York: Dodd, Mead, [1970]. 1st American edition. Dustwrapper. *(Dermont)* **$30 [≃£15]**

Shaffer, Peter
- Amadeus. New York: 1981. 1st US edition. Dustwrapper. *(Buckley)* **£15 [≃$28]**
- Equus. London: 1973. Dustwrapper (slightly abraded). *(Egret)* **£25 [≃$47]**
- Equus. London: Deutsch, 1973. Dustwrapper. *(Lewton)* **£30 [≃$57]**
- Five Finger Exercise. London: Hamilton, 1958. Dustwrapper. His 1st book. *(Lewton)* **£27.50 [≃$53]**
- Five Finger Exercise. London: Hamish Hamilton, 1958. Large inscription on front fly. Dustwrapper. *(Ash)* **£20 [≃$38]**
- The Royal Hunt of the Sun. London: Hamish Hamilton, 1964. Dustwrapper (slightly nicked). *(David Rees)* **£18 [≃$34]**

Shange, Ntozake
- A Daughter's Geography. New York: 1983. One of 250 signed. Dustwrapper. Slipcase. *(Pettler & Liebermann)* **$65 [≃£33]**

Shannon, Dell
- Pseudonym used by Elizabeth Linington, q.v.

Shapiro, Karl
- Edsel. Bernard Geis Associates: [1971]. Uncorrected proof copy. Spiral bound (light soiling to wrappers). *(Dermont)* **$125 [≃£65]**
- V-Letter and Other Poems. Reynal & Hitchcock: 1944. Dustwrapper (spine darkened, one very short tear). *(Nouveau)* **$60 [≃£31]**

Sharpe, Tom
- Ancestral Vices. London: 1980. Dustwrapper. *(Lewton)* **£14 [≃$26]**
- Blott on the Landscape. London: Secker, 1975. Dustwrapper. *(Dyke)* **£55 [≃$105]**
- Blott on the Landscape. London: Secker & Warburg, 1975. 4-word gift inscription. Dustwrapper. *(Alphabet)* **$65 [≃£33]**
- Blott on the Landscape. London: Secker & Warburg, 1975. Small stamps on prelims. Dustwrapper. *(Ash)* **£50 [≃$95]**
- Blott on the Landscape. London: Secker & Warburg, 1975. Dustwrapper. *(Limestone Hills)* **$80 [≃£41]**
- Blott on the Landscape. Secker & Warburg, 1975. Embossed stamp on 1st 2 prelims. Dustwrapper. *(Moorhouse)* **£25 [≃$47]**
- The Great Pursuit. London: S&W, 1977. Dustwrapper. *(Lewton)* **£24 [≃$46]**
- (Contributes) In the Third Person, [to] Triangles. Original Stories edited by Alex Hamilton. London: Hutchinson, 1973. Dustwrapper. Name spelt incorrectly as Sharp. *(Moorhouse)* **£30 [≃$57]**
- Indecent Exposure. London: S&W, 1973. Dustwrapper. *(Lewton)* **£80 [≃$153]**
- Porterhouse Blue. London: Secker & Warburg, 1974. Uncorrected proof copy. Wrappers, with publisher's label. *(David Rees)* **£60 [≃$115]**
- Riotous Assembly. New York: Viking, (1971). Small crease to spine. Dustwrapper (usual spine fading). His 1st book. *(Between the Covers)* **$35 [≃£18]**
- The Throwback. London: S&W, 1978. Dustwrapper. *(Lewton)* **£20 [≃$38]**
- The Throwback. London: Secker, 1978. Dustwrapper (slightly creased). *(Dyke)* **£30 [≃$57]**
- Vintage Stuff. London: 1982. Dustwrapper. *(Lewton)* **£11.50 [≃$23]**
- Vintage Stuff. London: Secker, 1983. Dustwrapper. *(Dyke)* **£15 [≃$28]**
- Vintage Stuff. Secker & Warburg, 1982. Top edge slightly marked. Dustwrapper. *(Moorhouse)* **£7 [≃$13]**
- Wilt. London: Secker, 1976. Dustwrapper. *(Dyke)* **£35 [≃$67]**
- The Wilt Alternative. London: Secker, 1979. Dustwrapper. Signed by the author. *(Dyke)* **£45 [≃$86]**
- The Wilt Alternative. London: S&W, 1979. Dustwrapper. *(Lewton)* **£17.50 [≃$34]**
- Wilt on High. London: Secker, 1985. Dustwrapper. *(Dyke)* **£15 [≃$28]**

Shaw, Irwin
- The Assassin. New York: Random House, [1946]. Dustwrapper (moderate edgewear, small stain). *(Antic Hay)* **$45 [≃£23]**
- Mixed Company. London: Cape, 1952. Dust-

wrapper (slightly dusty). *(Dalian)* **£16 [≃$30]**

- Two Weeks in Another Town. London: Cape, 1960. Advance proof copy. Plain green wrappers (slightly faded). *(Dalian)* **£20 [≃$38]**
- Two Weeks in Another Town. London: Cape, 1960. Dustwrapper. *(Dalian)* **£15 [≃$28]**
- The Young Lions. New York: Random House, [1948]. Dustwrapper. *(Chapel Hill)* **$50 [≃£26]**
- The Young Lions. New York: Random House, (1948). Dustwrapper (small chips, nicks). *(Houle)* **$65 [≃£33]**

Shaw, Robert

- The Flag. London: Chatto & Windus, 1965. Dustwrapper (slightly dusty). *(Dalian)* **£16 [≃$30]**
- The Hiding Place. London: Chatto & Windus, 1959. Dustwrapper. Book Society wraparound band. His 1st book. *(Dalian)* **£35 [≃$67]**
- The Man in the Glass Booth. London: Chatto & Windus, 1967. Dustwrapper. *(Dalian)* **£15 [≃$28]**

Shepard, Lucius

- Green Eyes. London: Chatto, 1985. 1st hardbound edition. Dustwrapper. *(Michael Johnson)* **£40 [≃$76]**

Shepherd, Michael

- Pseudonym used by Robert Ludlum, q.v.

Shute, Nevil

- In the Wet. London: Heinemann, 1953. Dustwrapper. *(Limestone Hills)* **$45 [≃£23]**
- On the Beach. London: Heinemann, 1957. Dustwrapper. *(Limestone Hills)* **$85 [≃£44]**
- On the Beach. London: Heinemann, 1957. Dustwrapper (slightly rubbed). *(Paul Brown)* **£25 [≃$47]**
- Stephen Morris. London: Heinemann, 1961. Uncorrected proof copy. Wrappers. Dustwrapper. *(Limestone Hills)* **$55 [≃£28]**

Shuttle, Penelope

- All the Usual Hours of Sleeping. London: Calder, 1969. Dustwrapper. *(Hazeldene)* **£18 [≃$34]**

Signatures

- Signatures. Work in Progress. Michigan, 1936-38. Vols 1-3. All published. Wrappers. *(Any Amount)* **£35 [≃$67]**

Sillitoe, Alan

- Barbarians and Other Poems. Turret Books: 1973. One of 100 signed. Dustwrapper. *(Dalian)* **£30 [≃$57]**
- The Death of William Posters. London: 1965. Dustwrapper (faintly edge browned). *(Buckley)* **£20 [≃$38]**
- The Incredible Fencing Fleas. London: Robson Books, 1978. Laminate pictorial boards. No dustwrapper issued. *(Dalian)* **£35 [≃$67]**
- The Loneliness of the Long-Distance Runner. London: Allen, 1959. Dustwrapper (very slight wear). *(Ash)* **£100 [≃$191]**
- The Rats. London: Allen, 1960. Dustwrapper. Signed by the author. *(Whiteson)* **£24 [≃$46]**
- Storm: New Poems. London: 1974. Price-clipped dustwrapper. *(Buckley)* **£25 [≃$47]**
- Travels in Nihilon. London: 1971. Dustwrapper. *(Buckley)* **£15 [≃$28]**

Simenon, Georges

- Maigret Goes to School. London: Hamish Hamilton, 1957. 1st English edition. Dustwrapper (short closed tear). *(Mordida)* **$35 [≃£18]**
- Maigret in Society. London: Hamish Hamilton, 1962. 1st English edition. Dustwrapper. *(Mordida)* **$35 [≃£18]**
- Maigret's Failure. London: Hamilton, 1962. Dustwrapper. *(Janus)* **$45 [≃£23]**

Simon, Roger L.

- Heir. New York: Macmillan, 1968. Remainder dot. Dustwrapper. Signed by the author. His 1st book. *(Janus)* **$35 [≃£18]**

Simpson, N.F.

- Harry Bleachbaker. London: Harrap, 1976. Dustwrapper. *(Dalian)* **£15 [≃$28]**
- One Way Pendulum. London: Faber, 1960. Dustwrapper. *(Dalian)* **£16 [≃$30]**

Sims, George

- Poems. London: Fortune Press, 1944. Dustwrapper. *(Any Amount)* **£35 [≃$67]**

Sinclair, Clive

- Bibliosexuality. London: 1973. Dustwrapper (slightly rubbed). His 1st book. *(Ellis)* **£28 [≃$53]**
- Cosmetic Effects. London: Deutsch, 1989. Uncorrected proof copy. Wrappers. *(Paul Brown)* **£12.50 [≃$24]**
- Hearts of Gold. London: Allison & Busby,

1979. Dustwrapper. *(Alphabet)* **$40 [≃£20]**

Singer, Isaac Bashevis

- The Family Moskat. New York: 1950. Dustwrapper, fine. Author's signature laid in. *(Polyanthos)* **$125 [≃£65]**
- The Spinoza of Market Street. New York: Farrar, Straus & Cudahy, [1961]. Dustwrapper (usual browning spine, minor soil). *(Antic Hay)* **$40 [≃£20]**

Siodmak, Curt

- Donovan's Brain. New York: Knopf, 1943. Price-clipped dustwrapper (several tiny tears, very small internal tape repair). *(Mordida)* **$250 [≃£130]**

Sissman, L.E.

- Dying: An Introduction. Boston: Little, Brown, (1967). Dustwrapper. Author's 1st book. *(Woolmer)* **$50 [≃£26]**

Sisson, C.H.

- An Asiatic Romance. London: Gaberbocchus, 1953. Dustwrapper. His 1st book. *(Sklaroff)* **£32 [≃$61]**

Sitwell, Edith

- Augustan Books of Modern Poetry. (Selected Poems). London: Benn, (1926). The correct 1st edition in white printed wrappers. Covers slightly dusty and creased. *(Dalian)* **£15 [≃$28]**
- A Book of Winter. London: Macmillan, 1950. Dustwrapper (very slightly dusty). *(Dalian)* **£25 [≃$47]**
- The Canticle of the Rose. New York: (1949). Dustwrapper (chipped). Inscribed by the author. *(Black Sun)* **$80 [≃£41]**
- Clowns' Houses. Oxford: Blackwell, 1918. Endpapers slightly browned. Small name on endpaper. Wrappers (very slightly dusty). *(Dalian)* **£85 [≃$163]**
- Collected Poems. London: Macmillan, 1957. Dustwrapper (slightly tanned). *(Dalian)* **£25 [≃$47]**
- Fanfare for Elizabeth. London: 1946. Dustwrapper. Author's signed presentation copy. *(Words Etcetera)* **£25 [≃$47]**
- Five Variations on a Theme. London: Duckworth, 1933. Dustwrapper. *(Dalian)* **£45 [≃$86]**
- Green Song and Other Poems. London: Macmillan, 1944. Endpapers vers slightly foxed. Dustwrapper. *(Dalian)* **£25 [≃$47]**
- The Outcasts. London: Macmillan, 1962. Dustwrapper. *(Dalian)* **£25 [≃$47]**
- Poems Old and New. London: 1940. Printed boards. Dustwrapper. *(Roberts)* **£9 [≃$17]**
- Poor Men's Music. London: Fore Publications, 1950. Wrappers. Light soiling. Signed by the author. *(Chapel Hill)* **$150 [≃£78]**
- Popular Song. London: Faber, 1928. Signed limited edition. Boards slightly dull. *(Whiteson)* **£30 [≃$57]**
- Popular Song. London: Faber, Ariel Poem, 1928. Large Paper signed. *(Whiteson)* **£30 [≃$57]**
- The Queens and the Hive. London: Macmillan, 1962. Dustwrapper. *(Dalian)* **£45 [≃$86]**
- Rustic Elegies. London: Duckworth, 1927. Dustwrapper (very slightly rubbed). *(Dalian)* **£65 [≃$124]**

Sitwell, Osbert

- Collected Stories. London: Duckworth & Macmillan, 1953. Dustwrapper (very slightly rubbed). *(Dalian)* **£25 [≃$47]**
- Demos the Emperor. London: Macmillan, 1949. Signed limited edition. Wrappers. Envelope. *(Whiteson)* **£22 [≃$42]**
- Dumb-Animal. London: Duckworth, 1930. One of 110 signed by the author. Buckram, t.e.g., unopened. Dustwrapper. *(Sotheran's)* **£125 [≃$239]**
- Miss Mew. London: 1929. One of 101 signed. Boards. Author's presentation copy. *(Whiteson)* **£45 [≃$86]**
- Queen Mary and Others. London: Michael Joseph, 1974. Dustwrapper. *(Dalian)* **£20 [≃$38]**
- Who Killed Cock-Robin? Remarks on Poetry. London: C.W. Daniel, 1921. The 1st issue, with the wrapper loose over boards and without printer' stamp on back. Printed paper wrappers (slight mend lower cover). *(Dalian)* **£45 [≃$86]**

Sitwell, Sacheverell

- All at Sea ... With a Preface by Osbert Sitwell. London: Duckworth, 1927. Foredge slightly foxed. Dustwrapper (chipped and soiled). *(Dalian)* **£65 [≃$124]**
- The Augustan Books of English Poetry. London: Benn, (1928). The correct 1st edition in white printed wrappers (very slightly dusty). *(Dalian)* **£20 [≃$38]**
- A Background for Domenico Scarlatti, 1685 - 1757. London: Faber, 1935. Later issue red cloth. Dustwrapper. *(Dalian)* **£45 [≃$86]**
- Canons of Giant Art. London: Faber, 1933. Dustwrapper (slightly rubbed and nicked).

(Dalian) £45 [≃$86]

- Conversation Pieces. London: Batsford, 1936. Foredge and endpapers slightly browned. *(Dalian)* **£35 [≃$67]**
- The Cyder Feast. 1927. One of 165 signed. Unopened. Dustwrapper (some discolouration of top half of both panels, spine faded). *(Words Etcetera)* **£85 [≃$163]**
- Edinburgh. With Francis Bamford. London: Faber, 1938. Dustwrapper (slightly rubbed and nicked). *(Dalian)* **£40 [≃$76]**
- Exalt the Eglantine and Other Poems. London: The Fleuron, 1926. One of 350. Inscription on endpaper. Patterned boards (spine and part of covers sunned). *(Dalian)* **£55 [≃$105]**
- For Want of the Golden City. London: Thames & Hudson, 1974. Dustwrapper. *(Dalian)* **£25 [≃$47]**
- An Indian Summer. London: Macmillan, 1982. Dustwrapper. Signed by the author. *(Dalian)* **£35 [≃$67]**
- Notebook on Twenty Canons of Giant Art. Brackley: for the author, 1975. Printed wrappers. *(Dalian)* **£45 [≃$86]**
- Ritchie, Neil: Sacheverell Sitwell. An Annotated and Descriptive Bibliography, 1916-1986. Florence: The Giardo Press, 1987. One of 400 signed by the author. Dustwrapper. *(Dalian)* **£45 [≃$86]**

Skelton, Robin

- An Irish Gathering. Dublin: Dolmen, 1964. One of 500. Spine very slightly faded. Dustwrapper. His 1st book. *(Alphabet)* **$45 [≃£23]**

Smart, Elizabeth

- By Grand Central Station I Sat Down and Wept. London: Poetry London, 1945. Dustwrapper (some rubbing to spine hinges, a few small tears and creases). Author's presentation inscription signed ES (1977), signed in full on title. *(Words Etcetera)* **£300 [≃$575]**

Smith, Dodie

- The Hundred and One Dalmatians. London: Heinemann, 1956. Dustwrapper (slightly sunned, slightly repaired). *(Ash)* **£75 [≃$143]**

Smith, Edward E.

- Children of the Lens. Reading: Fantasy Press, [1954]. 1st binding. Dustwrapper. *(Dermont)* **$150 [≃£78]**

Smith, Ian Crichton

- From Bourgeois Land. London: Gollancz, 1969. Dustwrapper (slightly sunned). Signed by the author. *(David Rees)* **£15 [≃$28]**
- The Long River. Edinburgh: 1955. Limp vellum wrappers. Signed by the author. *(David Rees)* **£30 [≃$57]**
- Love Poems & Elegies. London: Gollancz, 1972. Dustwrapper. Signed by the author. *(David Rees)* **£20 [≃$38]**
- The Notebooks of Robinson Crusoe. London: Gollancz, 1975. Dustwrapper. Signed by the author. *(David Rees)* **£20 [≃$38]**
- The Village and Other Poems. Carcanet, 1989. Wrappers. Signed by the author. *(David Rees)* **£6 [≃$11]**

Smith, Lee

- Cakewalk. New York: 1981. Dustwrapper. Signed by the author and dated. *(Pettler & Liebermann)* **$40 [≃£20]**
- Fancy Strut. New York: Harper, (1973). Dustwrapper (very small wrinkle in lamination in one spot). *(Between the Covers)* **$100 [≃£52]**

Smith, Martin Cruz

- Gorky Park. London: Collins, 1981. Advance reading copy from uncorrected proofs. Printed wrappers. *(Dalian)* **£20 [≃$38]**
- Gorky Park. London: Collins, 1981. Dustwrapper. *(Ash)* **£25 [≃$47]**
- Nightwing. London: Deutsch, 1977. Dustwrapper. *(Dalian)* **£15 [≃$28]**
- Nightwing. New York: Norton, 1977. Dustwrapper. *(Janus)* **$50 [≃£26]**

Smith, Stevie

- The Best Beast. New York: 1969. Dustwrapper (spine little sunned, very small edge tear rear panel). *(Polyanthos)* **$25 [≃£13]**
- Francesca in Winter. Poem of the Month Club. Signed by the author. *(Whiteson)* **£20 [≃$38]**
- The Frog Prince and Other Poems. London: 1966. Dustwrapper (slightly chipped). *(Egret)* **£12 [≃$23]**
- A Good Time Was Had By All. London: Cape, 1937. Dustwrapper. *(Ash)* **£200 [≃$383]**
- Harold's Leap. London: 1950. Dustwrapper (slightly rubbed). *(Ellis)* **£60 [≃$115]**
- Harold's Leap. London: Chapman & Hall, 1950. Dustwrapper (slightly dusty). *(Dalian)* **£65 [≃$124]**

- Mother, What is Man? London: 1942. Dustwrapper (slightly rubbed and dusty). *(Clearwater)* **£65 [≃$124]**
- Tender Only to One. London: Cape, 1938. Page edges lightly foxed. Edges slightly rubbed. *(Virgo)* **£50 [≃$95]**
- Stevie Smith. A Bibliography, by Jack Barbara, William McBrien and Helen Bajan. Mansell Publishing: 1987. No dustwrapper issued. *(Dalian)* **£25 [≃$47]**

Snaith, Stanley

- Fieldfaring. Poems. London: Nelson, (1940). Endpapers slightly browned. Dustwrapper. *(Dalian)* **£25 [≃$47]**

Snodgrass, W.D.

- Heart's Needle. [Hessle, Yorkshire]: Marvell Press, (1960). 1st English edition. Dustwrapper. His 1st book. *(Houle)* **$165 [≃£85]**
- Vivaldi's Four Seasons. Targ Editions: 1984. One of 150 signed. Tissue dustwrapper. *(Nouveau)* **$100 [≃£52]**

Snow, C.P.

- The Light and the Dark. London: Faber, 1942. Dustwrapper. *(Limestone Hills)* **$85 [≃£44]**
- The New Men. London: Macmillan, 1954. Endpapers very slightly foxed. Dustwrapper (slightly dusty). *(Dalian)* **£45 [≃$86]**
- Recent Thoughts on the Two Cultures. An Oration Delivered at Birkbeck College London 12th December 1961. Printed wrappers (very slightly rubbed). *(Dalian)* **£30 [≃$57]**
- Science and Government. OUP: 1961. Price-clipped dustwrapper. *(Dalian)* **£16 [≃$30]**
- The Sleep of Reason. London: Macmillan, 1968. Dustwrapper. *(Limestone Hills)* **$25 [≃£13]**

Snyder, Gary

- The Back Country. Fulcrum Press, 1967. Printed wrappers (very slightly sunned). *(Dalian)* **£18 [≃$34]**
- Earth Household. London: Cape, 1970. Dustwrapper. *(Dalian)* **£45 [≃$86]**
- Myths and Texts. New Directions: 1978. Dustwrapper. Signed by the author. *(Words Etcetera)* **£36 [≃$69]**
- A Range of Poems. London: Fulcrum Press, (1966). Dustwrapper (spine very slightly darkened). *(Woolmer)* **$90 [≃£46]**
- Regarding Wave. Fulcrum Press: 1970. Printed wrappers (slightly rubbed). *(Dalian)* **£25 [≃$47]**
- Regarding Wave. Fulcrum: 1970. Dustwrapper. *(Any Amount)* **£15 [≃$28]**
- Riprap. [Ashland]: Origin Press, 1959. Name inside front cover with resulting ink marks on two pages. Japanese paper wrappers, sewn. His 1st book. *(Black Sun)* **$225 [≃£117]**

Solzhenitsyn, Aleksandr

- Cancer Ward. Part One. London: Bodley Head, [1968]. 1st English edition. Dustwrapper (lightly used). *(Nouveau)* **$45 [≃£23]**
- The First Circle. London: Collins, 1968. 1st English edition. Price-clipped dustwrapper. *(Nouveau)* **$40 [≃£20]**
- One Day in the Life of Ivan Denisovich. London: Gollancz, 1963. Name on endpaper. Price-clipped dustwrapper. *(Sklaroff)* **£21 [≃$40]**
- One Day in the Life of Ivan Denisovich. London: Gollancz, 1963. 1st English edition. Dustwrapper. *(Nouveau)* **$75 [≃£39]**
- Stories and Prose Poems. New York: FSG, (1971). Dustwrapper. Secretarial inscription, signed by the author. *(Between the Covers)* **$500 [≃£260]**

Somers, Jane

- Pseudonym used by Doris Lessing, q.v.

Sontag, Susan

- The Benefactor. Farrar: 1963. Dustwrapper (backstrip slightly darkened). Her 1st book. *(Nouveau)* **$45 [≃£23]**
- The Benefactor. London: Eyre & Spottiswoode, 1964. Dustwrapper. *(Hadley)* **£15 [≃$28]**
- Death Kit. New York: Farrar, Straus & Giroux, [1967]. 1st printing. Cloth and boards. Dustwrapper (slight wear). Signed by the author. *(Antic Hay)* **$75 [≃£39]**
- I, Etcetera. New York: Farrar, Straus & Giroux, [1978]. Dustwrapper. *(Antic Hay)* **$17.50 [≃£9]**
- Illness as Metaphor. New York: Farrar, Straus & Giroux, [1978]. 1st printing. Dustwrapper. Signed by the author. *(Antic Hay)* **$45 [≃£23]**

Southern, Terry

- Blue Movie. London: Calder, 1973. Dustwrapper. *(Paul Brown)* **£10 [≃$19]**
- Candy. With Mason Hoffenberg. New York: 1964. 1st US edition. Dustwrapper (chip at head of spine). *(Pettler & Liebermann)* **$20 [≃£10]**

- Flash and Filigree. New York: [1958]. Dustwrapper (chipped, closed tear). His 1st book. *(Buckley)* **£20 [≃$38]**
- The Magic Christian. London: 1959. Precedes New York edition. Dustwrapper (slightly rubbed and nicked). *(Buckley)* **£40 [≃$76]**

Spark, Muriel

- The Ballad of Peckham Rye. London: 1960. Covers faded. Dustwrapper (slightly scuffed). *(Egret)* **£25 [≃$47]**
- Collected Poems I. London: 1967. Dustwrapper. *(Egret)* **£15 [≃$28]**
- Doctors of Philosophy. London: 1963. Dustwrapper (slightly chipped). *(Buckley)* **£15 [≃$28]**
- The Driver's Seat. London: 1970. Dustwrapper. *(Buckley)* **£12 [≃$23]**
- Emily Bronte. With Derek Stanford. London: Peter Owen, 1953. Name on endpaper. 2nd impression price-clipped dustwrapper. *(Dalian)* **£35 [≃$67]**
- The Fanfarlo and Other Verse. Hand and Flower Press: 1952. Wrappers. *(David Rees)* **£35 [≃$67]**
- A Far Cry from Kensington. London: London Limited, 1988. One of 150 signed. *(Nouveau)* **$90 [≃£46]**
- The Go-Away Bird and Other Stories. Phila: Lippincott, 1960. 1st American edition. Dustwrapper (tiny tear, some sunning spine). *(Antic Hay)* **$35 [≃£18]**
- Going Up to Sotheby's and Other Poems. London: Granada, 1982. Pictorial wrappers. *(Dalian)* **£20 [≃$38]**
- Loitering with Intent. London: 1981. Dustwrapper. *(Words Etcetera)* **£10 [≃$19]**
- The Mandelbaum Gate. London: 1965. Price- clipped dustwrapper. *(Buckley)* **£20 [≃$38]**
- Not to Disturb. London: 1971. One of 500 signed by the author and by Michael Ayrton. Cloth backed boards (a little soiled along spine). *(Words Etcetera)* **£35 [≃$67]**
- Not to Disturb. London: Observer Books, 1971. One of 500 with an original etching etching by Michael Ayrton, signed by both. This copy unnumbered. *(Moorhouse)* **£45 [≃$86]**
- Not to Disturb. Observer Books, 1971. One of 500 signed by the author and by the illustrator, Michael Ayrton. Glassine dustwrapper. *(David Rees)* **£75 [≃$143]**
- Not to Disturb. London: Macmillan, 1971. Dustwrapper (a closed tear). *(Dalian)* **£25 [≃$47]**
- The Prime of Miss Jean Brodie. London: 1961. Dustwrapper. *(Georges)* **£40 [≃$76]**
- The Prime of Miss Jean Brodie. London: Macmillan, 1961. Spine a little spotted. Price-clipped dustwrapper. *(Dyke)* **£35 [≃$67]**
- The Prime of Miss Jean Brodie. London: 1961. Dustwrapper (very slightly rubbed). *(Ellis)* **£65 [≃$124]**
- The Public Image. London: Macmillan, 1968. Dustwrapper (slightly marked). *(Dalian)* **£20 [≃$38]**
- (Foreword to) Realizations. Newman's Selection of His Parochial and Plain Sermons. Edited with an Introduction by Vincent Ferrer Blehl. London: Daton, Longman & Todd, 1964. Dustwrapper. *(Dalian)* **£45 [≃$86]**
- Territorial Rights. London: Macmillan, 1979. Uncorrected proof copy. Printed wrappers (very slightly dusty, one closed tear top of front cover). *(Dalian)* **£35 [≃$67]**
- (Edits) Tribute to Wordsworth ... Edited with Introductions by Muriel Spark and Derek Stanford. London: Wingate, 1950. Name on endpaper. Cloth faded. Dustwrapper (slightly soiled, chipped at head). *(Dalian)* **£85 [≃$163]**
- Voices at Play. London: Macmillan, 1961. Price-clipped dustwrapper. *(Dalian)* **£25 [≃$47]**
- Muriel Spark. A Biographical and Critical Study by Derek Stanford. With a Bibliography by Bernard Stone. Centaur Press, 1953. Dustwrapper (slightly marked). *(Dalian)* **£45 [≃$86]**

Spencer, Colin

- Anarchists in Love. London: Eyre & Spottiswoode, 1963. Dustwrapper. *(Sklaroff)* **£21 [≃$40]**

Spencer, Elizabeth

- No Place for an Angel. New York: McGraw-Hill, [1967]. Dustwrapper. *(Antic Hay)* **$35 [≃£18]**
- The Voice at the Back Door. McGraw-Hill: 1956. Trace of shelf wear bottom edge. Dustwrapper. *(Nouveau)* **$65 [≃£33]**

Spender, Stephen

- Art Student. Poem of the Month Club. Signed by the author. *(Whiteson)* **£20 [≃$38]**
- Chaos and Control in Poetry. Washington: Library of Congress, 1966. Printed wrappers (faint stains). Signed by the author. *(Antic Hay)* **$50 [≃£26]**
- Citizens in War - and After. London: 1945.

Dustwrapper (rubbed and chipped). Signed by the author. *(Words Etcetera)* **£25 [≃$47]**
- Collected Poems. London: 1985. Dustwrapper. Signed by the author. *(Buckley)* **£20 [≃$38]**
- Cyril Connolly: A Memoir. London: 1978. One of 165. Signed by the author. *(Buckley)* **£70 [≃$134]**
- The Edge of Being. London: Faber, 1949. Dustwrapper (dusty). *(Dalian)* **£25 [≃$47]**
- Forward from Liberalism. London: 1937. Cloth issue. Black cloth. *(Words Etcetera)* **£20 [≃$38]**
- Forward from Liberalism. London: Gollancz, 1937. The black cloth issue (spine and covers slightly marked). *(Dalian)* **£20 [≃$38]**
- The New Realism. London: Hogarth Press, 1939. Wrappers. *(Woolmer)* **$45 [≃£23]**
- Nine Experiments by S.H.S. (Cincinnati: 1964). One of 500. Cloth, spine faded. Facsimile of his 1st book. *(Woolmer)* **$45 [≃£23]**
- Poems. London: Faber, 1934. 2nd edition, revised and enlarged. Dustwrapper (slightly frayed and dusty). *(Dalian)* **£25 [≃$47]**
- Poems of Dedication. London: 1947. Dustwrapper (chipped, two closed tears). *(Buckley)* **£15 [≃$28]**
- Poems. New York: 1934. Dustwrapper. Signed by the author. *(Polyanthos)* **$50 [≃£26]**
- Sirmione Peninsula. London: Faber, Ariel Poem, 1954. Wrappers. Envelope (worn). *(Woolmer)* **$15 [≃£7]**
- Stephen Spender. Verona: Corubolo & Castiglioni, American Authors Series, 1971. One of 30. Wrappers. *(Bromer)* **$250 [≃£130]**
- Vienna. London: Faber, 1934. Dustwrapper (little stained and dull). *(Whiteson)* **£35 [≃$67]**

Spillane, Mickey
- The Girl Hunters. New York: Dutton, 1962. Dustwrapper. *(Janus)* **$18.50 [≃£9]**

Stafford, Jean
- Children Are Bored on Sunday. London: Gollancz, 1954. Dustwrapper. *(Dalian)* **£30 [≃$57]**
- The Mountain Lion. London: Faber, 1948. Dustwrapper (very slightly dusty). *(Dalian)* **£25 [≃$47]**

Stafford, William E.
- Down in My Heart. Elgin, Illinois: Brethren Publishing House, (1947). Spine a little faded. Dustwrapper (minor wear at edges). *(Woolmer)* **$900 [≃£468]**

Stapledon, Olaf
- New Hope for Britain. London: Methuen, 1939. 1st issue dustwrapper with '5 shilling net' unclipped from front flap (very slight chipping to spine tips). *(Dalian)* **£75 [≃$143]**
- Philosophy and Living. Penguin Books: 1939. Slightly browned. Printed wrappers. *(Dalian)* **£22 [≃$42]**
- Sirius. London: 1944. Dustwrapper (slightly frayed). *(Clearwater)* **£45 [≃$86]**
- Waking World. London: Methuen, 1934. Spine and covers marked. *(Dalian)* **£25 [≃$47]**

Stark, Richard
- Pseudonym used by Donald Westlake, q.v.

Starrett, Vincent
- Coffins for Two. Chicago: Covici McGee, 1924. Some internal darkening. Dustwrapper (spine slightly worn and darkened). *(Mordida)* **$100 [≃£52]**

Stegner, Wallace
- All the Little Live Things. New York: Viking, (1967). Dustwrapper. *(Between the Covers)* **$50 [≃£26]**
- Angle of Repose. Garden City: Doubleday, 1971. Faint erasure on front fly. Dustwrapper (very short tear on rear panel). Author's long inscription. *(Between the Covers)* **$175 [≃£91]**
- The Big Rock Candy Mountain. New York: (1943). Foxing to page edges and endpapers. Dustwrapper. *(Between the Covers)* **$200 [≃£104]**

Steig, William
- The Agony of the Kindergarten. New York: Duell, Sloan & Pearce, [1950]. Dustwrapper (some browning, minor chipping, few short tears). *(Antic Hay)* **$45 [≃£23]**

Stein, Gertrude
- An Acquaintance with Description. Hammersmith: Seizin Press, 1929. One of 225 signed. Light soiling. *(Dermont)* **$400 [≃£208]**
- Alphabets & Birthdays. New Haven: Yale UP, 1957. Dustwrapper. *(Dermont)* **$45 [≃£23]**
- The Autobiography of Alice B. Toklas. New York: 1933. 1st issue dustwrapper and

binding. *(Pettler & Liebermann)* **$225 [≃£117]**

- Bee Time Vine and Other Pieces. Yale: UP, 1953. Corners bumped. Dustwrapper (slight wear and edge tears). *(Dermont)* **$35 [≃£18]**
- Bee Time Vine and Other Pieces. New Haven: Yale UP, 1953. Dustwrapper. *(Chapel Hill)* **$60 [≃£31]**
- Brewsie and Willie. New York: Random House, 1946. Dustwrapper (tear on backstrip). *(Nouveau)* **$50 [≃£26]**
- Brewsie and Willie. New York: Random House, [1946]. Slight darkening along front gutter from binder's glue. Dustwrapper (lightly used). *(Chapel Hill)* **$75 [≃£39]**
- Composition as Explanation. London: Hogarth Press, 1926. Printed boards, covers somewhat browned. Glassine dustwrapper (chipped). *(Limestone Hills)* **$145 [≃£75]**
- Everybody's Autobiography. London: Heinemann, 1938. Foredge slightly foxed. Dustwrapper (slightly rubbed, slightly soiled). *(Dalian)* **£110 [≃$211]**
- Everybody's Autobiography. London: 1938. Inscription. Dustwrapper (very slightly rubbed and nicked). *(Sclanders)* **£65 [≃$124]**
- Geography and Plays. Boston: Four Seas, [1922]. 1st issue binding, with lettering on front cover. Spine label brittle and cracking but complete. Dustwrapper flap laid in. *(Chapel Hill)* **$150 [≃£78]**
- How Writing is Written [Uncollected Writings Vol 2]. Los Angeles: Black Sparrow Press, 1974. One of 50 special hardbound. Copy of the 1939 1st edition of Stein's "Very Well I Thank You" in envelope on front pastedown. Dustwrapper. *(Houle)* **$175 [≃£91]**
- In Savoy or Yes is for a Very Young Man. London: The Pushkin Press, (1946). Wrappers. Dustwrapper (very slightly darkened and worn). *(Holmes)* **$35 [≃£18]**
- Last Operas and Plays. New York: (1949). Dustwrapper (minimally edge rubbed, one tiny closed tear rear panel). *(Polyanthos)* **$50 [≃£26]**
- Lectures in America. New York: (1935). 1st issue. Dustwrapper (one small tear). *(King)* **$125 [≃£65]**
- Lucy Church Amiably. Paris: 1930. Boards (spine slightly chipped). *(Patterson)* **£80 [≃$153]**
- Mrs. Reynolds and Five Earlier Novelettes. Yale: UP, 1952. Dustwrapper. *(Dermont)* **$45 [≃£23]**
- Narration. Chicago: UP, 1935. Price- clipped dustwrapper (two small tears, small piece missing top edge not affecting lettering). *(Polyanthos)* **$100 [≃£52]**
- Narration. US: 1935. 1st US edition. Covers dusty, tail of spine slightly scuffed. *(Ellis)* **£60 [≃$115]**
- A Primer for the Gradual Understanding of Gertrude Stein. Los Angeles: Black Sparrow Press, 1971. One of 60. Acetate dustwrapper. Slipcase. Stein's signature tipped on limitation page. *(Houle)* **$250 [≃£130]**
- Reflection on the Atomic Bomb [Uncollected Writings Vol 1]. Los Angeles: Black Sparrow Press, 1973. One of 50 special hardbound. Copy of the 1947 1st edition of Stein's "Literally True" in inserted envelope. Dustwrapper. *(Houle)* **$175 [≃£91]**
- Stanzas in Meditation. Yale: UP, 1956. Dustwrapper (edge tear). *(Dermont)* **$45 [≃£23]**
- Things As They Are. Pawlet: The Banyan Press, (1950). One of 516. Cloth, paper label. *(Black Sun)* **$250 [≃£130]**
- Two: Gertrude Stein and Her Brother and Other Early Portraits. Yale: UP, 1951. Dustwrapper (lightly used, small edge tear). *(Dermont)* **$45 [≃£23]**
- Wars I Have Seen. New York: Random House, [1945]. Gift inscription. Pinholes in endpapers and dampstaining at rear. Dustwrapper. *(Chapel Hill)* **$40 [≃£20]**
- Wars I Have Seen. London: Batsford, [1945]. 1st British edition. Dustwrapper. *(Dermont)* **$40 [≃£20]**
- Wars I Have Seen. London: Batsford, 1945. Dustwrapper. *(Paul Brown)* **£25 [≃$47]**
- The World is Round. New York: William R. Scott, [1939]. One of 350 signed by Stein and the illustrator, Clement Hurd. Boards (light soiling, some staining on rear board). Printed slipcase (worn). *(Dermont)* **$400 [≃£208]**
- Writings and Lectures 1911-1945. London: Peter Owen, [1967]. Dustwrapper. *(Limestone Hills)* **$45 [≃£23]**

Steinbeck, John

- America and Americans. New York: 1966. Spine reads from top to bottom. Tiny chip top edge rear cover. Dustwrapper (torn along flap). *(Polyanthos)* **$45 [≃£23]**
- America and Americans. London: Heinemann, 1966. Small name. Dustwrapper (slightly frayed and tanned). *(Dalian)* **£45 [≃$86]**
- Cannery Row. New York: 1945. Advance copy. printed wrappers (very slightly worn). *(Black Sun)* **$475 [≃£247]**
- Cannery Row. New York: Viking, 1945. 1st

issue, the advance issue in wrappers. Stiff blue wrappers (lower wrapper sunned). Slipcase. *(Houle)* **$875 [≃£455]**

- Cannery Row. New York: 1945. Advance review copy. Printed wrappers (slight wear). *(King)* **$475 [≃£247]**
- Cannery Row. New York: Viking, 1945. Slightly faded. *(Sklaroff)* **£30 [≃$57]**
- Cannery Row. New York: Viking, 1945. Some darkening along spine gutter of front cover, few spots top edge. Dustwrapper (moderate wear, some rubbing, short tears). *(Antic Hay)* **$50 [≃£26]**
- Cup of Gold. New York: (1936). 2nd issue, with 'Covici Friede' stamped in gilt on spine. Top of spine very slightly rubbed. Dustwrapper (slightly chipped, nicked, rubbed and sunned). His 1st book. *(Polyanthos)* **$300 [≃£156]**
- East of Eden. New York: 1952. Dustwrapper (little edge rubbed, few edge chips). *(Polyanthos)* **$50 [≃£26]**
- East of Eden. New York: Viking, 1952. Dustwrapper. *(Chapel Hill)* **$125 [≃£65]**
- East of Eden. New York: Viking, 1952. Edges very slightly dull. Dustwrapper (damaged). *(Whiteson)* **£60 [≃$115]**
- East of Eden. London: Heinemann, 1952. Dustwrapper (spine panel slightly foxed, tear on rear panel repaired). *(Sklaroff)* **£25 [≃$47]**
- The Forgotten Village. New York: Viking, 1941. *(Whiteson)* **£30 [≃$57]**
- The Grapes of Wrath. London: 1939. Inscription. Price-clipped dustwrapper (frayed, rubbed). *(Ellis)* **£120 [≃$230]**
- The Grapes of Wrath. London: Heinemann, 1939. *(Sklaroff)* **£40 [≃$76]**
- In Dubious Battle. London: Heinemann, 1936. Spine and covers marked and soiled. Front pastedown soiled. *(Dalian)* **£25 [≃$47]**
- Journal of a Novel. London: Heinemann, 1970. Dustwrapper. *(Dalian)* **£30 [≃$57]**
- A Letter from John Steinbeck. San Francisco: The Roxburgh Club, 1964. One of 150. Printed wrappers. *(Black Sun)* **$300 [≃£156]**
- The Long Valley. New York: 1938. 1st American edition. Spine darkened. Dustwrapper (slightly rubbed and chipped). *(First Issues)* **£125 [≃$239]**
- The Long Valley. New York: 1938. Spine minimally sunned. Dustwrapper (tiny edge nick, two very small edge tears, spine extremities minimally rubbed, fine). *(Polyanthos)* **$200 [≃£104]**
- The Moon is Down. New York: Viking, 1942. True 1st edition, with period on page 112. Dustwrapper (worn). *(Whiteson)* **£45 [≃$86]**
- The Moon Is Down. New York: Viking Press, 1942. 2nd issue, without the large period on p 112 and with the added notation 'By the Haddon Craftsmen' on title verso. Inscription on endpaper. Covers very slightly marked. Dustwrapper (torn and soiled). *(Dalian)* **£35 [≃$67]**
- Of Mice and Men. New York: (1937). 2nd state. Price-clipped dustwrapper (spine slightly sunned, extremities slightly rubbed). *(Polyanthos)* **$45 [≃£23]**
- The Pastures of Heaven. New York: Robert O. Ballou, 1932. 3rd issue, with the Ballou imprint on title page and spine. One corner lightly bumped. Early dustwrapper with the Brewer, Warren & Putnam imprint on spine (minor wear). *(Antic Hay)* **$250 [≃£130]**
- The Pastures of Heaven. London: Philip Allan, 1933. Spine faded, covers slightly marked, some wear to spine ends. *(Dalian)* **£35 [≃$67]**
- The Pearl. New York: Viking, 1947. 1st state, top edge stained blue. 1st state dustwrapper, with lower cover photo showing Steinbeck looking to the left (few nicks). *(Houle)* **$225 [≃£117]**
- The Pearl. New York: 1947. 2nd state dustwrapper (three minor tears, slight wear to extremities). *(King)* **$65 [≃£33]**
- The Pearl. New York: Viking, 1947. Later state, top edge unstained. Later state dustwrapper, with lower cover photo showing Steinbeck looking to the right. *(Houle)* **$150 [≃£78]**
- The Pearl. New York: Viking, 1947. Dustwrapper. *(Nouveau)* **$125 [≃£65]**
- The Pearl. London: Heinemann, 1948. 1st English edition. Two tiny nicks at spinal extremities. *(Limestone Hills)* **$85 [≃£44]**
- The Red Pony. New York: Viking, 1945. 1st illustrated edition. Variant 2. Slipcase. *(Antic Hay)* **$75 [≃£39]**
- The Short Reign of Pippin IV. London: Heinemann, 1957. Uncorrected proof copy. Printed wrappers (very slightly dusty). *(Dalian)* **£150 [≃$287]**
- The Short Reign of Pippin IV. London: Heinemann, 1957. Dustwrapper. *(Dalian)* **£35 [≃$67]**
- Sweet Thursday. New York: 1954. 1st printing. Price-clipped dustwrapper (slightly frayed and torn). *(King)* **$50 [≃£26]**
- Tortilla Flat. New York: Covici Friede, (1935). Dustwrapper (hint of fading at spine).

(Chapel Hill) **$2,000 [≃£1,041]**

- Tortilla Flat. London: 1935. 1st English edition. Prelims foxed. (Unrecorded) dustwrapper (spine browned, not price clipped). *(Words Etcetera)* **£1,250 [≃$2,399]**
- Tortilla Flat. With Seventeen Paintings by Peggy Worthington. New York: Viking, [1947]. 1st illustrated edition. Dustwrapper (small tear and crease head of spine). *(Antic Hay)* **$150 [≃£78]**
- The Wayward Bus. New York: 1947. Dustwrapper (one tear side of spine, two small tears, some edge wear, front flap fold rubbed). *(Polyanthos)* **$40 [≃£20]**
- The Wayward Bus. New York: Viking, 1947. Dustwrapper. *(Chapel Hill)* **$85 [≃£44]**
- The Wayward Bus. London: 1947. Dustwrapper (very slightly rubbed). *(Ellis)* **£80 [≃$153]**
- The Wayward Bus. London: Heinemann, 1947. 1st English edition. Dustwrapper (slightly worn, minutely nicked). *(Limestone Hills)* **$75 [≃£39]**
- Working Days. New York: Viking, (1989). Uncorrected proof copy. Wrappers. *(Lopez)* **$125 [≃£65]**
- (Contributes to) John Emery. By Zachary Scott. New York: privately printed, November 18, 1964. One of 200, none for sale. Leather backed decorated boards (very slight wear to one tip). *(Black Sun)* **$1,200 [≃£625]**

Steinbeck, John, IV

- In Touch. London: Deutsch, 1969. Dustwrapper. His 1st book. *(Sklaroff)* **£10 [≃$19]**

Steiner, George

- Anno Domini. New York: 1964. Dustwrapper. *(Polyanthos)* **$25 [≃£13]**

Stephen, Adrian

- The "Dreadnought" Hoax. Hogarth Press: 1936. Pictorial boards, spine a trifle browned. *(Words Etcetera)* **£85 [≃$163]**

Stevens, Shane

- Go Down Dead. New York: Morrow, 1966. Small label removed from endpaper. Dustwrapper (some tiny tears). *(Mordida)* **$45 [≃£23]**

Stevens, Wallace

- The Auroras of Autumn. New York: Knopf, 1950. Dustwrapper, fine. Inscribed by the author. *(Black Sun)* **$2,200 [≃£1,145]**
- The Auroras of Autumn. New York: Knopf, (1950). Dustwrapper (spine slightly faded, minor wear at foot). *(Woolmer)* **$250 [≃£130]**
- Selected Poems. London: Fortune Press, n.d. *(Words Etcetera)* **£40 [≃$76]**

Stewart, J.I.M.

- The Man Who Won the Pools. London: Gollancz, 1961. Dustwrapper. *(Marlborough B'shop)* **£27.50 [≃$53]**

Stone, Irving

- The Agony and the Ecstasy. Garden City: Doubleday, 1961. Dustwrapper (few nicks). Signed by the author. *(Houle)* **$65 [≃£33]**
- The Agony and the Ecstasy. Franklin Center: Franklin Library, 1977. Limited edition (number unspecified). Leather. Signed by the author. *(Between the Covers)* **$35 [≃£18]**
- Lust for Life. Franklin Center: Franklin Library, 1981. Leather. Signed by the author. *(Between the Covers)* **$35 [≃£18]**

Stone, Robert

- Children of Light. London: Deutsch, 1986. The correct 1st edition. Dustwrapper. *(Michael Johnson)* **£18 [≃$34]**
- Children of Light. New York: Knopf, 1986. 1st American edition. Dustwrapper. Signed by the author. *(Michael Johnson)* **£28 [≃$53]**
- Dog Soldiers. New York: Boston: Houghton, 1974. Dustwrapper. *(Michael Johnson)* **£45 [≃$86]**
- A Flag for Sunrise. New York: Knopf, 1981. Uncorrected proof copy. *(Lopez)* **$125 [≃£65]**
- A Hall of Mirrors. Boston: Houghton Mifflin, 1967. Dustwrapper. Signed by the author. His 1st book. *(Alphabet)* **$225 [≃£117]**
- A Hall of Mirrors. London: Bodley Head, (1968). Dustwrapper. *(Lopez)* **$225 [≃£117]**

Stoppard, Tom

- Jumpers. London: Faber, 1972. Wrappers. *(Moorhouse)* **£8 [≃$15]**
- Jumpers. London: 1972. Clothbound issue. Dustwrapper (one small mark on rear panel). *(Blakeney)* **£75 [≃$143]**
- Lord Malquist & Mr Moon. London: 1966. Dustwrapper. His 1st book. *(First Issues)* **£40 [≃$76]**
- On the Razzle. 1981. Actors' working playscript. Wrappers. *(Moorhouse)* **£45 [≃$86]**
- The Real Inspector Hound. London: Faber, 1968. Clothbound. Dustwrapper. *(Moorhouse)* **£65 [≃$124]**

- The Real Inspector Hound. London: Faber, 1968. Dustwrapper (slightly bruised, very faintly yellowed). *(Ash)* **£100 [≃$191]**

Storey, David

- Edward. A Story. London: Allen Lane, 1973. Dustwrapper (very slightly rubbed). *(Dalian)* **£12 [≃$23]**
- Flight into Camden. London: Longmans, 1960. Spine very faintly sunned. Dustwrapper (slightly nicked). *(Ash)* **£100 [≃$191]**
- Flight into Camden. London: Longmans, 1960. Dustwrapper (slightly rubbed). *(Dalian)* **£45 [≃$86]**
- Flight into Camden. London: Longmans, 1960. Dustwrapper. *(Lewton)* **£85 [≃$163]**
- Pasmore. London: Longman, 1972. Dustwrapper. *(Paul Brown)* **£15 [≃$28]**
- Pasmore. London: Longmans, 1972. Dustwrapper. *(Dalian)* **£15 [≃$28]**
- A Temporary Life. London: Lane, 1973. Dustwrapper. *(Sklaroff)* **£9 [≃$17]**
- This Sporting Life. London: 1960. Dustwrapper. His 1st book. *(Georges)* **£180 [≃$345]**
- This Sporting Life. London: 1960. Slight offsetting to endsheets. Boards dampstained. Dustwrapper (rubbed, slightly frayed, some soiling to lower panel). Author's signed presentation inscription. His 1st book. *(Blakeney)* **£110 [≃$211]**

Story, Jack Trevor

- Something for Nothing. London: Secker & Warburg, 1963. Dustwrapper (slightly creased). *(Sklaroff)* **£20 [≃$38]**

Stout, Rex

- And Be a Villain. New York: Viking, 1948. Two corners bumped. Dustwrapper (slightly rubbed and worn). *(Moorhouse)* **£25 [≃$47]**
- Corsage: A Bouquet of Rex Stout and Nero Wolfe. Bloomington: Rock, 1977. One of 250 hardbound numbered. Dustwrapper. *(Janus)* **$150 [≃£78]**
- Death of a Doxy. New York: Viking Press, 1966. Small stain on foredge. Dustwrapper (tiny wear at corners). *(Mordida)* **$65 [≃£33]**
- The Mother Hunt. New York: Viking Press, 1963. Dustwrapper. *(Mordida)* **$110 [≃£57]**
- Prisoner's Base. New York: Viking, 1952. Dustwrapper (minor wear). *(Mordida)* **$90 [≃£46]**
- Seeds on the Wind. New York: 1930. Cloth (covers soiled, spine slightly spotted). *(King)* **$60 [≃£31]**
- The Silent Speaker. New York: Viking Press, 1946. Pages darkened. Dustwrapper (unfaded, several tiny tears). *(Mordida)* **$150 [≃£78]**
- Too Many Clients. New York: Viking, 1960. Small label on pastedown. Dustwrapper (few small tears). *(Limestone Hills)* **$45 [≃£23]**

Strachey, Lytton

- Elizabeth and Essex. New York: 1928. One of 1060 signed by the author. *(Ellis)* **£95 [≃$182]**
- Landmarks in French Literature. London: [1912]. 1st issue. Hinges slightly tender. His 1st book. *(Buckley)* **£40 [≃$76]**
- Portraits in Miniature. London: 1931. One of 260 signed by the author. Slipcase (slightly rubbed, ink title). *(Ellis)* **£120 [≃$230]**

Straub, Peter

- Julia. London: 1976. 1st English edition. Dustwrapper. *(Words Etcetera)* **£30 [≃$57]**
- Julia. London: Cape, 1976. Dustwrapper. *(Lewton)* **£35 [≃$67]**
- Julia. New York: 1975. 1st US edition. Very slightly cocked. Dustwrapper (small chip at spine). *(Pettler & Liebermann)* **$75 [≃£39]**
- Marriages. New York: 1973. 1st US edition. Dustwrapper (somewhat worn). *(Pettler & Liebermann)* **$80 [≃£41]**

Streatfield, Noel

- Apple Bough. London: Collins, 1962. Dustwrapper. *(Green Meadow)* **£12.50 [≃$24]**
- Curtain Up. London: Dent, 1944. Dustwrapper. *(Green Meadow)* **£15 [≃$28]**
- Far to Go. London: Collins, 1976. Dustwrapper. *(Green Meadow)* **£15 [≃$28]**
- The Fearless Treasure. London: Michael Joseph, 1953. Dustwrapper. *(Green Meadow)* **£15 [≃$28]**
- Saplings. London: Collins, 1945. Dustwrapper. *(Green Meadow)* **£20 [≃$38]**
- The Silent Speaker. London: Collins, 1961. Dustwrapper. *(Green Meadow)* **£20 [≃$38]**

Strete, Craig

- If All Else Fails ... Garden City: Doubleday, 1980. Remainder spray. Dustwrapper. *(Lopez)* **$75 [≃£39]**

Stuart, Francis

- The Coloured Dome. London: 1932. Dustwrapper (frayed, repaired). *(Clearwater)* **£45 [≃$86]**

- The Pillar of Cloud. London: 1948. Spine bruised. Dustwrapper (repaired). Author's presentation inscription (1949). *(Clearwater)* **£50 [≃$95]**

Stuart, H. (i.e. Francis Stuart)

- We Have Kept The Faith. Dublin: 1923. Pages browned as usual. One corner bumped. *(Blakeney)* **£125 [≃$239]**

Stuart, Jesse

- Foretaste of Glory. New York: Dutton, 1946. Dustwrapper (few chips). Author's inscription (1946). *(Houle)* **$225 [≃£117]**

Sturgeon, Theodore

- The Dreaming Jewels. New York: Greenberg, [1950]. Dustwrapper (lightly used). *(Dermont)* **$35 [≃£18]**
- E Pluribus Unicorn. New York: Abelard Press, [1953]. Dustwrapper. *(Dermont)* **$60 [≃£31]**

Styron, William

- As He Lay Dead, A Bitter Grief. New York: Albondocani Press, 1981. One of 300 signed. Prospectus laid in. Wrappers. *(Alphabet)* **$65 [≃£33]**
- Confessions of Nat Turner. New York: Random, 1967. Dustwrapper. Signed by the author at time of publication. *(Michael Johnson)* **£40 [≃$76]**
- The Confessions of Nat Turner. New York: 1967. Dustwrapper. Signed by the author. *(Polyanthos)* **$35 [≃£18]**
- The Confessions of Nat Turner. PA: The Franklin Library, 1979. Limited edition signed. Leather gilt, a.e.g. Notes from the editors inserted. *(Polyanthos)* **$45 [≃£23]**
- The Confessions of Nat Turner. London: 1967. Dustwrapper. Author's signed presentation copy. *(Polyanthos)* **$40 [≃£20]**
- Lie Down in Darkness. Bobbs, Merrill: 1951. Dustwrapper. Signed by the author. *(Nouveau)* **$200 [≃£104]**
- Lie Down in Darkness. Indianopolis: 1951. Name. Spine and top edge of rear cover little sunned. Dustwrapper (spine and rear panel little sunned, spine extremities little rubbed, few edge nicks). Signed by the author. His 1st book. *(Polyanthos)* **$95 [≃£49]**
- Lie Down in Darkness. Indianopolis: Bobbs-Merrill, [1951]. Very slight fading to edges of cloth. Dustwrapper (couple of scratches in lower part of spine). His 1st book. *(Chapel Hill)* **$175 [≃£91]**
- Lie Down in Darkness. Indianopolis: 1951. Dustwrapper (top of spine minimally rubbed). Author's signed presentation copy. His 1st book. *(Polyanthos)* **$150 [≃£78]**
- Lie Down in Darkness. Indianopolis: Bobbs-Merrill, 1951. Name. Dustwrapper (chipped and torn). His 1st book. *(Alphabet)* **$100 [≃£52]**
- Lie Down in Darkness. New York: 1951. Name and date. Dustwrapper. His 1st book. *(Pettler & Liebermann)* **$90 [≃£46]**
- Lie Down in Darkness. London: Hamish Hamilton, 1952. His 1st book. *(Dalian)* **£20 [≃$38]**
- Set This House on Fire. New York: 1960. Name and date. Dustwrapper. *(Pettler & Liebermann)* **$25 [≃£13]**
- Set This House on Fire. New York: RH, (1960). Dustwrapper. *(Lopez)* **$40 [≃£20]**
- Set This House on Fire. London: Hamish Hamilton, 1961. Dustwrapper. Signed by the author. *(Nouveau)* **$90 [≃£46]**
- Sophie's Choice. New York: Random House, (1979). One of 500 signed. Slipcase. *(Houle)* **$175 [≃£91]**
- Sophie's Choice. London: Cape, 1979. 1st English edition. Price-clipped dustwrapper. Signed by the author. *(Nouveau)* **$55 [≃£28]**

Sutcliff, Rosemary

- Beowulf. The Great Anglo-Saxon Poem now retold ... London: Bodley Head, 1961. 1st issue. Uncorrected proof copy. Printed wrappers. Dustwrapper (edge creased). *(Bookmark)* **£25 [≃$47]**
- Chronicles of Robin Hood. OUP: 1950. Slightly marked, edges rubbed. Her 1st book. *(Bookmark)* **£30 [≃$57]**
- The Lantern Bearers. London: 1959. *(Bookmark)* **£15.50 [≃$30]**
- Sword at Sunset. London: 1963. Occasional slight fox flecks. Dustwrapper (torn). *(Bookmark)* **£18.50 [≃$36]**
- Sword at Sunset. London: Hodder & Stoughton, 1963. Dustwrapper. *(Green Meadow)* **£17.50 [≃$34]**

Sutton, David

- Out on a Limb. London: 1969. One of 100 signed. Dustwrapper. *(Buckley)* **£20 [≃$38]**

Swados, Harvey

- Out Went the Candle. New York: 1955. Name. Dustwrapper (spine slightly sunned). His 1st book. *(Pettler & Liebermann)* **$30 [≃£15]**

Swenson, May

- A Cage of Spines. New York: Rinehart, (1958). Dustwrapper. *(Woolmer)* **$75 [≃£39]**

Swift, Graham

- Learning to Swim. London: London Magazine Editions, 1982. Dustwrapper. *(Moorhouse)* **£40 [≃$76]**
- Out of this World. London: Viking, 1988. Dustwrapper. Signed by the author. *(Dyke)* **£20 [≃$38]**
- Out of this World. London: 1988. Dustwrapper. Signed by the author. Publicity photo loosely laid-in. *(First Issues)* **£15 [≃$28]**
- Out of this World. London: Viking, 1988. Dustwrapper. Signed by the author. *(Michael Johnson)* **£20 [≃$38]**
- Out of This World. London: 1988. Dustwrapper. *(Egret)* **£12 [≃$23]**
- Out of this World. Viking: 1988. Dustwrapper. *(Moorhouse)* **£6 [≃$11]**
- The Sweet Shop Owner. London: 1980. Dustwrapper (small faint stain inside front panel). His 1st book. *(Blakeney)* **£125 [≃$239]**

Sykes, Christopher

- Answer to Question 33. London: 1948. Boards faded. Dustwrapper (slightly nicked and frayed, sunned at spine). *(Blakeney)* **£15 [≃$28]**
- Four Studies in Loyalty. London: Collins, 1946. Endpapers slightly browned. Dustwrapper (tanned and slightly foxed). *(Dalian)* **£20 [≃$38]**
- High-Minded Murder. London: Home and Van Thal, 1944. Dustwrapper. *(Dalian)* **£22 [≃$42]**

Symons, Julian

- Confusions about X. London: Fortune Press, (1939). Dustwrapper (slightly dusty and tanned). His 1st book. *(Dalian)* **£175 [≃$335]**
- Critical Occasions. London: Hamish Hamilton, 1966. Price-clipped dustwrapper. *(Dalian)* **£20 [≃$38]**
- Did Sherlock Holmes Meet Hercule ... Council Bluffs: Yellow Barn Press, 1988. One of 200. No dustwrapper issued. Signed by the author. *(Janus)* **$125 [≃£65]**
- The Modern Crime Story. Edinburgh: The Tragara Press, 1980. One of 25 (of 125) signed. Wrappers. *(Limestone Hills)* **$65 [≃£33]**
- The Second Man. London: Routledge, 1943. Dustwrapper. *(Any Amount)* **£30 [≃$57]**

Talbot, Hake

- Rim of the Pit. New York: Simon, 1944. Softbound advance copy bound in jacket. *(Janus)* **$110 [≃£57]**

Tanner, Lt.-Col. W. ('Bill')

- The Book of Bond or Every Man His Own 007. London: Cape, 1965. Reversible dustwrapper. *(Alphabet)* **$45 [≃£23]**

Tapply, William G.

- Death at Charity's Point. New York: Scribner, 1984. Dustwrapper. *(Mordida)* **$85 [≃£44]**

Tate, Allen

- The Fathers. New York: 1938. Name and address. Dustwrapper (a bit worn). *(Pettler & Liebermann)* **$50 [≃£26]**
- On the Limits of Poetry. Swallow Press: 1948. Dustwrapper (lightly nicked and smudged). *(Nouveau)* **$80 [≃£41]**
- Poems 1920-45. London: Eyre & Spottiswoode, 1947. Endpapers tanned, top edges darkened. Signature. Dustwrapper (torn with loss). *(Hazeldene)* **£40 [≃$76]**
- Reason in Madness. New York: (1941). Dustwrapper (slightly nicked). Inscribed by the author. *(Black Sun)* **$150 [≃£78]**
- Two Conceits for the Eye to Sing, if possible. Cummington Press: 1950. One of 300 signed. Wrappers, printed label. In mailing envelope. *(Bromer)* **$165 [≃£85]**

Tate, James

- Land of Little Sticks. Worcester: Metacom Press, 1981. One of 300 numbered and signed. Sewn wrappers. *(Antic Hay)* **$50 [≃£26]**

Taylor, Elizabeth

- In a Summer Season. London: Peter Davies, 1961. Dustwrapper. *(Limestone Hills)* **$55 [≃£28]**
- Mossy Trotter. London: 1961. Dustwrapper (just a little creased at foot of spine). *(Blakeney)* **£35 [≃$67]**
- Mrs. Palfrey at the Claremont. London: Chatto & Windus, 1971. White dustwrapper (very slightly browned). *(Virgo)* **£25 [≃$47]**
- The Soul of Kindness. London: Chatto & Windus, 1964. Uncorrected proof copy. Wrappers (a bit stained & soiled). *(Holmes)* **$85 [≃£44]**
- The Soul of Kindness. London: Chatto &

Windus, 1964. Dustwrapper (slightly faded). *(Virgo)* **£30 [≃$57]**

Taylor, Peter

- The Collected Stories. Farrar: 1969. Dustwrapper. *(Nouveau)* **$60 [≃£31]**
- A Long Fourth and Other Stories. Introduction by Robert Penn Warren. New York: 1948. Name. Dustwrapper (edge tears, pieces missing, edge rubbed, little soiled). Bookplate signed by Warren. Author's signed presentation copy. His 1st book. *(Polyanthos)* **$175 [≃£91]**
- Miss Leonora When Last Seen. New York: Obolensky, (1963). Advance review copy with slip laid in. Dustwrapper (spine very slightly darkened). *(Between the Covers)* **$275 [≃£143]**
- The Old Forest and Other Stories. Garden City: Doubleday Doran / Dial, 1985. Uncorrected proof copy. Wrappers. *(Lopez)* **$85 [≃£44]**
- Summons to Memphis. New York: Knopf, 1986. Dustwrapper. *(Michael Johnson)* **£24 [≃$46]**
- Summons to Memphis. London: Chatto, 1987. 1st British edition. Dustwrapper. *(Michael Johnson)* **£15 [≃$28]**

Taylor, Phoebe Atwood

- Proof of the Pudding. New York: Norton, 1945. Dustwrapper. *(Janus)* **$40 [≃£20]**

Tennant, Emma

- Black Marina. London: Faber, 1985. Dustwrapper. *(Paul Brown)* **£7.50 [≃$15]**
- Black Marina. London: Faber, 1985. Dustwrapper. *(Dalian)* **£15 [≃$28]**
- The House of Hospitalities. Viking: 1987. Dustwrapper. *(Moorhouse)* **£4 [≃$7]**
- The Last of the Country House Murders. London: 1974. Dustwrapper. Author's presentation copy. *(Egret)* **£22 [≃$42]**
- Queen of Stones. London: Cape, 1972. Dustwrapper. Author's compliment slip tipped in. *(Dalian)* **£22 [≃$42]**
- Time of the Crack. London: Cape, 1973. Dustwrapper. *(Lewton)* **£18.50 [≃$36]**
- The Time of the Crack. London: 1973. Dustwrapper (spine a trifle faded). *(Words Etcetera)* **£30 [≃$57]**
- Wild Nights. London: Cape, 1979. Dustwrapper. *(Marlborough B'shop)* **£10 [≃$19]**
- Wild Nights. London: Cape, 1979. Dustwrapper. *(Dalian)* **£15 [≃$28]**

Theroux, Alexander

- Darconville's Cat. London: Hamish Hamilton, 1981. Dustwrapper. *(Dalian)* **£25 [≃$47]**
- Three Wogs. London: Chatto & Windus, 1973. Dustwrapper. His 1st book. *(Dalian)* **£85 [≃$163]**
- Three Wogs. London: Chatto & Windus, 1973. Dustwrapper. His 1st book. *(Moorhouse)* **£45 [≃$86]**
- Three Wogs. London: Chatto, 1972. The hardback edition. Dustwrapper. His 1st book. *(First Issues)* **£75 [≃$143]**

Theroux, Paul

- The Black House. Boston: Houghton Mifflin, 1974. Dustwrapper. *(Alphabet)* **$30 [≃£15]**
- The Black House. New York: Boston: Houghton Mifflin, 1974. Dustwrapper (slightly nicked and abraded). Signed by the author. *(Egret)* **£25 [≃$47]**
- The Black House. Boston: Houghton Mifflin, 1974. 1st US edition (precedes the UK edition). Dustwrapper (slightly browned, rubbed). *(Moorhouse)* **£25 [≃$47]**
- The Black House. London: 1974. Price-clipped dustwrapper. *(First Issues)* **£25 [≃$47]**
- The Black House. London: Hamish Hamilton, 1974. Price-clipped dustwrapper. *(Dalian)* **£35 [≃$67]**
- Chicago Loop. London: Hamish Hamilton, 1990. Uncorrected proof copy. Printed wrappers. Signed by the author. *(David Rees)* **£45 [≃$86]**
- Chicago Loop. London: Hamish Hamilton, 1990. Uncorrected proof copy. Printed wrappers. *(David Rees)* **£30 [≃$57]**
- Chicago Loop. London: Hamish Hamilton, 1990. Uncorrected proof copy. Pictorial wrappers. *(Michael Johnson)* **£20 [≃$38]**
- A Christmas Card. London: Hamish Hamilton, 1978. Dustwrapper. *(David Rees)* **£12 [≃$23]**
- The Consul's File. London: Hamish Hamilton, (1977). Uncorrected proof copy. Printed wrappers (very slightly dusty). *(Dalian)* **£35 [≃$67]**
- The Consul's File. London: Hamish Hamilton, 1977. Price-clipped dustwrapper. Signed by the author. *(David Rees)* **£60 [≃$115]**
- The Consul's File. Boston: Houghton Mifflin, 1977. 1st American edition. Dustwrapper. *(Dalian)* **£20 [≃$38]**
- Doctor Slaughter. London: 1984. Proof copy.

Wrappers. *(Words Etcetera)* **£30 [≃$57]**

- Doctor Slaughter. London: 1984. Dustwrapper. *(Words Etcetera)* **£10.50 [≃$21]**
- Doctor Slaughter. London: 1984. Dustwrapper. *(Buckley)* **£13 [≃$24]**
- Doctor Slaughter. London: Hamish Hamilton, 1984. Dustwrapper. Signed by the author. *(David Rees)* **£15 [≃$28]**
- The Family Arsenal. Boston: Houghton Mifflin, 1976. 1st American edition. Dustwrapper (slightly rubbed). Signed by the author. *(First Issues)* **£25 [≃$47]**
- The Family Arsenal. Boston: 1976. Dustwrapper (minimally rubbed). *(Polyanthos)* **$25 [≃£13]**
- Fong and the Indians. London: Hamish Hamilton, 1976. Price-clipped dustwrapper. Signed by the author. *(David Rees)* **£25 [≃$47]**
- Fong and the Indians. London: 1976. Dustwrapper. Signed by the author. *(Egret)* **£40 [≃$76]**
- Fong and the Indians. London: Hamilton, 1976. Dustwrapper. *(Sklaroff)* **£45 [≃$86]**
- Fong and the Indians. London: Hamish Hamilton, 1976. Dustwrapper. *(Dalian)* **£35 [≃$67]**
- Girls at Play. London: 1969. Slightly shaken. Dustwrapper (slightly soiled, two small tears, internal strengthening). *(Words Etcetera)* **£75 [≃$143]**
- The Great Railway Bazaar. Boston: HM, 1975. Price-clipped dustwrapper. *(Lopez)* **$65 [≃£33]**
- The Great Railway Bazaar. London: Hamilton, 1975. Dustwrapper. *(Lewton)* **£45 [≃$86]**
- Half Moon Street. Boston: Houghton, Mifflin, 1984. Uncorrected proof copy. Printed wrappers. Signed by the author. *(Antic Hay)* **$100 [≃£52]**
- Half Moon Street. Boston: Houghton: 1984. Advance uncorrected proof copy. Wrappers. *(Nouveau)* **$75 [≃£39]**
- Half Moon Street. Boston: 1984. Dustwrapper. *(Polyanthos)* **$25 [≃£13]**
- The Imperial Way. Boston: 1985. Dustwrapper. Signed by the author. *(David Rees)* **£18 [≃$34]**
- The Imperial Way. London: Hamilton, 1985. Dustwrapper. *(Lewton)* **£10 [≃$19]**
- Jungle Lovers. Boston: Houghton Mifflin, 1971. Slight manufacturer's defect on top edge. Price-clipped dustwrapper. *(Alphabet)* **$125 [≃£65]**
- Jungle Lovers. Boston: Houghton: 1971. Dustwrapper. *(Nouveau)* **$65 [≃£33]**
- The Kingdom by the Sea. Boston: Houghton: 1983. One of 250 signed. Slipcase. *(Nouveau)* **$100 [≃£52]**
- The Kingdom by the Sea. Boston: HM, 1983. Dustwrapper (tiny nick at head). Signed by the author. *(Lopez)* **$65 [≃£33]**
- The London Embassy. London: 1982. Price-clipped dustwrapper. *(Buckley)* **£18 [≃$34]**
- The London Embassy. Boston: 1983. Dustwrapper. *(Polyanthos)* **$20 [≃£10]**
- London Snow. Russell, 1979. One of 150 (of 450) for the UK signed by the author and by the illustrator, John Lawrence. Glassine dustwrapper. *(David Rees)* **£65 [≃$124]**
- London Snow. Boston: 1980. Dustwrapper. *(Polyanthos)* **$30 [≃£15]**
- The Mosquito Coast. London: Hamish Hamilton, 1981. Dustwrapper. *(Dalian)* **£25 [≃$47]**
- The Mosquito Coast. Boston: 1981 [sic]. Advance reading copy. Pictorial wrappers (front wrapper slightly creased). *(Polyanthos)* **$30 [≃£15]**
- The Mosquito Coast. Boston: Houghton: 1982 [sic]. Advance reading copy. decorated wrappers. *(Nouveau)* **$35 [≃£18]**
- My Secret History. London: London Limited Editions, 1989. One of 150 signed. Glassine dustwrapper. *(Michael Johnson)* **£40 [≃$76]**
- O-Zone. London: Hamish Hamilton, 1986. Uncorrected proof copy. Printed wrappers. Signed by the author. *(David Rees)* **£45 [≃$86]**
- O-Zone. London: Hamish Hamilton, 1986. Review slip. Dustwrapper. Signed by the author. *(David Rees)* **£10 [≃$19]**
- The Old Patagonian Express. London: Hamish Hamilton, 1979. Price-clipped dustwrapper. *(David Rees)* **£18 [≃$34]**
- The Old Patagonian Express. London: Hamish Hamilton, 1979. Dustwrapper. Signed by the author. *(David Rees)* **£35 [≃$67]**
- The Old Patagonian Express. London: Hamilton, 1979. Dustwrapper. *(Lewton)* **£20 [≃$38]**
- Picture Palace. London: 1978. Dustwrapper. *(Words Etcetera)* **£10 [≃$19]**
- Picture Palace. Boston: HM, 1978. Couple of tiny spots top edge of pages. Dustwrapper. Signed by the author. *(Lopez)* **$65 [≃£33]**
- Picture Palace. London: 1978. Dustwrapper. *(Buckley)* **£15 [≃$28]**
- Sailing through China. Salisbury: 1983. 1st

trade edition. Dustwrapper. *(Limestone Hills)* **$35 [≃£18]**

- Sailing through China. London: (1983). 1st English edition. Small stain foredge of half-title. Dustwrapper. Signed by the author. *(Lopez)* **$65 [≃£33]**
- Sailing through China. Boston: 1984. One of 400 signed by author and illustrator. Dustwrapper. *(Polyanthos)* **$60 [≃£31]**
- Saint Jack. Boston: Houghton Mifflin, 1973. 1st US edition (precedes the UK edition). Dustwrapper (slightly soiled, several short tears). *(Moorhouse)* **£20 [≃$38]**
- Saint Jack. Boston: Houghton: 1973. Dustwrapper (one short tear). *(Nouveau)* **$40 [≃£20]**
- The Shortest Day of the Year. Leamington Spa: Sixth Chamber Press, 1986. One of 175 signed. *(Georges)* **£50 [≃$95]**
- The Shortest Day of the Year. Sixth Chamber Press: 1986. One of 175 signed. *(David Rees)* **£70 [≃$134]**
- Sinning with Annie & Other Stories. Boston: Houghton Mifflin, 1972. Price-clipped dustwrapper. *(Alphabet)* **$75 [≃£39]**
- Sinning with Annie. London: Hamish Hamilton, 1975. Dustwrapper. Signed by the author. *(David Rees)* **£125 [≃$239]**
- Sinning with Annie. London: Hamilton, 1975. Dustwrapper. *(Lewton)* **£50 [≃$95]**
- Sunrise with Seamonsters. Boston: 1985. Dustwrapper. *(Polyanthos)* **$25 [≃£13]**
- V.S. Naipaul: an Introduction to his Work. London: Deutsch, 1972. Lacks front endpaper. Two library stamps. Dustwrapper. *(Moorhouse)* **£5 [≃$9]**
- Waldo. Boston: Houghton Mifflin, 1967. Dustwrapper. His 1st book. *(Alphabet)* **$110 [≃£57]**
- Waldo. London: 1968. Price-clipped dustwrapper, bright. Author's presentation copy. *(Egret)* **£160 [≃$307]**
- Waldo. London: 1968. Top corner slightly bumped. Dustwrapper (some internal staining lower panel, nick, 2-inch closed tear). His 1st book. *(Ellis)* **£85 [≃$163]**
- The White Man's Burden. London: 1987. Dustwrapper. *(Words Etcetera)* **£20 [≃$38]**
- World's End. Boston: HM, 1980. Dustwrapper. Signed by the author. *(Lopez)* **$65 [≃£33]**
- World's End and Other Stories. Boston: 1980. Dustwrapper. *(Polyanthos)* **$25 [≃£13]**
- World's End and Other Stories. London: 1980. Dustwrapper. *(Words Etcetera)* **£16 [≃$30]**

Thomas, D.M.

- Ararat. London: 1983. Dustwrapper. Inscribed by the author. *(First Issues)* **£15 [≃$28]**
- Ararat. London: Gollancz, 1983. Dustwrapper. Signed by the author. *(Hazeldene)* **£20 [≃$38]**
- Ararat. London: Gollancz, 1983. Dustwrapper. *(Dalian)* **£18 [≃$34]**
- The Devil and the Floral Dance. London: Robson Books, 1978. Paper boards. No dustwrapper issued. *(Hazeldene)* **£10 [≃$19]**
- The Flute-Player. London: Gollancz, 1979. Dustwrapper. Signed by the author. *(Hazeldene)* **£40 [≃$76]**
- The Flute Player. London: Gollancz, 1979. Dustwrapper. *(Michael Johnson)* **£20 [≃$38]**
- The Flute Player. New York: Dutton, (1979). 1st American edition. Advance review copy. Dustwrapper. *(Lopez)* **$35 [≃£18]**
- Lilith-Prints. London: 1974. Wrappers. Signed by the author. *(Egret)* **£10 [≃$19]**
- Logan Stone. London: 1971. Author's inscription. *(Egret)* **£16 [≃$30]**
- News from the Front. By D.M. Thomas and Sylvia Kantaris. Todmorden: 1983. Wrappers. Signed by the authors. *(Egret)* **£12 [≃$23]**
- Penguin Modern Poets II. Thomas, Redgrove and D.M. Black. Penguin: 1968. Dustwrapper (slightly rubbed). Signed by Thomas and Redgrove. *(Egret)* **£18 [≃$34]**
- Selected Poems. London: 1983. Dustwrapper. *(First Issues)* **£15 [≃$28]**
- Sphinx. London: 1986. Dustwrapper. *(First Issues)* **£15 [≃$28]**
- Swallow. London: Gollancz, 1984. Uncorrected proof copy. Wrappers. Proof dustwrapper. *(Dalian)* **£25 [≃$47]**
- Symphony in Moscow. Richmond, Surrey: The Keepsake Press, 1974. One of 180. Card printed wrappers. Envelope. *(Dalian)* **£45 [≃$86]**
- Two Voices. London: 1968. 1st edition thus. Wrappers (head of spine little creased). Signed by the author. *(Egret)* **£15 [≃$28]**
- Two Voices. London: Cape Goliard, 1968. Pictorial boards. *(Lewton)* **£17.50 [≃$34]**
- The White Hotel. New York: 1981. 1st US edition (precedes the English edition). Dustwrapper. Signed by the author. *(Egret)* **£60 [≃$115]**
- The White Hotel. New York: Viking, 1981. 1st American edition (precedes British edition). Dustwrapper. *(Michael Johnson)* **£40 [≃$76]**

- The White Hotel. London: Gollancz, 1981. Dustwrapper. *(Sklaroff)* **£200 [≃$383]**

Thomas, Dylan

- Adventures in the Skin Trade. London: Putnam, (1955). 1st edition thus. Dustwrapper. *(Houle)* **$175 [≃£91]**
- Adventures in the Skin Trade. London: Putnam, 1955. 1st edition in book form. Dustwrapper. *(Limestone Hills)* **$110 [≃£57]**
- A Child's Christmas in Wales. Norfolk, Conn.: New Directions, [1954]. 1st separate edition. Dustwrapper. *(Limestone Hills)* **$65 [≃£33]**
- The Collected Letters. London: Dent, 1985. Dustwrapper. *(Paul Brown)* **£15 [≃$28]**
- Collected Poems. London: 1952. Gilt lettering on spine faintly rubbed. *(Words Etcetera)* **£20 [≃$38]**
- Collected Poems. London: 1952. One of 65 signed. *(Words Etcetera)* **£1,600 [≃$3,071]**
- Conversation About Christmas. New Directions: Christmas 1954. Wrappers. *(Woolmer)* **$35 [≃£18]**
- Conversation about Christmas. [New York?]: New Directions, 1954. 1st edition thus. Stiff wrappers. *(Houle)* **$150 [≃£78]**
- Deaths and Entrances. London: Dent, 1946. Inscription. Prelims very slightly foxed. dustwrapper (sunned, dusty, slightly chipped). *(Tiger Books)* **£65 [≃$124]**
- Deaths and Entrances. Gregynog Press: 1984. One of 250. Piper illustrations. Morocco backed cloth. Slipcase. *(Words Etcetera)* **£275 [≃$527]**
- The Doctor and the Devils. London: Dent, 1953. Uncorrected proof copy. Wrappers (lacks small chip from upper wrapper). *(David Rees)* **£60 [≃$115]**
- The Followers. London: Dent, 1976. Pictorial wrappers. *(Sklaroff)* **£15 [≃$28]**
- From In Memory of Anne Jones; A Poem. Caseg Broadsheet: (1942). Single sheet. Specially made half leather folder. *(Words Etcetera)* **£100 [≃$191]**
- In Country Sleep. New York: 1952. One of 100 signed. Slipcase (somewhat worn). *(Blakeney)* **£750 [≃$1,439]**
- In Country Sleep and Other Poems. New York: (1952). Tiny corner rub. Dustwrapper (extremities sunned, spine little chipped, two small tears). *(Polyanthos)* **$75 [≃£39]**
- In Country Sleep and Other Poems. New York: New Directions, 1952. Boards. Dustwrapper (spine trifle browned). *(Words Etcetera)* **£60 [≃$115]**
- In Country Sleep and Other Poems. New York: New Directions, (1952). Review slip. Dustwrapper. *(Bromer)* **$275 [≃£143]**
- Letters to Vernon Watkins. London: Dent, London: Faber, [1957]. 1st English edition. Dustwrapper (tiny tear). *(Antic Hay)* **$50 [≃£26]**
- Me and My Bike. New York: McGraw-Hill, 1965. Precedes the English edition. Cloth. *(Dalian)* **£35 [≃$67]**
- Me and my Bike. London: 1965. One of 500. Dustwrapper. Slipcase. *(Words Etcetera)* **£32 [≃$61]**
- New Poems. Norfolk: New Directions, Poets of the Year Series, [1943]. Printed wrappers. *(Antic Hay)* **$75 [≃£39]**
- The Notebooks. New York: New Directions, 1967. Dustwrapper. *(Alphabet)* **$30 [≃£15]**
- Poem On His Birthday: In the Mustardseed Sun. [Market Drayton]: Tern Press, (1983). 1st edition thus. One of 85 signed by Nicholas Parry, the illustrator. *(Houle)* **$150 [≃£78]**
- Portrait of the Artist as a Young Dog. Norfolk: New Directions, (1940). Cloth. *(Houle)* **$85 [≃£44]**
- A Prospect of the Sea: And Other Stories and Prose Writings. London: Dent, (1955). Dustwrapper. *(Houle)* **$150 [≃£78]**
- Quite Early One Morning. London: Dent, 1954. 1st issue. Dustwrapper. *(Limestone Hills)* **$75 [≃£39]**
- Quite Early One Morning. London: 1954. Dustwrapper (rubbed, very slightly chipped). *(Buckley)* **£45 [≃$86]**
- Quite Early One Morning. London: Dent, 1954. Dustwrapper (slightly soiled and nicked). *(Dalian)* **£25 [≃$47]**
- The Selected Dylan Thomas. New York: New Directions, 1946. Dustwrapper (chipped, internally repaired). *(Glyn's)* **£32 [≃$61]**
- Twelve More Letters. Turret Books: 1969. One of 175. Yellow buckram gilt. *(Words Etcetera)* **£85 [≃$163]**
- Twenty Years a-Growing. London: Dent, 1964. Dustwrapper. *(Green Meadow)* **£45 [≃$86]**
- Under Milkwood. Llaregub. A Piece for Radio. [In] Boteghe Oscure IX, Rome, 1952. Cream wrappers. *(First Issues)* **£125 [≃$239]**
- Under Milk Wood. [In] Mademoiselle: February, 1954. Precedes book publication. Spine worn. *(Woolmer)* **$25 [≃£13]**
- Under Milk Wood, a Play for Voices. London: 1954. Dustwrapper (slightly creased and nicked). *(Georges)* **£75 [≃$143]**

- Under Milk Wood. A Play for Voices. Dent, 1954. Top edge slightly spotted. Dustwrapper (slightly rubbed). *(Moorhouse)* **£75 [≃$143]**
- Under Milk Wood. London: Dent, 1954. Dustwrapper (slightly edge scuffed rubbed chipped, minor loss to spine). *(Paul Brown)* **£50 [≃$95]**
- Under Milk Wood. London: Dent, 1954. Edges tanned. Later issue dustwrapper. *(Hazeldene)* **£50 [≃$95]**
- Under Milk Wood. London: Dent, 1954. Inscription first free endpaper. Prelims and foredge very slightly foxed. Dustwrapper (dusty, minor chips). *(Tiger Books)* **£55 [≃$105]**

Thomas, Gwyn

- All Things Betray Thee. London: Michael Joseph, 1949. Dustwrapper (slightly nicked). *(Dalian)* **£20 [≃$38]**
- The Love Man. London: Gollancz, 1958. Dustwrapper. *(Dalian)* **£15 [≃$28]**
- Where Did I Put My Pity? Folk Tales. Progress Publishing Company, (1946). Dustwrapper. His 1st book. *(Dalian)* **£45 [≃$86]**

Thomas, Leslie

- Dangerous Davies. The Last Detective. London: Eyre Methuen, 1976. Dustwrapper. *(Limestone Hills)* **$40 [≃£20]**
- The Virgin Soldiers. Constable, 1966. Price-clipped dustwrapper. *(Glyn's)* **£20 [≃$38]**
- The Virgin Soldiers. London: 1966. Dustwrapper. *(Ellis)* **£20 [≃$38]**
- The Virgin Soldiers. London: Constable, 1966. Dustwrapper. *(Lewton)* **£10 [≃$19]**

Thomas, R.S.

- The Bread of Truth. London: 1963. Dustwrapper (tiny nick). *(Egret)* **£30 [≃$57]**
- The Bread of Truth. London: 1963. Dustwrapper (slightly browned, one tear). *(Words Etcetera)* **£22 [≃$42]**
- The Bread of Truth. London: 1963. Dustwrapper. *(Egret)* **£30 [≃$57]**
- The Bread of Truth. London: Hart Davis, 1963. Name and date on fly. Dustwrapper. *(Halsey)* **£35 [≃$67]**
- Destinations. Celandine Press: 1985. One of 75 signed. Slipcase (slightly rubbed). *(Ellis)* **£120 [≃$230]**
- Destinations. Rampant Lions for Celandine Press, 1985. One of 300. Buckram backed marbled boards. *(Dyke)* **£30 [≃$57]**
- Judgement Day. Poetry Book Society: 1960. One of 1000. Wrappers. *(David Rees)* **£8 [≃$15]**
- Laboratories of the Spirit. London: 1975. Dustwrapper (spine faded). *(Egret)* **£18 [≃$34]**
- Not That He Brought Flowers. London: 1968. Dustwrapper. *(Words Etcetera)* **£22 [≃$42]**
- Pieta. London: 1966. Dustwrapper. *(Words Etcetera)* **£25 [≃$47]**
- Pieta. London: Hart Davis, 1966. Dustwrapper. *(Halsey)* **£30 [≃$57]**
- Poet's Meeting. Celandine Press: (1983). One of 85 (of 125) signed. Wrappers. *(Waterfield's)* **£30 [≃$57]**
- Poetry for Supper. London: Hart-Davis, 1958. Dustwrapper (slightly marked and nicked). Poetry Book Society wraparound. *(Dalian)* **£45 [≃$86]**
- Sea Christmas. [Ca 1980]. Single card. Signed and inscribed by the author. *(Words Etcetera)* **£50 [≃$95]**
- Selected Poems 1946-1968. London: 1973. Dustwrapper. *(Egret)* **£15 [≃$28]**
- Song. Oxford: Fishpaste Hors-serie 3, 1968. Postcard. *(Dalian)* **£45 [≃$86]**
- The Stones of the Field. Carmarthen: 1946. Cloth backed boards spotted and slightly bumped at top edge. Dustwrapper (slightly creased, a little chipped at top of spine, a few short closed tears). His 1st book. *(Blakeney)* **£275 [≃$527]**
- Tares. London: 1961. Dustwrapper (very slightly dusty). Inscribed by the author. *(Words Etcetera)* **£75 [≃$143]**
- Tares. London: Hart Davis, 1961. Name on fly. Dustwrapper (slightly soiled, several nicks to top edge). *(Halsey)* **£35 [≃$67]**
- Three Poems. Words Press: 1988. One of 75 signed. Wrappers. *(David Rees)* **£25 [≃$47]**
- Three Poems. Words Press: 1988. One of 125 unsigned. Wrappers. *(David Rees)* **£10 [≃$19]**
- The Way of it. Ceolfrith Press, 1977. Printed wrappers. *(Dalian)* **£25 [≃$47]**

Thomas, Ross

- Briarpatch. New York: Simon and Schuster, 1984. Uncorrected proof copy. Wrappers. *(Mordida)* **$85 [≃£44]**
- Cast a Yellow Shadow. New York: Morrow, 1967. Dustwrapper. *(Mordida)* **$100 [≃£52]**
- Chinaman's Chance. New York: Simon and Schuster, 1978. Dustwrapper (minor scrape spine edge). *(Mordida)* **$45 [≃£23]**

- The Eighth Dwarf. New York: Simon & Schuster, 1979. Dustwrapper. Signed by the author. *(Mordida)* **$37.50 [≃£19]**
- The Eighth Dwarf. London: Hamish Hamilton, 1979. 1st English edition. Dustwrapper (ink lines through price on inner flap). *(Limestone Hills)* **$25 [≃£13]**
- The Fools in Town are on Our Side. New York: Morrow, 1971. 1st American edition. Edges spotted. Dustwrapper. *(Mordida)* **$85 [≃£44]**
- The Highbinders. By Oliver Bleeck. New York: Morrow, 1974. Dustwrapper. *(Mordida)* **$50 [≃£26]**
- Missionary Stew. New York: Simon and Schuster, 1983. Dustwrapper. *(Mordida)* **$30 [≃£15]**
- The Money Harvest. New York: Morrow, 1975. Dustwrapper (short closed tear, tiny wear). *(Mordida)* **$65 [≃£33]**
- The Money Harvest. London: Hamish Hamilton, 1975. Dustwrapper (small crease on back panel). *(Limestone Hills)* **$45 [≃£23]**
- The Mordida Man. New York: Simon & Schuster, 1981. Dustwrapper (tiny wear at base of spine). *(Mordida)* **$35 [≃£18]**
- The Porkchoppers. New York: Morrow, 1972. Dustwrapper. Signed by the author. *(Janus)* **$50 [≃£26]**
- The Porkchoppers. New York: Morrow, 1972. Price-clipped dustwrapper. *(Alphabet)* **$50 [≃£26]**
- The Procane Chronicle. By Oliver Bleeck. New York: Morrow, 1972. Slightly leaned. Dustwrapper. *(Janus)* **$140 [≃£72]**
- Protocol for a Kidnapping. By Oliver Bleeck. Morrow: 1971. Dustwrapper. *(Nouveau)* **$90 [≃£46]**
- Seersucker Whipsaw. London: Hodder, 1968. 1st British edition. Dustwrapper. *(Michael Johnson)* **£20 [≃$38]**
- Yellow-Dog Contract. New York: Morrow, 1977. Dustwrapper. Signed by the author. *(Janus)* **$45 [≃£23]**

Thompson, Flora

- Lark Rise. London: OUP, 1939. Dustwrapper (slightly dusty, frayed at head of spine, split three quarters of the front outer hinge). *(Blakeney)* **£65 [≃$124]**
- Lark Rise. OUP: 1939. Modern morocco gilt extra by Bayntun-Riviere. *(Ash)* **£250 [≃$479]**

Thompson, Hunter S.

- The Curse of Lono. New York: Bantam, (1983). Wrappers. *(Lopez)* **$30 [≃£15]**
- Fear and Loathing in Las Vegas. New York: 1971. Front board faded. Price-clipped dustwrapper (slightly creased). *(Blakeney)* **£75 [≃$143]**
- Fear and Loathing in Las Vegas. New York: RH, (1971). Sticker removal mark on front endpaper. Dustwrapper. *(Lopez)* **$75 [≃£39]**
- Fear and Loathing in Las Vegas. New York: Random House, [1971]. Dustwrapper (minor wear). *(Antic Hay)* **$85 [≃£44]**
- Fear and Loathing in Las Vegas. New York: RH, (1971). Tiny bit of fading to upper edges of covers. Dustwrapper. *(Lopez)* **$100 [≃£52]**
- Fear and Loathing on the Campaign Trail '72. (San Francisco): Straight Arrow, (1973). 1st issue dustwrapper (slightly rubbed). *(Lopez)* **$85 [≃£44]**
- Fear and Loathing on the Campaign Trail '72. (San Francisco): Straight Arrow, (1973). 2nd issue dustwrapper. *(Lopez)* **$65 [≃£33]**
- Fear and Loathing on the Campaign Trail '72. New York: 1973. Dustwrapper (very slightly rubbed, spine very slightly faded). *(Blakeney)* **£35 [≃$67]**
- Generation of Swine. New York: Summit Books, [1988]. Uncorrected proof copy. Wrappers. *(Dermont)* **$50 [≃£26]**
- The Great Shark Hunt. New York: Summit, (1979). Dustwrapper. *(Lopez)* **$45 [≃£23]**

Thompson, Jim

- The Kill-Off. New York: Lion, 1957. Wrappers, sticker scar on front cover. *(Alphabet)* **$35 [≃£18]**
- The Nothing Man. New York: Dell Publishing, 1954. Paperback original. Wrappers (tiny rub and crease at lower corner of front cover). *(Mordida)* **$125 [≃£65]**

Thubron, Colin

- Emperor. London: Heinemann, 1978. Dustwrapper. *(Dalian)* **£20 [≃$38]**
- Falling. London: Heinemann, 1989. Dustwrapper. Signed by the author. *(David Rees)* **£18 [≃$34]**
- Falling. London: Heinemann, 1989. Dustwrapper. Signed by the author. *(Paul Brown)* **£20 [≃$38]**
- Falling. London: Heinemann, 1989. Dustwrapper. *(Moorhouse)* **£5 [≃$9]**
- The Hills of Adonis. London: Heinemann, 1968. Price-clipped dustwrapper. Author's presentation copy. *(David Rees)* **£35 [≃$67]**
- The Hills of Adonis. London: Heinemann, 1968. Price-clipped dustwrapper. *(Dalian)* **£35 [≃$67]**

Thurber, James

- The Beast in Me and Other Animals. New York: Harcourt, Brace, [1948]. 2nd state. Dustwrapper (a few internal repairs). *(Antic Hay)* **$50 [≃£26]**
- Credos and Curios. New York: Harper & Row, [1962]. Dustwrapper (few tiny tears). *(Antic Hay)* **$30 [≃£15]**
- Further Fables for Our Time. New York: Simon & Schuster, 1956. 1st trade edition. Dustwrapper (few tears, moderate browning). *(Antic Hay)* **$27.50 [≃£14]**
- Lanterns & Lances. New York: Harper, [1961]. Dustwrapper (minor wear). *(Antic Hay)* **$35 [≃£18]**
- Many Moons. London: Hamish Hamilton, 1944. Dustwrapper (torn). *(Green Meadow)* **£20 [≃$38]**
- Men, Women and Dogs. New York: 1943. Dustwrapper (a bit chipped at head). *(Pettler & Liebermann)* **$40 [≃£20]**
- Thurber's Men, Women and Dogs. London: Hamish Hamilton, 1944. 1st English edition. Dustwrapper. *(Limestone Hills)* **$65 [≃£33]**
- My Life and Hard Times. New York: 1933. Dustwrapper. *(Sclanders)* **£60 [≃$115]**
- The Owl in the Attic and Other Perplexities. New York: 1931. Spine sunned, covers dust soiled. *(Polyanthos)* **$75 [≃£39]**
- The Thurber Carnival. New York: Harper, 1945. *(Green Meadow)* **£10 [≃$19]**
- The White Deer. London: Hamish Hamilton, 1946. Dustwrapper. *(Green Meadow)* **£30 [≃$57]**
- The Wonderful O. New York: Simon & Schuster, [1957]. Light soiling at edges. Price-clipped dustwrapper. *(Chapel Hill)* **$60 [≃£31]**

Thwaite, Anthony

- Home Truths. Marvell Press: 1957. Dustwrapper. Signed by the author. His 1st collection. *(Words Etcetera)* **£28 [≃$53]**
- The Owl in the Trees. OUP: 1963. Spine slightly spotted. Dustwrapper. *(Hazeldene)* **£25 [≃$47]**
- Stones of Emptiness. OUP: 1967. Dustwrapper. Signed by the author. *(Hazeldene)* **£20 [≃$38]**

Tidyman, Ernest

- Shaft. New York: Macmillan, 1970. Dustwrapper (short crease on inner front flap). *(Mordida)* **$25 [≃£13]**

Tindall, Gillian

- No Name in the Street. London: Cassell, (1959). Advance proof copy. Wrappers (tiny pinholes affecting front cover and first two pages of text). Her 1st book. *(Holmes)* **$65 [≃£33]**

Tinniswood, Peter

- A Touch of Daniel. London: Hodder & Stoughton, 1968. Page edges slightly tanned. Dustwrapper. *(Glyn's)* **£20 [≃$38]**

Toklas, Alice B.

- The Alice B. Toklas Cookbook ... see Stein, Gertrude.
- Aromas and Flavours of Past and Present. London: 1959. Dustwrapper (very slightly frayed, spine tanned). *(Ellis)* **£25 [≃$47]**
- Staying On Alone. London: Angus & Robertson, 1974. Dustwrapper. *(Hazeldene)* **£20 [≃$38]**
- What is Remembered. New York: Holt, Rinehart, 1963. Dustwrapper. *(Whiteson)* **£30 [≃$57]**

Tolkien, J.R.R.

- Farmer Giles of Ham. London: Allen & Unwin, 1949. Dustwrapper (torn and rubbed). *(Dalian)* **£45 [≃$86]**
- The Letters. Edited by Humphrey Carpenter. Boston: Houghton, 1981. 1st US edition. Dustwrapper. *(Nouveau)* **$20 [≃£10]**
- The Middle English "Lozenger". Paris: 1953. Offprint. Wrappers with small ink traces. *(Blakeney)* **£125 [≃$239]**
- Pictures. London: 1979. Slipcase. *(Words Etcetera)* **£35 [≃$67]**
- The Return of the King. London: Allen & Unwin, 1955. Later dustwrapper. *(Green Meadow)* **£175 [≃$335]**
- The Silmarillion. London: 1977. Dustwrapper. *(First Issues)* **£10 [≃$19]**
- The Silmarillion. London: Allen & Unwin, 1977. One of the copies printed by William Clowes (not by Billing & Sons by offset lithography). Dustwrapper. *(Hazeldene)* **£60 [≃$115]**
- Sir Gawain and the Green Knight. With E.V. Gordon. Oxford: 1925. Errata slip. Text heavily annotated in pencil. Cloth little spotted. *(Polyanthos)* **$100 [≃£52]**
- Smith of Wootton Manor. Boston: Houghton: 1967. 1st US edition. Price-clipped dustwrapper. *(Nouveau)* **$65 [≃£33]**
- Tom Bombadil. London: Allen & Unwin, 1962. Ex-library. Dustwrapper. *(Green Meadow)* **£35 [≃$67]**

- Unfinished Tales. London: 1980. Dustwrapper. *(Roberts)* **£10 [≃$19]**

Tomlinson, Charles

- American Scenes. London: 1966. Dustwrapper. Author's presentation copy. *(Egret)* **£20 [≃$38]**
- In Black & White. London: 1975. Dustwrapper (very slightly torn). *(Egret)* **£18 [≃$34]**
- A Peopled Landscape. London: 1963. Dustwrapper (part faded). Signed by the author. *(Egret)* **£30 [≃$57]**
- Relations and Contraries. Aldington, Kent: Hand and Flower Press, 1951. Wrappers. His 1st collection. *(Egret)* **£65 [≃$124]**
- Relations and Contraries. Hand and Flower Press: 1951. Wrappers. *(Buckley)* **£50 [≃$95]**
- Selected Poems 1951-1974. London: 1978. Dustwrapper. *(Buckley)* **£10 [≃$19]**
- The Way of a World. London: 1969. Name on flyleaf. Wrappers. Author's inscription. *(Egret)* **£15 [≃$28]**

Towne, Stuart

- See Rawson, Clayton.

Townsend, Sue

- The Secret Diary of Adrian Mole. London: Methuen, 1982. Dustwrapper. *(Green Meadow)* **£15 [≃$28]**
- The Secret Diary of Adrian Mole. London: 1982. Dustwrapper. *(Buckley)* **£10 [≃$19]**

Transition

- Transition. Edited by Eugene Jolas and Elliot Paul. Paris: 1927-38. Numbers 1-27 (16/17 & 19/20 double issues), all published. With the 2 supplements pertaining to Gertrude Stein. *(Blakeney)* **£2,250 [≃$4,319]**

Treece, Henry

- The Black Seasons. London: Faber, 1945. Faint discolouration to edges of boards. Dustwrapper (slightly dusty). *(Ash)* **£20 [≃$38]**
- The Dream-Time. London: Brockhampton Press, 1967. One of 30 specially bound. White cover slightly soiled. *(Any Amount)* **£35 [≃$67]**

Tremain, Rose

- The Cupboard. London: Macdonald, 1981. Dustwrapper. *(Lewton)* **£17.50 [≃$34]**
- Sadler's Birthday. London: 1976. Dustwrapper. *(Egret)* **£25 [≃$47]**
- The Swimming Pool Season. London: Hamilton, 1985. Dustwrapper. Signed by the author. *(Lewton)* **£24 [≃$46]**

Trevanian

- The Eiger Sanction. New York: Crown, 1972. Price-clipped dustwrapper. *(Mordida)* **$60 [≃£31]**

Trevelyan, Julian

- Indigo Days. London: MacGibbon, 1957. Dustwrapper. *(Any Amount)* **£16 [≃$30]**

Trevor, William

- Angels at the Ritz and Other Stories. London: 1975. Uncorrected proof. Wrappers. Slightly cocked, a little wear to base of spine, one corner creased. *(Blakeney)* **£35 [≃$67]**
- Angels at the Ritz and Other Stories. London: Bodley Head, 1975. Dustwrapper. *(Dalian)* **£45 [≃$86]**
- Angels at the Ritz. London: 1975. Dustwrapper. *(Egret)* **£25 [≃$47]**
- The Ballroom of Romance. London: Bodley Head, 1972. One corner bumped. Dustwrapper. *(Moorhouse)* **£75 [≃$143]**
- Beyond the Pale and Other Stories. London: Bodley Head, 1981. Dustwrapper. *(Dalian)* **£25 [≃$47]**
- Beyond the Pale. London: Bodley Head, 1981. Dustwrapper. *(Virgo)* **£18.50 [≃$36]**
- The Boarding-House. London: 1965. Dustwrapper (spine very slightly tanned). *(Ellis)* **£80 [≃$153]**
- The Boarding-House. London: Bodley Head, 1965. Dustwrapper (slightly soiled, small chips from corners, one small closed tear in back panel). *(Virgo)* **£60 [≃$115]**
- The Children of Dynmouth. London: 1976. Dustwrapper. *(Blakeney)* **£40 [≃$76]**
- Family Sins and Other Stories. London: Bodley Head, 1990. Uncorrected proof copy. Printed wrappers. Dustwrapper. *(Limestone Hills)* **$45 [≃£23]**
- Family Sins. London: 1990. Dustwrapper. Signed by the author. *(Lewton)* **£16 [≃$30]**
- Fools of Fortune. London: 1983. Dustwrapper. Signed by the author. *(First Issues)* **£35 [≃$67]**
- Fools of Fortune. London: Bodley Head, 1983. Dustwrapper (very slightly marked). *(Dalian)* **£25 [≃$47]**
- The Last Lunch of the Season. London: Covent Garden Press, 1973. One of 600. Wrappers. Signed by the author. *(Moorhouse)* **£50 [≃$95]**

- The Love Department. London: 1966. Dustwrapper (faint staining to bottom third). *(First Issues)* **£40 [≃$76]**
- The Love Department. London: 1966. Dustwrapper. *(Lewton)* **£55 [≃$105]**
- Lovers of Their Time. London: Bodley Head, 1978. Dustwrapper. *(Virgo)* **£30 [≃$57]**
- Miss Gomez and the Brethren. London: 1971. Dustwrapper. *(Ellis)* **£35 [≃$67]**
- Mrs. Eckdorf in O'Neill's Hotel. London: Bodley Head, 1969. Dustwrapper, fine. *(Dalian)* **£65 [≃$124]**
- Nights at the Alexandra. London: Hutchinson, 1987. Dustwrapper, *(Virgo)* **£10 [≃$19]**
- The Old Boys. London: Davis-Poynter, 1971. Wrappers. Signed by the author. His dramatic adaptation of his own novel. *(Moorhouse)* **£25 [≃$47]**
- The Old Boys. London: Davis-Poynter, 1971. Wrappers. *(Dalian)* **£25 [≃$47]**
- The Old Boys. London: Davis-Poynter, 1971. Wrappers. *(Lewton)* **£17.50 [≃$34]**
- Other People's Worlds. London: 1980. Dustwrapper. *(Egret)* **£15 [≃$28]**
- Other People's Worlds. London: Bodley Head, 1980. Dustwrapper. *(Virgo)* **£25 [≃$47]**
- Scenes from an Album. Dublin: Co-op Books, 1981. Wrappers. *(First Issues)* **£15 [≃$28]**
- Scenes from an Album. Dublin: Co-op Books, 1981. Wrappers. *(Moorhouse)* **£12 [≃$23]**
- The Silence in the Garden. London: 1988. Uncorrected proof copy. Oversize dustwrapper (slightly rubbed). *(First Issues)* **£15 [≃$28]**
- The Silence in the Garden. London: Bodley Head, 1988. Dustwrapper. *(Limestone Hills)* **$35 [≃£18]**

Trocchi, Alexander

- Cain's Book. London: Calder, 1963. Dustwrapper. *(Paul Brown)* **£15 [≃$28]**

Tuten, Frederic

- The Adventures of Mao on the Long March. New York: Citadel, (1971). Price-clipped dustwrapper. *(Lopez)* **$75 [≃£39]**

Tyler, Anne

- The Accidental Tourist. New York: Knopf, 1985. Uncorrected proof copy. 2nd issue (red) proof. Spine worn. *(Lopez)* **$40 [≃£20]**
- The Accidental Tourist. New York: Knopf, 1985. 1st US edition. Dustwrapper. *(Lewton)* **£15 [≃$28]**
- The Accidental Tourist. New York: Knopf, 1985. Dustwrapper. *(Michael Johnson)* **£20 [≃$38]**
- Breathing Lessons. Pennsylvania: Franklin Library, 1988. Limited edition signed. Leather. *(Moorhouse)* **£45 [≃$86]**
- Breathing Lessons. New York: Knopf, 1988. Dustwrapper. *(Michael Johnson)* **£17.50 [≃$34]**
- Celestial Navigation. New York: Knopf, 1974. Slight soiling bottom edge. Dustwrapper (lightly worn). *(Between the Covers)* **$75 [≃£39]**
- Celestial Navigation. London: Chatto & Windus, 1974. Dustwrapper. *(Dalian)* **£65 [≃$124]**
- Celestial Navigation. London: Chatto & Windus, 1975. 1st English edition. Dustwrapper (slightly nicked). *(Limestone Hills)* **$75 [≃£39]**
- The Clock Winder. London: 1973. Dustwrapper. *(Egret)* **£55 [≃$105]**
- The Clock Winder. London: Chatto & Windus, 1973. 1st English edition. Dustwrapper. *(Alphabet)* **$200 [≃£104]**
- The Clock Winder. London: Chatto & Windus, 1973. Dustwrapper (top front edge slightly stained). *(Lewton)* **£40 [≃$76]**
- Dinner at the Homesick Restaurant. New York: Knopf, 1982. Uncorrected proof copy. Printed wrappers. Promotional material stapled inside front cover. *(Antic Hay)* **$125 [≃£65]**
- Dinner at the Homesick Restaurant. New York: Knopf, 1982. Dustwrapper. *(Alphabet)* **$45 [≃£23]**
- Dinner at the Homesick Restaurant. New York: Knopf, 1982. Dustwrapper. *(Michael Johnson)* **£33 [≃$63]**
- Dinner at the Homesick Restaurant. New York: Knopf, 1982. Dustwrapper. *(Nouveau)* **$40 [≃£20]**
- Dinner at the Homesick Restaurant. London: Chatto & Windus, 1982. 1st English edition. Dustwrapper. *(Limestone Hills)* **$55 [≃£28]**
- Earthly Possessions. New York: Knopf, 1977. Dustwrapper. *(Lopez)* **$75 [≃£39]**
- Earthly Possessions. New York: Knopf, 1977. Usual fading to edges of boards. Price-clipped dustwrapper. *(Between the Covers)* **$60 [≃£31]**
- Earthly Possessions. New York: Knopf, 1977. Price-clipped dustwrapper. *(Alphabet)* **$50 [≃£26]**
- Earthly Possessions. New York: Knopf,

1977. Red mark on bottom edge. Dustwrapper. *(Nouveau)* **$50 [≃£26]**

- If Morning Ever Comes. New York: Knopf, 1964. Dustwrapper (two short tears at mid spine). Her 1st book. *(Alphabet)* **$450 [≃£234]**
- Morgan's Passing. London: Chatto, 1980. 1st English edition. Dustwrapper. *(Lopez)* **$50 [≃£26]**

Tynan, Kenneth

- Oh! Calcutta!. New York: Grove, (1969). Dustwrapper (few very short tears). *(Between the Covers)* **$45 [≃£23]**

Undset, Sigrid

- Madame Dorothea. New York: Knopf, 1940. 1st American edition. Dustwrapper. Signed by the author. *(Chapel Hill)* **$195 [≃£101]**

Unsworth, Barry

- The Greeks have a Word for It. London: 1967. Dustwrapper (top of spine slightly chipped). *(First Issues)* **£20 [≃$38]**
- The Hide. London: 1970. Dustwrapper. *(First Issues)* **£30 [≃$57]**
- The Partnership. London: 1966. Edges very slightly spotted. Covers slightly spotted, spine ends slightly bruised. Dustwrapper (slightly spotted, few small nicks). His 1st book. *(Ellis)* **£45 [≃$86]**
- The Partnership. London: Hutchinson, 1966. Dustwrapper. His 1st book. *(Clearwater)* **£28 [≃$53]**
- The Partnership. London: New Authors, 1966. Dustwrapper. *(Lewton)* **£27.50 [≃$53]**

Updike, John

- The Angels. King & Queen Press, 1968. One of 50. Original envelope. *(Nouveau)* **$750 [≃£390]**
- Assorted Prose. New York: 1965. Name. Slight dustiness to boards. Dustwrapper with some overprinting off-centre. *(Pettler & Liebermann)* **$45 [≃£23]**
- Bech is Back. New York: 1982. Dustwrapper. Author's signed presentation copy. *(Polyanthos)* **$45 [≃£23]**
- Bech is Back. New York: Knopf, 1982. 1st trade edition. Dustwrapper. *(Nouveau)* **$20 [≃£10]**
- Bech is Back. New York: Knopf, 1982. Dustwrapper. Signed by the author. *(Between the Covers)* **$65 [≃£33]**
- Bech is Back. London: Deutsch, 1983. Dustwrapper. *(Dalian)* **£16 [≃$30]**
- Bech: A Book. London: Deutsch, 1970. Price-clipped dustwrapper. *(Dalian)* **£25 [≃$47]**
- Buchanan Dying. New York: Knopf, 1974. Dustwrapper. Signed by the author. *(Between the Covers)* **$85 [≃£44]**
- Buchanan Dying. London: 1974. Price-clipped dustwrapper. Author's signed presentation copy. *(Polyanthos)* **$50 [≃£26]**
- The Carpentered Hen and Other Tame Creatures. New York: Harper, (1958). Dustwrapper. Inscribed by the author. *(Bromer)* **$950 [≃£494]**
- The Carpentered Hen and Other Tame Creatures. New York: Harper, [1958]. Dustwrapper (short tear, some soiling rear panel). His 1st book. *(Antic Hay)* **$350 [≃£182]**
- The Centaur. London: Deutsch, [1963]. 1st English edition. Dustwrapper (lightly used). *(Dermont)* **$45 [≃£23]**
- The Coup. New York: Knopf, 1978. One of 350 signed. Dustwrapper. Slipcase. *(Houle)* **$150 [≃£78]**
- The Coup. New York: 1978. Dustwrapper. Author's signed presentation copy. *(Polyanthos)* **$50 [≃£26]**
- The Coup. London: Deutsch, 1979. Dustwrapper. *(Dalian)* **£20 [≃$38]**
- Couples. London: Deutsch, 1968. Dustwrapper. *(Sklaroff)* **£20 [≃$38]**
- Couples. London: Deutsch, 1968. 1st English edition. Dustwrapper. *(Limestone Hills)* **$55 [≃£28]**
- Cunts: (Upon receiving the Swingers Life Club Membership Solicitation). New York: Frank Hallman, (1974). One of 250 signed. *(Houle)* **$165 [≃£85]**
- Ego and Art in Walt Whitman. Targ Editions: 1980. One of 350 signed. Dustwrapper. *(Nouveau)* **$90 [≃£46]**
- Emersonianism. Ewert: 1985. One of 200 (of 203) signed. *(Nouveau)* **$90 [≃£46]**
- Facing Nature. New York: Knopf, 1985. Dustwrapper. Author's signed presentation inscription. *(Woolmer)* **$150 [≃£78]**
- From the Journal of a Leper. Lord John: 1978. One of 300 signed. *(Nouveau)* **$90 [≃£46]**
- Getting the Words Out. Lord John Press: 1988. One of 250 signed. *(Dermont)* **$50 [≃£26]**
- A Good Place ... [New York]: Aloe Editions, 1973. 1st edition thus. One of 100 (of 126) signed. Stiff wrappers. *(Houle)* **$275 [≃£143]**
- A Good Place. Aloe: (1973). One of 100 signed. Wrappers. *(Lopez)* **$300 [≃£156]**
- Hawthorne's Creed. Targ: 1981. One of 250

signed. *(Nouveau)* **$80 [≈£41]**

- Hoping for a Hoopoe. London: 1959. Dustwrapper. Author's signed presentation copy. His 1st book (in US The Carpentered Hen). *(Polyanthos)* **$125 [≈£65]**
- Hoping for a Hoopoe. London: Gollancz, 1959. 1st English edition of The Carpentered Hen. Dustwrapper. *(First Issues)* **£40 [≈$76]**
- Hoping for a Hoopoe. London: Gollancz, 1959. 1st English edition. Dustwrapper. His 1st book. *(Nouveau)* **$65 [≈£33]**
- Hoping for a Hoopoe. London: 1959. Dustwrapper. *(Buckley)* **£28 [≈$53]**
- Jester's Dozen. Lord John: 1984. One of 150 signed. *(Nouveau)* **$80 [≈£41]**
- Just Looking. New York: Knopf, 1989. One of 350 signed. Slipcase. *(Nouveau)* **$150 [≈£78]**
- Just Looking. New York: Knopf, 1989. Dustwrapper. *(Nouveau)* **$35 [≈£18]**
- Marry Me. New York: 1976. One of 300 signed. Dustwrapper. Slipcase. *(Pettler & Liebermann)* **$85 [≈£44]**
- Marry Me. New York: 1976. Dustwrapper. Signed by the author. *(Polyanthos)* **$45 [≈£23]**
- Marry Me. London: Deutsch, 1977. Dustwrapper. *(Dalian)* **£20 [≈$38]**
- A Month of Sundays. New York: 1975. Spine extremities slightly rubbed. Dustwrapper. Author's signed presentation copy. *(Polyanthos)* **$50 [≈£26]**
- A Month of Sundays. New York: 1975. Dustwrapper. *(Antic Hay)* **$25 [≈£13]**
- A Month of Sundays. New York: Knopf, 1975. Price-clipped dustwrapper. Signed by the author. *(Between the Covers)* **$85 [≈£44]**
- More Stately Mansions. Nouveau Press: 1987. One of 300 signed. *(Nouveau)* **$65 [≈£33]**
- The Music School. New York: Knopf, 1966. 1st issue, lines on page 46 transposed. Small bookplate. Dustwrapper. *(Nouveau)* **$150 [≈£78]**
- The Music School. London: Deutsch, 1967. Foredge and prelims slightly foxed. Price-clipped dustwrapper. *(Dalian)* **£25 [≈$47]**
- An Oddly Lovely Day Alone. Richmond, Virginia: Waves Press, 1979. One of 276 signed. Broadside. *(Black Sun)* **$75 [≈£39]**
- Of the Farm. New York: Knopf, 1965. Price-clipped dustwrapper. *(Nouveau)* **$60 [≈£31]**
- Of the Farm. New York: 1965. Dustwrapper. *(Words Etcetera)* **£75 [≈$143]**
- Of the Farm. London: Deutsch, 1966. Dustwrapper (very slightly rubbed). *(Dalian)* **£45 [≈$86]**
- Picked-Up Pieces. London: Deutsch, 1976. 1st English edition. Dustwrapper. *(Nouveau)* **$65 [≈£33]**
- Pigeon Feathers and Other Stories. New York: 1962. Dustwrapper (faintly sunned). *(Buckley)* **£35 [≈$67]**
- The Poorhouse Fair. New York: Knopf, 1959. Dustwrapper (small nick, tape repair). *(Houle)* **$175 [≈£91]**
- The Poorhouse Fair. London: Gollancz, 1959. 1st British edition. Page edges slightly foxed. Dustwrapper (slightly nicked). *(Michael Johnson)* **£80 [≈$153]**
- Problems and Other Stories. New York: 1979. Dustwrapper. Signed by the author. *(Polyanthos)* **$35 [≈£18]**
- Rabbit is Rich. New York: 1981. Dustwrapper. Signed by the author. *(Polyanthos)* **$35 [≈£18]**
- Rabbit is Rich. New York: Knopf, 1981. 1st trade edition. Dustwrapper. *(Nouveau)* **$25 [≈£13]**
- Rabbit, Run. New York: Knopf, 1960. Price-clipped dustwrapper (lightly rubbed). *(Nouveau)* **$150 [≈£78]**
- S. London: Deutsch, (1988). One of 87 (of 95) signed. Quarter leather. Slipcase. *(Lopez)* **$275 [≈£143]**
- S. New York: 1988. Dustwrapper. Author's signed presentation copy. *(Polyanthos)* **$45 [≈£23]**
- Self-Consciousness. New York: Knopf, 1989. Uncorrected proof copy. Wrappers. *(Lopez)* **$100 [≈£52]**
- Self-Consciousness. New York: Knopf, 1989. Dustwrapper. Signed by the author. *(Michael Johnson)* **£30 [≈$57]**
- 75 Aromatic Years of Leavitt & Peirce [In] The Recollection of 31 Harvard Men. Cambridge, MA: Leavitt & Peirce, 1958. Wrappers. *(Lopez)* **$85 [≈£44]**
- Sunday in Boston. N.p.: Rook Broadsides, 1975. One of 300. Broadside. *(Black Sun)* **$25 [≈£13]**
- Talk from the Fifties. Northridge: Lord John Press, 1979. One of 300 (of 375) signed. *(Houle)* **$125 [≈£65]**
- Telephone Poles. London: Deutsch, 1964. 1st English edition. Dustwrapper. *(Nouveau)* **$45 [≈£23]**
- Telephone Poles. London: 1964. Dustwrapper. *(First Issues)* **£10 [≈$19]**
- Three Illuminations in the Life of an American Author. Targ Editions: 1979. One of 350 signed. Tissue dustwrapper.

(Dermont) **$75 [≃£39]**

- Three Illuminations in the Life of an American Actor. New York: Targ Editions, 1979. One of 350 signed. This copy unnumbered and marked "review copy". Tissue dustwrapper. *(Antic Hay)* **$175 [≃£91]**
- Trust Me. New York: Knopf, 1987. 1st trade edition. Dustwrapper. *(Nouveau)* **$20 [≃£10]**
- The Witches of Eastwick. Franklin Center: The Franklin Library, 1984. Signed limited edition (limitation unknown). Leather, a.e.g. *(Antic Hay)* **$60 [≃£31]**

Upfield, Arthur W.

- The Body at Madman's Bend. Garden City: Doubleday, 1963. Precedes British and Australian editions. Dustwrapper. *(Janus)* **$65 [≃£33]**
- Bony and the Kelly Gang. London: Heinemann, 1960. 1st English edition (published in the US as Valley of Smugglers). Price-clipped dustwrapper. *(Mordida)* **$35 [≃£18]**
- Bony Buys a Woman. London: Heinemann, 1957. Dustwrapper (worn but bright). *(Limestone Hills)* **$45 [≃£23]**
- Man of Two Tribes. London: Heinemann, 1956. 1st English edition. Price-clipped dustwrapper. *(Mordida)* **$90 [≃£46]**
- The Mystery of Swordfish Reef. Sydney: Angus & Robertson, 1939. 1st edition. Light foxing on edges, ring mark on front cover. Dustwrapper (minor wear). *(Mordida)* **$435 [≃£226]**
- The Mystery of Swordfish Reef. London: Heinemann, 1960. 1st English edition. Dustwrapper (slightly chipped). *(Limestone Hills)* **$55 [≃£28]**
- The Widows of Broome. Garden City: Doubleday, 1950. Dustwrapper. *(Janus)* **$55 [≃£28]**
- The Will of the Tribe. London: Heinemann, 1962. 1st English edition. Price-clipped dustwrapper. *(Janus)* **$50 [≃£26]**

Upward, Edward

- The Spiral Ascent: a Trilogy. London: Heinemann, 1977. Dustwrapper. Signed by the author. *(Sklaroff)* **£65 [≃$124]**

Uris, Leon

- The Angry Hills. New York: Random House, [1955]. Price-clipped dustwrapper (lightly used). *(Antic Hay)* **$75 [≃£39]**
- Battle Cry. New York: Putnam, (1953). Advance copy, with publisher's letter laid in. Dustwrapper (small chips). Author's inscription. *(Houle)* **$250 [≃£130]**
- Battle Cry. New York: Putnam's, [1953]. Paper covered boards (minor soil top and bottom edge). Price-clipped dustwrapper (two tiny chips). Signed by the author. His 1st book. *(Antic Hay)* **$175 [≃£91]**
- Exodus. London: 1959. Dustwrapper (slightly creased, very little marked). *(Blakeney)* **£15 [≃$28]**
- Ob VII. Garden City: Doubleday, 1970. Publisher's Compliments stamp on pastedown. Dustwrapper. *(Antic Hay)* **$35 [≃£18]**
- Trinity. Garden City: Doubleday, 1976. 1st trade edition. Dustwrapper (minor rubbing). Signed by the author on tipped in leaf. *(Antic Hay)* **$75 [≃£39]**

Uttley, Alison

- Grey Rabbit's May Day. London: Collins, 1963. Dustwrapper. *(Green Meadow)* **£17.50 [≃$34]**
- Hare and the Easter Eggs. London: Collins, 1952. Dustwrapper (lightly repaired). *(Green Meadow)* **£15 [≃$28]**
- Moonshine and Magic. London: Faber, 1932. Pictorial cloth. *(Green Meadow)* **£25 [≃$47]**

Vachss, Andrew

- Blue Belle. New York: Knopf, 1988. Special Advance Readers Edition. Pictorial wrappers. *(Michael Johnson)* **£35 [≃$67]**
- Blue Belle. New York: Knopf, 1988. Dustwrapper. Signed by the author. *(Michael Johnson)* **£25 [≃$47]**
- Flood. New York: Donald I. Fine, 1985. Dustwrapper. Signed by the author. *(Michael Johnson)* **£35 [≃$67]**
- Flood. New York: Don I Fine, 1985. Dustwrapper. *(Michael Johnson)* **£20 [≃$38]**
- Flood. London: Collins, 1986. 1st British edition. Hardbound. Dustwrapper. Signed by the author. *(Michael Johnson)* **£18 [≃$34]**
- Hard Candy. New York: Knopf, 1989. Dustwrapper. Signed by the author. *(Michael Johnson)* **£24 [≃$46]**
- Strega. New York: Knopf, 1987. Dustwrapper. Signed by the author. *(Michael Johnson)* **£25 [≃$47]**

Valin, Jonathan

- Final Notice. New York: Dodd, 1980. Closed tear on one page. Dustwrapper. *(Janus)* **$50 [≃£26]**

Van der Post, Laurens

- The Hunter and the Whale. London: 1967. Dustwrapper. Author's signed presentation copy. *(Polyanthos)* **$45 [≃£23]**

Van Dine, S.S.

- The Dragon Murder Case. New York: Scribner, 1933. Small hole on one page. Dustwrapper (tiny wear spine ends and corners). *(Mordida)* **$450 [≃£234]**
- The Garden Murder Case. New York: Scribner, 1935. Dustwrapper (tiny wear spine ends and corners). *(Mordida)* **$200 [≃£104]**

Van Doren, Carl

- The Great Rehearsal. New York: 1948. One of 350 signed. Box. *(Polyanthos)* **$75 [≃£39]**

Van Doren, Mark

- The Country Year. New York: Sloane, [1946]. Dustwrapper (minor wear). Signed by the author. *(Antic Hay)* **$75 [≃£39]**

Van Gulik, Robert

- The Chinese Bell Murders. London: Michael Joseph, 1958. 1st English edition. Gilt on spine dulled. Price-clipped dustwrapper (corners very slightly worn, top of back panel slightly creased). *(Virgo)* **£65 [≃$124]**
- The Chinese Gold Murders. New York: Harpers, [1959]. Dustwrapper. *(Dermont)* **$30 [≃£15]**
- The Chinese Gold Murders. New York: Harper, [1959]. 1st American edition. Dustwrapper (some wear, rear panel soiled). *(Antic Hay)* **$25 [≃£13]**
- The Chinese Nail Murders. New York: Harper & Row, [1961]. 1st American edition. Dustwrapper. *(Antic Hay)* **$50 [≃£26]**
- De Gong An: Three Murder Cases Solved by Judge Dee. Tokyo: Privately Printed, 1949. One of 1200 signed. Pages browned. Board edges rubbed. Dustwrapper (soiled). *(Mordida)* **$900 [≃£468]**
- The Haunted Monastery. London: Heinemann, 1963. 1st English edition. Small label on pastedown. Dustwrapper. *(Mordida)* **$80 [≃£41]**
- The Lacquer Screen. London: Heinemann. 1964. Dustwrapper (very slightly rubbed). *(Dalian)* **£35 [≃$67]**
- The Monkey and the Tiger. London: Heinemann, 1965. Dustwrapper. *(Mordida)* **$75 [≃£39]**
- Murder in Canton. London: Heinemann, 1966. Dustwrapper (corners and edges rubbed). *(Mordida)* **$95 [≃£49]**
- The Red Pavilion. Kuala Lumpur: Art Printing Works, 1961. 1st edition. Top corner slightly bumped. Stiff wrappers. *(Mordida)* **$550 [≃£286]**
- The Red Pavilion. London: Heinemann, 1964. Dustwrapper (lacks one inch from front panel). *(Dalian)* **£35 [≃$67]**
- The Red Pavilion. New York: Scribner's, [1968]. 1st American edition. Dustwrapper. *(Antic Hay)* **$45 [≃£23]**

Van Vogt, A.E.

- The Mind Cage. New York: Simon & Schuster, 1957. Dustwrapper. *(Dermont)* **$35 [≃£18]**
- The Mixed Man. New York: Gnome Press, [1952]. Dustwrapper (slight wear). *(Dermont)* **$50 [≃£26]**
- The World of A. New York: Simon & Schuster, 1958. Dustwrapper (lightly dust soiled). *(Dermont)* **$35 [≃£18]**

Vance, John Holbrook

- The Man in the Cage. New York: Random House, 1960. Top edge slightly discoloured. Name. Dustwrapper (short tear back panel, tiny wear at spine ends). *(Mordida)* **$115 [≃£59]**
- The Pleasant Grove Murders. Indianopolis: Bobbs-Merrill, 1967. Light staining on top edge. Dustwrapper (several short closed tears, spine slightly faded). *(Mordida)* **$85 [≃£44]**

Vickers, Roy

- (Introduces) Some Like Them Dead. London: Hodder and Stoughton, 1960. Dustwrapper (spine slightly faded, back panel soiled). *(Mordida)* **$350 [≃£182]**

Vidal, Gore

- The City and the Pillar. London: John Lehmann, 1949. Edges spotted. Dustwrapper (rubbed and nicked, spine faded). *(Moorhouse)* **£25 [≃$47]**
- Creation. New York: Random House, (1981). One of 500 signed. Slipcase. *(Houle)* **$125 [≃£65]**
- Creation. New York: Random House, [1981]. One of 500 signed. Slipcase, shrink-wrap, unopened. *(Antic Hay)* **$100 [≃£52]**
- Creation. New York: Random House, 1981. Dustwrapper. *(Nouveau)* **$20 [≃£10]**
- Death Before Bedtime. By Edgar Box. New York: Dutton, 1953. Dustwrapper (used). *(Alphabet)* **$40 [≃£20]**
- Death Before Bedtime. By Edgar Box. London: 1954. Some browning to flyleaf.

Dustwrapper (torn at head of spine). *(Words Etcetera)* **£45 [≃$86]**

- Death Likes It Hot. By Edgar Box. London: 1955. Dustwrapper (trifle rubbed and frayed at extreme edges). *(Words Etcetera)* **£55 [≃$105]**
- Duluth. New York: 1983. Dustwrapper. Bookplate signed by the author. *(Polyanthos)* **$30 [≃£15]**
- 1876. New York: Random House, (1976). One of 300 signed. Slipcase. *(Houle)* **$135 [≃£70]**
- 1876. New York: Random House, 1976. One of 300 signed. Slipcase. *(Nouveau)* **$100 [≃£52]**
- Empire. New York: 1987. Dustwrapper. Signed by the author. *(Polyanthos)* **$35 [≃£18]**
- An Evening with Richard Nixon. New York: 1972. Dustwrapper. Bookplate signed by the author. *(Polyanthos)* **$30 [≃£15]**
- Hollywood: A Novel of America in the 1920s. New York: RH, (1990). Uncorrected proof copy. *(Lopez)* **$40 [≃£20]**
- In a Yellow Wood. New York: Dutton, 1947. Little foxing on endpapers. Dustwrapper (trace of rubbing to extremities). *(Between the Covers)* **$325 [≃£169]**
- The Judgment of Paris. New York: Dutton, 1952. Dustwrapper (small repaired nick on rear panel). *(Alphabet)* **$125 [≃£65]**
- Kalki. New York: Random House, 1978. Dustwrapper. *(Nouveau)* **$20 [≃£10]**
- Lincoln. Franklin Center: The Franklin Library, 1984. Signed, limited edition. Blue calf gilt, a.e.g., ribbon marker. *(Antic Hay)* **$75 [≃£39]**
- Lincoln. New York: Random House, (1984). One of 350 signed. Slipcase. *(Houle)* **$150 [≃£78]**
- Messiah. Dutton, 1954. Dustwrapper. *(Nouveau)* **$50 [≃£26]**
- Myra Breckinridge. Boston: 1968. Dustwrapper (two tiny edge tears). Bookplate signed by the author. *(Polyanthos)* **$30 [≃£15]**
- Myra Breckinridge. London: Blond, 1968. Dustwrapper (rubbed). *(Glyn's)* **£15 [≃$28]**
- Myron. New York: Random House, 1974. Dustwrapper. *(Nouveau)* **$25 [≃£13]**
- Reflections from a Sinking Ship. Boston: Little, Brown, 1969. Dustwrapper. *(Nouveau)* **$35 [≃£18]**
- Rocking the Boat. Boston: Little, Brown, 1962. Dustwrapper. *(Nouveau)* **$40 [≃£20]**
- Romulus. The Broadway Adaptation. New York: Grove, (1966). Price-clipped dustwrapper. *(Lopez)* **$45 [≃£23]**
- Romulus: The Broadway Adaptation. New York: Grove, [1966]. Bookplate. Price-clipped dustwrapper. *(Antic Hay)* **$25 [≃£13]**
- The Season of Comfort. New York: Dutton, 1949. Dustwrapper (internal tape strengthening). *(Lopez)* **$75 [≃£39]**
- The Second American Revolution and Other Essays. New York: 1982. Dustwrapper. Bookplate signed by the author. *(Polyanthos)* **$30 [≃£15]**
- Sex, Death and Money. New York: Bantam, (1968). Paperback. *(Lopez)* **$40 [≃£20]**
- A Thirsty Evil. London: Heinemann, 1958. Light foxing. Dustwrapper. *(Paul Brown)* **£15 [≃$28]**
- Two Sisters. Boston: Little, Brown, [1970]. Uncorrected proof copy. Wrappers. *(Dermont)* **$45 [≃£23]**
- Two Sisters. Boston: Little, Brown, 1970. Dustwrapper (nicked, lightly rubbed). *(Nouveau)* **$30 [≃£15]**
- Washington, D.C. Boston: Little, Brown, 1967. Dustwrapper. *(Nouveau)* **$30 [≃£15]**
- Williwaw. New York: Dutton, (1946). Name on front fly. Dustwrapper (very slight rubbing, very minor piece of tape internally). His 1st book. *(Between the Covers)* **$375 [≃£195]**
- Williwaw. US: 1946. 1st US edition. Spine ends rubbed. Dustwrapper (rubbed, chipped). *(Ellis)* **£75 [≃$143]**

Vine, Barbara

- Pseudonym used by Ruth Rendell, q.v.

Vollman, William T.

- The Rainbow Stories. London: Deutsch, (1989). Dustwrapper. Signed by the author. *(Lopez)* **$65 [≃£33]**
- You Bright and Risen Angels; A Cartoon. London: Deutsch, 1987. Small rubber stamp on bottom edge. Price-clipped dustwrapper. His 1st book. *(Alphabet)* **$30 [≃£15]**

Vonnegut, Kurt

- Bluebeard. New York: Delacorte, (1987). Dustwrapper. Signed by the author. *(Between the Covers)* **$85 [≃£44]**
- Breakfast of Champions. New York: 1973. Dustwrapper. Bookplate signed by the author. *(Polyanthos)* **$40 [≃£20]**
- Breakfast of Champions. New York: Delacorte, 1973. Dustwrapper (two small internal repairs). Author's inscription.

(Between the Covers) **$100 [≃£52]**

- Deadeye Dick. New York: Delacorte, [1982]. One of 350 signed. Slipcase, shink-wrap, unopened. *(Antic Hay)* **$100 [≃£52]**
- Deadeye Dick. New York: Delacorte, (1982). Dustwrapper. Signed by the author. *(Between the Covers)* **$85 [≃£44]**
- Jailbird. New York: Delacorte / Seymour Lawrence, (1979). One of 500 signed. Slipcase. *(Houle)* **$135 [≃£70]**
- Jailbird. New York: Delacorte, Lawrence, [1979]. Dustwrapper. *(Antic Hay)* **$25 [≃£13]**
- Mother Night. New York: Gold Medal Original, 1962. Wrappers (tanned). Priced at 35c. *(Hazeldene)* **£20 [≃$38]**
- Mother Night. New York: Harper, 1966. Bookplate. Three small initials bottom edge. Dustwrapper. *(Nouveau)* **$85 [≃£44]**
- Mother Night. London: 1968. 1st English edition. Dustwrapper (very slightly browned). *(Words Etcetera)* **£45 [≃$86]**
- Mother Night. London: 1968. Dustwrapper (slightly soiled, one short closed tear, spine lightly browned). *(Sclanders)* **£35 [≃$67]**
- Palm Sunday. New York: 1981. One of 500 signed. Box. *(Polyanthos)* **$75 [≃£39]**
- Palm Sunday. New York: Delacorte, [1981]. One of 500 signed. Slipcase, shink-wrap, unopened. *(Antic Hay)* **$85 [≃£44]**
- The Sirens of Titan. Dell, 1959. Wrappers. *(Nouveau)* **$40 [≃£20]**
- Slapstick. New York: 1976. Price-clipped dustwrapper. Signed by the author. *(Polyanthos)* **$30 [≃£15]**
- Slaughterhouse Five. New York: Delacorte, (1969). Bottom corner bumped. Dustwrapper (slight offsetting rear panel). *(Between the Covers)* **$125 [≃£65]**
- Slaughterhouse-Five. New York: 1969. Signed by the author. *(Polyanthos)* **$75 [≃£39]**
- Slaughterhouse 5. London: 1970. Slightly cocked. Dustwrapper (slightly rubbed). *(Ellis)* **£45 [≃$86]**
- Wampeters, Foma and Granfalloons. New York: Delacorte, (1974). Uncorrected proof copy. Wrappers. *(Lopez)* **$200 [≃£104]**
- Wampeters Foma and Granfalloons. New York: 1974. Dustwrapper. Bookplate signed by the author. *(Polyanthos)* **$40 [≃£20]**

Wade, Henry

- The Verdict of You All. London: Constable, 1926.. His 1st book. *(Any Amount)* **£24 [≃$46]**

Wah, Fred

- Lardeau. Toronto: Island Press, 1965. One of 344 (of 350). Tape bound wrappers. Author's presentation. His 1st book. *(Alphabet)* **$115 [≃£59]**

Wain, John

- Mixed Feelings. Nineteen Poems. Reading: School of Art, Reading University, 1951. One of 120. With a single-page "List of Subscribers before Publication". Wrappers (slightly soiled, backstrip very slightly bumped at head). His 1st book. *(Georges)* **£75 [≃$143]**
- The Smaller Sky. London: Macmillan, 1967. Dustwrapper. *(Paul Brown)* **£10 [≃$19]**
- Strike the Father Dead. London: Macmillan, 1962. Price-clipped dustwrapper. *(Paul Brown)* **£10 [≃$19]**

Wakoski, Diane

- Coins & Coffins. New York: Hawk's Well Press, 1962. Wrappers. Her 1st book. *(Any Amount)* **£30 [≃$57]**
- The Magellanic Clouds. Santa Barbara: Black Sparrow, 1970. One of 250 signed. Acetate dustwrapper (slightly chipped). *(Any Amount)* **£30 [≃$57]**

Walcott, Derek

- The Castaway. London: 1965. Dustwrapper. *(Egret)* **£40 [≃$76]**
- Dream on Monkey Mountain and Other Plays. London: Cape, 1972. Advance proof copy. Wrappers. Proof dustwrapper. *(Dalian)* **£45 [≃$86]**
- The Gulf. London: 1969. Dustwrapper. *(Egret)* **£35 [≃$67]**
- In a Green Night. London: Cape, 1962. Small stamp on title. Price-clipped dustwrapper. Author's signed and dated (1962) presentation copy. *(Dalian)* **£125 [≃$239]**
- In a Green Night. London: 1962. Spine ends slightly bruised. Dustwrapper (rubbed, slightly frayed, head of spine nicked). *(Ellis)* **£50 [≃$95]**
- The Joker of Seville & O Babylon. London: Cape, 1979. Wrappers. *(Dalian)* **£18 [≃$34]**
- Selected Poems. New York: Farrar, (1964). 1st US edition. Dustwrapper (edges darkened). *(Woolmer)* **$75 [≃£39]**
- The Star-Apple Kingdom. New York: Farrar Straus & Giroux, 1979. Dustwrapper. *(Dalian)* **£20 [≃$38]**

Waldman, Anne

- Giant Knight. New York: Corinth, 1970. Dustwrapper (three small stains on lower cover). Signed presentation copy. Her 1st book. *(Any Amount)* **£25 [≃$47]**

Waley, Arthur

- Chinese Poems. London: Allen & Unwin, 1946. Endpapers slightly browned. Dustwrapper (slightly rubbed, very slightly nicked). *(Dalian)* **£25 [≃$47]**
- The Life and Times of Po Chu-I. London: Allen & Unwin, 1949. Dustwrapper (slightly chipped and rubbed). *(Dalian)* **£35 [≃$67]**
- More Translations from the Chinese. London: Allen & Unwin, 1919. Variant in white printed wrappers. *(Dalian)* **£75 [≃$143]**
- The Nine Songs. London: Allen & Unwin, 1955. Dustwrapper (slightly rubbed, very slightly nicked). *(Dalian)* **£45 [≃$86]**
- Poems from the Chinese. The Augustan Books of English Poetry. London: Benn, (1927). White printed wrappers (very slightly dusty). *(Dalian)* **£16 [≃$30]**
- The Temple and Other Poems. London: Allen & Unwin, 1923. Dustwrapper, fine. *(Dalian)* **£85 [≃$163]**
- Translations from the Chinese. New York: Knopf, 1941. Illustrated by C.L. Baldridge. Slipcase. *(Wreden)* **$45 [≃£23]**
- Johns, Francis A.: A Bibliography of Arthur Waley. New Brunswick: Rutgers UP, 1968. 1st American edition. No dustwrapper issued. *(Dalian)* **£25 [≃$47]**

Walker, Alice

- The Color Purple. London: 1986. 1st English hardback edition. Dustwrapper. *(First Issues)* **£15 [≃$28]**
- Color Purple. London: Women's Press, 1986. 1st British edition. Hardbound. Dustwrapper. *(Michael Johnson)* **£20 [≃$38]**
- Meridian. New York: HBJ, (1976). Dustwrapper. *(Lopez)* **$200 [≃£104]**
- Temple of My Familiar. New York: Harcourt, Brace, 1989. Dustwrapper. Signed by the author. *(Michael Johnson)* **£32 [≃$61]**
- The Temple of My Familiar. San Diego: 1989. Dustwrapper. Signed by the author. *(Polyanthos)* **$35 [≃£18]**
- Temple of My Familiar. London: Women's Press, 1989. 1st British edition. Uncorrected proof copy. Pink wrappers (ink line on corner of front panel, a few creases). *(Michael Johnson)* **£45 [≃$86]**
- You Can't Keep a Good Woman Down. New York: HBJ, (1981). Small owner's name. Dustwrapper. *(Between the Covers)* **$175 [≃£91]**

Wallant, Edward Lewis

- The Children at the Gate. New York: Harcourt, Brace & World, [1964]. Dustwrapper. *(Dermont)* **$60 [≃£31]**

Warhol, Andy

- Andy Warhol's Exposures. London: Hutchinson, 1979. Dustwrapper. Signed by the author 'Andy'. *(Any Amount)* **£80 [≃$153]**

Warner, Marina

- In a Dark Wood. London: 1977. Dustwrapper. *(First Issues)* **£15 [≃$28]**

Warner, Rex

- Poems and Contradictions. London: John Lane; The Bodley Head, 1943. Dustwrapper (slightly dusty and nicked). *(Dalian)* **£25 [≃$47]**
- Why Was I Killed? A Dramatic Dialogue. London: John Lane; The Bodley Head, 1943. Cloth very slightly sunned. Name. No endpapers issued. Dustwrapper. *(Dalian)* **£35 [≃$67]**
- The Wild Goose Chase. Boriswood, 1937. Foredge and endpapers very slightly foxed. Dustwrapper (very slightly dusty). *(Dalian)* **£55 [≃$105]**

Warner, Sylvia Townsend

- Azrael & Other Poems. Libanus Press: 1978. One of 200. Wrappers. *(Egret)* **£35 [≃$67]**
- Elinor Barley. London: Cresset Press, 1930. One of 350 signed. Vellum spine (soiled), boards (edges rubbed). *(Virgo)* **£175 [≃$335]**
- The Innocent and the Guilty. London: 1971. Spine a trifle bumped. Dustwrapper. *(Egret)* **£15 [≃$28]**
- Kingdoms of Elfin. London: 1977. Dustwrapper. *(Egret)* **£18 [≃$34]**
- Letters. London: 1982. Dustwrapper. *(Egret)* **£9 [≃$17]**
- Lolly Willowes. London: Chatto & Windus, 1926. Dustwrapper (frayed and chipped). *(Virgo)* **£30 [≃$57]**
- Mr Fortune's Maggot. London: 1927. Dustwrapper (very slightly rubbed and chipped). *(Buckley)* **£75 [≃$143]**
- Mr Fortunes Maggot. London: Chatto & Windus, 1927. Dustwrapper. *(Virgo)* **£45 [≃$86]**
- The Museum of Cheats and Other Stories.

London: Chatto & Windus, 1947. Endpapers slightly browned. Dustwrapper (rubbed). *(Dalian)* **£20 [≃$38]**
- One Thing Leading to Another. London: 1984. Dustwrapper. *(Egret)* **£10 [≃$19]**
- The Salutation. London: 1932. Two corners slightly bumped. Dustwrapper (spine darkened, slightly stained at one edge). *(Buckley)* **£35 [≃$67]**
- T.H. White. London: 1967. Dustwrapper. *(Egret)* **£25 [≃$47]**
- Twelve Poems. London: 1980. Price-clipped dustwrapper. *(Egret)* **£10 [≃$19]**

Warren, Robert Penn
- All the King's Men. London: 1948. Inscription and owner's stamp. Dustwrapper (slightly chipped and rubbed). *(Clearwater)* **£50 [≃$95]**
- At Heaven's Gate. New York: Harcourt, Brace, [1943]. Dustwrapper (edge wear and light chipping at crown and mostly to rear panel). *(Dermont)* **$100 [≃£52]**
- Audubon. New York: 1969. Price-clipped dustwrapper. Bookplate signed by the author. *(Polyanthos)* **$45 [≃£23]**
- Audubon. New York: Random House, 1969. Dustwrapper (reinforced, few short closed tears). *(Nouveau)* **$40 [≃£20]**
- Band of Angels. New York: Random House, 1955. Dustwrapper. *(Nouveau)* **$60 [≃£31]**
- Being Here. Poetry 1977-1980. New York: RH, (1980). Price-clipped dustwrapper. Signed by the author. *(Lopez)* **$65 [≃£33]**
- Brother to Dragons. New York: 1979. Dustwrapper. Author's signed presentation copy. *(Polyanthos)* **$65 [≃£33]**
- Brother to Dragons. New York: Random House, 1953. Dustwrapper (one short tear, one insignificant chip). Signed by the author. *(Nouveau)* **$90 [≃£46]**
- The Cave. New York: 1959. Dustwrapper. Bookplate signed by the author. *(Polyanthos)* **$50 [≃£26]**
- The Cave. New York: Random House, 1959. Price-clipped dustwrapper (rubbed, chip at top of spine). Signed by the author. *(Nouveau)* **$65 [≃£33]**
- The Cave. New York: RH, (1959). Price-clipped dustwrapper. Signed by the author. *(Lopez)* **$85 [≃£44]**
- Chief Joseph of the Nez Perce. New York: 1983. Pictorial wrappers. Author's signed presentation copy. *(Polyanthos)* **$45 [≃£23]**
- Chief Joseph of the Nez Perce. New York: 1983. Dustwrapper. Author's signed presentation copy. *(Polyanthos)* **$65 [≃£33]**
- The Circus in the Attic. Harcourt, 1947. Tape remnants on endpapers. Dustwrapper. *(Nouveau)* **$85 [≃£44]**
- Democracy and Poetry. Harvard: UP, 1975. Inscription on half-title. Dustwrapper (short tear front panel, very slightly rubbed). Signed by the author. *(Nouveau)* **$65 [≃£33]**
- (Contributes to) Driftwood Flames. Nashville: Poetry Guild, (1923). One of 325. Few small library stamps. Small stain upper edge rear cover. His 1st book appearance. *(Lopez)* **$375 [≃£195]**
- Eleven Poems on the Same Theme. New Directions: 1942. Wrappers (slight fading at edges). Signed by the author. *(Nouveau)* **$150 [≃£78]**
- Flood. New York: 1964. Price-clipped dustwrapper. Bookplate signed by the author. *(Polyanthos)* **$45 [≃£23]**
- Flood. New York: RH, (1964). Dustwrapper. Signed by the author. *(Lopez)* **$85 [≃£44]**
- (Contributes to) Fugitives: An Anthology of Verse. New York: Harcourt Brace, (1928). Spine label darkened, slight shelfwear. *(Lopez)* **$275 [≃£143]**
- Homage to Theodore Dreiser. New York: 1971. Price-clipped dustwrapper. Signed by the author. *(Polyanthos)* **$40 [≃£20]**
- Incarnations. Poems 1966-1968. New York: RH, (1968). One of 250 signed. Dustwrapper. Slipcase (one edge slightly sunned). *(Lopez)* **$100 [≃£52]**
- Incarnations. New York: 1968. Dustwrapper. Bookplate signed by the author. *(Polyanthos)* **$50 [≃£26]**
- Jefferson Davis Gets his Citizenship Back. Kentucky: UP, 1980. Dustwrapper. *(Polyanthos)* **$25 [≃£13]**
- Jefferson Davis Gets His Citizenship Back. Lexington: Kentucky UP, (1980). Dustwrapper. Signed by the author. *(Lopez)* **$85 [≃£44]**
- John Greenleaf Whittier's Poetry. Minneapolis: University of Minnesota, (1971). Hardcover issue. Dustwrapper. Signed by the author. *(Lopez)* **$85 [≃£44]**
- John Greenleaf Whittier's Poetry. Univ Minn Press: 1971. Dustwrapper. Signed by the author. *(Nouveau)* **$55 [≃£28]**
- Meet Me in the Green Glen. New York: Random, (1971). Dustwrapper (some tears and nicks). Signed by the author. *(Between the Covers)* **$65 [≃£33]**
- New and Selected Poems: 1923-1985. New York: Random House, 1985. One of 350 signed. Slipcase. *(Nouveau)* **$125 [≃£65]**

- Night Rider. Boston: 1939. Small sticker on rear pastedown. Dustwrapper (bit of chipping at spine). *(Pettler & Liebermann)* **$300 [≃£156]**
- Now and Then. Poems 1976-1978. New York: RH, (1978). One of 200 signed. Slipcase. *(Lopez)* **$75 [≃£39]**
- Or Else. New York: 1974. Small area lower side of spine little rubbed. Dustwrapper. Author's signed presentation copy. *(Polyanthos)* **$55 [≃£28]**
- A Place to Come to. New York: 1977. Remainder stamp. Dustwrapper. Signed by the author. *(Pettler & Liebermann)* **$50 [≃£26]**
- A Place to Come to. New York: 1977. Dustwrapper. Author's signed presentation copy. *(Polyanthos)* **$55 [≃£28]**
- A Place to Come To. New York: Random, (1977). Remainder mark bottom edge. Dustwrapper. Signed by the author. *(Between the Covers)* **$65 [≃£33]**
- Portrait of a Father. Kentucky: UP, 1988. Dustwrapper. Bookplate signed by the author. *(Polyanthos)* **$35 [≃£18]**
- Remember the Alamo! New York: Random, (1958). Dustwrapper, fine. *(Between the Covers)* **$250 [≃£130]**
- Remember the Alamo. New York: RH / Landmark, (1958). Dustwrapper. *(Lopez)* **$125 [≃£65]**
- Rumor Verified. New York: 1981. Wrappers. Author's signed presentation copy. *(Polyanthos)* **$35 [≃£18]**
- Selected Essays. New York: 1958. Dustwrapper. *(Pettler & Liebermann)* **$45 [≃£23]**
- Selected Poems 1923-1975. Franklin Library: 1976. Leather. *(Nouveau)* **$65 [≃£33]**
- Selected Poems 1923-1975. PA: The Franklin Library, 1981. Limited edition signed. Leather gilt, a.e.g. *(Polyanthos)* **$50 [≃£26]**
- Six Poems. Tamazunchale: 1987. One of 250. Leather, gilt edges. *(Nouveau)* **$50 [≃£26]**
- Who Speaks for the Negro? New York: Random, (1965). Faint spotting to covers. Dustwrapper. Author's inscription. *(Between the Covers)* **$150 [≃£78]**
- Wilderness. New York: Random House, 1961. Dustwrapper. Signed by the author. *(Nouveau)* **$75 [≃£39]**
- Wilderness. London: Eyre & Spottiswoode, 1962. 1st English edition. Dustwrapper. *(Nouveau)* **$50 [≃£26]**
- Wilderness. New York: RH, (1961). Dustwrapper. Signed by the author. *(Lopez)* **$85 [≃£44]**
- World Enough and Time. New York: 1950. Limited edition. Acetate dustwrapper (two short tears, tiny piece missing). Bookplate signed by the author. *(Polyanthos)* **$75 [≃£39]**
- World Enough and Time. New York: Random House, [1950]. Special Limited Edition, numbered (limitation unknown). Acetate dustwrapper. *(Antic Hay)* **$150 [≃£78]**

Watkins, Vernon

- Ballad of the Marie Lwyd and Other Poems. London: 1941. Review slip. Name on fly. Dustwrapper. *(Words Etcetera)* **£35 [≃$67]**

Watson, Colin

- The Flaxborough Crab. London: 1969. Dustwrapper (creased, small portion missing base of front cover). *(First Issues)* **£30 [≃$57]**
- The Naked Nuns. London: Eyre Methuen, 1975. Dustwrapper. *(Dalian)* **£25 [≃$47]**
- The Puritan. London: 1966. Date on endpaper. One short nick to top of lower panel. *(First Issues)* **£35 [≃$67]**

Watson, Ian

- The Embedding. London: 1973. Dustwrapper (slightly creased, a number of pin pricks to the upper panel). His 1st book. *(Blakeney)* **£75 [≃$143]**
- The Embedding. London: 1973. Dustwrapper. His 1st book. *(Ellis)* **£80 [≃$153]**
- The Jonah Kit. London: 1975. Dustwrapper. *(First Issues)* **£15 [≃$28]**
- The Jonah Kit. London: 1975. Two corners slightly bumped. Dustwrapper. *(Ellis)* **£30 [≃$57]**
- The Jonah Kit. London: Gollancz, 1975. Dustwrapper. *(Sklaroff)* **£20 [≃$38]**

Waugh, Auberon

- The Foxglove Saga. London: 1960. Dustwrapper (slightly rubbed, one nick). Signed by the author. His 1st book. *(Ellis)* **£25 [≃$47]**
- The Foxglove Saga. London: Chapman & Hall, 1960. Edges and endpapers spotted. Dustwrapper (tanned, chipped). *(Hazeldene)* **£15 [≃$28]**
- Who are the Violets Now? London: Chapman & Hall, 1965. Dustwrapper. *(Tiger Books)* **£15 [≃$28]**

Waugh, Evelyn

- Basil Seal Rides Again. Boston: (1963). One

of 1000 signed. *(Black Sun)* **$250 [≃£130]**

- Basil Seal Rides Again. Boston: 1963. One of 1000 signed. Blue boards gilt, t.e.g. *(First Issues)* **£135 [≃$259]**
- Basil Seal Rides Again. Boston: (1963). 1st edition issued in America. One of 1000 signed. *(Black Sun)* **$250 [≃£130]**
- Basil Seal Rides Again. Boston: Little, Brown, [1963]. 1st American edition. One of 1000 signed. Top third of rear cover spotted. *(Chapel Hill)* **$135 [≃£70]**
- Basil Seal Rides Again. Boston: 1963. One of 1000 signed. Blue cloth gilt, t.e.g. *(First Issues)* **£175 [≃$335]**
- Basil Seal Rides Again. London: 1963. One of 750 signed by the author. Part of upper cover and spine slightly faded. Cellophane dustwrapper (chipped, 3-inch closed tear). *(Ellis)* **£300 [≃$575]**
- Black Mischief. London: Chapman & Hall, 1932. One of 250 Large Paper signed. Spine faded, covers slightly discoloured in places. *(Clearwater)* **£350 [≃$671]**
- Black Mischief. London: Chapman & Hall, 1932. Page edges very slightly browned. Dustwrapper (soiled, slightly chipped). *(Virgo)* **£225 [≃$431]**
- Black Mischief. London: Chapman & Hall, 1932. Faint spotting. Dustwrapper (slightly browned and rubbed). *(Ash)* **£250 [≃$479]**
- Black Mischief. London: Chapman & Hall, 1932. Some foxing. Bookplate removed from flyleaf. *(Clearwater)* **£36 [≃$69]**
- Black Mischief. London: Chapman & Hall, 1932. Erased inscription on endpaper. Spine very slightly faded. *(Sklaroff)* **£45 [≃$86]**
- Black Mischief. London: Chapman & Hall, 1932. Bookplate. *(Marlborough B'shop)* **£34 [≃$65]**
- Brideshead Revisited. Boston: Little Brown, 1945. 1st American edition. Dustwrapper (very slightly rubbed). *(Dalian)* **£85 [≃$163]**
- The Diaries. Edited by Michael Davie. London: Weidenfeld & Nicolson, 1976. Inscription on endpaper. Dustwrapper (slightly nicked). *(Virgo)* **£20 [≃$38]**
- The End of the Battle. Boston: Little, Brown, 1961. 1st US edition. Dustwrapper (slightly chipped). *(Whiteson)* **£30 [≃$57]**
- A Handful of Dust. London: 1934. Some very light spotting. *(Words Etcetera)* **£125 [≃$239]**
- A Handful of Dust. New York: Farrar & Rinehart, 1934. 1st American edition. Dustwrapper (minimal wear to corners and spine ends). *(Words Etcetera)* **£250 [≃$479]**
- Helena. London: Chapman & Hall, 1950. Dustwrapper (slightly chipped, a few short tears). *(Limestone Hills)* **$75 [≃£39]**
- The Holy Places. London: The Queen Anne Place, 1953. One of 950. Dustwrapper (spine sunned, tiny piece missing top, few tiny edge tears, little soiled). *(Polyanthos)* **$150 [≃£78]**
- The Letters. London: Weidenfeld & Nicholson, 1980. Dustwrapper. *(Virgo)* **£25 [≃$47]**
- A Little Learning. London: Chapman & Hall, 1964. Proof copy. Printed wrappers. *(Black Sun)* **$225 [≃£117]**
- A Little Learning. London: 1964. Dustwrapper (slightly torn). Signed by the author. *(Clearwater)* **£75 [≃$143]**
- The Loved One. Boston: Little, Brown, 1948. 1st American edition. Dustwrapper. *(Chapel Hill)* **$50 [≃£26]**
- The Loved One. Boston: 1948. Precedes UK edition. Dustwrapper (slightly stained). *(Buckley)* **£30 [≃$57]**
- The Loved One. London: Chapman & Hall, (1948). Dustwrapper (very slightly rubbed). *(Lewton)* **£25 [≃$47]**
- The Loved One. London: Chapman & Hall, 1948. Dustwrapper (one small internal repair). *(Glyn's)* **£25 [≃$47]**
- Men at Arms. London: Chapman & Hall, 1952. *(Sklaroff)* **£21 [≃$40]**
- Men at Arms. London: 1952. Dustwrapper (torn). *(Words Etcetera)* **£12.50 [≃$24]**
- Mexico; an Object Lesson. Boston: 1939. 1st American edition of Robbery Under Law. Endpapers slightly foxed. Dustwrapper (minutely chipped at head of spine, spine slightly browned). *(Words Etcetera)* **£185 [≃$355]**
- Mr Loveday's Little Outing. London: 1936. *(Words Etcetera)* **£75 [≃$143]**
- Mr. Loveday's Little Outing and Other Stories. Boston: Little Brown, 1936. 1st American edition. One of 700 (of 750). Spine slightly sunned. *(Dalian)* **£145 [≃$278]**
- Ninety-Two Days. London: 1934. Edges foxed. Head of spine slightly scuffed. *(Ellis)* **£120 [≃$230]**
- Ninety-Two Days. New York: Farrar & Rinehart, (1934). 1st American edition. Dustwrapper. *(Houle)* **$600 [≃£312]**
- Officers and Gentlemen. London: 1955. Dustwrapper (slightly torn and nicked). *(Words Etcetera)* **£12.50 [≃$24]**
- The Ordeal of Gilbert Pinfold. London: 1957. Dustwrapper (extreme head of spine very slightly frayed).

(Words Etcetera) **£20 [≃$38]**

- The Ordeal of Gilbert Pinfold. London: 1957. Dustwrapper (very slightly chipped at rear). *(Buckley)* **£35 [≃$67]**
- The Ordeal of Gilbert Pinfold. London: 1957. Dustwrapper (very slightly frayed). *(Roberts)* **£10.50 [≃$21]**
- The Ordeal of Gilbert Pinfold. London: 1957. Dustwrapper (very slightly frayed, few small nicks). *(Ellis)* **£30 [≃$57]**
- Put Out More Flags. London: Chapman & Hall, 1942. Dustwrapper (chipped and torn, lacks portion at base of spine). *(Moorhouse)* **£50 [≃$95]**
- Put Out More Flags. London: 1942. Bookplate. *(Ellis)* **£30 [≃$57]**
- Put Out More Flags. London: 1942. Slight foxing near endpapers. *(Buckley)* **£20 [≃$38]**
- Put Out More Flags. London: Chapman & Hall, 1942. *(Marlborough B'shop)* **£10 [≃$19]**
- Remote People. London: 1931. Edges foxed. *(Ellis)* **£120 [≃$230]**
- Remote People. London: Duckworth, 1931. Name. Spine very slightly faded. *(Alphabet)* **$125 [≃£65]**
- Robbery Under Law. London: 1939. Spine a little darkened, covers trifle marked around edges. *(Words Etcetera)* **£110 [≃$211]**
- Rossetti. London: Duckworth, 1928. Covers faded. *(Clearwater)* **£120 [≃$230]**
- Rossetti. New York: Dodd, Mead, 1928. Edges slightly rubbed. *(First Issues)* **£135 [≃$259]**
- Scoop. London: Chapman & Hall, 1938. Mottled cloth (very slight wear to edges). *(Whiteson)* **£25 [≃$47]**
- Scott-King's Modern Europe. London: 1947. Dustwrapper. *(Buckley)* **£25 [≃$47]**
- Scott-King's Modern Europe. Boston: Little Brown, 1949. 1st American edition. Endpapers slightly marked. Dustwrapper. *(Dalian)* **£35 [≃$67]**
- Tactical Exercise. Boston: Little, Brown, [1954]. Not published in England. Dustwrapper (small abrasion rear panel). *(Antic Hay)* **$75 [≃£39]**
- A Tourist in Africa. London: 1960. Dustwrapper (very slightly nicked). *(Ellis)* **£25 [≃$47]**
- A Tourist in Africa. London: Chapman & Hall, 1960. Dustwrapper. *(Limestone Hills)* **$55 [≃£28]**
- A Tourist in Africa. London: Chapman & Hall, 1960. Dustwrapper (slightly frayed). *(Glyn's)* **£13.50 [≃$26]**
- Unconditional Surrender. London: 1961. Uncorrected proof copy. Printed wrappers, a little handled and skewed, spine slightly chafed. *(Clearwater)* **£65 [≃$124]**
- Unconditional Surrender. London: 1961. Price-clipped dustwrapper. *(Buckley)* **£30 [≃$57]**
- Unconditional Surrender. London: Chapman & Hall, 1961. Dustwrapper (slightly worn and stained). *(Limestone Hills)* **$55 [≃£28]**
- Waugh in Abyssinia. London: 1936. Prelims slightly foxed. Slightly cocked. Small snag head of spine. Spine lightly scratched and with small stain. *(Ellis)* **£100 [≃$191]**
- Waugh in Abyssinia. London: 1936. Tape or rust marks to corners of both fly leaves. *(Words Etcetera)* **£85 [≃$163]**
- When the Going Was Good. London: 1946. Name. Dustwrapper (frayed, chipped). *(Ellis)* **£120 [≃$230]**
- When the Going Was Good. London: Duckworth, 1946. Two staple marksd to rear pastedown. Slight spotting to foredge and prelims. *(Lloyd-Roberts)* **£25 [≃$47]**
- Wine in Peace and War. London: (1947). Pastedowns foxed. Tissue dustwrapper (slightly frayed, slightly scratched). *(Ellis)* **£180 [≃$345]**
- Wine in Peace and War. London: Saccone & Speed, 1947. Endpapers foxed. Plain dustwrapper (somewhat chipped). *(David Rees)* **£90 [≃$172]**
- Wine in Peace and War. London: Saccone & Speed, n.d. Cream boards (insides slightly spotted). Tissue dustwrapper (torn bottom edge). *(Larkhill)* **£130 [≃$249]**

Waughburton, Richard (pseudonym)

- See Byron, Robert & Sykes, Christopher.

Webb, Charles

- The Graduate. New York: NAL, (1963). Dustwrapper. His 1st book. *(Lopez)* **$50 [≃£26]**

Webb, James

- Fields of Fire. Englewood Cliffs: 1978. Dustwrapper. His 1st book. *(Pettler & Liebermann)* **$50 [≃£26]**

Welch, Denton

- Brave and Cruel. London: Hamish Hamilton, 1948. Dustwrapper. *(Any Amount)* **£36 [≃$69]**
- Dumb Instrument. Enitharmon Press: 1976. One of 660. Dustwrapper. *(Lewton)* **£17.50 [≃$34]**
- Journals. London: 1952. Head of spine and

tips of two corners slightly bumped. dustwrapper (worn).
(Clearwater) **£20 [≃$38]**
- The Journals. London: Allison & Busby, 1984. 1st unabridged edition. Dustwrapper. *(Virgo)* **£14 [≃$26]**
- A Last Sheaf. London: Lehmann, 1951. Dustwrapper. *(Any Amount)* **£28 [≃$53]**
- A Voice through a Cloud. London: John Lehmann, (1950). Dustwrapper (few nicks). *(Houle)* **$37.50 [≃£19]**

Weldon, Fay
- Female Friends. London: 1975. Dustwrapper. Signed by the author. *(Egret)* **£40 [≃$76]**
- Letters to Alice. London: Michael Joseph, 1984. Dustwrapper. *(Lewton)* **£7.50 [≃$15]**
- Letters to Alice. London: Michael Joseph, Rainbow, 1984. Dustwrapper. *(Paul Brown)* **£7.50 [≃$15]**
- The Life and Loves of a She-Devil. London: 1983. Dustwrapper. Signed by the author. *(Egret)* **£40 [≃$76]**
- Polaris & Other Stories. London: 1985. Dustwrapper. Signed by the author. *(Egret)* **£20 [≃$38]**
- Praxis. London: 1978. Dustwrapper. Signed by the author. *(Egret)* **£20 [≃$38]**
- Praxis. London: 1978. Dustwrapper. Signed by the author. *(Egret)* **£20 [≃$38]**
- Puffball. London: 1980. Dustwrapper (slightly rubbed). Signed by the author. *(Egret)* **£18 [≃$34]**
- Puffball. London: Hodder, 1980. Dustwrapper. *(Paul Brown)* **£12.50 [≃$24]**
- Remember Me. London: 1976. Dustwrapper. Signed by the author. *(First Issues)* **£20 [≃$38]**
- Remember Me. London: 1976. Dustwrapper. Signed by the author. *(Egret)* **£30 [≃$57]**
- The Rules of Life. London: 1987. Dustwrapper. Signed by the author. *(Egret)* **£18 [≃$34]**
- The Shrapnel Academy. London: 1986. Dustwrapper. Signed by the author. *(Egret)* **£18 [≃$34]**

Wells, H.G.
- See the companion IRBP volume Literature.

Welsh, James
- Death of Jim Lonely. New York: Harper & Row, 1979. Dustwrapper. *(Michael Johnson)* **£32 [≃$61]**
- Winter in the Blood. New York: Harper & Row, 1974. Dustwrapper. *(Michael Johnson)* **£30 [≃$57]**

Welty, Eudora
- The Bride of Innisfallen. New York: 1955. 2nd issue (stated 1st with multiple copyright dates). Price-clipped dustwrapper. *(Pettler & Liebermann)* **$65 [≃£33]**
- The Bride of the Innisfallen. Harcourt, 1955. 2nd issue. Slight shelf wear. Dustwrapper (a few creases, two repaired tears). Signed by the author. *(Nouveau)* **$125 [≃£65]**
- The Bride of the Innisfallen and Other Stories. London: Hamish Hamilton, 1955. Prelims very slightly foxed. Dustwrapper. *(Dalian)* **£65 [≃$124]**
- Conversations with Eudora Welty. Edited by Peggy Prenshaw. Miss Univ Press, 1980. Advance review copy with slip. Dustwrapper. *(Nouveau)* **$40 [≃£20]**
- 'Delta Wedding". Complete in The Atlantic for January, February, March, April 1946. Wrappers. *(Limestone Hills)* **$75 [≃£39]**
- Delta Wedding. Harcourt, 1946. Name on half-title. Light rub spot. Dustwrapper. Signed by the author. *(Nouveau)* **$225 [≃£117]**
- Delta Wedding. London: Bodley Head, 1947. Slight offsetting to front cover. Dustwrapper. *(Dalian)* **£75 [≃$143]**
- The Golden Apples. New York: 1949. Spine lightly sunned. Dustwrapper. Signed by the author. *(Pettler & Liebermann)* **$250 [≃£130]**
- The Golden Apples. New York: 1949). One tiny spot of foxing on foredge. Dustwrapper, fine. *(Between the Covers)* **$350 [≃£182]**
- In Black and White. Introduction by Anne Tyler. Northridge: Lord John, 1985. One of 100 deluxe signed by Welty and Tyler. Slipcase. *(Lopez)* **$225 [≃£117]**
- In Black and White. Introduction by Anne Tyler. Northridge: Lord John, 1985. One of 400 signed by Welty. *(Lopez)* **$100 [≃£52]**
- Losing Battles. New York: Random House, 1970. 1st trade edition. Dustwrapper. Signed by the author. *(Nouveau)* **$70 [≃£36]**
- One Writer's Beginnings. Cambridge: Harvard, (1984). Uncorrected proof copy. Wrappers (slightly sunned). *(Lopez)* **$250 [≃£130]**
- The Optimist's Daughter. London: Deutsch, 1973. Dustwrapper. *(Dalian)* **£25 [≃$47]**
- Photographs. Jackson: Univ of Miss., (1989). One of 375 signed. Slipcase. *(Between the Covers)* **$275 [≃£143]**
- Photographs. Univ Press Miss, 1989. 1st

trade edition. Dustwrapper.
(Nouveau) **$60 [≃£31]**

- The Ponder Heart. Harcourt, 1954. Light shelf wear. Price-clipped dustwrapper. Signed by the author. *(Nouveau)* **$150 [≃£78]**
- The Reading and Writing of Short Stories [In] The Atlantic, February and March 1949. Pictorial wrappers, a bit worn. *(Limestone Hills)* **$45 [≃£23]**
- Retreat. Palaemon, 1981. One of 150 signed. *(Nouveau)* **$125 [≃£65]**
- The Robber Bridegroom. London: 1944. Decorated boards. *(First Issues)* **£20 [≃$38]**

Wescott, Glenway

- A Calendar of Saints for Unbelievers. Paris: Harrison of Paris, 1932. One of 695 signed. Cloth, t.e.g.. Glassine dustwrapper. Slipcase. Prospectus laid-in. *(Antic Hay)* **$250 [≃£130]**
- The Grandmothers. New York: Harper, 1927. One of 250 signed. Cloth and boards. *(Antic Hay)* **$75 [≃£39]**

Wesker, Arnold

- Chips with Everything. London: Cape, 1962. Dustwrapper. *(Lewton)* **£12.50 [≃$24]**
- The Journalists. London: Cape, 1979. Dustwrapper. Signed by the author. *(Moorhouse)* **£10 [≃$19]**
- Their Very Own and Golden City. London: Cape, 1966. Price-clipped dustwrapper. *(Moorhouse)* **£10 [≃$19]**

Wesley, Mary

- Harnessing Peacocks. London: Macmillan, 1985. Dustwrapper. *(Lewton)* **£16 [≃$30]**
- Jumping the Queue. London: Macmillan, 1983. Dustwrapper. Signed by the author. *(Ash)* **£50 [≃$95]**
- Jumping the Queue. London: Macmillan, 1983. Dustwrapper. *(Lewton)* **£18.50 [≃$36]**
- Jumping the Queue. London: 1983. Dustwrapper. Signed by the author. *(Egret)* **£40 [≃$76]**
- Jumping the Queue. London: 1983. Dustwrapper. Signed by the author. *(Egret)* **£45 [≃$86]**
- Jumping the Queue. London: Macmillan, 1983. Dustwrapper. Her 1st book. *(Dalian)* **£30 [≃$57]**
- Second Fiddle. London: Macmillan, 1988. Dustwrapper. *(Lewton)* **£8.50 [≃$17]**
- Second Fiddle. London: 1988. Dustwrapper. Signed by the author. *(First Issues)* **£25 [≃$47]**

West, Jessamyn

- The Friendly Persuasion. New York: Harcourt, Brace, [1945]. Dustwrapper. HHer 1st book. *(Chapel Hill)* **$150 [≃£78]**

West, Nathanael

- A Cool Million. New York: Covici Friede, (1934). 1st issue binding (later issued in green cloth). Advance review slip tipped in. Tan cloth stamped in green. Dustwrapper (minimal wear). *(Chapel Hill)* **$1,300 [≃£677]**
- The Day of the Locust. London: The Grey Walls Press, 1951. Dustwrapper (slightly tanned). *(Dalian)* **£45 [≃$86]**

West, Rebecca

- Harriet Hume. London: Hutchinson, [1929]. Scattered foxing top edge. Dustwrapper (moderate wear, some soiling). *(Antic Hay)* **$135 [≃£70]**
- Henry James. A Study. London: Nisbet, 1916. Spine and covers sunned. Her 1st book. *(Dalian)* **£35 [≃$67]**
- The Judge. New York: Doran, [1922]. 1st American edition. Minor scattered spotting to edges. Dustwrapper (some soil, faint stain along upper edge of spine and front panel). *(Antic Hay)* **$85 [≃£44]**
- The Return of the Soldier. New York: Century, 1918. Top edge slightly foxed. Dustwrapper (lightly chipped and soiled). *(Bromer)* **$325 [≃£169]**
- The Return of the Soldier. London: Nisbet, 1918. Cloth slightly faded and marked. Part of dustwrapper pasted to front endpaper. *(Dalian)* **£35 [≃$67]**
- The Return of the Soldier. London: Nisbet, 1918. *(Ash)* **£50 [≃$95]**
- The Thinking Reed. London: Hutchinson, 1936. Covers slightly marked. Dustwrapper (repaired). *(Dalian)* **£30 [≃$57]**
- The Thinking Reed. London: Hutchinson, [1936]. Scattered foxing, especially to edges. Dustwrapper (somewhat worn, few tears and tiny chips). Signed by the author on tipped in sheet. *(Antic Hay)* **$100 [≃£52]**
- The Thinking Reed. London: Hutchinson, 1936. Spring 1936 adverts. Dustwrapper (spine extremities lightly worn). *(Alphabet)* **$150 [≃£78]**

Westheimer, David

- Von Ryan's Express. Garden City: Doubleday, 1964. Dustwrapper. Signed by the author. *(Houle)* **$125 [≃£65]**

Westlake, Donald E.

- Adios, Scheherazade. New York: Simon and Schuster, 1970. Dustwrapper (slight darkening of spine, couple of tiny nicks and tears). *(Mordida)* **$40 [≃£20]**
- Bank Shot. New York: Simon & Schuster, 1972. Dustwrapper. Signed by the author. *(Limestone Hills)* **$75 [≃£39]**
- The Fugitive Pigeon. New York: Random House, 1965. Dustwrapper (stains on back panel, some short closed tears). *(Mordida)* **$35 [≃£18]**
- God Save the Mark. New York: Random House, 1967. Dustwrapper. Author's presentation copy. *(Limestone Hills)* **$55 [≃£28]**
- Kahawa. New York: Viking, 1982. Dustwrapper. Signed by the author. *(Limestone Hills)* **$60 [≃£31]**
- Lemons Never Lie. By Richard Stark. New York: World, 1971. Dustwrapper. *(Janus)* **$65 [≃£33]**
- The Mercenaries. London: 1961. Dustwrapper (very slightly rubbed). His 1st book. *(Dalian)* **£25 [≃$47]**
- 361. New York: Random House, 1962. Name. Dustwrapper (tiny wear at foot of spine, short creases on inner flaps). *(Mordida)* **$75 [≃£39]**

Wharton, William

- Birdy. London: Cape, 1979. Dustwrapper. His 1st bok. *(Dalian)* **£25 [≃$47]**
- Birdy. Cape, 1979. Dustwrapper. *(Paul Brown)* **£15 [≃$28]**
- Dad. London: Cape, 1981. Dustwrapper. *(Dalian)* **£16 [≃$30]**
- Franky Furbo. Henry Holt, 1989. One of 250 signed. Dustwrapper. *(Nouveau)* **$50 [≃£26]**
- A Midnight Clear. London: Cape, 1982. Uncorrected proof copy. Wrappers. *(Dalian)* **£20 [≃$38]**
- Pride. London: Cape, 1989. Uncorrected proof copy. Wrappers. *(Dalian)* **£20 [≃$38]**
- Pride. London: Cape, 1989. Dustwrapper. *(Dalian)* **£15 [≃$28]**

Wheatley, Dennis

- File on Bolitho Blane. New York: Morrow, 1936. 1st US edition of Murder off Miami. Solution seal broken but complete. *(Janus)* **$75 [≃£39]**
- File on Bolitho Blane. With J.G. Links. New York: Morrow, 1936. 1st US edition of Murder off Miami. *(Janus)* **$45 [≃£23]**
- Murder Off Miami. London: Hutchinson, [1936]. Buff wrappers. Complete with samples. Seal opened. Signed by the author. *(Sklaroff)* **£75 [≃$143]**
- Who Killed Robert Prentice? London: Hutchinson, [1937]. All evidence present. Solution unopened. Wrappers (slightly yapped and worn). *(Moorhouse)* **£60 [≃$115]**

White, Antonia

- The Lost Traveller. London: Eyre & Spottiswoode, 1950. Edges foxed. Dustwrapper. *(Ash)* **£20 [≃$38]**

White, E.B.

- Charlotte's Web. London: Hamish Hamilton, 1952. Dustwrapper. *(Green Meadow)* **£55 [≃$105]**
- Stuart Little. New York: Harper, 1945. Dustwrapper, fine. *(Alphabet)* **$250 [≃£130]**

White, Edmund

- The Beautiful Room is Empty. London: Picador, 1987. Dustwrapper. *(Dalian)* **£16 [≃$30]**
- Nocturnes for the King of Naples. London: Deutsch, 1979. Dustwrapper (slightly rubbed). *(Moorhouse)* **£25 [≃$47]**

White, Patrick

- The Aunt's Story. 1948. Foredges text leaves creased. Dustwrapper (head of spine and one corner slightly torn). *(Words Etcetera)* **£85 [≃$163]**
- The Eye of the Storm. London: Cape, 1973. Advance uncorrected proof copy. Wrappers (very slightly dusty, slightly chipped). Proof dustwrapper. *(Dalian)* **£35 [≃$67]**
- Flaws in the Glass. London: 1981. Proof copy. Wrappers. *(Polyanthos)* **$75 [≃£39]**
- Flaws in the Glass. London: Cape, 1981. *(Dalian)* **£25 [≃$47]**
- Happy Valley. 1939. Spine very slightly cocked. Dustwrapper (slight wear to extremities of spine and two corners). *(Words Etcetera)* **£600 [≃$1,151]**
- Riders in the Chariot. London: Eyre & Spottiswoode, 1961. Dustwrapper. *(Dalian)* **£35 [≃$67]**
- Riders in the Chariot. New York: 1961. Dustwrapper. *(Polyanthos)* **$65 [≃£33]**
- Three Uneasy Pieces. London: 1988. Proof copy. Wrappers. Proof dustwrapper (two edge tears). *(Polyanthos)* **$55 [≃£28]**
- The Tree of Man. London: 1956. Dustwrapper. *(Buckley)* **£30 [≃$57]**
- The Tree of Man. London: 1956. Dustwrapper. *(Egret)* **£45 [≃$86]**

- The Tree of Man. London: Eyre & Spottiswoode, 1956. Dustwrapper. *(Sklaroff)* **£35 [≃$67]**
- The Tree of Man. London: Eyre & Spottiswoode, 1956. Foredge foxed. Dustwrapper (slightly marked). *(Dalian)* **£45 [≃$86]**
- The Vivisector. London: Cape, 1970. Uncorrected proof copy. Wrappers. Proof dustwrapper. *(Dalian)* **£45 [≃$86]**
- Voss. London: 1957. Dustwrapper (edges slightly rubbed). *(First Issues)* **£25 [≃$47]**
- Voss. London: 1957. Dustwrapper (slightly rubbed and marked). *(Buckley)* **£25 [≃$47]**

White, T.H.

- America at Last. New York: Putnam's, [1965]. 1st American edition. A few early pages creased. Dustwrapper. *(Limestone Hills)* **$50 [≃£26]**
- America at Last. New York: [1965]. Dustwrapper. *(Clearwater)* **£45 [≃$86]**
- The Book of Beasts. London: 1954. Two corners slightly bruised. Dustwrapper (slightly frayed). *(Clearwater)* **£40 [≃$76]**
- The Book of Merlyn. London: Univ of Texas Press & Collins, [1977]. Dustwrapper. *(Limestone Hills)* **$45 [≃£23]**
- Burke's Steerage. London: 1938. Dustwrapper (slightly chipped and dusty). *(Clearwater)* **£50 [≃$95]**
- Earth Stopped or Mr Marx's Sporting Tour. London: 1934. Covers a little worn and marked. *(Edrich)* **£30 [≃$57]**
- England Have My Bones. New York: Macmillan, 1936. 1st American edition. Dustwrapper (small chips). *(Antic Hay)* **$75 [≃£39]**
- Farewell Victoria. London: 1933. Spine sunned, covers worn and faded. *(Edrich)* **£30 [≃$57]**
- The Godstone and the Blackymor. New York: Putnam, 1959. 1st US edition. Binding dull and slightly rubbed. *(Whiteson)* **£18 [≃$34]**
- The Goshawk. London: 1951. Dustwrapper (slightly worn and torn). *(Clearwater)* **£20 [≃$38]**
- The Goshawk. London: Cape, 1951. Dustwrapper. *(Lewton)* **£22.50 [≃$44]**
- The Green Bay Tree; or, The Wicked Man Touches Wood. [Cambridge: W. Heffer & Sons, Songs for Sixpence Series, 1929]. Illustrated wrappers (small snag). His 1st book. *(Black Sun)* **$300 [≃£156]**
- Mistress Masham's Repose. New York: Putnam's, 1946. Dustwrapper (slightly soiled and nicked). *(Dalian)* **£25 [≃$47]**
- Mistress Masham's Repose. London: Cape, 1947. Dustwrapper (slightly rubbed). *(Dalian)* **£30 [≃$57]**
- The Once and Future King. London: Collins, 1958. 1st complete edition. Dustwrapper. *(Limestone Hills)* **$125 [≃£65]**
- The Sword in the Stone. London: Collins, 1938. A few faint marks, a few unobtrusive library marks in text. Dustwrapper (slightly chipped). *(Ash)* **£200 [≃$383]**
- The Sword in the Stone. London: Collins, 1938. *(Whiteson)* **£16 [≃$30]**
- The Sword in the Stone. New York: Putnam, 1939. 1st American edition. Dustwrapper (chipped). *(Dalian)* **£85 [≃$163]**
- The Sword in the Stone. New York: Putnam, 1939. 1st US edition. Dustwrapper. *(Glyn's)* **£125 [≃$239]**

Wideman, John Edgar

- A Glance Away. New York: 1967. Dustwrapper. His 1st book. *(Pettler & Liebermann)* **$75 [≃£39]**

Wiener, Norbert

- God & Golem, Inc. London: Chapman & Hall, [1964]. Dustwrapper. *(Sklaroff)* **£45 [≃$86]**

Wiesel, Elie

- Dawn. London: MacGibbon & Kee, 1961. Name. Dustwrapper (edge worn at spine top). *(Alphabet)* **$50 [≃£26]**
- The Gates of the Forest. New York: Holt, 1966. Dustwrapper. Signed by the author on tipped in card. *(Nouveau)* **$60 [≃£31]**

Wilbur, Richard

- Advice to a Prophet. London: Faber, 1962. 1st English edition. Advance review copy. Dustwrapper. *(Nouveau)* **$60 [≃£31]**
- Poems 1943-1956. London: Faber, 1957. Dustwrapper (slightly tanned). *(Dalian)* **£45 [≃$86]**
- Walking to Sleep. London: Faber, 1969. Dustwrapper. *(Dalian)* **£25 [≃$47]**

Wilder, Thornton

- The Angel that Troubled the Waters and Other Plays. London: Longmans, Green, 1928. One of 260 signed. Covers very slightly rubbed. *(Dalian)* **£45 [≃$86]**
- The Angel that Troubled the Waters and Other Plays. New York: Coward-McCann, 1928. 1st trade edition. One of 2000 signed by

the publishers. Name. Dustwrapper (spine little torn, few pieces missing at edges, but both panels intact). *(Polyanthos)* **$30 [≈£15]**

- The Bridge of San Luis Rey. New York: Boni, 1927. Dustwrapper (faintly chipped). Author's presentation inscription on title. Chemise & slipcase provided. *(Bromer)* **$1,250 [≈£651]**
- The Bridge of San Luis Rey. New York: Boni, 1927. 1st American edition. Dustwrapper (slightly used, few internal tape reinforcements, shallow chip to of rear panel). *(Chapel Hill)* **$225 [≈£117]**
- The Cabala. By Thornton Niven Wilder. New York: Albert & Charles Boni, 1926. 1st state, with issue points on pp 196, 202, 186. Spine a bit browned, wear to corners. *(Houle)* **$125 [≈£65]**
- The Cabala. New York: Boni, 1926. 1st printing, with "conversation" for "conversion" on p 196, line 13. Small abraded area on front pastedown. Blue cloth. His 1st book. *(Chapel Hill)* **$75 [≈£39]**
- The Cabala. New York: 1926. 1st issue. *(Polyanthos)* **$35 [≈£18]**
- The Cabala. London: Longmans Green, 1926. Foredge slightly foxed. Dustwrapper (slightly dusty and tanned). His 1st book. *(Dalian)* **£85 [≈$163]**
- Heaven's My Destination. London: Longmans, Green, 1934. Precedes the American edition. Bookplate. Foredge slightly foxed. Dustwrapper (chipped). *(Dalian)* **£35 [≈$67]**
- The Ides of March. New York: Harper, [1948]. Dustwrapper (moderate wear). *(Antic Hay)* **$45 [≈£23]**
- The Ides of March. New York: Harper, [1948]. One of 750 signed. Dustwrapper (moderate edgewear). *(Antic Hay)* **$100 [≈£52]**
- The Ides of March. New York: Harper, (1948). 1st edition ('M-W'). Dustwrapper (few nicks). *(Houle)* **$50 [≈£26]**
- James Joyce 1883-1941. (Aurora, New York: Wells College Press, 1944). One of 150. Wrappers (edges a little darkened). *(Woolmer)* **$250 [≈£130]**

Willans, Geoffrey

- Down with Skool. London: Max Parrish, 1953. Spine gilt rubbed. Edges tanned and spotted. Dustwrapper (spotted). *(Hazeldene)* **£18 [≈$34]**

Willeford, Charles

- The Burnt Orange Heresy. New York: Crown, 1971. Label removed from front endpaper, faint short tape marks on pastedowns. Dustwrapper. *(Mordida)* **$100 [≈£52]**
- Cockfighter. Chicago: Chicago Paperback House, 1962. Paperback original. Pages darkened. Wrappers. *(Mordida)* **$100 [≈£52]**
- Cockfighter. New York: Crown, 1972. Dustwrapper (several closed tears, punch-tear on spine, chipped corner on back panel, rubbing at foot of spine). *(Mordida)* **$80 [≈£41]**
- A Guide for the Undehemorrhoided. Boynton Beach: Star Publishing, 1977. Dustwrapper. Signed by the author. *(Mordida)* **$75 [≈£39]**
- High Priest of California & Wild Wives. San Francisco: Re/Search Publications, 1987. 1st hardcover edition. One of 250 signed. Dustwrapper. *(Mordida)* **$75 [≈£39]**
- Kiss Your Ass Goodbye. Miami Beach: Dennis McMillan, 1987. One of 400 signed. Dustwrapper. *(Alphabet)* **$125 [≈£65]**
- Miami Blues. New York: St. Martin's Press, 1984. Dustwrapper. *(Mordida)* **$75 [≈£39]**
- New Hope for the Dead. New York: St. Martin's Press, 1985. Dustwrapper. *(Mordida)* **$45 [≈£23]**
- Off the Wall. Montclair: Pegasus Rex Press, 1980. Dustwrapper. *(Mordida)* **$50 [≈£26]**
- (Contributes to) The Outcast Poets. Yonkers: 1947. Small broadsides laid into envelope, fine. *(Pettler & Liebermann)* **$200 [≈£104]**
- Proletarian Laughter. Yonkers: Alicat Bookshop Press, 1948. Pages darkened. Wrappers. His 1st book. *(Mordida)* **$100 [≈£52]**
- Proletarian Laughter. Yonkers: The Alicat Chapbooks XII, 1948. Wrappers. His 1st solo book. *(Pettler & Liebermann)* **$150 [≈£78]**
- Something About a Soldier. New York: Random House, 1986. Dustwrapper. *(Mordida)* **$27.50 [≈£14]**

Williams, Alan

- Holy of Holies. New York: Rawson, Wade, [1980]. Uncorrected proof copy. Printed wrappers. *(Antic Hay)* **$45 [≈£23]**

Williams, Charles

- Arthurian Torso. OUP: 1948. Spine lettering dull. Dustwrapper. *(Dalian)* **£65 [≈$124]**
- Bacon. London: 1933. Edges foxed. Bookplate. Dustwrapper (slightly frayed, spine slightly faded). *(Ellis)* **£60 [≈$115]**
- Collected Plays. OUP: 1963. Dustwrapper. *(Dalian)* **£45 [≈$86]**

- Cranmer of Canterbury. Acting Edition for the Festival of the Friends of Canterbury Cathedral. Canterbury: J.H. Goulden, 1936. "Precedes the First Edition". Very slightly foxed. Printed wrappers. *(Dalian)* **£85 [≃$163]**
- Descent into Hell. New York: Pellegrini & Cudahy, 1949. 1st American edition. Dustwrapper (spine a bit faded). *(Alphabet)* **$40 [≃£20]**
- The Figure of Beatrice. London: Faber, 1943. Bookplate. Dustwrapper. *(Dalian)* **£65 [≃$124]**
- Flecker of Dean Close. The Canterbury Press, 1946. Foredge slightly foxed. Dustwrapper, fine. *(Dalian)* **£85 [≃$163]**
- The House of the Octopus. Edinburgh House Press: 1945. Dustwrapper. *(Ash)* **£20 [≃$38]**
- Poems of Conformity. OUP: Humphrey Milford, 1917. 1st issue, with Milford at base of spine. Covers slightly marked. *(Virgo)* **£65 [≃$124]**
- Poems of Conformity. OUP: 1917. Endpapers slightly browned. Covers slightly marked. *(Dalian)* **£85 [≃$163]**
- Reason and Beauty in the Poetic Mind. London: 1933. Dustwrapper (slightly frayed, several nicks). *(Ellis)* **£45 [≃$86]**
- The Region of the Summer Stars. London: Editions Poetry, 1944. Dustwrapper (very slightly rubbed and nicked). *(Dalian)* **£75 [≃$143]**
- Religion and Love in Dante. Dacre Press: n.d. Some foxing. Wrappers. *(Ellis)* **£25 [≃$47]**
- A Short Life of Shakespeare. OUP: 1933. Dustwrapper (torn). *(Dalian)* **£35 [≃$67]**
- A Short Life of Shakespeare. OUP: 1933. *(Dalian)* **£25 [≃$47]**
- Taliesin through Logres. OUP: 1938. Slight fading edges and spine. *(Whiteson)* **£35 [≃$67]**
- Thomas Cranmer of Canterbury. OUP: 1936. Dustwrapper. *(Dalian)* **£95 [≃$182]**
- War in Heaven. London: Gollancz, 1930. Endpapers slightly browned. Cloth very slightly rubbed. *(Dalian)* **£65 [≃$124]**
- Witchcraft. London: Faber, 1941. Spine slightly faded. *(Any Amount)* **£20 [≃$38]**
- Glenn, Lois: Charles W.S. Williams. A Checklist. Kent State UP: 1975. No dustwrapper issued. *(Dalian)* **£35 [≃$67]**

Williams, Emlyn

- A Murder Has Been Arranged. London: Collins, 1931. Front endpaper slightly marked. Covers slightly rubbed. His 1st book. *(Dalian)* **£25 [≃$47]**

Williams, Heathcote

- The Speakers. London: Hutchinson, 1964. Dustwrapper. His 1st book. *(Paul Brown)* **£12.50 [≃$24]**
- The Speakers. New York: Grove, 1964. Dustwrapper. His 1st book. *(Any Amount)* **£20 [≃$38]**

Williams, Joan

- The Morning and the Evening. Atheneum: 1961. Dustwrapper (lightly rubbed and nicked). Signed by the author. Her 1st book. *(Nouveau)* **$60 [≃£31]**

Williams, Tennessee

- Cat on a Hot Tin Roof. New York: New Directions, (1955). Dustwrapper (few nicks). *(Houle)* **$125 [≃£65]**
- Cat on a Hot Tin Roof. New York: New Directions, [1955]. Dustwrapper. *(Chapel Hill)* **$75 [≃£39]**
- Cat on a Hot Tin Roof. New York: (1955). Spine extremities little rubbed, tiny stain front cover. Dustwrapper (extremities of spine and corners little chipped, two tiny edge tears rear panel). *(Polyanthos)* **$65 [≃£33]**
- Eight Mortal Ladies Possessed. New York: 1974. Price-clipped dustwrapper (tiny tear side of spine). *(Polyanthos)* **$20 [≃£10]**
- Five Plays. London: Secker & Warburg, 1962. 1st English edition. Dustwrapper. *(Nouveau)* **$65 [≃£33]**
- The Glass Menagerie. London: 1948. 1st hardback edition. Endpapers slightly browned. Dustwrapper. *(Buckley)* **£25 [≃$47]**
- Grand. New York: House of Books, 1964. One of 300 signed. Cloth. Glassine dustwrapper (minor wear). *(Antic Hay)* **$275 [≃£143]**
- Grand. New York: House of Books, 1964. One of 300 signed. Glassine dustwrapper. *(Houle)* **$295 [≃£153]**
- Hard Candy. [Norfolk]: New Directions, [1954]. Limited edition. Some darkening spine. Slipcase (moderate wear). *(Antic Hay)* **$85 [≃£44]**
- Hard Candy. N.p., [1954]. Stated limited edition. Box (lightly worn). *(Between the Covers)* **$85 [≃£44]**
- In the Winter of Cities: Poems. Norfolk: New Directions, 1956. Name on half-title.

Dustwrapper (one small chip, several old internal tape repairs, tape removed). *(Alphabet)* **$45 [≃£23]**

- The Knightly Quest. New Directions: 1966. Small sticker endpaper. Dustwrapper (light edge wear). *(Nouveau)* **$75 [≃£39]**
- Letters to Donald Windham. Verona: Mardersteig, 1976. One of 500. Dustwrapper. Slipcase. *(Between the Covers)* **$150 [≃£78]**
- Memoirs. Garden City: Doubleday, 1975. Dustwrapper. *(Between the Covers)* **$35 [≃£18]**
- Moise & The World of Reason. New York: Simon & Schuster, 1975. Dustwrapper. Signed by the author. *(Alphabet)* **$85 [≃£44]**
- Moise and the World of Reason. London: Secker & Warburg, 1978. Dustwrapper. *(Dalian)* **£18 [≃$34]**
- The Night of the Iguana. New York: New Directions, 1962. Top edge very slightly faded. Dustwrapper (slightly browned, one tiny closed tear). *(Virgo)* **£60 [≃$115]**
- One Arm and Other Stories. Norfolk: New Directions, (1948). One of 50 signed. Parchment backed boards, t.e.g. Publisher's slipcase. *(Chapel Hill)* **$2,500 [≃£1,302]**
- Orpheus Descending. London: Secker & Warburg, 1958. Dustwrapper (very slightly nicked). *(Dalian)* **£30 [≃$57]**
- The Remarkable Rooming-House of Mme. Le Monde. Albondocani: 1984. One of 150 numbered. Wrappers. *(Nouveau)* **$65 [≃£33]**
- The Roman Spring of Mrs. Stone. New York: New Directions, (1950). One of 500 signed. Vellum spine (slightly sunned). Box (spine and edges slightly sunned). *(Polyanthos)* **$375 [≃£195]**
- The Roman Spring of Mrs. Stone. New York: New Directions, [1950]. Dustwrapper (lightly soiled and rubbed). *(Chapel Hill)* **$55 [≃£28]**
- The Roman Spring of Mrs. Stone. New Directions: 1950. Dustwrapper (light wear, a few short tears). *(Nouveau)* **$60 [≃£31]**
- The Roman Spring of Mrs. Stone. London: John Lehmann, 1950. 1st English edition. Boards a bit bowed. Dustwrapper. *(Alphabet)* **$75 [≃£39]**
- The Rose Tattoo. New York: New Directions, (1950) [sic]. 1st edition (so stated). Dustwrapper (few nicks). *(Houle)* **$125 [≃£65]**
- The Rose Tattoo. New York: New Directions, 1951 [sic]. 1st binding, rose cloth. Minimal rubbing to spine extremities. Dustwrapper (little torn along side, extremities slightly rubbed). *(Polyanthos)* **$65 [≃£33]**
- Small Craft Warnings. London: Secker & Warburg, 1973. Dustwrapper. *(Dalian)* **£20 [≃$38]**
- Sweet Bird of Youth. London: Secker & Warburg, 1959. Dustwrapper. *(Dalian)* **£25 [≃$47]**
- The Two-Character Play. New York: New Directions, (1969). One of 350 signed. Box (very small stain). *(Polyanthos)* **$375 [≃£195]**
- The World of Tennessee Williams. Edited by Richard F. Leavitt. New York: Putnam, (1978). One of 250 signed by both. Errata slip. Dustwrapper. Slipcase. *(Houle)* **$175 [≃£91]**

Williams, Valentine

- Death Answers the Bell. London: Hodder & Stoughton, 1931. Dustwrapper (lower cover chipped, slight rubbing). *(Houle)* **$65 [≃£33]**

Williams, William Carlos

- The Autobiography. London: MacGibbon & Kee, 1968. Dustwrapper (very slightly rubbed). *(Dalian)* **£35 [≃$67]**
- The Broken Span. CT: New Directions, Poet of the Month, 1941. Wrappers. Dustwrapper (spine little sunned with one tiny tear). *(Polyanthos)* **$60 [≃£31]**
- The Build-Up. New York: 1952. Dustwrapper. *(Polyanthos)* **$75 [≃£39]**
- The Build-Up. New York: [1952]. Dustwrapper (slightly used). *(Dermont)* **$60 [≃£31]**
- The Clouds, Aigeltinger, Russia &c. Cummington Press and The Wells College Press: [1948]. One of 310. Rough cloth, paper label, fine. *(Black Sun)* **$275 [≃£143]**
- The Collected Later Poems. New York: New Directions, (1950). One of 100 signed. Deluxe issue, specially bound. Box (little edge sunned). *(Polyanthos)* **$600 [≃£312]**
- The Collected Later Poems. New Directions: (1950). Dustwrapper (slightly used). With the booklet The Rose inserted as required. Inscribed presentation by the author. *(Black Sun)* **$475 [≃£247]**
- A Dream of Love. Direction 6: [1948]. Wrappers (light wear and soiling). *(Dermont)* **$50 [≃£26]**
- Go Go. Manikin Number Two. New York: Monroe Wheeler, (1923). One of 150. Printed stiff wrappers, string-tied, mint. *(Black Sun)* **$700 [≃£364]**

- In the Money. White Mule Part II. CT: New Directions, (1940). Author's signed presentation copy. *(Polyanthos)* **$200 [≃£104]**
- The Knife of the Times: and Other Stories. Ithaca: Dragon Press, (1932). Dustwrapper (short tear). *(Houle)* **$850 [≃£442]**
- Make Light Of It. New York: 1950. Dustwrapper (three short closed tears). *(Polyanthos)* **$30 [≃£15]**
- Make Light Of It. New York: Random House, 1950. Review slip. Dustwrapper. *(Alphabet)* **$85 [≃£44]**
- Paterson (Book Two). New York: New Directions, (1948). Dustwrapper (spine darkened, crown chipped). *(Lopez)* **$135 [≃£70]**
- Paterson. New York: New Classics / New Directions, (1948). 1st one-volume edition of the first two books. Dustwrapper. Signed by the author. *(Lopez)* **$300 [≃£156]**
- Paterson (Book Five). New York: (1958). Name. Dustwrapper (slightly soiled, two tiny tears spine extremities). *(Polyanthos)* **$60 [≃£31]**
- Spring and All. Dijon: Contact Press, [1923]. One of 300. Wrappers (slightly sunned at edges). *(Black Sun)* **$600 [≃£312]**
- Spring and All. Paris: Contact Press, 1923. Wrappers, unopened (a little browned round the edges). *(Words Etcetera)* **£250 [≃$479]**
- The Wedge. The Cummington Press: 1944. One of 380. Decorated boards (edges very slightly rubbed). Tissue dustwrapper (a bit chipped). Folding cloth case. *(Black Sun)* **$400 [≃£208]**
- White Mule. London: MacGibbon & Kee, 1965. Dustwrapper. *(Dalian)* **£45 [≃$86]**
- Wallace, Emily Mitchell: A Bibliography of William Carlos Williams. Wesleyan UP: 1968. Name on fly. Spine dull. *(Halsey)* **£15 [≃$28]**

Williamson, Henry

- The Children of Shallowford. London: Faber, 1939. Dustwrapper. *(Clearwater)* **£36 [≃$69]**
- A Clear Water Stream. London: Faber, 1957. Dustwrapper. *(Clearwater)* **£20 [≃$38]**
- The Dark Lantern. London: Macdonald, 1951. Dustwrapper (couple of small tears). *(Hadley)* **£45 [≃$86]**
- The Dark Lantern. London: Macdonald, 1951. *(Clearwater)* **£15 [≃$28]**
- The Dream of Fair Women. London: Faber, 1931. Cloth slightly marked. *(Dalian)* **£30 [≃$57]**
- The Dream of Fair Women. London: 1931. Dustwrapper (spine sunned, one-inch chip top of spine). *(Polyanthos)* **$30 [≃£15]**
- The Flax of Dream. London: Faber, 1936. Covers slightly discoloured. *(Clearwater)* **£20 [≃$38]**
- The Gale of the World. London: Macdonald, 1969. 2nd state, with the corrections demanded by the author. Dustwrapper (slightly worn). *(Ash)* **£75 [≃$143]**
- Genius of Friendship. 'T.E. Lawrence'. London: Faber, 1941. Endpapers foxed. Corners slightly bumped. *(Virgo)* **£65 [≃$124]**
- The Gold Falcon. London: Faber, 1933. Dustwrapper. Published anonymously. *(Ash)* **£75 [≃$143]**
- The Gold Falcon. London: Faber, 1933. dustwrapper (dust marked, rather frayed). Anonymous. *(Clearwater)* **£35 [≃$67]**
- The Golden Virgin. London: Macdonald, 1957. Edges fox spotted. Dustwrapper. *(Clearwater)* **£36 [≃$69]**
- Goodbye West Country. London: Putnam, 1937. Covers discoloured. Dustwrapper (slightly worn and marked, repaired). *(Clearwater)* **£34 [≃$65]**
- The Innocent Moon. London: Macdonald, 1961. Dustwrapper (slightly marked). *(Clearwater)* **£36 [≃$69]**
- It Was the Nightingale. London: Macdonald, 1962. Dustwrapper. *(Clearwater)* **£25 [≃$47]**
- The Labouring Life. London: 1932. Dustwrapper (minimal wear). *(Words Etcetera)* **£30 [≃$57]**
- The Linhay on the Downs ... London: Woburn Books, 1929. One of 530 initialled. Remains of dustwrapper. *(Clearwater)* **£35 [≃$67]**
- The Linhay on the Downs. London: Woburn Books, 1929. One of 500 initialled. Tiny chip top of spine. Dustwrapper (torn along spine, few edge tears). *(Polyanthos)* **$50 [≃£26]**
- The Lone Swallows. London: Collins, [1922]. Cloth backed boards, rather marked in places and rubbed at corners. No dustwrapper called for. *(Clearwater)* **£40 [≃$76]**
- The Lone Swallows. New York: 1926. Extremities of spine sunned, minimally rubbed. Dustwrapper. *(Polyanthos)* **$30 [≃£15]**
- Lucifer Before Sunrise. London: Macdonald, 1967. Dustwrapper. *(Virgo)* **£15 [≃$28]**

- Lucifer Before Sunrise. London: Macdonald, 1967. Dustwrapper. *(Clearwater)* **£15 [≃$28]**
- On Foot in Devon. London: 1933. Dustwrapper. *(Words Etcetera)* **£35 [≃$67]**
- On Foot in Devon. London: Maclehose, 1933. Dustwrapper. *(Clearwater)* **£35 [≃$67]**
- The Pathway. London: 1928. Fine. Dustwrapper (unchipped). *(Words Etcetera)* **£30 [≃$57]**
- The Patriot's Progress. New York: [1930]. 1st American edition. Dustwrapper (chipped). *(Clearwater)* **£30 [≃$57]**
- The Phasian Bird. London: Faber, 1948. Dustwrapper. *(Clearwater)* **£15 [≃$28]**
- The Phasian Bird. Boston: 1950. 1st American edition. Dustwrapper. *(Clearwater)* **£20 [≃$38]**
- The Phoenix Generation. London: Macdonald, 1965. Dustwrapper. *(Virgo)* **£16 [≃$30]**
- The Phoenix Generation. London: Macdonald, 1965. Dustwrapper. *(Clearwater)* **£18 [≃$34]**
- The Power of the Dead. London: Macdonald, 1963. Dustwrapper. *(Clearwater)* **£16 [≃$30]**
- Salar the Salmon. London: Faber, 1935. Dustwrapper (very slightly tanned and nicked). *(Dalian)* **£45 [≃$86]**
- Salar the Salmon. London: Faber, 1935. *(Green Meadow)* **£35 [≃$67]**
- The Scandaroon. London: Macdonald, 1972. Dustwrapper. *(Clearwater)* **£13 [≃$24]**
- The Scandaroon. London: MacDonald, 1972. Dustwrapper. *(Dalian)* **£22 [≃$42]**
- Scribbling Lark. London: Faber, 1949. Dustwrapper. *(Clearwater)* **£35 [≃$67]**
- A Solitary War. London: Macdonald, 1966. Dustwrapper. *(Virgo)* **£15 [≃$28]**
- A Solitary War. London: Macdonald, 1966. Dustwrapper. *(Clearwater)* **£18 [≃$34]**
- The Star-Born. London: Faber, 1933. Covers water stained, endpapers foxed. *(Clearwater)* **£20 [≃$38]**
- The Sun in the Sands. London: Faber, 1945. Dustwrapper. *(Clearwater)* **£14 [≃$26]**
- Tales of Moorland and Estuary. London: Macdonald, 1953. Dustwrapper. *(Clearwater)* **£35 [≃$67]**
- Tarka the Otter. Putnam's, 1927. 1st trade edition. Very slightly sunned. Dustwrapper (somewhat browned and worn). *(Ash)* **£100 [≃$191]**
- Tarka the Otter. London: Putnam, 1927. 1st regular public edition. Dustwrapper (slightly torn and rubbed). *(Clearwater)* **£100 [≃$191]**
- A Test to Destruction. London: 1960. Uncorrected proof copy with publisher's stamp. *(Buckley)* **£30 [≃$57]**
- The Village Book. London: Cape, 1930. Dustwrapper. *(Clearwater)* **£30 [≃$57]**
- The Wet Flanders Plain. London: Beaumont Press, 1929. One of 320. Corners slightly rubbed. *(Virgo)* **£65 [≃$124]**
- The Wet Flanders Plain. London: Faber, 1929. 1st regular public edition. Dustwrapper. *(Clearwater)* **£50 [≃$95]**
- Young Phillip Maddison. London: Macdonald, 1953. Dustwrapper (chipped). *(Clearwater)* **£40 [≃$76]**

Willingham, Calder

- End as a Man. London: John Lehmann, 1952. Dustwrapper (slightly dusty). His 1st book. *(Dalian)* **£35 [≃$67]**

Wilson, A.N.

- Gentlemen in England. London: Hamish Hamilton, 1985. Dustwrapper. *(Dalian)* **£15 [≃$28]**
- Kindly Light. London: Secker & Warburg, 1979. Price-clipped dustwrapper. *(Virgo)* **£27.50 [≃$53]**
- Love Unknown. London: Hamish Hamilton, 1986. Dustwrapper. *(Dalian)* **£16 [≃$30]**
- The Sweets of Pimlico. London: Secker & Warburg, 1977. Dustwrapper (slightly rubbed, one inch tear in upper panel). His 1st book. *(Moorhouse)* **£45 [≃$86]**

Wilson, Angus

- Anglo Saxon Attitudes. London: 1956. Dustwrapper (repaired). *(Roberts)* **£10.50 [≃$21]**
- Anglo Saxon Attitudes. Secker & Warburg, 1956. Dustwrapper (a little worn). *(Tiger Books)* **£18 [≃$34]**
- Anglo-Saxon Attitudes. London: 1956. Dustwrapper (slightly chipped). *(Buckley)* **£20 [≃$38]**
- A Bit Off the Map. London: 1957. Dustwrapper. *(Roberts)* **£14 [≃$26]**
- Hemlock and After. London: 1952. Dustwrapper. *(Roberts)* **£12.50 [≃$24]**
- Late Call. London: 1964. Dustwrapper (minimal browning). *(Roberts)* **£12.50 [≃$24]**
- The Middle Age of Mrs Eliot. London: Secker & Warburg, 1958. Dustwrapper. *(Sklaroff)* **£18 [≃$34]**

- The Middle Age of Mrs Eliot. Secker & Warburg, 1958. Dustwrapper. Signed by the author. *(Tiger Books)* **£30 [≃$57]**
- The Mulberry Bush. London: Secker & Warburg, 1956. Dustwrapper. *(Dalian)* **£25 [≃$47]**
- The Old Men at the Zoo. London: Secker & Warburg, 1961. Dustwrapper. *(Dalian)* **£18 [≃$34]**
- Such Darling Dodos. London: 1950. Dustwrapper. *(Roberts)* **£30 [≃$57]**
- The Wild Garden. London: Secker & Warburg, 1963. Dustwrapper (slightly chipped). *(Tiger Books)* **£18 [≃$34]**

Wilson, Colin

- The Outsider. London: Gollancz, 1956. Edges tanned. Dustwrapper (tanned, torn with loss). His 1st book. *(Hazeldene)* **£30 [≃$57]**
- The Outsider. Boston: Houghton, 1956. 1st US edition. Dustwrapper (lightly rubbed). *(Nouveau)* **$40 [≃£20]**
- Religion and the Rebel. London: Gollancz, 1957. Dustwrapper. *(Nouveau)* **$50 [≃£26]**
- Ritual in the Dark. London: 1960. Dustwrapper. *(First Issues)* **£15 [≃$28]**
- The Space Vampires. New York: Random House, 1976. Precedes the English edition. Dustwrapper. *(Dalian)* **£25 [≃$47]**
- The World of Violence. London: Gollancz, 1963. Dustwrapper. *(Dalian)* **£30 [≃$57]**

Wilson, Edmund

- Corrections & Comments. Iowa City: The Windhover Press, 1976. One of 175. Decorated paper boards. *(Alphabet)* **$135 [≃£70]**
- Devil Take the Hindmost. US: 1932. 1st US edition. Top corners slightly bumped. Some abrasion to endpapers. Dustwrapper (frayed, slightly chipped). *(Ellis)* **£80 [≃$153]**
- I Thought of Daisy. New York: Scribners, 1929. Spine extremities chipped. Author's presentation inscription. *(Alphabet)* **$250 [≃£130]**
- Memoirs of Hecate Country. New York: 1946. Dustwrapper (spine extremities little chipped, tiny piece missing top of front panel, few tiny chips extremities and a little rubbed). *(Polyanthos)* **$50 [≃£26]**
- Memoirs of Hecate Country. London: W.H. Allen, (1952). Dustwrapper (slightly nicked). *(Dalian)* **£20 [≃$38]**
- The Shock of Recognition. Edited by Edmund Wilson. New York: 1943. Top of spine minimally rubbed. Dustwrapper (little sunned and edge rubbed, half-inch piece missing top of spine, lower spine little rubbed, rear flap slightly defective). *(Polyanthos)* **$100 [≃£52]**
- This Room & This Gin & These Sandwiches. New York: The New Republic, 1937. Illustrated wrappers (wallet-edges a little used). *(Alphabet)* **$185 [≃£96]**
- To the Finland Station. New York: 1940. Dustwrapper (spine sunned, front panel some small pieces missing and little rubbed, tiny chips flap folds). *(Polyanthos)* **$100 [≃£52]**
- The Undertaker's Garland. With John Peale Bishop. New York: Knopf, 1922. 1st trade edition ('September, 1922'). His 1st appearance in book form. *(Houle)* **$275 [≃£143]**

Wilson, Harry Leon

- Merton of the Movies. New York: 1922. Dustwrapper (few small edge tears). *(Polyanthos)* **$100 [≃£52]**

Wingfield, Sheila

- Poems. London: Cresset Press, (1938). Unopened. Dustwrapper. Her 1st book. *(Dalian)* **£45 [≃$86]**

Winsor, Kathleen

- Forever Amber. London: Macdonald, [1944]. 1st English edition. Dustwrapper. *(Limestone Hills)* **$40 [≃£20]**

Winterson, Jeanette

- Boating for Beginners. London: Methuen, 1985. Dustwrapper. *(David Rees)* **£40 [≃$76]**
- Oranges Are Not the Only Fruit. Pandora: 1985. Wrappers. *(David Rees)* **£20 [≃$38]**
- The Passion. London: Bloomsbury, 1987. Dustwrapper. *(Moorhouse)* **£8 [≃$15]**
- The Passion. London: Bloomsbury, 1987. Dustwrapper. *(David Rees)* **£20 [≃$38]**
- Sexing the Cherry. London: Bloomsbury, 1989. Dustwrapper. Signed by the author. *(Moorhouse)* **£18 [≃$34]**
- Sexing the Cherry. London: 1989. Dustwrapper. Signed by the author. *(First Issues)* **£20 [≃$38]**

Wodehouse, P.G.

- America I Like You. New York: 1956. Cloth backed boards. Dustwrapper. *(Words Etcetera)* **£40 [≃$76]**

- America I Like You. New York: Simon & Schuster, 1956. 1st edition. Dustwrapper (minimally chipped). *(Limestone Hills)* **$95 [≃£49]**
- Aunts Aren't Gentlemen. London: Barrie & Jenkins, 1974. Dustwrapper. *(Limestone Hills)* **$85 [≃£44]**
- Author! Author! New York: Simon & Schuster, 1962. 1st American edition, 1st printing. Price-clipped dustwrapper. *(Limestone Hills)* **$95 [≃£49]**
- Bachelors Anonymous. London: Barrie & Jenkins, 1973. Price-clipped dustwrapper. *(Limestone Hills)* **$75 [≃£39]**
- Bertie Wooster Sees it Through. New York: Simon & Schuster, 1955. 1st American edition. Dustwrapper (slightly rubbed and chipped). *(Limestone Hills)* **$85 [≃£44]**
- The Best of Wodehouse. New York: Pocket Books, 1949. 1st printing. Pictorial wrappers. *(Limestone Hills)* **$55 [≃£28]**
- Biffen's Millions. New York: Simon & Schuster, 1964. 1st printing. Tiny flaw on rear panel. Dustwrapper (a few short tears along edges without loss). *(Limestone Hills)* **$90 [≃£46]**
- Big Money. London: Jenkins, 1931. 1st English edition, 1st printing. Orange cloth, lightly soiled. *(Limestone Hills)* **$150 [≃£78]**
- Big Money. New York: 1931. Spine little sunned, extremities very slightly rubbed, rear cover little soiled. *(Polyanthos)* **$30 [≃£15]**
- Bill the Conqueror. London: Methuen, 1924. 8-page catalogue dated 924 (September '24). Red cloth, black letters. *(Limestone Hills)* **$165 [≃£85]**
- Bill the Conqueror. London: Methuen, 1924. Cloth slightly marked. *(David Rees)* **£25 [≃$47]**
- Bill the Conqueror. His Invasion of England in the Springtime. New York: Doran, [1924]. 1st American edition. Yellow cloth, green letters. Dustwrapper (a few small chips). *(Limestone Hills)* **$350 [≃£182]**
- Bill the Conqueror. New York: Doran, (1924). 1st American edition. Dustwrapper (few small nicks). *(Houle)* **$750 [≃£390]**
- Bill the Conqueror. Toronto: Goodchild, [1924]. 1st Canadian edition. "Printed in Great Britain", and Methuen style red cloth. Name. *(Alphabet)* **$100 [≃£52]**
- Blandings Castle and Elsewhere. London: Jenkins, 1935. 1st printing. Some fading, especially of spine. Dustwrapper (short edge tears and creases repaired). *(Limestone Hills)* **$450 [≃£234]**
- Bring on the Girls. With Guy Bolton. London: Jenkins, 1954. 1st British edition. Dustwrapper (slightly rubbed). *(Dyke)* **£45 [≃$86]**
- Bring on the Girls. With Guy Bolton. London: 1954. Dustwrapper. *(Polyanthos)* **$75 [≃£39]**
- Brinkley Manor. Boston: Little, Brown, 1934. 1st American edition. Dustwrapper (chipped and soiled). *(Limestone Hills)* **$250 [≃£130]**
- The Butler Did It. New York: Simon & Schuster, 1957. 1st American edition (published in England as "Something Fishy'). Dustwrapper (chip at head of spine just affecting lettering, few short tears). *(Antic Hay)* **$50 [≃£26]**
- Carry on Jeeves. London: 1925. Minimal foxing of half-title. *(Roberts)* **£50 [≃$95]**
- Carry on Jeeves. London: 1925. Some foxing of prelims and edges. Spine faded. *(Roberts)* **£37.50 [≃$72]**
- Carry On, Jeeves! London: Jenkins, 1925. *(Limestone Hills)* **$135 [≃£70]**
- The Clicking of Cuthbert. London: Jenkins, 1922. Green pictorial cloth, fading moisture spot lower inner corner of rear panel, top edges darkened, front edges lightly foxed, corners wearing. *(Limestone Hills)* **$120 [≃£62]**
- Cocktail Time. London: Jenkins, 1958. Price-clipped dustwrapper (lightly chipped). *(Limestone Hills)* **$95 [≃£49]**
- Cocktail Time. London: Jenkins, 1958. Endpapers slightly foxed. Dustwrapper. *(Lewton)* **£17.50 [≃$34]**
- Cocktail Time. London: Jenkins, 1958. Dustwrapper. *(Sklaroff)* **£35 [≃$67]**
- The Code of the Woosters. London: 1938. *(Roberts)* **£45 [≃$86]**
- The Coming of Bill. London: 1920. Spine creased and darkened, cloth slightly bubbled. *(Blakeney)* **£45 [≃$86]**
- Company for Henry. London: Jenkins, 1967. Dustwrapper. *(Dyke)* **£30 [≃$57]**
- Do Butlers Burgle Banks? London: Jenkins, 1968. Price-clipped dustwrapper. *(Limestone Hills)* **$65 [≃£33]**
- A Few Quick Ones. New York: Simon & Schuster, 1959. 1st edition (precedes and differs from English edition). Dustwrapper. *(Limestone Hills)* **$65 [≃£33]**
- A Few Quick Ones. London: 1959. Dustwrapper. *(First Issues)* **£30 [≃$57]**
- A Few Quick Ones. London: Jenkins, [1959].

1st English edition. Dustwrapper (edges rubbed, lower rear corner chipped away, internal marginal repairs of short tears and creases). *(Limestone Hills)* **$75 [≃£39]**

- A Few Quick Ones. London: Jenkins, 1959. Price-clipped dustwrapper (rubbed, very slightly frayed), spine a touch faded). *(Moorhouse)* **£25 [≃$47]**
- The First Time I Went to New York [in] The First Time I ... Edited by Theodora Benson. London: Chapman & Hall, 1935. Dustwrapper (spine browned). *(Limestone Hills)* **$75 [≃£39]**
- French Leave. London: Jenkins, 1955. Dustwrapper (two small chips front lower panel, several small tears). *(Limestone Hills)* **$95 [≃£49]**
- Frozen Assets. London: Jenkins, 1964. 1st English edition. Price-clipped dustwrapper (two short tears rear bottom edge, small chip head of backstrip). *(Limestone Hills)* **$85 [≃£44]**
- Full Moon. London: Jenkins, (1947). Dustwrapper (small closed tear, slight rubbing and marking). *(Lewton)* **£28 [≃$53]**
- Full Moon. London: Jenkins, 1947. Page edges lightly spotted. Price-clipped dustwrapper (a little worn, slightly frayed at spine head). *(Glyn's)* **£22.50 [≃$44]**
- Full Moon. London: Jenkins, [1947]. 1st English edition, 1st printing. Dustwrapper. *(Limestone Hills)* **$85 [≃£44]**
- Full Moon. London: [1947]. Dustwrapper. *(Clearwater)* **£40 [≃$76]**
- Galahad at Blandings. London: Jenkins, 1965. 1st English edition. Dustwrapper. *(Limestone Hills)* **$85 [≃£44]**
- The Girl in Blue. New York: 1971. Dustwrapper. *(Polyanthos)* **$25 [≃£13]**
- Golf Without Tears. New York: Doran, [1924]. 1st American edition, 1st issue. Green cloth with green letters, coloured decorated endpapers, corners a bit bumped. *(Limestone Hills)* **$200 [≃£104]**
- Good Morning Bill. London: Methuen, 1928. 8 pages advertisements dated 1027 (October 1927). Unclipped dustwrapper (crease marks smoothed, missing letters at spine ends supplied in facsimile). *(Limestone Hills)* **$825 [≃£429]**
- Good Morning Bill. London: Methuen, 1928. Adverts at end. Blue cloth. *(Whiteson)* **£35 [≃$67]**
- Hot Water. London: Jenkins, 1932. 1st printing. Covers irregularly faded, rear inner hinge tender. *(Limestone Hills)* **$70 [≃£36]**
- Ice in the Bedroom. London: Jenkins, [1961]. 1st English edition. 1st issue price-clipped dustwrapper (very lightly edgeworn). *(Limestone Hills)* **$95 [≃£49]**
- If I Were You. Garden City: Doubleday, Doran, 1931. 1st edition (precedes English edition). Dustwrapper (lacks 2 1/4 inches at base of spine, numerous small tears and chips). *(Limestone Hills)* **$250 [≃£130]**
- The Inimitable Jeeves. London: Jenkins, 1923. Light green pictorial cloth, two tiny spots at foot of front panel and frontispiece, bottom edges lightly foxed. *(Limestone Hills)* **$185 [≃£96]**
- The Intrusion of Jimmy. New York: Watt, (1910). 1st issue, with gilt stamped spine. Precedes the English issue as 'Gentleman of Leisure'. Decorated cloth with coloured pictorial label, bright. *(Houle)* **$750 [≃£390]**
- Jeeves & the Tie that Binds. New York: 1971. 1st edition. Dustwrapper. *(Whiteson)* **£25 [≃$47]**
- Jeeves and the Tie that Binds. New York: 1971. Price-clipped dustwrapper. *(Polyanthos)* **$25 [≃£13]**
- Jeeves in the Offing. London: Jenkins, 1960. 1st English edition. Dustwrapper. *(Limestone Hills)* **$120 [≃£62]**
- Joy in the Morning. New York: Doubleday, 1946. 1st edition. Light indentation front cover. Dustwrapper. *(Limestone Hills)* **$85 [≃£44]**
- Laughing Gas. Garden City: Doubleday, Doran, 1936. 1st American edition. Dustwrapper. *(Limestone Hills)* **$450 [≃£234]**
- Laughing Gas. London: Jenkins, 1936. Dustwrapper (creased and repaired at bottom of front panel, small loss base of spine). *(Limestone Hills)* **$950 [≃£494]**
- The Little Warrior. New York: Doran, [1920]. 1st edition. Owner's signature and bookplate. Crease on front panel, front inner hinge tender. *(Limestone Hills)* **$195 [≃£101]**
- Love Among the Chickens. New York: The Circle Publishing Company, 1909. 1st American edition. Advance copy. Tan pictorial cloth, blue lettering, pictorial design in red and blue, top edge slightly darkened. *(Limestone Hills)* **$750 [≃£390]**
- The Luck of the Bodkins. Boston: Little, Brown, 1936. Name on endpaper. Dustwrapper (couple of small repairs). *(Dyke)* **£250 [≃$479]**

- The Mating Season. London: [1949]. 1st printing, so stated. Two tiny stains. Dustwrapper (slightly sunned, extremities minimally rubbed, tiny closed edge tear). *(Polyanthos)* **$65 [≃£33]**
- The Mating Season. New York: Didier, 1944. 1st American edition. Dustwrapper (minor edge wear, one closed tear). *(Limestone Hills)* **$185 [≃£96]**
- Mike at Wrykyn. New York: Meredith Press, [1953]. 1st American edition. Dustwrapper. *(Limestone Hills)* **$75 [≃£39]**
- Money in the Bank. London: Jenkins, [1946]. 1st English edition, 1st printing. Lower corners lightly bumped. 1st iss dustwrapper, with Quick Service the last title on front flap, (lightly chipped). *(Limestone Hills)* **$115 [≃£59]**
- The Most of P.G. Wodehouse. New York: Simon & Schuster, 1960. 1st edition (no English edition). Dustwrapper (scuffed, one tear on front flap). *(Limestone Hills)* **$75 [≃£39]**
- The Most of P.G. Wodehouse. New York: 1960. Dustwrapper (small pinhole to upper panel, very slight creasing to foot of spine). *(Words Etcetera)* **£45 [≃$86]**
- Mr. Mulliner Speaking. London: Jenkins, 1929. Foredge and prelims slightly foxed. *(Dalian)* **£35 [≃$67]**
- Much Obliged Jeeves. London: Barrie & Jenkins, 1971. Dustwrapper (half inch chip out of lower edge of back panel). *(Limestone Hills)* **$75 [≃£39]**
- Mulliner Nights. London: Jenkins, 1933. 1st printing. Patchy fading of front and black panels but lettering and design bright. *(Limestone Hills)* **$95 [≃£49]**
- No Nudes is Good Nudes. New York: Simon & Schuster, 1970. 1st American edition. Price- clipped dustwrapper. *(Limestone Hills)* **$95 [≃£49]**
- Nothing Serious. London: Jenkins, [1950]. *(Sklaroff)* **£20 [≃$38]**
- Over Seventy. London: Jenkins, 1957. Dustwrapper (lightly chipped, small piece missing from base of spine). *(Limestone Hills)* **$75 [≃£39]**
- P.G. Wodehouse. Methuen's Library of Humour. Edited by E.V. Knox. London: 1934. Dustwrapper (lightly soiled, missing very small pieces at spine ends). *(Blakeney)* **£150 [≃$287]**
- Pearls, Girls and Monty Bodkin. London: Barrie & Jenkins, 1972. Dustwrapper (small tears at top of front panel). *(Limestone Hills)* **$75 [≃£39]**
- A Pelican at Blandings. London: Jenkins, 1969. Dustwrapper. *(Limestone Hills)* **$135 [≃£70]**
- Pigs Have Wings. London: Jenkins, 1952. Dustwrapper. *(Marlborough B'shop)* **£60 [≃$115]**
- The Plot That Thickened. New York: Simon & Schuster, 1973. 1st American edition. Dustwrapper. *(Limestone Hills)* **$65 [≃£33]**
- The Pothunters. London: Black, 1902. 2nd issue. Slight foxing. Decorated cloth (little dull). *(Whiteson)* **£420 [≃$806]**
- The Prince and Betty. New York: Watt, 1912. Precedes the British edition. Black cloth, two oval portraits on upper cover. *(Dyke)* **£275 [≃$527]**
- The Prince and Betty. New York: W.J. Watt, 1912. Precedes and differs from the British edition. Black cloth gilt, with two oval onlays. *(Ash)* **£500 [≃$959]**
- Psmith in the City. London: Adam & Charles Black, 1910. Pictorial cloth (slightly rubbed, front endpaper cracked at hinge). *(Ash)* **£400 [≃$767]**
- Psmith in the City. London: Black, 1910. Advertisement leaf. Blue pictorial cloth, upper corners bumped. *(Limestone Hills)* **$800 [≃£416]**
- The Purloined Paperweight. New York: Simon & Schuster, [1967]. 1st edition, 1st printing. Dustwrapper. *(Limestone Hills)* **$60 [≃£31]**
- The Return of Jeeves. New York: Simon & Schuster, 1954. 1st American edition of Ring for Jeeves (much revised). 1st printing. Unclipped dustwrapper (some soiling on rear panel). *(Limestone Hills)* **$150 [≃£78]**
- Right Ho Jeeves. London: Jenkins, 1934. Covers slightly soiled, faint stain on rear. *(Limestone Hills)* **$210 [≃£109]**
- Service with a Smile. London: Jenkins, 1961. 1st English edition. Edges lightly foxed. Dustwrapper (one tiny chip base of spine). *(Limestone Hills)* **$95 [≃£49]**
- The Small Bachelor. London: Methuen, [1927]. 8 pages advertisements dated 327 (March 1927). Blue cloth, black lettering, minimally rubbed. *(Limestone Hills)* **$120 [≃£62]**
- Something Fishy. London: 1957. Dustwrapper (little creased and chipped around edges). *(Words Etcetera)* **£35 [≃$67]**
- Something Fishy. London: Jenkins, 1957. Price-clipped dustwrapper (torn and creased

but complete). *(Limestone Hills)* **$75 [≃£39]**

- Spring Fever. London: Jenkins, 1948. 1st English edition (published simultaneously with American). Unclipped dustwrapper (repaired, 2 replaced chips on spine, 1/4 inch at head, 2 inches at foot). *(Limestone Hills)* **$80 [≃£41]**
- Stiff Upper Lip, Jeeves. London: Jenkins, 1963. 1st British edition. Dustwrapper. *(Dyke)* **£45 [≃$86]**
- Stiff Upper Lip, Jeeves. London: Jenkins, 1963. 1st English edition. Dustwrapper (one small internally closed tear at foot of backstrip). *(Limestone Hills)* **$95 [≃£49]**
- Summer Moonshine. Garden City: Doubleday Doran, 1937. Dustwrapper (slightly worn). *(Limestone Hills)* **$250 [≃£130]**
- Sunset at Blandings. London: Chatto & Windus, 1977. Dustwrapper. *(Sklaroff)* **£18 [≃$34]**
- Sunset at Blandings. London: Chatto & Windus, 1977. Dustwrapper. *(Marlborough B'shop)* **£15 [≃$28]**
- Ukridge. London: Jenkins, 1924. Light spotting and foxing. Bright green pictorial cloth. *(Limestone Hills)* **$245 [≃£127]**
- Uncle Dynamite. London: Jenkins, [1948]. 1st printing. Price-clipped dustwrapper (three interior tape marks, tape mark back panel, tiny chip at spine extremities). *(Limestone Hills)* **$120 [≃£62]**
- Uncle Dynamite. London: [1948]. Dustwrapper (slightly torn). *(Clearwater)* **£40 [≃$76]**
- Uncle Dynamite. New York: Didier, 1948. 1st American edition. Dustwrapper (few unobtrusive chips and closed tears). *(Limestone Hills)* **$225 [≃£117]**
- Uncle Fred in the Springtime. London: Jenkins, [1939]. 1st printing. Top edges lightly foxed. Unclipped dustwrapper (edgeworn, repaired, spine ends chipped affecting 2 letters, head of front panel chipped affecting 1 letter, foot of spine chipped affecting 2 letters). *(Limestone Hills)* **$525 [≃£273]**
- Uncle Fred in the Springtime. New York: 1939. Spine little sunned, extremities little rubbed. *(Polyanthos)* **$30 [≃£15]**
- The Uncollected Wodehouse. New York: Seabury Press, 1976. 1st edition (no English edition). Dustwrapper. *(Limestone Hills)* **$55 [≃£28]**
- The Uncollected Wodehouse. New York: Continuum Books, [1976]. Price-clipped dustwrapper. *(Limestone Hills)* **$65 [≃£33]**
- Very Good, Jeeves. Garden City: Doubleday, Doran, 1930. 1st edition. Inner hinges tender, spine a bit rubbed. *(Limestone Hills)* **$95 [≃£49]**
- William Tell Told Again. London: Black, 1905. 2nd issue, with brown letters on front cover, gold on spine. Advertisement leaf. Front edge foxing. Front free endsheet replaced. Tan pictorial cloth, t.e.g. *(Limestone Hills)* **$400 [≃£208]**
- Wodehouse Nights. New York: Heinemann, 1983. 1st American edition. Dustwrapper. *(Limestone Hills)* **$35 [≃£18]**
- The World of Uncle Fred. London: Hutchinson, 1983. Price-clipped dustwrapper (spine extremities a little creased). *(Limestone Hills)* **$60 [≃£31]**
- Young Men in Spats. London: Jenkins, 1936. Two corners of spine faded. Unclipped dustwrapper (minor creases and edge tears repaired). *(Limestone Hills)* **$450 [≃£234]**

Wolfe, Thomas

- The Crisis in Industry. Chapel Hill: North Carolina University, 1919. Printed grey wrappers, slight fold, small foxed spot on top margin of leaves. His 1st book. One of 200. *(Chapel Hill)* **$6,500 [≃£3,385]**
- The Hills Beyond. New York: 1941. Dustwrapper (top of spine minimally chipped, tiny piece missing top corner). *(Polyanthos)* **$65 [≃£33]**
- The Hills Beyond. New York: Harper, 1941. Some spotting of lower parts of boards. Dustwrapper (light edgewear). *(Nouveau)* **$75 [≃£39]**
- Look Homeward, Angel. London: Heinemann, [1930]. 1st English edition. Endpapers foxed, a bit dusty. *(Chapel Hill)* **$95 [≃£49]**
- Mannerhouse. New York: 1948. One of 500. Dustwrapper (spine slightly sunned). Box (very slightly edge rubbed). *(Polyanthos)* **$150 [≃£78]**
- Mannerhouse. New York: Harpers, 1948. One of 500. Dustwrapper (spine darkened). Slipcase (slightly worn). *(Bromer)* **$250 [≃£130]**
- Of Time & The River. New York: Scribners, 1935. Dustwrapper (light edgewear at spine extremities). *(Alphabet)* **$150 [≃£78]**
- Of Time and the River. London: Heinemann, 1935. 1st English edition. Dustwrapper (slightly chipped).

(Limestone Hills) **$135 [≃£70]**

- The Story of a Novel. New York: Scribners, 1936. Dustwrapper (light rubbing, few closed tears). *(Nouveau)* **$125 [≃£65]**
- The Story of a Novel. London: Heinemann, 1936. Cloth slightly marked. *(Dalian)* **£25 [≃$47]**
- You Can't Go Home Again. New York: Harpers, [1940]. Dustwrapper (lightly used). *(Dermont)* **$100 [≃£52]**
- You Can't Go Home Again. London: Heinemann, 1947. Dustwrapper (slightly rubbed and chipped). *(Dalian)* **£35 [≃$67]**

Wolfe, Tom

- The Bonfire of the Vanities. New York: Farrar Straus, 1987. One of 250 signed. Slipcase. *(First Issues)* **£160 [≃$307]**
- The Bonfire of the Vanities. New York: Farrar Straus Giroux, 1987. Dustwrapper. *(Moorhouse)* **£30 [≃$57]**
- The Bonfire of the Vanities. New York: 1987. Dustwrapper. *(Polyanthos)* **$50 [≃£26]**
- The Bonfire of the Vanities. London: Cape, 1988. Price-clipped dustwrapper. *(Moorhouse)* **£25 [≃$47]**
- Electric Kool Aid Acid Test. New York: Farrar, 1968. Dustwrapper. *(Michael Johnson)* **£40 [≃$76]**
- The Electric Kool-Aid Acid Test. New York: 1968. Spine extremities little sunned. Dustwrapper (slightly soiled, few tiny edge chips). *(Polyanthos)* **$45 [≃£23]**
- From Bauhaus to Our House. New York: 1981. Dustwrapper with release. *(Polyanthos)* **$30 [≃£15]**
- From Bauhaus to Our House. London: Cape, 1982. 1st English edition. Uncorrected proof copy. Wrappers. *(Limestone Hills)* **$50 [≃£26]**
- In Our Time. New York: 1980. Wrappers. *(Polyanthos)* **$20 [≃£10]**
- The Kandy-Kolored Tangerine-Flake Streamline Baby. New York: 1965. Covers very slightly soiled. His 1st book. *(Polyanthos)* **$35 [≃£18]**
- The Kandy-Kolored Tangerine Flake Streamline Baby. London: 1966. Dustwrapper (slight wear at edges). His 1st book. *(Sclanders)* **£30 [≃$57]**
- Mauve Gloves & Madmen, Clutter & Vine. New York: Farrar, Straus & Giroux, 1976. 1st printing. Dustwrapper (one nick on front panel). *(Limestone Hills)* **$45 [≃£23]**
- The Mid-Atlantic Man. London: Weidenfeld & Nicolson, 1969. Dustwrapper. Published in the US as The Pump House Gang. *(Moorhouse)* **£25 [≃$47]**
- The Painted Word. Farrar, 1975. Price-clipped dustwrapper. Signed by the author. *(Nouveau)* **$60 [≃£31]**
- The Painted Word. New York: 1975. Dustwrapper. *(Polyanthos)* **$35 [≃£18]**
- The Pump House Gang. New York: 1968. Dustwrapper. *(Polyanthos)* **$45 [≃£23]**
- The Purple Decades. New York: 1982. Proof copy. Wrappers. *(Polyanthos)* **$50 [≃£26]**
- The Purple Decades. New York: 1982. Dustwrapper (tiny nick lower spine). *(Polyanthos)* **$40 [≃£20]**
- The Purple Decades. London: Cape, 1983. 1st English edition. Dustwrapper. *(Limestone Hills)* **$30 [≃£15]**
- Radical Chic & Mau-Mauing the Flak Catchers. New York: Farrar, 1970. Dustwrapper. *(Nouveau)* **$45 [≃£23]**
- Radical Chic and Mau-Mauing the Flak Catchers. New York: 1970. Dustwrapper. *(Polyanthos)* **$25 [≃£13]**
- The Right Stuff. New York: 1979. Dustwrapper. *(Polyanthos)* **$30 [≃£15]**
- The Right Stuff. New York: Farrar, 1979. Dustwrapper. *(Michael Johnson)* **£30 [≃$57]**
- The Right Stuff. New York: Nov. 1980. 1st Bantam edition. Special edition, not for sale. Wrappers. *(Polyanthos)* **$20 [≃£10]**

Wolff, Tobias

- Hunters in the Snow. London: Cape, 1982. Dustwrapper. *(Dalian)* **£25 [≃$47]**

Woolf, Douglas

- The Hypocritic Days. Palma De Mallorca: Divers Press, 1955. Paper wrappers, small mark on front cover. His 1st book. *(Alphabet)* **$65 [≃£33]**

Woolf, Leonard

- Essays on Literature History Politics ... London: 1927. Dustwrapper (dull and slightly discoloured). *(Whiteson)* **£55 [≃$105]**
- The Hotel. London: Hogarth Press, 1939. Dustwrapper. *(Buckley)* **£35 [≃$67]**
- Quack, Quack. London: Hogarth Press, 1935. *(Whiteson)* **£30 [≃$57]**

Woolf, Virginia

- Beau Brummel. New York: 1930. One of 550 signed. Cloth backed boards. Slipcase (badly

foxed, broken along lower edge, slightly sunned along upper edge).
(Words Etcetera) **£450 [≈$863]**

- Beau Brummell. New York: Rimington & Hooper, 1930. 1st separate edition. One of 550 signed. Foredge slightly spotted. Covers a little soiled and browned around edges, spine faded with small splits at head.
(Virgo) **£300 [≈$575]**

- The Captain's Death Bed: and Other Essays. New York: Harcourt, Brace, (1950). 1st edition ('first American edition'). Dustwrapper. *(Houle)* **$125 [≈£65]**

- The Captain's Death Bed: and Other Essays. London: Hogarth Press, 1950. 1st English edition. Dustwrapper. *(Houle)* **$125 [≈£65]**

- The Common Reader: Second Series. Hogarth Press: 1932. Edges slightly spotted. Dustwrapper (very slightly chipped and soiled). *(Virgo)* **£225 [≈$431]**

- Contemporary Writers. London: 1965. Proof copy. Wrappers.
(Words Etcetera) **£50 [≈$95]**

- Contemporary Writers. London: Hogarth Press, 1965. Dustwrapper.
(Virgo) **£35 [≈$67]**

- The Death of the Moth and Other Essays. London: Hogarth Press, 1942. Name on endpaper. Covers faded.
(Sklaroff) **£25 [≈$47]**

- The Diaries. 1915-1941. London: 1977-84. 5 vols. Vols 1-3 lower edge splashed. Dustwrappers (vols 1 & 2 slightly browned round edges). *(Virgo)* **£125 [≈$239]**

- Flush. London: 1933. Large Paper. Dustwrapper (trifle foxed, unchipped).
(Words Etcetera) **£125 [≈$239]**

- Granite and Rainbow. London: 1958. Dustwrapper (spine a little browned).
(Words Etcetera) **£45 [≈$86]**

- Granite and Rainbow. London: 1958. Name and bookplate. Dustwrapper (rubbed, nicked, frayed). *(Ellis)* **£40 [≈$76]**

- Granite and Rainbow. New York: 1958. Spine extremities little sunned. Dustwrapper.
(Polyanthos) **$35 [≈£18]**

- Granite and Rainbow. New York: Harcourt, Brace, (1958). 1st American edition. Dustwrapper (slight browning to spine).
(Houle) **$85 [≈£44]**

- A Haunted House and Other Stories. London: 1943. Dustwrapper (spine extremities and two corners slightly torn).
(Words Etcetera) **£75 [≈$143]**

- Hours in a Library. New York: (1957). Privately printed. No dustwrapper issued.
(Polyanthos) **$35 [≈£18]**

- Jacob's Room. Richmond: The Hogarth Press, 1922. One corner slightly bumped, some rubbing to head of spine. Signed by the author. *(Black Sun)* **$3,200 [≈£1,666]**

- A Letter to a Young Poet. Hogarth Press: 1932. Covers slightly soiled.
(Virgo) **£25 [≈$47]**

- A Letter to a Young Poet. Hogarth Press: 1932. Ownership inscription. Wrappers.
(First Issues) **£15 [≈$28]**

- A Letter to a Young Poet. London: Hogarth Press, 1932. Wrappers (trifle marked in places). *(Words Etcetera)* **£28 [≈$53]**

- The London Scene. New York: Frank Hallman, 1975. One of 750. No dustwrapper issued. *(Polyanthos)* **$35 [≈£18]**

- The Moment and Other Essays. Hogarth Press: 1947. Dustwrapper (slightly chipped, spine and edges faded). *(Virgo)* **£25 [≈$47]**

- The Moment and Other Essays. London: Hogarth Press, 1947. Dustwrapper (slightly chipped). *(Sklaroff)* **£40 [≈$76]**

- The Moment: and Other Essays. London: Hogarth Press, 1947. Dustwrapper (top of spine and upper cover chipped).
(Houle) **$125 [≈£65]**

- Mrs. Dalloway. London: Hogarth Press, 1925. Rubbed, spine repaired, extremities chafed or worn, marks of label removal from front cover. *(Clearwater)* **£60 [≈$115]**

- Nurse Lugton's Golden Thimble. London: Hogarth Press, 1966. Purple cloth.
(First Issues) **£25 [≈$47]**

- Orlando. London: 1928. Dustwrapper (three small closed tears to upper panels, three slightly larger ones to lower panel).
(Words Etcetera) **£125 [≈$239]**

- Orlando. New York: Crosby Gaige, 1928. One of 861 signed. Small name on pastedown. No dustwrapper issued.
(Alphabet) **$500 [≈£260]**

- Reviewing. Hogarth Press: 1939.
(Virgo) **£25 [≈$47]**

- Reviewing. London: Hogarth Press, 1939. Wrappers. *(Holmes)* **$85 [≈£44]**

- Reviewing. London: Hogarth Press, 1939. Wrappers. *(Woolmer)* **$50 [≈£26]**

- Roger Fry. London: 1940. Spine slightly faded. Dustwrapper (slightly chipped, a few nicks). *(Ellis)* **£160 [≈$307]**

- Roger Fry. New York: Harcourt Brace, 1940. 1st American edition. Endpapers a little browned. Dustwrapper (slightly soiled and faded, small chips at corners and spine ends). *(Virgo)* **£70 [≃$134]**

- A Room of One's Own. London: The Hogarth Press, 1929. 1st English edition. Cloth boards (slightly worn). Signed inscription by the author dated Oct. 1922. *(Black Sun)* **$2,000 [≃£1,041]**
- A Room of One's Own. Hogarth Press, 1929. Dustwrapper (repaired, with loss at head of spine). *(Tiger Books)* **£75 [≃$143]**
- A Room of One's Own. London: 1929. Price-clipped dustwrapper (chipped, rubbed, lower panel lightly stained, some loss at spine ends). *(Ellis)* **£200 [≃$383]**
- A Room of One's Own. Fountain Press / Hogarth Press, 1929. One of 492 signed. Name on fly. *(Words Etcetera)* **£750 [≃$1,439]**
- Street Haunting. San Francisco: Westgate Press, 1930. One of 500 signed. Morocco backed boards (spine slightly faded). Slipcase. *(Words Etcetera)* **£450 [≃$863]**
- Thoreau. California: Upstairs Press, 1977. One of 100. Wrappers. *(Words Etcetera)* **£45 [≃$86]**
- Three Guineas. London: Hogarth Press, 1938. Inscription. Spine darkened. *(Sklaroff)* **£25 [≃$47]**
- Three Guineas. London: 1938. Yellow cloth. Dustwrapper (slightly worn and torn). *(Whiteson)* **£45 [≃$86]**
- Three Guineas. London: The Hogarth Press, 1938. Slight darkening to flyleaf. Dustwrapper (slightly chipped). Signed presentation inscription by the author. *(Black Sun)* **$3,500 [≃£1,822]**
- Three Guineas. New York: (1938). Dustwrapper (bit of darkening to spine, couple of very short tears). *(Between the Covers)* **$125 [≃£65]**
- To the Lighthouse. Hogarth Press: 1927. Edges slightly spotted, foxing on endpapers and end leaves. Spine slightly dulled, two tiny pin holes. Dustwrapper (rather soiled and worn, small pieces missing from spine ends, chips from corners and edges). *(Virgo)* **£400 [≃$767]**
- To the Lighthouse. London: Hogarth Press, 1927. Bookplate. Small split spot on slightly dull spine. *(Blakeney)* **£75 [≃$143]**
- Two Stories. [The Mark on the Wall] By Virginia Woolf and [Three Jews by] Leonard S. Woolf. Richmond: The Hogarth Press, 1917. With both flyleaves. Japanese paper wrappers, sewn, fine. *(Black Sun)* **$8,500 [≃£4,427]**
- Walter Sickert. London: 1934. Wrappers (rubbed). *(Ellis)* **£60 [≃$115]**
- Walter Sickert. London: Hogarth Press, 1934. Wrappers (very slightly browned at edges). *(Buckley)* **£40 [≃$76]**
- Walter Sickert. London: Hogarth Press, 1934. Wrappers just a little dusty, very slightly sunned at spine. *(Blakeney)* **£65 [≃$124]**
- The Waves. Hogarth Press, 1931. Edges of text browned. Boopklate. Dampstaining at spine ends. Dustwrapper (browned, pieces missing from spine ends). *(Tiger Books)* **£60 [≃$115]**
- The Waves. London: Hogarth Press, 1931. Spine slightly faded. *(Sotheran's)* **£98 [≃$188]**
- A Writer's Diary. Hogarth Press: 1953. Dustwrapper (rather browned, chipped and frayed). *(Virgo)* **£30 [≃$57]**
- A Writer's Diary. London: Hogarth Press, 1953. Endpapers and prelims foxed. Spine slightly faded, top edge of covers very faintly spotted. Dustwrapper (top edges and spine slightly browned). *(Virgo)* **£40 [≃$76]**
- The Years. London: Hogarth, 1937. Some foxing to endpapers. Dustwrapper (some foxing front panel). *(Between the Covers)* **$450 [≃£234]**
- The Years. New York: 1937. Spine very slightly sunned. *(Polyanthos)* **$30 [≃£15]**

Woolrich, Cornell

- Cover Charge. New York: 1926. Bookplate. One page carelessly opened, not affecting text. His 1st book. *(Polyanthos)* **$75 [≃£39]**
- Night Has a Thousand Eyes. By George Hopley. New York: Farrar Rinehart, 1945. Small stain on bottom edge. Dustwrapper (crease on front and back panels, minor wear at top of spine and along front flap fold, couple of tiny tears). *(Mordida)* **$200 [≃£104]**
- Nightwebs. New York: Harper & Row, 1971. Price-clipped dustwrapper (minor wear spine ends). *(Mordida)* **$65 [≃£33]**

Wouk, Herman

- The 'Caine' Mutiny. London: Cape, 1951. Inscription on flyleaf. Dustwrapper (worn). *(Sklaroff)* **£25 [≃$47]**

Wright, Charles

- The Grave of the Right Hand. Wesleyan UP: (1970). Dustwrapper. His 1st book. *(Woolmer)* **$45 [≃£23]**

Wright, James

- Two Citizens. New York: Farrar Straus Giroux, (1973). Dustwrapper. Signed by the author. *(Lopez)* **$100 [≃£52]**

Wright, Richard

- Black Boy. London: Gollancz, 1945. 1st British edition. Dustwrapper. *(Michael Johnson)* **£30 [≃$57]**
- The Weekend Man. Toronto: Macmillan, 1970. Dustwrapper (very slight edge wear at spine). His 1st book. *(Alphabet)* **$50 [≃£26]**

Wylie, Eleanor

- Mr. Hodge and Mr. Hazard. London: Heinemann, 1928. Prelims and foredge slightly foxed. Dustwrapper (slightly tanned and chipped). *(Dalian)* **£35 [≃$67]**
- The Venetian Glass Nephew. London: Heinemann, 1926. Cloth slightly faded and marked. *(Dalian)* **£20 [≃$38]**

Wyndham, John

- Chocky. London: Michael Joseph, (1969). Dustwrapper. *(Lopez)* **$65 [≃£33]**
- Chocky. London: Michael Joseph, 1968. Dustwrapper. *(Sklaroff)* **£15 [≃$28]**
- Consider Her Ways & Others. London: Michael Joseph, 1961. Dustwrapper. *(Sklaroff)* **£30 [≃$57]**
- Consider Her Ways and Others. London: Joseph, 1961. Dustwrapper. *(Limestone Hills)* **$45 [≃£23]**
- The Day of the Triffids. London: Michael Joseph, 1951. Covers slightly dull. "London edition with textual alterations". His 1st book. *(Whiteson)* **£60 [≃$115]**
- The Midwich Cuckoos. London: 1957. Dustwrapper (slightly darkened, internally repaired). *(Sclanders)* **£50 [≃$95]**
- The Midwich Cuckoos. New York: Ballantine, 1957. 1st American edition. One of 500. Dustwrapper (one tiny wrinkled tear at lower foredge corner, gilt unblemished). *(Alphabet)* **$150 [≃£78]**
- The Seeds of Time. London: Michael Joseph, 1956. Dustwrapper. *(Limestone Hills)* **$85 [≃£44]**
- The Space Machine. By John Beynon. [In] Modern Wonder, 1937. Vols 1-3 (68 issues), all published. Bound in 2 vols. Cloth. *(Sklaroff)* **£150 [≃$287]**
- Trouble With Lichen. London: Michael Joseph, 1960. Dustwrapper. *(Limestone Hills)* **$95 [≃£49]**

Yates, Dornford

- B-Berry and I Look Back. London: Ward Lock, 1958. Dustwrapper. *(Glyn's)* **£7.50 [≃$15]**
- The Berry Scene. London: Ward Lock, 1947. Dustwrapper (slightly frayed). *(Tiger Books)* **£18 [≃$34]**
- The House That Berry Built. London: 1945. Dustwrapper (slightly faded at spine, one short tear). *(Blakeney)* **£15 [≃$28]**
- Ne'er Do Well. London: Ward Lock, 1954. Dustwrapper (slightly worn). *(Glyn's)* **£7.50 [≃$15]**
- Red in the Morning. London: Ward Lock, 1946. Inscription. Dustwrapper (spine browned). *(Tiger Books)* **£18 [≃$34]**
- Wife Apparent. London: Ward Lock, 1956. 1st issue 'Lady in Waiting' dustwrapper. *(Glyn's)* **£15 [≃$28]**
- Wife Apparent. London: Ward, Lock, 1956. Dustwrapper (overstamped with new title). *(Ash)* **£25 [≃$47]**

Yates, Richard

- Revolutionary Road. Boston: 1961. Dustwrapper. His 1st book. *(Pettler & Liebermann)* **$60 [≃£31]**
- Revolutionary Road. London: Deutsch, 1962. Dustwrapper (slightly creased, very slightly repaired). *(Dalian)* **£35 [≃$67]**

Yeates, V.M.

- Winged Victory. New York: 1934. 1st American edition. Covers slightly scratched. *(Clearwater)* **£35 [≃$67]**

Yeats, W.B.

- Autobiographies. New York: Macmillan, 1927. One of 250 signed. Cloth and boards. No dustwrapper issued. *(Antic Hay)* **$375 [≃£195]**
- A Book of Irish Verse. London: Methuen, 1900. Revised edition. Endpapers slightly foxed. *(Dalian)* **£35 [≃$67]**
- The Collected Poems. London: Macmillan, 1933. Name on endpaper. Endpapers slightly browned. Dustwrapper (slightly tanned, slightly marked). *(Dalian)* **£35 [≃$67]**
- Deirdre. London: Bullen, 1907. Boards dull

and slightly marked, slight wear to edges. *(Whiteson)* **£25 [≃$47]**

- Dramatis Personae. New York: 1936. Dustwrapper (little soiled, few tiny nicks). *(Polyanthos)* **$60 [≃£31]**
- Essays. New York: Macmillan, 1924. One of 250 signed. Cloth and boards. No dustwrapper issued. *(Antic Hay)* **$475 [≃£247]**
- The Great Clock Tower. New York: Macmillan, 1935. 1st US edition. *(Whiteson)* **£25 [≃$47]**
- Ideas of Good and Evil. New York: 1903. Spine extremities minimally rubbed. *(Polyanthos)* **$75 [≃£39]**
- Michael Robartes and the Dancer. Cuala Press: 1920. One of 400. Spine label chipped. *(Woolmer)* **$150 [≃£78]**
- Modern Poetry. London: BBC, 1936. Printed wrappers (slightly tanned). *(Dalian)* **£85 [≃$163]**
- New Poems. Dublin: Cuala Press, 1938. One of 450. *(Woolmer)* **$125 [≃£65]**
- Plays. London: Macmillan, 1931. Partly unopened. Dustwrapper (slightly dull). *(Whiteson)* **£15 [≃$28]**
- Sophocles' King Oedipus. London: Macmillan, 1928. Wrappers (slightly dusty). *(Dalian)* **£35 [≃$67]**
- Tribute to Thomas Davis. Oxford: Blackwell, 1947. Printed wrappers (edges very slightly faded). *(Dalian)* **£45 [≃$86]**
- The Winding Stair. London: Macmillan, 1933. Dustwrapper (dull, slightly worn). *(Whiteson)* **£15 [≃$28]**
- See also the companion IRBP volume Literature.

Yevtushenko, Yevgeny

- A Precocious Autobiography. London: 1963. Dustwrapper. *(First Issues)* **£10 [≃$19]**
- Wild Berries. London: 1984. Dustwrapper. *(First Issues)* **£10 [≃$19]**

Young, Andrew

- Winter Harvest. London: Nonesuch Press, 1933. Cloth backed boards. Dustwrapper (slightly soiled and dusty, top edge a little frayed). *(Blakeney)* **£30 [≃$57]**

Catalogue Booksellers Contributing to IRBP

The booksellers who have provided catalogues during 1990 specifically for the purpose of compiling the various titles in the *IRBP* series, and from whose catalogues books have been selected, are listed below in alphabetical order of the abbreviation employed for each. This listing is therefore a complete key to the booksellers contributing to the series as a whole; only a proportion of the listed names is represented in this particular subject volume.

The majority of these booksellers issue periodic catalogues free, on request, to potential customers. Sufficient indication of the type of book handled by each bookseller can be gleaned from the individual book entries set out in the main body of this work and in the companion titles in the series.

Agvent	=	Charles Agvent, R.D.2, Box 377A, Mertztown, PA 19539, U.S.A. (215 682 4750)
Alphabet	=	Alphabet Bookshop, 145 Main Street West, Port Colborne, Ontario L3K 3V3, Canada (416 834 5323)
Antic Hay	=	Antic Hay Rare Books, P.O. Box 2185, Asbury Park, NJ 07712, U.S.A. (201 774 4590)
Any Amount	=	Any Amount of Books, 62 Charing Cross Road, London WC2H 0BB, England (071 240 8140)
Ars Artis	=	Ars Artis, 31 Abberbury Road, Oxford OX4 4ET, England (0865 770714)
Ars Libri	=	Ars Libri, Ltd., 560 Harrison Avenue, Boston, Massachusetts 02118, U.S.A. (617 357 5212)
Ash	=	Ash Rare Books, 25 Royal Exchange, London EC3V 3LP, England (071 626 2665)
Baldwin	=	Stuart A. Baldwin, Fossil Hall, Boars Tye Road, Silver End, Witham, Essex CM8 3QA, England (0376 83502)
Bates & Hindmarch	=	Bates and Hindmarch, Antiquarian Bookseller, Fishergate, Boroughbridge, North Yorkshire Y05 9AL, England (0423 324258)
Beech	=	John Beech Rare Books, 63 Station Road, Histon, Cambridge CB4 4LQ, England (Cambridge 232210)
Bell	=	Peter Bell, Bookseller & Publisher, 4 Brandon Street, Edinburgh EH3 5DX, Scotland (031 556 2198)
Bernett	=	F.A. Bernett Inc., 2001 Palmer Avenue, Larchmont, N.Y. 10538, U.S.A. (914 834 3026)
Between the Covers	=	Between the Covers, 575 Collings Avenue, Collingswood, NJ 08107, U.S.A. (609 869 0512)
Bickersteth	=	David Bickersteth, 4 South End, Bassingbourn, Royston, Hertfordshire SG8 5NG, England (0763 45619)
Black Sun	=	Black Sun Books, P.O. Box 7916 - F.D.R. Sta., New York, New York 10150-1915, U.S.A. (212 688 6622)
Blakeney	=	Adam Blakeney, Apartment 8, 59 Devonshire Street, London W1N 1LT, England (071 323 0937)
Book Block	=	The Book Block, 8 Loughlin Avenue, Cos Cob, Connecticut 06807, U.S.A. (203 629 2990)
Bookline	=	Bookline, 35 Farranfad Road, Downpatrick BT30 8NH, Northern Ireland (039687 712)
Bookmark	=	Bookmark, Children's Books, Fortnight, Wick Down, Broad Hinton, Swindon, Wiltshire SN4 9NR, England (0793 731693)
Bookpress	=	The Bookpress Ltd., Post Office Box KP, Williamsburg, Virginia 23187, U.S.A. (804 229 1260)

Boswell	=	Boswell Books and Prints, 44 Great Russell Street, London WclB 3PA, England (071 580 7200) *or* Boswell Books and Prints, 2261 Market Street, Suite 288, San Francisco, CA 94114, U.S.A. (415 431 3021)
Bow Windows	=	Bow Windows Book Shop, 128 High Street, Lewes, East Sussex BN7 1XL, England (0273 480780)
Bromer	=	Bromer Booksellers, 607 Boylston Street, at Copley Square, Boston, MA 02116, U.S.A. (617 247 2818)
Paul Brown	=	Paul Brown, 3 Melbourne Terrace, Melbourne Grove, London SE22 8RE, England (081 299 4195)
Buccleuch	=	Buccleuch Books, 40 Buccleuch Street, Edinburgh EH8 9LP, Scotland (031 6681353)
Buckley	=	Brian & Margaret Buckley, 11 Convent Close, Kenilworth, Warwickshire CV8 2FQ, England (0926 55223)
Burmester	=	James Burmester, Manor House Farmhouse, North Stoke, Bath BA1 9AT, England (0272 327265)
Central Africana	=	Central Africana, The Coach House, Serpentine Road, Sevenoaks TN13 3XP, England (071 242 3131)
Chapel Hill	=	Chapel Hill Rare Books, P.O. Box 456, Carrboro, NC 27510, U.S.A. (919 929 8351)
Clark	=	Robert Clark, 6a King Street, Jericho, Oxford OX2 6DF, England (0865 52154)
Clearwater	=	Clearwater Books, 19 Matlock Road, Ferndown, Wimborne, Dorset BH22 8QT, England (0202 893263)
Claude Cox	=	Claude Cox, The White House, Kelsale, Saxmundham, Suffolk IP17 2PQ, England (0728 602786)
Dalian	=	Dalian Books, David P. Williams, 81 Albion Drive, London Fields, London E8 4LT, England (071 249 1587)
de Beaumont	=	Robin de Beaumont, 25 Park Walk, Chelsea, London SW10 0AJ, England (071 352 3440)
Dermont	=	Joseph A. Dermont, 13 Arthur Street, P.O. Box 654, Onset, MA 02558, U.S.A. (508 295 4760)
Dramatis Personae	=	Dramatis Personae, 71 Lexington Avenue, New York, New York 10010, U.S.A. (212 679 3705)
Dyke	=	Martin Dyke, 4 Gordon Road, Clifton, Bristol BS8 1AP, England (0272 742090)
Edrich	=	I.D. Edrich, 17 Selsdon Road, London E11 2QF, England (081 989 9541)
Egret	=	Egret Books, 6 Priory Place, Wells, Somerset BA5 1SP, England (0749 679312)
Ellis	=	Peter Ellis, 31 Museum Street, London WC1A 1LH, England (071 637 5862)
Emerald Isle	=	Emerald Isle Books, 539 Antrim Road, Belfast BT15 3BU, Northern Ireland (0232 370798)
Fenning	=	James Fenning, 12 Glenview, Rochestown Avenue, Dun Laoghaire, County Dublin, Eire (01 857855)
Finch	=	Simon Finch Rare Books, Clifford Chambers, 10 New Bond Street, London W1Y 9PF, England (071 499 0974)
First Issues	=	First Issues Ltd, 17 Alfoxton Avenue, London N15 3DD, England (081 881 6931)
Frew Mackenzie	=	Frew Mackenzie plc, 106 Great Russell Street, London WC1B 3NA, England (071 580 2311)
Fye	=	W. Bruce Fye, Antiquarian Medical Books, 1607 North Wood Avenue, Marshfield, Wisconsin 54449, U.S.A. (715 384 8128)
Gage	=	Gage Postal Books, P.O. Box 105, Westcliff-on-Sea, Essex SS0 8EQ, England ()

Gaskell	=	Roger Gaskell, 17 Ramsey Road, Warboys, Cambridgeshire PE17 2RW, England (0487 823059)
Gemmary	=	The Gemmary, Inc, PO Box 816, Redondo Beach, CA 90277, U.S.A. (213 372 5969)
Georges	=	Georges, 52 Park Street, Bristol BS1 5JN, England (0272 276602)
Glyn's	=	Glyn's Books, 4 Bryn Draw Terrace, Wrexham, Clwyd LL13 7DF, Wales (0978 364473)
Goodrich	=	James Tait Goodrich, Antiquarian Books & Manuscripts, 214 Everett Place, Englewood, New Jersey 07631, U.S.A. (201 567 0199)
Gough	=	Simon Gough Books, 5 Fish Hill, Holt, Norfolk, England (026371 2650)
Grayling	=	David A.H. Grayling, Lyvennet, Crosby Ravensworth, Penrith, Cumbria CA10 3JP, England (09315 282)
Green Meadow	=	Green Meadow Books, Kinoulton, Nottingham NG12 3EN, England (0949 81723)
Gretton	=	John R. Gretton, 5 Quebec Road, Dereham, Norfolk NR19 2DP, England (0362 692707)
Hadley	=	Peter J. Hadley, 20th Century Books, 132 Corve Street. Ludlow, Shropshire SY8 2PG, England (0584 874441)
Halsey	=	Alan Halsey, The Poetry Bookshop, 22 Broad Street, Hay-on-Wye, Via Hereford HR3 5DB, England (0497 820 305)
Hannas	=	Torgrim Hannas, 29a Canon Street, Winchester, Hampshire SO23 9JJ, England (0962 862730)
Hatchwell	=	Richard Hatchwell, The Old Rectory, Little Somerford, Chippenham, Wiltshire SN15 5JW, England (0666 823261)
Hazeldene	=	Hazeldene Bookshop, A.H. & L.G. Elliot, 61 Renshaw Street, Liverpool L1 2SJ, England (051 708 8780)
Hemlock	=	Hemlock Books, 170 Beach 145th Street, Neponsit, New York 11694, U.S.A. (718 318 0737)
Henly	=	John Henly, Bookseller, Brooklands, Walderton, Chichester, West Sussex PO18 9EE, England (0705 631426)
Heritage	=	Heritage Book Shop, Inc., 8540 Melrose Avenue, Los Angeles, California 90069, U.S.A. (213 659 3674)
High Latitude	=	High Latitude, P.O. Box 11254, Bainbridge Island, WA 98110, U.S.A. (206 598 3454)
Hollett	=	R.F.G. Hollett and Son, 6 Finkle Street, Sedbergh, Cumbria LA10 5BZ, England (05396 20298)
Holmes	=	David J. Holmes, 230 South Broad Street, Third Floor, Philadelphia, Pennsylvania 19102, U.S.A. (215 735 1083)
Horowitz	=	Glenn Horowitz, 141 East 44th Street, Suite 808, New York, New York 10017, U.S.A. (212 557 1381)
Houle	=	George Houle, 7260 Beverly Boulevard, Los Angeles, California 90036, U.S.A. (213 937 5858)
Humber	=	Humber Books, 688 Beverley Road, Hull, North Humberside HU6 7JH, England (0482 802239)
James	=	Marjorie James, The Old School, Oving, Chichester, West Sussex PO20 6DG, England (0243 781354)
Janus	=	Janus Books, Post Office Box 40787, Tucson, Arizona 85717, U.S.A. (602 881 8192)
Jarndyce	=	Jarndyce, Antiquarian Booksellers, 46 Great Russell Street, Bloomsbury, London WC1B 3PA, England (071 631 4220)
C.R. Johnson	=	C.R. Johnson, 21 Charlton Place, London N1 8AQ, England (071 354 1077)
Michael Johnson	=	Michael Johnson Books, Oak Lodge, Kingsway, Portishead, Bristol BS20 8HW, England (0272 843798)

Karmiole	=	Kenneth Karmiole, Bookseller, 1225 Santa Monica Mall, Santa Monica, California 90401, U.S.A. (213 451 4342)
King	=	John K. King, P.O. Box 33363, Detroit, Michigan 48232-5363, U.S.A., U.S.A. (313 961 0622)
Lamb	=	R.W. & C.R. Lamb, Talbot House, 158 Denmark Rd., Lowestoft, Suffolk NR32 2EL, England (0502 564306)
Larkhill	=	Larkhill Books, Larkhill House, Tetbury, Gloucestershire GL8 8SY, England (0666 502343)
Lewis	=	John Lewis, 35 Stoneham Street, Coggeshall, Essex CO6 1UH, England (0376 561518)
Lewton	=	L.J. Lewton, Old Station House, Freshford, Bath BA3 6EQ, England (0225 723351)
Limestone Hills	=	Limestone Hills Book Shop, P.O. Box 1125, Glen Rose, Texas 76043, U.S.A. (817 897 4991)
Lloyd-Roberts	=	Tom Lloyd-Roberts, Old Court House, Caerwys, Mold, Clwyd CH7 5BB, Wales (0352 720276)
Lopez	=	Ken Lopez, Bookseller, 51 Huntington Road, Hadley, MA 01035, U.S.A. (413 584 4827)
McBlain	=	McBlain Books, P.O. Box 5062 Hamden, CT 06518, U.S.A. (203 281 0400)
McCann	=	Joey McCann, 76 Oliver Road, Cowley, Oxford OX4 2JF, England (0865 715001)
MacDonnell	=	Mac Donnell Rare Books, 9307 Glenlake Drive, Austin, Texas 78730, U.S.A. (512 345 4139)
McGilvery	=	Laurence McGilvery, Post Office Box 852, La Jolla, California 92038, U.S.A. (619 454 4443)
Marlborough B'Shop	=	Marlborough Bookshop, 6 Kingsbury Street, Marlborough, Wiltshire, England (0672 514074)
Mendelsohn	=	H.L. Mendelsohn, Fine European Books, P.O. Box 317, Belmont, Massachusetts 02178, U.S.A. (617 484 7362)
Meyer Boswell	=	Meyer Boswell Books, Inc., 982 Hayes Street, San Francisco, CA 94117, U.S.A. (415 346 1839)
Moon	=	Michael Moon, Antiquarian, Booksellers & Publishers, 41, 42 & 43 Roper Street, Whitehaven, Cumbria CA28 7BS, England (0946 62936)
Moorhouse	=	Hartley Moorhouse Books, 142 Petersham Road, Richmond, Surrey TW10 6UX, England (081 948 7742)
Mordida	=	Mordida Books, P.O. Box 79322, Houston, Texas 77279, U.S.A. (713 467 4280)
Newnham	=	Anthony Newnham, 72 Dundas Street, Edinburgh EH3 6QZ, Scotland (031 556 3705)
New Wireless	=	New Wireless Pioneers, Box 398, Elma N.Y. 14059, U.S.A. (716 681 3186)
Nouveau	=	Nouveau Rare Books, Steve Silberman, P.O. Box 12471, 5005 Meadow Oaks Park Drive, Jackson, Mississippi 39211, U.S.A. (601 956 9950)
Oak Knoll	=	Oak Knoll Books, 414 Delaware Street, New Castle, Delaware 19720, U.S.A. (302 328 7232)
Offenbacher	=	Emile Offenbacher, 84-50 Austin Street, P.O. Box 96, Kew Gardens, New York 11415, U.S.A. (718 849 5834)
Parmer	=	J. Parmer, Booksellers, 7644 Forrestal Road, San Diego, CA 92120, U.S.A. (619 287 0693)
Patterson	=	Ian Patterson, 21 Bateman Street, Cambridge CB2 1NB, England (0223 321658)
Petrilla	=	R & A Petrilla, Roosevelt, NJ 08555-0306, U.S.A. (609 426 4999)
Pettler & Liebermann	=	Pettler & Liebermann, 8033 Sunsett Blvd. £977, Los Angeles, CA 90046, U.S.A. (213 474 2479)

Phillips	=	Phillips of Hitchin, (Antiques) Ltd., The Manor House, Hitchin, Hertfordshire, England (0462 432067)
Pickering	=	Pickering & Chatto, 17 Pall Mall, London SW1Y 5NB, England (071 930 8627)
Polyanthos	=	Polyanthos Park Avenue Books, P.O. Box 343, Huntington, NY 11743, U.S.A. (516 271 5558)
Rankin	=	Alan Rankin, 72 Dundas Street, Edinburgh EH3 6QZ, Scotland, Scotland (031 556 3705)
Reese	=	William Reese Company, 409 Temple Street, New Haven, Connecticut 06511, U.S.A. (203 789 8081)
David Rees	=	David Rees, 18A Prentis Road, London SW16 1QD, England (081 769 2453)
Reference Works	=	Reference Works, 12 Commercial Road, Dorset BH19 1DF, England (0929 424423)
Respess	=	L & T Respess Books, PO Box 236, Bristol, RI 02809, U.S.A. (401 253 1639)
Roberts	=	John Roberts Bookshop, 43 Triangle West, Clifton, Bristol BS8 1ES, Scotland (2 268568)
Robertshaw	=	John Robertshaw, 5 Fellowes Drive, Ramsey, Huntingdon, Cambridgeshire PE17 1BE, England (0487 813330)
Rootenberg	=	B & L. Rootenberg, P.O. Box 5049, Sherman Oaks, California 91403-5049, U.S.A. (818 788 7765)
Rostenberg & Stern	=	Leona Rostenberg and Madeleine, Stern, Rare Books, 40 East 88 Street, New York, N.Y. 10128., U.S.A. (212 831 6628)
Sanders	=	Sanders of Oxford Ltd., 104 High Street, Oxford OX1 4BW, England (0865 242590)
Savona	=	Savona Books, 9 Wilton Road, Hornsea, North Humberside HU18 1QU, England (0964 535195)
Schoyer	=	Schoyer's Books, 1404 South Negley Avenue, Pittsburgh, PA 15217, U.S.A. (412 521 8464)
Sclanders	=	Andrew Sclanders, 73 Duckett Road, London N4 1BL, England (081 340 6843)
Sklaroff	=	L.J. Sklaroff, The Totland Bookshop, The Broadway, Totland, Isle of Wight PO39 0BW, England (0983 754960)
Sotheran's	=	Henry Sotheran Ltd., 2 Sackville Street, Piccadilly, London W1X 2DP, England (071 439 6151)
Spelman	=	Ken Spelman, 70 Micklegate, York YO1 1LF, England (0904 624414)
Stewart	=	Andrew Stewart, 11 High Street, Helpringham, Sleaford, Lincolnshire NG34 9RA, England (052 921 617)
Sumner & Stillman	=	Sumner & Stillman, P.O. Box 225, Yarmouth, ME 04096, U.S.A. (207 846 6070)
Michael Taylor	=	Michael Taylor Rare Books, The Gables, 8 Mendham Lane, Harleston, Norfolk IP20 9DE, England (0379 853889)
Peter Taylor	=	Peter Taylor, 4A Ye Corner, Aldenham Road, Watford, Hertfordshire WD1 4BS, England (0923 50342)
Temple	=	Robert Temple, 65 Mildmay Road, London N1 4PU, England (071 254 3674)
Terramedia	=	Terramedia Books, 19 Homestead Road, Wellesley, MA 02181, U.S.A. (617 237 6485)
Tiger Books	=	Tiger Books, Yew Tree Cottage, Westbere, Canterbury Kent CT2 0HH, England (0227 710030)
Trophy Room Books	=	Trophy Room Books, Box 3041, Agoura, CA 91301, U.S.A. (818 889 2469)
Vanbrugh	=	Vanbrugh Rare Books, Pied Bull Yard, Bury Place, Bloomsbury, London EC1A 2JR, England (071 404 0733)

Virgo	=	Virgo Books, Little Court, South Wraxall, Bradford-on-Avon, Wiltshire BA15 2SE, England (02216 2040)
Walcot	=	Patrick Walcot, 60 Sunnybank Road, Sutton Coldfield, West Midlands B73 5RJ, England (021 382 6381)
Washton	=	Andrew D. Washton, 411 East 83rd Street, New York, New York 10028, U.S.A. (212 751 7027)
Waterfield's	=	Waterfield's, 36 Park End Street, Oxford OX1 1HJ, England (0865 721809)
West Side	=	West Side Books, 113 W. Liberty, Ann Arbor, MI 48103, U.S.A. (313 995 1891)
Wheldon & Wesley	=	Wheldon & Wesley Ltd., Lytton Lodge, Codicote, Hitchin, Hertfordshire SG4 8TE, England (0438 820370)
Whitehart	=	F.E. Whitehart, Rare Books, 40 Priestfield Road, Forest Hill, London SE23 2RS, England (081 699 3225)
Whiteson	=	Edna Whiteson, 66 Belmont Avenue, Cockfosters, Hertfordshire EN4 9LA, England (081 449 8860)
Willow	=	Willow House Books, 58-60 Chapel Street, Chorley, Lancashire PR7 1BS, England (02572 69280)
Woolmer	=	J. Howard Woolmer, Revere, Pennsylvania 18953, U.S.A. (215 847 5074)
Words Etcetera	=	Words Etcetera, Julian Nangle, Hod House, Child Okeford, Dorset DT11 8EH, England (0258 73338)
Worldwide	=	Worldwide Antiquarian, Post Office Box 391, Cambridge, MA 02141, U.S.A. (617 876 6220)
Wreden	=	William P. Wreden, 206 Hamilton Avenue, P.O. Box 56, Palo Alto, CA 94302-0056, U.S.A. (415 325 6851)
Ximenes	=	Ximenes: Rare Books, Inc., 19 East 69th Street, New York, NY 10021, U.S.A. (212 744 0226)
Young's	=	Young's Antiquarian Books, Tillingham, Essex CM0 7ST, England (062187 8187)
Zwisohn	=	Jane Zwisohn Books, 524 Solano Drive N.E., Albuquerque, New Mexico 87108, U.S.A. (505 255 4080)